TECHNICAL COMMUNICATION

Custom Edition for HUMBER COLLEGE

Taken from:

Technical Communication, Fourth Canadian Edition
by John M. Lannon and Don Klepp

Grammar at Work for Technical Communication
by Don Klepp

Technical Communication, Third Canadian Edition
by John M. Lannon and Don Klepp

Technical Communication: A Practical Approach, Fourth Canadian Edition
by William Sanborn Pfeiffer and Jan Boogerd

Technically-Write!, Canadian Seventh Edition
by Ron Blicq and Lisa Moretto

Custom Publishing

New York Boston San Francisco
London Toronto Sydney Tokyo Singapore Madrid
Mexico City Munich Paris Cape Town Hong Kong Montreal

Cover art: courtesy of PhotoDisc/Getty Images.

Excerpts taken from:

Technical Communication, Fourth Canadian Edition
by John M. Lannon and Don Klepp
Copyright © 2009, 2006, 2003, 2000 by Pearson Education Canada
Published by Longman
Toronto, Ontario

Grammar at Work for Technical Communication
by Don Klepp
Copyright © 2009 by Pearson Education Canada

Technical Communication, Third Canadian Edition
by John M. Lannon and Don Klepp
Copyright © 2006, 2003, 2000 by Pearson Education Canada
Published by Longman

Technical Communication: A Practical Approach, Fourth Canadian Edition
by William Sanborn Pfeiffer and Jan Boogerd
Copyright © 2007, 2004, 2000, 1997 by Pearson Education Canada
Published by Prentice Hall

Technically-Write!, Canadian Seventh Edition
by Ron Blicq and Lisa Moretto
Copyright © 2008, 2004 by Pearson Education Canada
Published by Prentice Hall

Printed in Canada

10 9 8 7 6 5 4 3 2 1

2008560113

MH

Pearson Custom Publishing
is a division of

PEARSON

www.pearsonhighered.com

ISBN 10: 0-555-01469-X
ISBN 13: 978-0-555-01469-1

BRIEF CONTENTS

All frontmatter, Chapters 1–6, 8–18, and 20–21 were taken from *Technical Communication*, Fourth Canadian Edition, by John M. Lannon and Don Klepp. Chapter 19 was taken from *Technical Communication*, Third Canadian Edition, by John M. Lannon and Don Klepp. Chapter 7 was compiled of a combination of original material provided by the adopters of this text, and material taken from *Technical Communication*, Fourth Canadian Edition, by John M. Lannon and Don Klepp; *Technical Communication: A Practical Approach*, Fourth Canadian Edition, by William Sanborn Pfeiffer and Jan Boogerd; and *Technically Write!*, Canadian Seventh Edition, by Ron Blicq and Lisa Moretto. Part III was taken from *Grammar at Work for Technical Communication* by Don Klepp.

All frontmatter, Chapters 1–6, 8–18, and 20–21 were taken from *Technical Communication*, Fourth Canadian Edition, by John M. Lannon and Don Klepp. Chapter 19 was taken from *Technical Communication*, Third Canadian Edition, by John M. Lannon and Don Klepp. Chapter 7 was compiled of a combination of original material provided by the adopters of this text, and material taken from *Technical Communication*, Fourth Canadian Edition, by John M. Lannon and Don Klepp; *Technical Communication: A Practical Approach*, Fourth Canadian Edition, by William Sanborn Pfeiffer and Jan Boogerd; and *Technically Write!*, Canadian Seventh Edition, by Ron Blicq and Lisa Moretto. Part III was taken from *Grammar at Work for Technical Communication* by Don Klepp.

Thank you for using this book. Together with Pearson Education Canada editors and page designers, I've worked very hard to make *Technical Communication* informative and practical.

I see this book as more than a university or college text; I also view it as a workplace tool that you can use for many years. Some aspects of the book, such as resource URLs and information about electronic communication media, may become outdated. However, the book's advice about writing processes, document structures, and effective language will remain relevant because that advice is based on practical experience and on solid rhetorical theory.

You'll notice, though, that rhetoric and other communications theory is rarely discussed directly in this book. The book is primarily interested in practical applications, not in theory for its own sake. So, for example, *Technical Communication* does not discuss genre analysis; instead, Chapters 17 and 13 show how the *action structure* can be profitably adapted to a wide variety of business and technical documents.

WHAT'S NEW?

In keeping with our continuing emphasis on usability and relevance, this edition contains new material or more emphasis on the following topics:

- electronic communication media, in Chapter 1
- managing conflict, in conjunction with discussion of collaborative communications, in Chapter 1
- environmental noise and dyadic versus group communication, in Chapter 2
- productive collaborative writing, in Chapter 3
- international and intercultural communication
- a new approach in research methods, in Chapter 15, to reflect changes in methods for gaining access to electronic information sources
- CSE and IEEE documentation formats
- email usage, in Chapter 13
- "new correspondence media," in Chapter 13—blogs, vlogs, podcasting, and text messaging

Also, the text includes new writing samples and exercises:

- a new scenario, re: four communications challenges, in Chapter 1, reflects contemporary issues in Alberta oil sands operations.
- a new whistle-blowing case study appears in Chapter 12.
- a group of new ethics case study exercises concludes Chapter 12.
- new examples of technical marketing materials are found in Chapter 8.
- more information and examples re: web page design are now available in Chapter 10.

The most dramatic development in this 4th edition is the inclusion of 57 **"On the Job"** boxes that quote technical communications practitioners—these features provide valuable perspectives from people whose writing and speaking skills are critical to their business success.

SUPPLEMENTS

For Students

A Text Enrichment Site (TES) accompanies this textbook at **www.pearsoned.ca/lannon**. This updated and expanded site contains

- a variety of editing and proofreading exercises, including exercises that are set in a context that helps one to identify errors and phrasing problems;
- examples of technical reports and manuals;
- ethics case study exercises;
- forms and templates found in the textbook;
- detailed examples of MLA, APA, IEEE, and CSE documentation formatting; and
- an annotated list of links to over 150 technical communication resources found on the internet.

For Instructors

An **Instructor's Resource Manual** is available to instructors who use the Fourth Canadian edition of *Technical Communication*. The manual includes teaching notes and resources, sample documents, test questions, answers to test questions, and answers for exercises found at the TES.

Twenty-four PowerPoint slide presentations are also available to instructors. The slides offer summaries of key points and illustrations from the textbook that can be used to augment lectures and in-class discussions.

Instructors can download the slides and the Instructor's Resource Manual from a password-protected location on Pearson Education Canada's online catalogue (**vig.pearsoned.ca**). Search for this text, then click on "Instructors" under "Resources" in the left-hand menu. Contact your local Pearson Education sales representative for more information.

For More Resources

If you have comments or requests, email me at **dklepp@shaw.ca**. I will respond. Also, please use the website. And, you may wish to visit my blog at **www.commtalk.blogspot.com**. That blog contains my reactions to current trends and developments in the wide field of professional communication. It will also contain your responses to my posts. Ideally, "Commtalk" will become a forum for students and professors who use *Technical Communication*.

Grammar at Work responds to a need for supplementary material and exercises to help writers improve their skills—this workbook focuses on grammar, sentence structure, vocabulary and usage, and mechanics such as spelling, punctuation, and numbers. The book provides self-directed instruction and exercises that students can use to improve their mastery of business and technical English. *Grammar at Work* can operate in conjunction with the 4th Canadian edition of Technical Communication or as a stand-alone workbook.

This book contains these self-help components:

- **A Diagnostic Test.** Exercises test your current knowledge and skill levels. You can then use the self-evaluated results to determine which skill areas you most need to improve.
- **Essential Grammar, Usage, and Mechanics.** Each of five exercise sections begins by reviewing basic principles and rules. Each section then allows you to test your skills as you progress.
- **Self-improvement Exercises.** In three stages, each section of exercises helps you gain command of English grammar, mechanics, and usage. First, practice exercises help you determine how well you have understood the principles discussed in that section. Then, sentence exercises contain errors that you will need to eradicate in workplace writing. Finally, the document critiques will sharpen your evaluation and editing skills. Page 643 provides the standard proofreading marks and Correction Symbols that you'll need to complete the document critiques.

Starting on page 617, you will find answer keys for the exercises in this workbook.

ACKNOWLEDGMENTS

This book results from a collaboration of many people. Pearson Education Canada editors Chris Helsby, Carolin Sweig, Amanda Wesson, and Charlotte Morrison-Reed, technical guru Larry Sulky, and freelance editors Valerie Adams and Colleen Ste. Marie have all made valuable contributions to this edition. I acknowledge the contributors who provided quotes for the book's 57 "On the Job" boxes—you'll see their names in those boxes. I also thank Ken Langedyk, Roger Webber, Flightcraft, Humber College's media department, Norco's Peter Stace-Smith, Dr. Ron Marken, and Permachart's Suzanne Tyson for graciously providing print and website material that appears either in the book or in the TES.

I appreciate the valuable suggestions and challenges posed by reviewers from universities and colleges across Canada:

Anne Loxley Baker, Thompson Rivers University
Jim Catton, Algonquin College
Martin Cooney, Durham College
Kim Davis, Carleton University
Carolyn Hay, University of British Columbia, Okanagan
Carolyn Ives, Thompson Rivers University
Alyson King, University of Ontario Institute of Technology
Donna Meade, College of the North Atlantic
Lisa Meyer, Carleton University
Jessica Mudry, Concordia University
Patricia Sackville, British Columbia Institute of Technology
Linda Szekely, University of Alberta
David Thompson, University College of the Fraser Valley
Jana Weerasinghe-Segits, University of Western Ontario
Diana Wegner, Douglas College
Shelley Zwicker, Nova Scotia Community College

Finally, I thank my wife, Betty Chan Klepp, whose courageous, positive approach to life remains a constant inspiration.

Acknowledgments (Humber Edition)

This edition required the collaborative efforts of the faculty members who teach COMM 213 and COMM 313 at Humber College. In particular, the material in Chapter 14 was revised, with original material, by Elizabeth Jones and Judy Moorhouse. Thanks to all who participated in the preparation of this edition.

PART I

CHAPTER 1

Introduction to Technical Writing

LEARNING OBJECTIVES

After reading this chapter, you should be able to

- Appreciate the nature, purpose, and range of technical writing.
- Understand the challenges faced by technical writers.
- Identify the skills needed to collaborate with others in producing technical documents.

As a technical writer, you interpret and communicate specialized information for your readers, who may need your information to perform a task, answer a question, solve a problem, or make a decision. Your memo, letter, report, or manual must advance the goals of your readers and of the company or organization you represent. You often collaborate with others to plan, prepare, and present important documents and oral presentations.

TECHNICAL WRITING SERVES PRACTICAL NEEDS

Unlike poetry and fiction, which appeal mainly to our *imagination*, technical documents appeal to our *understanding*. Technical writing rarely seeks to entertain, create suspense, or invite differing interpretations. If you have written a lab or research report, you know that technical writing must be clear, reader oriented, and efficient.

Technical Documents Meet Reader Needs

Instead of focusing on the *writer's desire* for self-expression, a technical document addresses the *reader's desire* for information. This need should not make your writing sound like something produced by a robot, without any personality (or *voice*) at all. Your document may in fact reveal a lot about you (your competence, knowledge, integrity, and so on), but it rarely focuses on you personally. Readers are interested in *what you have done,* in *what you recommend,* or in *how you speak for your company;* they have only a professional interest in *who you are* (your feelings, hopes, dreams, visions). A personal essay, then, is not technical writing. Consider this essay fragment:

Focuses on the feelings

> Computers are not a particularly forgiving breed. The wrong key struck or the wrong command entered is almost sure to avenge itself on the inattentive user by banishing the document to some electronic trashcan.

This personal view communicates a good deal about the writer's resentment and anxiety but very little about computers themselves. The following example can be called technical writing because it focuses (see italics) on the subject, on what the writer has done, and on what the reader should do:

Focuses on the subject, actions taken, and actions required

> On MK 950 terminals, the *BREAK key* is adjacent to keys used for text editing and special functions. Too often, users inadvertently strike the BREAK key, causing the program to quit prematurely. To prevent the problem, *we have modified all database management terminals:* to quit a program, *you must now strike BREAK twice successively.*

This next example also can be called technical writing because it focuses on what the writer recommends:

Focuses on the recommendation

> Our Linux server should be upgraded to (1) increase the number of simultaneous users from 60 to 80, (2) increase the system's responsiveness, and (3) provide sorely needed disk storage for word processing and company databases.

As the above examples illustrate, documents don't always make the writer "disappear," but they should focus on what is most important to the readers.

Technical Documents Strive for Efficiency

Educators read to *test* our knowledge; colleagues, customers, and supervisors read to *use* our knowledge. Workplace readers hate waste and demand efficiency; instead of reading a document from beginning to end, they are more likely to use it for reference and want only as much as they need: "When it comes to memos, letters, proposals, and reports, there's no extra credit for extra words. And no praise for elegant prose. Bosses want employees to get to the point—quickly, clearly, and concisely" (Spruell 32). Efficient documents save time, energy, and money in the workplace.

No reader should have to spend 10 minutes deciphering a message worth only five minutes. Consider, for example, this wordy message:

An inefficient message

> At this point in time, we are presently awaiting an on-site inspection by vendor representatives relative to electrical utilization adaptations necessary for the new computer installation. Meanwhile, all staff members are asked to respect the off-limits designation of said location, as requested, due to liability insurance provisions requiring the on-line status of the computer.

Inefficient documents drain a reader's energy; they are too easily misinterpreted; they waste time and money. Notice how hard you had to work with the previous message to extract information that could be expressed this efficiently:

A more efficient message

> Hardware consultants soon will inspect our new computer room to recommend appropriate wiring. Because our insurance covers only an *operational* computer, this room must remain off limits until the computer is fully installed.

When readers sense they are working too hard, they tune out the message—or they stop reading altogether.

Inefficient documents have varied origins. Even when the information is accurate, errors like the following make readers work too hard:

Causes of inefficient documents

- more (or less) information than readers need
- irrelevant or uninterpreted information
- confusing organization
- jargon or vague technical expressions readers cannot understand
- more words than readers need
- uninviting appearance or confusing layout
- no visual aids when readers need or expect them

An efficient document sorts, organizes, and interprets its information to suit the audience's needs, abilities, and interests. Instead of merely happening, an efficient document is carefully designed to include these elements:

Elements of efficient documents

- *content* that makes the document worth reading
- *organization* that guides readers and emphasizes important material
- *style* that is economical and easy to read
- *visuals* (graphs, diagrams, pictures) that clarify concepts and relationships, and that substitute for words whenever possible
- *format* (layout, typeface) that is accessible and appealing
- *supplements* (abstracts, appendices) that enable readers with different needs to read only those sections required for their work

Reader orientation and efficiency are not abstract rules: writers are accountable for their documents. In questions of liability, faulty writing is no different from any other faulty product. If your inaccurate, unclear, or incomplete information leads to injury, damage, or loss, you can be held legally responsible.

ON THE JOB...

The Importance of Written Communication

"As an environmental consultant, I spend 75 percent of my work week writing and editing correspondence, proposals, and reports. I'd like to spend more time in the field, but it's critical to communicate what you've learned and what you think it means. That's what the client is paying for! And in providing that information and analysis, we're dealing with some serious health and safety issues, so we have to be very careful in interpreting and reporting the data we collect...."

—Dave Ayriss, project manager, Occupational Health and Safety, Golder Associates, Ltd., Calgary

WRITING IS PART OF MOST CAREERS

Although you might not anticipate a career as a "writer," your writing skills will be tested routinely in situations like these:

Ways in which your career may test your writing skills

- proposing various projects to management or to clients
- contributing articles to employee newsletters
- describing a product to employees or customers
- writing procedures and instructions for employees or customers
- justifying to management a request for funding or personnel
- editing and reviewing documents written by colleagues
- designing material that will be read on a computer screen or transformed into sound and pictures

ON THE JOB...

Writing on the Job

"I worked in Kelowna at Industry Canada, which places a high value on interpersonal and writing skills. I was quite surprised at how much writing I did. About 20 to 25 percent of my time was spent writing reports, manuals, letters, and memos.

For example, I wrote letters and memos upgrading our database of who has transmitters and receivers and where they're located. I reported on repairs and equipment modifications. I reported LAN maintenance...."

—Dave Parsons, electronics co-op student

So, whatever your career plans, you can expect to write as part of your job.

Your value to any organization will depend on how clearly and persuasively you communicate. Many working professionals spend at least 40 percent of their time writing or dealing with someone else's writing. The higher their position, the more they write (Barnum and Fisher 9–11).

Good writing gives you and your ideas *visibility* and *authority* within your organization. Bad writing, on the other hand, is not only useless to readers and potentially damaging to the writer, but also expensive: written communication in North American business and industry costs billions of dollars every year. More than 60 percent of the writing is inefficient; it is unclear, misleading, irrelevant, deceptive, or otherwise wasteful of time and money (Max 5–6).

In your career, you'll have to write well. Employers first judge your writing by your application letter and résumé. In a large organization, your future may be decided by executives you've never met. One concrete measure of your job performance will be your letters, memos, and reports. As you advance, communication skills become more important than technical background. The higher your goals, the better you need to communicate.

THE ELECTRONIC INFORMATION AGE REQUIRES EXCELLENT WRITING SKILLS

Information has become our prized commodity:

> *The new source of wealth is not material; it is information, knowledge applied to work to create value. The pursuit of wealth is now largely the pursuit of information, and the application of information to the means of production.* (Wriston 8)

To a large extent, that information is stored and transmitted electronically. Several electronic technologies, collectively known as *information technology* (IT),[1] enhance the speed, volume, and variety of means of creating and transmitting messages:

Information is the ultimate product

- *Integrated software* facilitates the inclusion of verbal, graphic, and video elements from word processors, internet sources, digital recording and storage media, electronic spreadsheets and databases, and oral presentation software.
- *Basic email* helps people exchange ideas and information, while email attachments allow for sophisticated formatting of documents.
- *Wireless laptop computers* allow users to receive and send email from locations (hotel conference rooms, airport lounges, classrooms, etc.) that support wireless transmission.
- *The BlackBerry and other hand-held computers* combine all the advantages of wireless communication (phone, email, text messaging, instant messaging, internet access) with organizer applications and more. Some of these personal digital assistants (PDAs) can be centrally managed and supported by IT departments using proprietary servers and software. ITworldcanada.com says that the North American market for hand-held service will grow to "63 million units per year by 2010 from just 7.3 million" in 2005 (Nystedt).
- Many brands of *cell phones* (or "smart phones") now have capabilities that rival those of PDAs.
- *Virtual private networks (VPNs)* connect home-based workers to their office intranet, without allowing their messages to be monitored by anyone outside that intranet.
- *Voice over Internet Protocol* (*VoIP*) technology is in the process of replacing traditional phone systems, partly because of massive long distance phone call savings, and partly because it enables a host of communications "convergence" features (Lima "Calling All Workstations" 22). *Converged messaging* (also known as "unified messaging") allows voice mails and faxes to be automatically forwarded as email attachments, which the recipient can view or listen to on a smart phone.

ON THE JOB...

Types of Writing

"I generate emails constantly. These include status reports, replies to queries, requests for missing information, etc. I sometimes have to write instructions for media projects. I write bids and invoices. I sometimes have to write for returns for equipment that isn't up to expectation. I sometimes write introductory messages to try to get new sales, and occasionally I write copy for websites."

—Lorraine Patsco, director of prepress and multimedia production

---

1. Howard Solomon reports that companies such as Hewlett-Packard are trying to replace the term *information technology* with the term *business technology*, to reflect the integration of software, hardware, and related services in meeting a company's internal and external business communication needs.

- *Electronic document sharing* uses file transfer software for sharing and editing drafts. The best software allows participants to comment on each other's work online so that each participant's comments are distinct from everyone else's and from the original text.
- *Teleconferencing,* using speakerphones, is good for small rooms with 15 or fewer people seated around a table. Many job interviews are now conducted via teleconference.
- *Videoconferencing* provides live online meetings in which participants at different sites can edit and comment on each other's ideas while observing each other's non-verbal messages.

These technologies have had a profound effect on office communication:

IT has changed the office environment

- Small and medium-sized companies, which comprise 95 percent of all Canadian businesses, are slower than large companies to adopt emerging technologies, such as VoIP, wireless networking, and videoconferencing. However, almost all have desktop computers and email access, and many have laptops, PDAs, cell phones, and websites (Lima, "Small Firms" E2).

The virtual office

- Instead of being housed in one location, the virtual company may have branches in widespread locations, or just one central office, to which employees "commute" electronically. Such arrangements require workers to be skillful communicators who must master the latest technologies, use proper e-communication etiquette, and know how to compensate for the lack of face-to-face contact (Marron "Close Encounters" C1). A special class of worker has emerged—the "virtual assistant," who works on contract, at home, for one or more firms. A virtual assistant might answer phones, direct emails, produce and edit documents, update websites, or maintain databases and inventories. He or she can even go into a client firm's computer (via an internet connection) to work on material stored on that computer's hard drive (Buckler E5).
- Instead of relying on secretaries, most managers compose and send their own messages via email. Many also compose, design, and deliver their own reports and proposals.
- On desktop publishing networks, the composition, layout, graphics design, and printing of external documents and webpages are done in-house.
- Paper documents (such as résumés) can be optically scanned and stored electronically. Many documents are stored as PDF files.
- Computer-supported cooperative work systems, instant messaging, and videoconferencing enable employees worldwide to converse in real time. Email listservs announce daily developments in prices, policies, and procedures.

Intercultural challenges face globally outsourced offices

- As well, "enterprise rights management (ERM) technology allows a company to restrict the access to and use of all documents and e-mails throughout the organization" (Gooderham "It Was" E1). Restricted access is especially important when part of a firm is halfway around the world, in a location where "ethics [may be] questionable and corruption is rampant" (E1). Overseas outsourcing has become possible for small companies as well as large ones, according to business reporter Mary Gooderham. Canadian firms might outsource administrative functions, call centres, design work, or even product design to workers in India, Finland, or Singapore. One main challenge in managing the outsourced office is fitting those workers into the company culture while respecting the workers' own cultural values and practices.

Today's workers depend heavily on computer technology

However, there's a price to be paid for the efficient, convenient electronic office. For example, knowledge workers depend on IT professionals (network technicians and others), who are the *wunderkinds* of the new office environment. Their expertise is essential to maintaining not only the computers, but also the hardware networks and associated software. In a short time, today's workers have become totally dependent on computer technology.

Electronic multitasking can exact a heavy personal price

We pay another price for full-time connectiveness and electronic multi-tasking—we have scant time for quiet reflection. Dr. Edward Hallowell, author of *Crazy Busy: Overstretched, Overbooked, and About to Snap*, sees symptoms of attention-deficit disorder in adult executives who are "caught up in a dust storm of information competing for our attention" (qtd. in Immen, "The Next Great Curse" C1).

Also, despite the opportunities for multitasking brought by electronic devices, those tools facilitate interruptions. The Basex research firm found that, on average, interruptions consume 28 percent of a knowledge worker's day. Further, a study of Microsoft employees found that they took an average of 15 minutes to return to "serious mental tasks" after responding to emails or text messages (Galt, "Drive-by Interruptions" B9).

There is no substitute for human critical thinking

And, despite the tremendous advantages brought by IT, information does not write itself. Information technology provides tools; it does not substitute for human interaction. Only humans can answer the following questions:

- Which information is most relevant?
- What does this data mean?
- Can I verify the accuracy of this data?
- How will others interpret it?
- With whom should I share it?
- What action does it suggest?

IN BRIEF WRITING REACHES A GLOBAL AUDIENCE

Our linked global community shares social, political, and financial interests that demand cooperation as well as competition. Multinational corporations often use parts that are manufactured in one country and shipped to another for assembly into a product that will be marketed elsewhere. Medical, environmental, and other research crosses national boundaries, and professionals in all fields transact with colleagues from other cultures.

Here is a sample of documents that might address global audiences (Weymouth 143):

- studies of global pollution and industrial emissions
- specifications for hydroelectric dams and other engineering projects
- operating instructions for appliances and electronic equipment
- catalogues, promotional literature, and repair manuals
- contracts and business agreements

To communicate effectively across cultural and national boundaries, any document must respect not only language differences but also cultural differences. One writer offers this helpful definition of culture:

> Our cultures, our accumulated knowledge and experiences, beliefs and values, attitudes and roles, shape us as individuals and differentiate us as a people. Inbred through family life, religious training, and educational and

(continued)

work experiences . . . cultures manifest themselves . . . in our thoughts and feelings, our actions and reactions, and our views of the world . . . [and] in our information needs and our styles of communication. . . . Our cultures define our expectations as to how information should be organized, what should be included in its content, and how it should be expressed. (Hein 125)

Cultures define appropriate social behaviours, business relationships, contract negotiation, and communication practices. A communication style considered perfectly acceptable in one culture may be offensive elsewhere.

Effective communicators recognize these differences but withhold judgment or evaluation, focusing instead on similarities. For example, needs assessment and needs satisfaction know no international boundaries; technical solutions are technical solutions without regard to nationality, creed, or language; courtesy and goodwill are universal values. In a diverse global context, the writer must establish trust and enhance human relationships.

TECHNICAL WRITERS FACE INTERRELATED CHALLENGES

No matter how sophisticated our communication technology, computers cannot *think* for us. More specifically, computers cannot solve the challenges faced by all people who write in the technical professions. These challenges include

- *the information challenge:* different readers in different situations have different information needs
- *the persuasion challenge:* people often disagree about what the information means and about what should be done
- *the ethics challenge:* the interests of your company may conflict with the interests of your readers
- *the global context challenge:* diverse people work together on information for a diverse audience

Information has to have meaning for its audience, but people differ in their interpretations of facts, and so they may need persuading that one viewpoint is preferable to another. Persuasion, however, can be powerful and unethical. Even the most useful and efficient document could deceive or harm. Therefore, solving the persuasion challenge doesn't mean manipulating readers by using "whatever works"; rather, it means building a case from honest and reasonable interpretation of the facts. Figure 1.1 offers one way of visualizing how these challenges relate.

The following scenario shows a professional facing the challenges of communicating in the workplace.

The Information Analysis Challenge

"What does all this data really mean?"

Erika Song, with a background in biology and environmental studies, works for Enviro Associates, an Edmonton-based environmental assessment firm. On contract to the Alberta Environment ministry, Enviro monitors water flow and water quality in the Athabasca River near the Fort McMurray oil sands projects.

Erika's task is to compile and analyze Enviro's 2006 monitoring data and compare it to both Enviro's 2005 data and to 2006 data made public by the Wood Buffalo Environmental Association and the Regional Environmental Monitoring Association (REMA). Alberta Environment wants Enviro's data and conclusions *and* it wants to know whether there is any redundancy in the three collections of data.

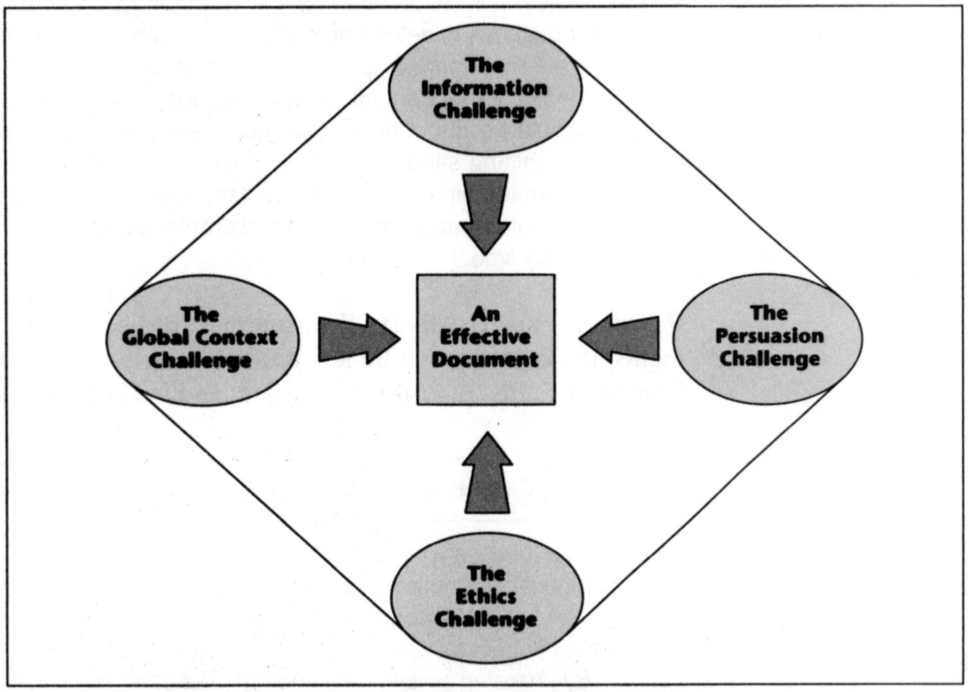

Figure 1.1 Writers Face Four Related Challenges

After analyzing the reams of data, Erika's next challenge is to organize and present the data for technical and non-technical readers. She has to answer such questions as: *How much explaining do I need to do? Do I need visuals? How much of the hundreds of pages of raw data should I include in the appendices? What conclusions can I draw?*

To some extent, Erika also faces a persuasion challenge. She sees some striking discrepancies between the Enviro data and data released by REMA, an initiative funded by oil sands producers. Further examination reveals that some discrepancies have resulted from the contrasting locations of monitoring stations. (Most of REMA's stations are downstream from the oil sands developments, while half of Enviro's stations are upstream and half are downstream.)

The Persuasion Challenge

Sources of collaborative conflict

Before writing her report, Erika must persuade her boss, Dr. Russ Klingbeil, to include the data discrepancies, only some of which resulted from the location of monitoring stations. For 16 days in July 2006, Enviro's main downstream station recorded wild fluctuations in water flows because of an electrical short that was eventually diagnosed and repaired. Dr. Klingbeil is reluctant to admit this equipment failure. He is about to propose a contract extension to Alberta Environment.

Erika's associates have asserted that Enviro's monitoring methods are superior to REMA's methods, but Erika sees little evidence in the 2005 and 2006 data to support this belief. Enviro's stations might be better placed to record sediment deposits, but not to measure stream flow or water levels. Also, it seems that REMA and Enviro use similar methods to determine benthic invertebrate communities (a biological indicator that is an important component of fish habitats).

Finally, Erika concludes that measuring sediment quality is not very useful and should be discontinued—varying flows affect which parts of the riverbanks get eroded; shifting sand bars affect sedimentation and obscure the effect of releasing water from the oil sands production facilities; and deposited hydrocarbon sediments, which occur naturally from the hydrocarbons found in the riverbanks, have historically varied very little.

If Erika persuades Alberta Environment to discontinue the sediment measurements, the contract will be less profitable for her firm, so she will face pressure from her boss to "re-examine" the data and her conclusions.

The Ethics Challenge

The ethics of omitting information

What is more important—personal integrity or business success? (See Case Study Exercise 1 on page 89.)

Erika can choose what data to include and what to omit. Does she report the 16-day equipment malfunction and the faulty data, or simply omit the information that reflects badly on Enviro Associates? Admitting the malfunction may jeopardize her firm's continuing contract.

By choosing certain data and omitting other facts, Erika could show that Enviro's methods are superior to the methods employed by REMA, and thus strengthen her firm's case for continuing to monitor the Athabasca River, and she could show that multiple sets of monitoring data are not redundant. Further, recommending that sediment measurements be discontinued may affect her firm's bottom line and perhaps her own employment.

Situations that jeopardize truth and fairness present the hardest choices of all. Some aspects of Erika's ethical challenges are: *How much am I obligated to report? What do I feel is fair? What would be the consequences of omitting some of the data and interpreting the data to favour Enviro Associates?*

In addition to meeting these various challenges, Erika collaborates with others to produce the final report. Technologist Avre Ostif, who collected and downloaded most of the data, will review Erika's data presentation; Russ Klingbeil will proofread and edit the report; and a graphic artist will create professional, bound copies.

Finally, Erika's audience will extend beyond her own group of technical experts. Government bureaucrats will use the report to aid their decision making. Erika's readers will even extend beyond her own culture.

The Global Context Challenge

Content and phrasing choices need to reflect multiple readers' needs

Eventually, Alberta Environment will place the report on its website, where it will be available to a worldwide audience of interested oil-industry businesspeople and environmentalists. Also, Enviro Associates is negotiating with Alice Earth, an Australian-based company that wants to buy Enviro and incorporate it into its global environmental practice. If the acquisition occurs, all of Enviro's reports will be placed In Alice Earth's database for associates in Australia, the United States, China, Singapore, and Malaysia to read. Thus, Erika and her colleagues have been urged to write reports that will be understood by an international audience.

Possibly, Erika will soon start to develop working relationships with people she has never met and whose cultural expectations differ from hers.

TECHNICAL WRITERS COLLABORATE

The increasingly complex nature of doing business requires input from diverse sources, which is facilitated by electronic communication. Workplace documents (especially long reports, proposals, and manuals) are produced by teams who share information, expertise, ideas, and responsibilities. For example, the aviation manual writing process used by technical writer Roger Webber for clients, such as Bombardier and Flightcraft, requires collaboration at nearly every one of the many stages outlined in Figure 1.2.

ON THE JOB...

Collaborating on Complex Documents

"I've collaborated with others on complex documents. Collaborative writing means having to accommodate different perspectives and needs.... That's why the group must agree on common goals and an overall framework. Then the members must follow style guidelines, to produce a consistent document."

—Marilyn Riley Nault, freelance writer and editor

Successful collaboration combines the best that each team member has to offer. It enhances critical thinking by providing feedback, new perspectives, group support, and the chance to test ideas in group discussion.

Not all members of a collaborative team do the actual writing—some might research, edit, proofread, or test the document's *usability*. The more important the document, the more it will be reviewed. Notice the engineering approval, technical review, verification, and quality control checks in Figure 1.2.

Effective Roles in Groups[2]

Most groups, including collaborative writing teams, function best when certain key roles are established and followed. Two main types of roles have been identified: *task roles* and *maintenance roles*. Often, such roles are established informally.

2. Adapted from Larry J. Barker et al. *Groups in Process.* 3rd ed. Englewood Cliffs, NJ: Prentice-Hall, 1987.

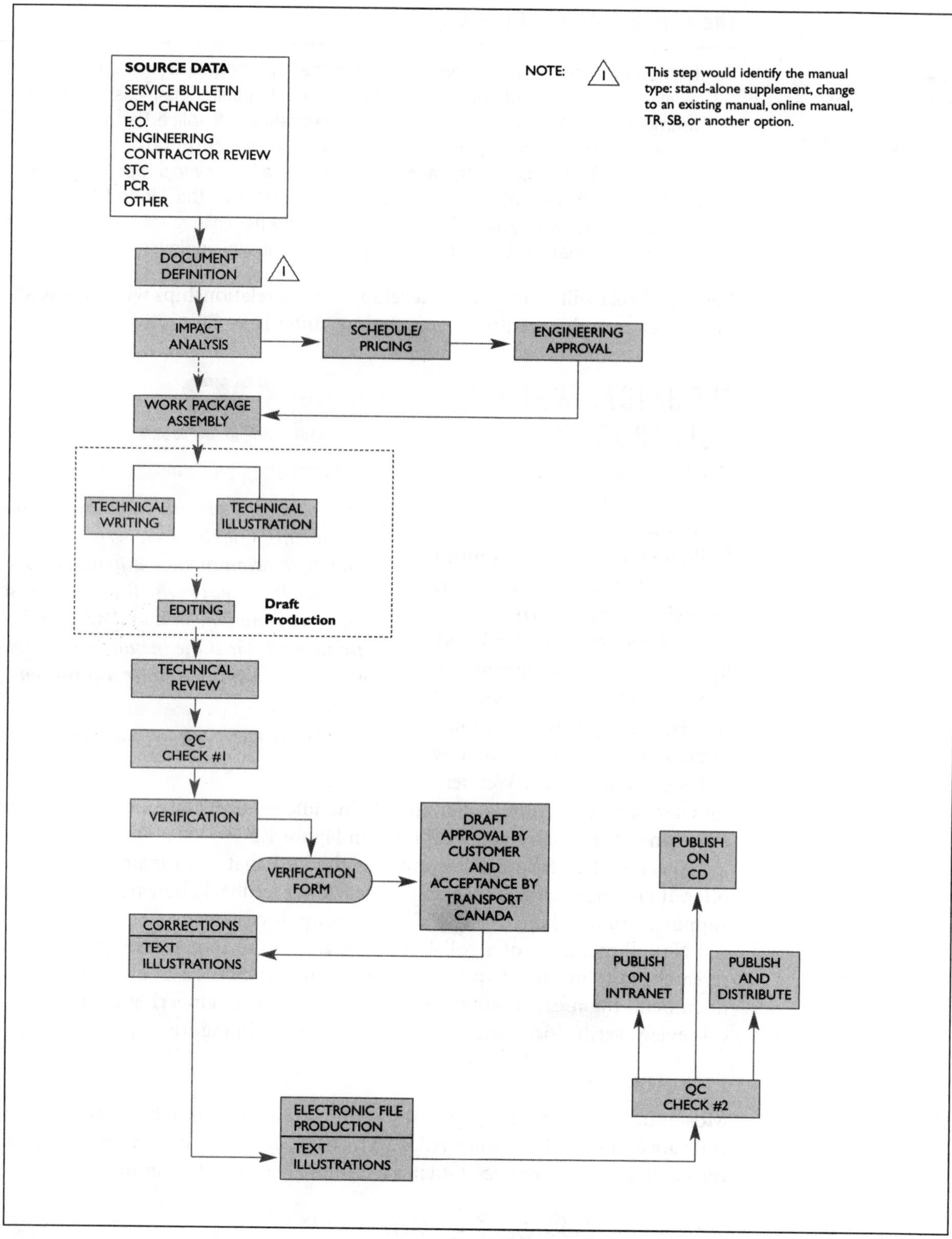

Figure 1.2 Publications Production Flow Chart for Aviation Documents

Source: Roger Webber, Torbay Technical Services.

Task Roles. In order to accomplish its set task, a group has to have its members successfully complete various task roles. Some people play one or two of these roles exclusively, but most people slide easily in and out of most of the roles.

- *Initiators* propose and define tasks; they also suggest solutions to problems or ways of solving problems.
- *Information seekers* notice where facts are needed; they push the group to find those facts. *Information givers* have the information at hand or they know how to find the needed information.
- *Opinion seekers* actively canvass group members for their ideas and opinions concerning a problem. *Opinion givers* volunteer input, respond readily when asked, and help set the criteria for solving problems.
- *Summarizers* draw together various ideas, facts, and opinions into a coherent whole; they review solutions, decisions, or problem-solving criteria. Often, the group's elected chair or appointed manager assumes this role.

Group Maintenance Roles. All successful groups need a supportive group climate in order for group members to give their best efforts. A positive group climate does not usually happen by accident; members have to consciously perform some of the following roles in order to develop and sustain a good working relationship.

- *Encouragers* help other group members feel accepted and valued. In particular, they go out of their way to reward those group members who are shy about contributing to the group's tasks.
- *Feeling expressers* try to get all group members to state their feelings about the group and those members' roles in the group.
- *Harmonizers* help deal with unproductive conflict by removing the personal, emotional aspects of disputes and concentrating on the objective issues. They recognize the good points made by the respective disputants and they help the "warring members" recognize the merits of each other's positions.
- *Gatekeepers* try to draw quiet group members into the discussion so that the louder, more aggressive group members do not dominate. When everyone contributes, two main advantages result: (1) the group has a better chance of getting the ideas and information it needs and (2) group morale improves.

Conflict Within Groups

Interpersonal sources of collaborative conflict

In any group effort, conflict can arise. Members might fail to get along because of differences in personality, working style, commitment, standards, or ability to take criticism. Some might disagree about exactly what or how much the group should accomplish, who should do what, or who should have the final say. Some might feel intimidated or hesitant to speak out. These interpersonal problems actually can worsen when the group communicates exclusively via email.

Generation gaps produce "natural" conflict

Members of collaborative writing groups are susceptible to the normal sources of human discord—defensiveness, rivalry, mistrust, clashing roles, and contrasting personal needs. In addition, today's younger workers are more likely than previous generations to question authority; these workers also want their opinions to be heard and their contributions to be valued. They present a special challenge for "old-school" managers (Moses, "The Challenge").

Misused power corrodes group effectiveness

A special form of unnecessary conflict ensues when persons in positions of power misuse their organizational authority, their prestige, or their personal charisma to get their way. Mistrust and sagging morale inevitably follow, often with negative effects on employee productivity and job satisfaction.

Any collaborative effort stands the best chance of succeeding when each group member feels included. A big mistake is to ignore personal differences, to assume everyone shares one viewpoint, one communication style, and one approach to problem solving. However, gender and cultural differences in collaborative groups can create perceptions of inequality and can lead to serious misunderstandings. Some of the sources of gender and cultural misunderstanding are introduced in the following In Brief section.

IN BRIEF GENDER AND CULTURAL DIFFERENCES IN COLLABORATIVE GROUPS

Gender Differences

Research on ways men and women communicate in meetings indicates a definite gender gap. Communication specialist Kathleen Kelley-Reardon offers this assessment of gender differences in workplace communication:

> Women and men operate according to communication rules for their gender, what experts call "gender codes." They learn, for example, to show gratitude, ask for help, take control, and express emotion, deference, and commitment in different ways. (88–89)

Professor Kelley-Reardon describes specific elements of a female gender code: women are more likely than men to take as much time as needed to explore an issue, build consensus and relationship among members, use tact in expressing views, use care in choosing their words, consider the listener's feelings, speak softly, allow interruptions, make requests instead of giving commands ("Could I have the report by Friday?" versus "Have this ready by Friday"), preface assertions in ways that avoid offending ("I don't want to seem disagreeable here, but...").

One study of mixed-gender interaction among peers indicates that women tend to be more agreeable, solicit and admit the merits of other opinions, ask questions, and express uncertainty (e.g., with qualifiers, such as *maybe, probably, it seems as if*) more often than men (Wojahn 747).

None of these traits, of course, is gender specific. Some people—regardless of gender—are more soft-spoken, contemplative, and reflective. But such traits most often are attributed to the "feminine" stereotype. Moreover, any woman who breaches the gender code, for instance, by being assertive, may be seen by peers as "too controlling" (Kelley-Reardon 6). In fact, studies suggest that women have less freedom than their male peers to alter their communication strategies: less assertive males often are still considered persuasive, whereas more assertive females often are not (Perloff 273).

Cultural Differences

International business expert David A. Victor describes cultural codes that influence interaction in collaborative groups: some cultures value silence more than speech, intuition and ambiguity more than hard evidence or data, politeness and personal relationships more than business relationships.

Cultures differ in their perceptions of time. Some want to get the job done immediately; others take as long as needed to weigh all the issues, engage in small talk and digressions, and inquire about family, health, and other personal matters.

Cultures may differ in their willingness to express disagreement, question or be questioned, leave things unstated, touch, shake hands, kiss, hug, or backslap.

Direct eye contact is not always a good indicator of listening. In some cultures it is considered offensive. Other eye movements, such as squinting, closing the eyes, staring away, or staring at legs or other body parts, are acceptable in some cultures but insulting in others.

(continued)

Influence of Online Communication

Some observers argue that online communication eliminates many such problems encountered in face-to-face meetings, because every participant, in effect, has as much time as needed to contribute to the electronically mediated discussion. Also, "status cues" such as age, gender, appearance, or ethnicity virtually disappear online. Other observers disagree, arguing that the interpersonal chemistry of communication transcends specific media (Wojahn 747–48).

Managing and Resolving Group Conflict

Faced with conflict, many groups seek short-term solutions while not dealing with the underlying causes of the disagreement. Often, then, the unresolved conflict poisons subsequent working relationships, igniting severe conflicts that ought to have been easily handled. In some cases, unresolved conflict is allowed to fester because the protagonists aren't sufficiently committed to dealing with the situation. In other words, they don't care enough to confront the situation.

Avoidance is a common response to conflict

Avoiding Conflict. In other cases, people are afraid of conflict and so they avoid confronting the situation that makes them uncomfortable. Unfortunately, the avoidance response fails to recognize that conflict is natural and inevitable, even in the most compatible work groups.

People who avoid conflict tend to discount the benefits that successfully managed conflict can bring, especially the increased understanding that accrues from carefully examining the nature and causes of a dispute. This process usually produces better decisions. Also, employees are encouraged to clarify their ideas and positions and are motivated to develop innovative solutions to problems (Graves).

Power plays sow the seeds of future conflicts

Using Power to Resolve Conflict. The two most common forms of power resolution are the use of authority and the formation of voting blocs. In the former approach, a problem might be referred up the chain of command, or a disputant might fall back on regulations of the law. Lawsuits represent an extreme version of this resolution method, but litigation often leaves deep wounds that inflame subsequent conflicts. The second kind of power play, which is found in more democratic organizations, usually involves lobbying behind the scenes to help a "combatant" form a successful voting bloc. Again, this type of force erodes the quality of working relationships.

Both types of power plays can result in "win–lose" outcomes, although if both sides of the dispute are able to muster enough support, the battle may turn into a dispute that neither can win—a "lose–lose" outcome.

"Win–win" strategies focus on solving problems, not on "winning battles"

Resolving Conflict Collaboratively. "Win–win" outcomes rarely result from exercising power and influence. The parties in a dispute are more likely to be satisfied by collaborative approaches. The stage can be set for resolving potential conflicts by maintaining a supportive communications climate in the work group—in such a climate, workers feel welcome to express their concerns and proposals, and they know that they will be rewarded, not censured, for confronting issues.

In collaborative approaches, participants emphasize solving problems, not fighting battles. They use their common goals as a starting point, and they get good information as the basis for a productive discussion. They show support for others in the discussion and, more to the point, they discuss issues; they don't debate with the intention of winning a battle. Participants explain their reactions and the source of their disagreement or discomfort. Sometimes, a mediator may be employed to help the group members through this process.

Collaborative conflict resolution shares many features with case study problem-solving methods taught at Harvard (hence the name, Harvard Case Study Model) and at Canadian business schools. Sample cases may be found at **www.pearsoned.ca/lannon**, the text enrichment website for this book.

Further advice, including a five-stage structured approach, is available at Industry Canada's Strategis website. Although it is aimed at entrepreneurs looking to succeed in business negotiations, its advice applies to any negotiation (see **http://strategis.ic.gc.ca/sc_mangb/stepstogrowth/engdoc/skills/skill-3-5.php**).

GUIDELINES for Active Listening

1. *Don't dictate.* If you are leading the group, don't express your view until everyone else has had a chance.
2. *Be receptive.* Take in different views and evaluate them later.
3. *Keep an open mind.* Judgment stops thought (Hayakawa 42). Reserve judgment until everyone has had his or her say.
4. *Be courteous.* Don't smirk, roll your eyes, whisper, or wisecrack.
5. *Show genuine interest.* Non-verbals are vital (eye contact, nodding, smiling, leaning toward the speaker). Make it a point to remember everyone's name.

4. *Hear the speaker out.* Instead of "tuning out" a message you find disagreeable, allow the speaker to continue without interruption (except to ask for clarification). Delay your own questions, comments, and rebuttals until the speaker has finished.

7. *Focus on the message.* Instead of thinking about what you want to say next, try to get a clear understanding of the speaker's position.
8. *Ask for clarification.* If anything is unclear, say so: "Can you repeat that?" To ensure accuracy, paraphrase the message: "So you're saying that…"
9. *Be agreeable.* Don't turn the conversation into a contest, and don't insist on having the last word.

Source: Adapted from H. Armstrong 24; Bashein and Markus 37; Cooper 78–84; Dumont and Lannon 648–51; Pearce, Johnson and Barker 28–32.

Ethical Issues in Workplace Collaboration

Our lean, downsized corporate world spells competition among workers:

Teamwork versus "survival of the fittest"

> Many companies send mixed signals... saying they value teamwork while still rewarding individual stars, so that nobody has any real incentive to share the glory. (Fisher, "My Team Leader" 291)

The resulting mistrust interferes with fair and open teamwork and promotes unethical behaviour, which may be especially tempting to ambitious employees eager to climb the organizational ladder.

Intimidating Co-workers. A dominant personality may intimidate peers into silence or agreement, or the group leader may allow no other viewpoints (Matson, "The Seven Sins" 30). Intimidated employees resort to "mimicking"—merely repeating what the boss says (Haskin, "Meetings Without Walls" 55).

Claiming Credit for Others' Work. Workplace plagiarism occurs when the team or project leader claims all the credit. Even with good intentions, "the person who speaks for a team often gets the credit, not the people who had the ideas or did the work" (Nakache 287–88). Team expert James Stern describes one strategy for avoiding plagiarism among co-workers:

How to ensure that the deserving team members get credit

> Some companies list "core" and "contributing" team members, to distinguish those who did the heavy lifting from those were less involved. (qtd. in Fisher 291)

Stern advises groups to decide beforehand—and in writing—what credit will be given for which contributions.

Hoarding Information. Surveys reveal that the biggest obstacle to workplace collaboration is people's "tendency to hoard their own know-how"(Cole-Gomoloski 6) when confronted with questions like these:

Information that people need to do their jobs

- Whom do we contact for what?
- Where do we get the best price, the quickest repair, the most dependable service?
- What's the best way to do X?

Despite all the technology available for information sharing, fewer than 10 percent of companies succeed in persuading employees to share ideas on a routine basis (Koudsi 233). People hoard information that they think gives them power or self-importance, or when having exclusive knowledge might provide job security (Devlin 179). In a worse case, they withhold information in order to sabotage peers.

COMMUNICATION SKILLS REQUIRED BY CONSULTANTS

The communication skills discussed in this chapter certainly apply to *consultants*—people who are paid to provide assessments, advice, technical solutions, and business solutions for external clients. Although many prefer the security of working for consulting firms, others choose an *entrepreneurial* path. These risk takers are willing to work long and hard to identify and meet clients' needs.

Many types of clients require consultant services

People provide consulting services in almost any field—engineering, environmental assessment and improvement, manufacturing, project management, health care, criminal justice, municipal services, business management, education, and computer technology. The list could go on and on.

Consultants provide assessment and other analytical services; they determine causes of problems and recommend solutions; they plan and lead projects; they provide skills assessment and training; they guide their clients through procedures that the consultants have recommended; they write reports for private and government organizations.

Whether they work for a firm or are self-employed, consultants rely on several critical communication skills:

Consultants must be skilled communicators

1. *They must be active listeners.* In conversation or in writing, they help clients identify needs and priorities. All successful consulting begins with an understanding of the pressing issues and problems. Often, the consultant supplements this knowledge with secondary research into the history and/or technical context of the situation.
2. *Consultants must be good analysts and problem solvers.* Often, they will need creative, innovative strategies to deal with unique situations. There are very few "cookie cutter" solutions in the world of consulting. So, consultants need to be open to new ways of doing things.
3. *Consultants must handle the pressure of looming deadlines and client expectations.* Even the least assertive client expects high-quality work in return for what he or she may perceive as high fees.
4. *Consultants must project a professional image,* through their written correspondence, personal appearance, and timely communication. Phone calls, text messages, and emails should be acknowledged and returned promptly. Consultants must fully prepare for client meetings.
5. *Consultants must have excellent interpersonal skills* to work with all levels of client understanding and a variety of personality types.
6. *Consultants must possess team-building and leadership skills.* Almost every project, at some stage or other, requires collaborative effort. Often, the consultant will lead or supervise that team effort.

Consultants win most of their contracts through proposals

7. *Above all, consultants must display strong oral and written skills for networking, marketing, reporting, and proposal writing.* The independent consultant will learn about opportunities through his or her contact network or through advertised requests for proposals. The next step will be to prepare and present a proposal. More often than not, this proposal must compete with rival proposals. (Chapter 14 discusses proposal processes, types, and structures.)

WEB CONNECT

These sites discuss the nature of technical writing, technical writing careers, and job listings for technical writers, collaborative writing techniques, and hints for effective technical documents:

http://en.wikipedia.org/wiki/Technical_communication
www.stc.org/membership/interestedTC01.asp
www.jeanweber.com/about/edrole.htm

This site provides internet resources for technical communicators:

www.soltys.ca/techcomm.html

For information about VPNs, see the Virtual Private Network Consortium website:

www.vpnc.org

Industry Canada discusses conflict resolution within the context of business negotiations:

http://strategis.ic.gc.ca/sc_mangb/stepstogrowth/engdoc/skills/skill-3-1.php

Here's an entertaining and useful conflict resolution game:

www.crnhq.org/crgame.html

EXERCISES

1. Locate a brief example of a technical document (or a section of one). Make a photocopy, bring it to class, and explain why your selection can be called technical writing.
2. Research the kinds of writing you will do in your future career. (Begin with the *Dictionary of Occupational Titles* in your library.) You might interview a member of your chosen profession. Why will you write on the job? For whom will you write? Explain in a memo to your instructor. (See Chapter 13 for memo elements and format.)
3. In a memo to your instructor, describe the skills you seek to develop in your technical writing course. How exactly will you apply these skills to your career?
4. Assume a friend in your major thinks that writing skills are obsolete, and that administrative assistants or word processors can fix any writing. Write your friend a letter, explaining why you think these assumptions are mistaken. Use examples to support your position. (See Chapter 13 for letter elements and format.)

COLLABORATIVE PROJECT

Divide into small groups of mixed genders. Read "In Brief" (page 16) and complete the following tasks to test the hypothesis that women and men communicate differently in the workplace.

Each group member prepares the following brief messages—without consulting with other members:

- A thank-you note to a co-worker who has done you a favour.
- A note asking a colleague for help with a problem or project.
- A note asking a collaborative peer to be more cooperative or stop interrupting or complaining.
- A note offering support to a good friend and co-worker.
- A note to a new colleague, welcoming this person to the company.
- The meeting is out of hand, so you decide to take control. Write what you would say.
- Some members of your group are dragging their feet on a project. Write what you would say.

As a group, compare messages, draw conclusions about the original hypothesis, and appoint one member to present the findings to the class.

CHAPTER 2

Preparing to Write: Audience/ Purpose Analysis

LEARNING OBJECTIVES

After reading this chapter, you should be able to

- Identify the factors to consider in analyzing the communication in a given situation.
- Understand why communication can easily break down.
- Choose the appropriate level of technicality for a given message and audience.
- Develop an audience/purpose profile to help choose the content, structure, design, and tone for a document.

As a technical writer, you'll need to consider your readers' needs. Perhaps you want your readers to support a proposal; perhaps you are responding to your supervisor's request for information about your progress on a project. Whatever you write, you must think very carefully about your audience and your purpose for writing in *any* kind of technical or business communication, written or spoken.

For example, when preparing for a job interview, consider more than the points you hope to make about your qualifications and skills; also consider what the interviewer hopes to gain. Analyzing the interviewer's role—to find an ideal candidate for the job—will help you anticipate the questions.

Can you predict how a listener will react to statements in a job interview, or how a reader will interpret a report's facts and conclusions? The answer is that you can't know *for certain*. However, you *can* make some shrewd guesses. The following communication model can help you anticipate receiver reactions so that you can adapt the content and presentation of your messages.

USE A COMMUNICATION MODEL

Certain factors affect each communication

Whether you have a quiet talk with a friend or write a high-powered report for an important client, certain key factors affect the nature and outcome of that communication. The following model develops those factors, to show how the factors interact and contribute to the success of that exchange.

Let's analyze a conversation between a consulting mechanical engineer, Daphne McCrae, and McCrae's client, Max Lauder, the maintenance supervisor for the Trendmark Ski Resort. Lauder has heard about a neighbouring ski hill's problem with the massive cast-metal gripping mechanisms that clamp the chairs of a high-speed chair lift onto the cable of that lift. Lauder wants McCrae's advice about whether to replace the grips on Trendmark's high-speed quad lift. Thus, McCrae has tested several grips and is giving a preliminary oral report of her findings.

Identify the primary message

First, in the communications model, let's identify the conversation's primary *message* as Daphne McCrae's semi-technical answer to Lauder's question. McCrae is the *sender* of that message; Lauder is the *receiver.* Their conversation, which occurs in the ski resort's maintenance building, uses an oral verbal *channel* and several non-verbal *channels.*

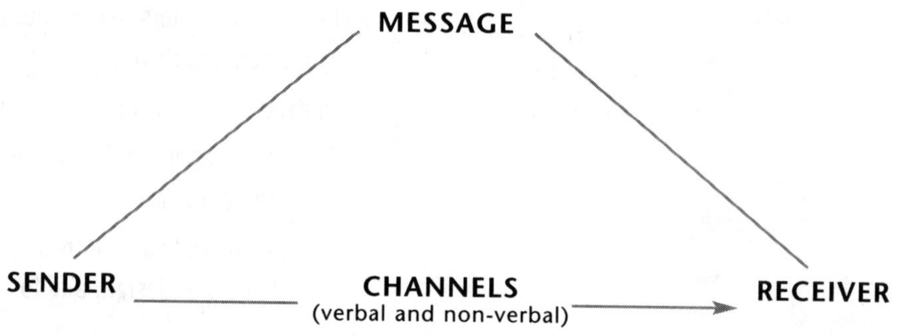

"Content" verbal messages are mediated by "relational" non-verbal messages

The conversation between McCrae and Lauder seems to depend on the verbal channel of speech. After all, McCrae uses words to convey her knowledge about the factors that might contribute to cast-alloy failure. Such *content* messages are often assumed to constitute the entire message.

However, several non-verbal channels, such as facial expression, vocal inflections, posture, and gestures, send accompanying messages about the sender's confidence in his own knowledge, degree of certainty, and level of concern for his client's current problem. How Max Lauder receives these non-verbal *relational* messages affects how he judges the accuracy and value of McCrae's words.

Has Daphne McCrae chosen an appropriate channel to convey her initial reaction to her client's question? The answer is "yes," especially if she wants to alleviate her receiver's immediate concerns. However, if McCrae were to communicate a full technical analysis of the grips she has tested, she should use a formal written report to present her findings. McCrae's choice of communication channels illustrates a basic communication principle: senders need to choose their primary communication channels carefully in order to reach their receivers.

Here are some other questions to help assess which channels should be used in a given situation:

1. *Has the sender chosen a channel used by the receiver?* For example, Daphne McCrae won't reach Max Lauder via email on days when Lauder is working on the lifts, away from his office computer.

2. *Has the sender taken advantage of the chosen channel's particular strengths?* The main advantage of presenting McCrae's initial analysis *orally* is that it allows her to accompany her semi-technical comments with reassuring vocal tones and other non-verbal messages.
3. *Have both the sender and receiver blocked out external "noise"?* The maintenance building could be very noisy, as workers repair and maintain equipment, so perhaps the conversation should be held in Lauder's office. However, in this case, the two participants need to examine the equipment as they talk, so they meet in the maintenance shed, where they need to block out the noise in order to focus on each other's messages.
4. *Has the sender considered both the verbal and non-verbal aspects of the transmission?* McCrae's subsequent written analysis will need to use a formal report format, to correspond to the subject's serious nature and to signal the writer's credibility.

Choosing the right channel is only the beginning. The sender also has to encode the message so that the receiver has at least a hope of decoding it as the sender intended. Proper encoding means choosing the right words, sentence patterns, and message structures to suit the sender's purpose and the reader's interests and needs. This collection of choices requires careful thought; that's why this text emphasizes audience/purpose analysis for all writing and speaking assignments.

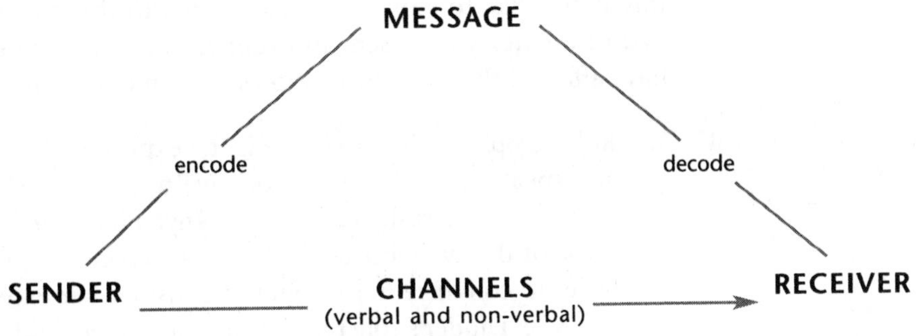

Decode messages carefully

Does Max Lauder understand Daphne McCrae's explanations? Perhaps. If McCrae uses a great deal of technical jargon, Lauder may be perplexed. And if McCrae oversimplifies her message, Lauder won't get the full picture and thus will not understand McCrae's advice about the grips.

Indeed, decoding messages is often harder than encoding them. To start with, many receivers do not know how to listen or read effectively and so they miss much of the intended message. Even the alert, skilled receiver may have difficulty following the sender's train of thought if the encoded message has been poorly organized, or if the sender has chosen an inappropriate level of phrasing or detail, or if the sender's verbal and non-verbal messages contradict each other.

Even when the receiver is confident that she or he has understood the message, communication can break down. That's because senders and receivers often have different meanings for the same words. (Your English professor, for example, might intend the word *decode* to interpret written and spoken words, but you might think of deciphering Morse code and other coded messages if you have a military background or a passion for spy novels.)

Now let's introduce more psychology to our communication model:

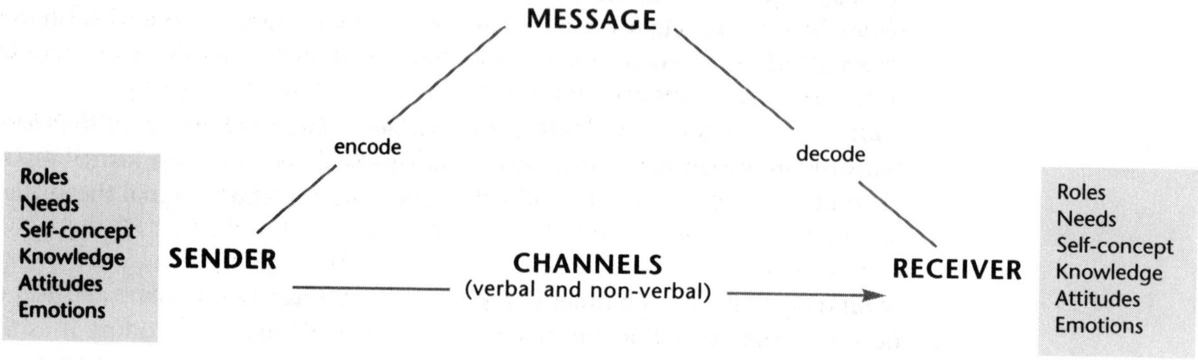

The terms beside *sender* and *receiver* in the model refer to factors that may affect each person at the time the communication occurs. These terms will now be discussed. The discussion will analyze the McCrae/Lauder conversation, but you might also like to stop at various points to think of a recent conversation you've had or a letter you've sent in order to see how each of the following factors may have affected the communication's outcome in each of those cases.

Consider the factors that affect the encoding and decoding processes

1. *Roles.* Daphne McCrae's role is the expert analyst, which compels her to think and speak carefully and rationally. In that role, she must not jump to conclusions or make rash statements. Why? First, her job role requires her to make sense of the available technical data. Second, she has to maintain credibility in order to convince her listener to consider her expert advice.

   Max Lauder's role requires him to understand and absorb McCrae's analysis and advice. Thus, Lauder listens very attentively.

   Now, think of how your role influences your behaviour at this moment. Probably, you're reading this page because your student role requires you to do so. So your receiving behaviour is role-dominated. But what if you find yourself getting really interested in this subject? What if you are now starting to think of how *role* affects your communication with your friends and your colleagues at work or school? If so, your *personal needs* are starting to influence your receiving behaviour.
2. *Needs.* It's obvious that we all have strong reasons for communicating with others: *practical needs* associated with making a living, basic *physical needs,* and *social needs* for acceptance, affection, and control. Also, *identity needs* seem always to influence our behaviour, even when we're taking care of our basic physical needs or our practical business needs. Much of our communication has us trying to determine who we are and then trying to assert that identity to others. If we allow our identity needs to dominate, however, problems may result. For

example, if Daphne McCrae were to have a strong identity need to appear forceful and infallible, she might be driven to make definite conclusions even if there's insufficient data to support such conclusions. If her identity need overruns her role requirement, she might provide disastrous advice to her client.

3. *Self-concept.* Our self-beliefs affect our sending and receiving behaviours. If, for example, Daphne McCrae sees herself as analytical and intelligent, her word choices and speaking pace will reflect those self-perceptions. And if Max Lauder sees himself as very practical but lacking education, he may defer to some of McCrae's conclusions even if his instincts tell him that she is wrong.
4. *Knowledge.* A sender like Daphne McCrae has to know her subject well before she can successfully explain, for example, resistance to stress in cast-metal chairlift grips. Similarly, Max Lauder has to have a rudimentary knowledge in order to understand any of the complexities in McCrae's analysis. From a practical viewpoint, Lauder probably understands these stresses well: he has observed the chairlift in action. However, he probably does not understand how to measure shear forces or how metal breaks down.
5. *Attitudes.* In the conversation we've been analyzing, both participants have a serious attitude toward the topic being discussed. They concentrate on the technical and practical aspects of a potential problem. Another factor lies in their degree of respect for each other. As it turns out, both are in their late 30s with over 15 years' experience in their field. Each is aware of the other's expertise, so each chooses words carefully.

   Actually, our attitudes are usually shown non-verbally. In the McCrae/Lauder conversation, the most likely channels revealing their attitudes toward the situation and each other would be posture, facial expressions, and tone of voice.
6. *Emotions.* You have experienced many situations where your emotions have affected how you spoke or how you listened. Indeed, one's emotions can totally block effective communication. In business, we should not allow that to happen, and it's not likely to happen in the conversation between Lauder and McRae.

Reasons for communication breakdown

As this chapter has hinted, communication can break down for many reasons:

- poor choice of channels
- receiver inattentiveness
- poor sender decoding
- lack of knowledge in sender or receiver
- conflicting roles or contrasting personal needs

Feedback can help communication

However, most misunderstandings can be prevented by timely and useful *feedback*, which is so important for two-way channels, such as face-to-face conversations, telephone calls, and email. Let's introduce that feedback loop next (see next page).

Feedback could be particularly useful in the McCrae/Lauder meeting—Lauder could immediately signal that he didn't understand some aspect of the message he heard, and McCrae could use different terminology or a different order of explanation to convey her message.

While two-way channels provide timely, direct feedback, written channels (letters, memos, reports) do not. That's why you should consider the reader's role,

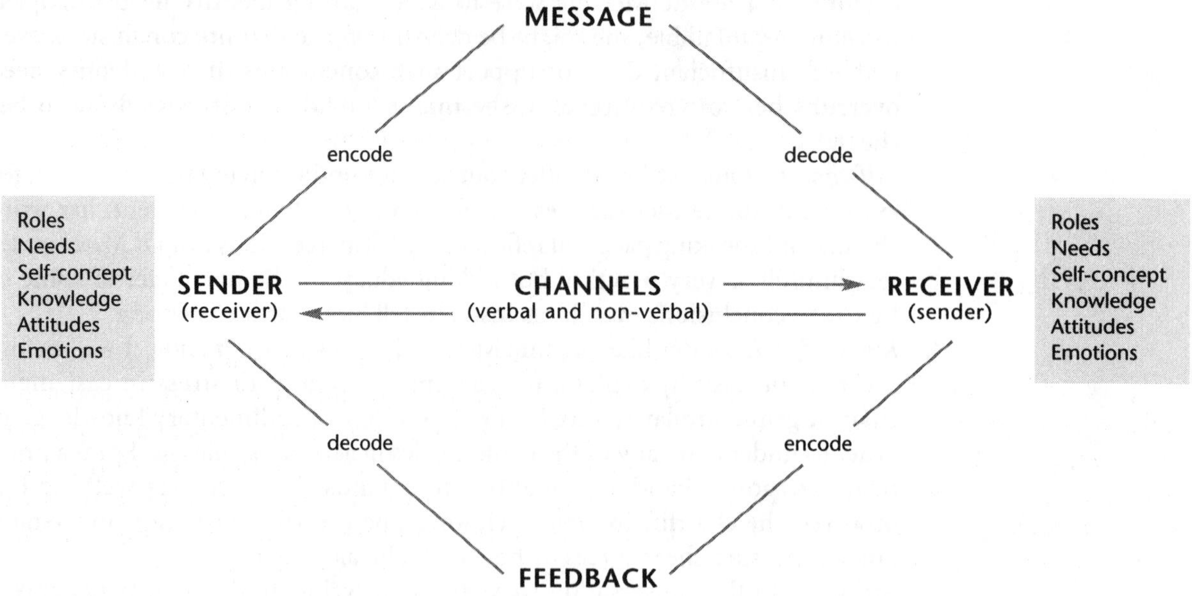

needs, and knowledge levels when you choose the content, structure, and style of your written messages.

Environmental noise can be distracting

The above model does not include the impact of the *environment* in which the communication occurs. The *physical environment* can introduce audio or visual "noise." Some people can receive and send messages in noisy environments; others cannot. Employers are now recognizing that the noise generated by phone rings, fax machines, printers, speakerphones, email prompts, and CD players creates undue stress for many employees. Consequently, steps are being taken to reduce and/or mask noise (Johne). Visual stimuli, such as loud wallpaper or bright shiny walls, too many pictures, a constant flow of people passing by, bright lighting, or superfluous computer monitors, provide additional noise.

Social conventions affect sending behaviours

The *social environment* further affects how we act and how we interpret messages. For example, we use a lot more slang in conversations with friends than we do in business meetings.

Senders and receivers should consider each other's cultural filters

Another important environmental consideration is the *cultural context.* Friends in social settings usually share culturally biased perceptual patterns. But the workplace, especially in Canada's cultural mosaic, can present a bewildering array of belief systems, non-verbal communication behaviours, and ways of interpreting messages. Many business encounters misfire when sender and receiver interpret their exchange through different cultural filters. (Pages 41 and 42 advise how to communicate with people from different cultural backgrounds.)

Small group communication is more complex than dyadic communication

It should be noted that *small group communication* (three to 15 people) is quite different from *dyadic communication* (one on one). Groups provide significantly more opportunities for interaction than two-person dyads do. For example, a three-person group has potential for four sets of interaction as compared to just one potential interaction in a dyad. A four-person group produces 10 potential interaction sets. Increasing group complexity increases the potential for information sharing but also the potential for disagreement and conflict (Barker et al.).

Small groups always contain an audience or observer, unlike one-on-one dyads, and speakers often modify their comments when they're aware of being observed. When they do consider the others in the group, speakers reveal a persuasive motive—in the small group, majority coalitions can form and alliances may therefore be more important than evidence or other forms of logical persuasion.

Now, let's look at assessing your readers' information needs.

ON THE JOB...

Audiences

"I write procedures for technicians who install and service photocopiers and other business machines. When our company introduces a new machine... all district offices get the technical information, and a set of procedures written by the engineers who designed the equipment. I then rewrite the procedures to make it easier for technicians to follow. I also give follow-up training sessions to provide our technicians with hands-on experience...."

—Leslie Jacobs, service rep and former technician

ASSESS READERS' INFORMATION NEEDS

Good writing connects with readers by recognizing their different backgrounds, needs, and preferences. A single message may appear in several versions for several audiences. For instance, an article describing a new cancer treatment might appear in a medical journal read by doctors and nurses. A less technical version might appear in a medical textbook read by medical and nursing students. An even simpler version might appear in *Reader's Digest.* All three versions treat the same topic, but each meets the needs of a different audience.

Technical writing is intended to be *used.* You become the teacher and the reader becomes the student. Because your readers may know less than you, they may have questions.

TYPICAL READER QUESTIONS ABOUT WORKPLACE DOCUMENTS

- Who should read the document?
- What is being described or explained?
- What does it look like?
- How did you do it?
- Why did it happen?
- Why should we do it?
- What are the risks?
- When will it happen?
- How much will it cost?

Always write to enable a specific audience to grasp the information and follow the discussion. To be useful, the writing must connect with the reader's level of understanding.

IDENTIFY LEVELS OF TECHNICALITY

When you write for a close acquaintance (friend, computer crony, co-worker, professor, or supervisor), you know a good deal about your reader's background. You deliberately adapt your document to that reader's knowledge, interests, and needs. But sometimes you write for less-defined audiences, particularly when the audience is large (e.g., when you are writing a journal article, a computer manual, a set of first-aid procedures, or a report of an accident). Even though you have only a general notion about your audience's background, you must decide whether your document should be *highly technical, semi-technical,* or *non-technical,* as depicted in Figure 2.1.

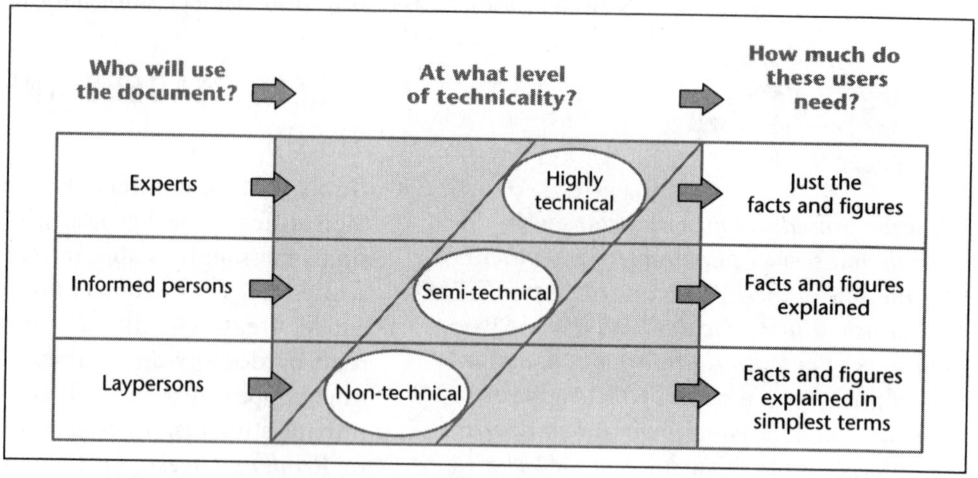

Figure 2.1 Deciding on a Document's Level of Technicality

The Highly Technical Document

Readers at the specialized level expect the technical facts and figures they need, without long explanations. The following report of treatment given to a heart attack victim is highly technical. The writer, an emergency room physician, is reporting to the patient's doctor. This reader needs an exact record of the patient's symptoms and treatment.

A Highly Technical Version

Expert readers need merely the facts and figures, which they can interpret for themselves

The patient was brought to the emergency room by ambulance at 0100 hours, September 27, 2007. The patient complained of severe chest pains, dyspnea, and vertigo. Auscultation and EKG revealed a massive cardiac infarction and pulmonary edema marked by pronounced cyanosis. Vital signs: blood pressure, 80/40; pulse, 140/min; respiration, 35/min. Lab: WBC, 20 000; elevated serum transaminase; urea nitrogen, 60 mg%. Urinalysis showed 4+ protein and 4+ granular casts/field, indicating acute renal failure secondary to the hypotension.

The patient received 10 mg of morphine stat, subcutaneously, followed by nasal oxygen and D5W intravenously. At 0125 the cardiac monitor recorded an irregular sinus rhythm, indicating left ventricular fibrillation. The patient was defibrillated stat and given a 50 mg bolus of Xylocaine intravenously. A Xylocaine drip was started and sodium bicarbonate administered until a normal heartbeat was established. By 0300, the oscilloscope was recording a normal sinus rhythm.

As the heartbeat stabilized and cyanosis diminished, the patient received 5 cc of heparin intravenously, to be repeated every six hours. By 0500 the BUN had fallen to 20 mg% and vital signs had stabilized: blood pressure, 110/60; pulse, 105/min; respiration, 22/min. The patient was now conscious and responsive.

This highly technical report is clear only to the medical expert. Because her reader has extensive background, this writer defines no technical terms (*pulmonary edema, sinus rhythm*). Nor does she interpret lab findings (4+ protein, elevated serum transaminase). She uses abbreviations her reader understands (WBC, BUN, D5W). Because her reader knows the reasons for specific treatments and medications (defibrillation, Xylocaine drip), she includes no theoretical background. Her report answers concisely the main questions she can anticipate from her reader: What happened? What treatment was given? What were the results?

The Semi-technical Document

One broad class of readers may have some technical background but less than the experts. For instance, first-year medical students have specialized knowledge but not as much as second-, third-, and fourth-year students. Yet students in all four groups could be considered semi-technical readers. When you write for a semi-technical audience, identify the *lowest* level of understanding in the group and write to that level. Too much explanation is better than too little.

Here is a partial version of the earlier medical report. Written at a semi-technical level, it might appear in a textbook for first-year medical or nursing students, in a report for a medical social worker, in a patient's history for the medical technology department, or in a monthly report for the hospital administration.

A Semi-technical Version

Informed but non-expert readers need enough explanation to understand what the facts mean

Examination by stethoscope and electrocardiogram revealed a massive failure of the heart muscle along with fluid buildup in the lungs, which produced a cyanotic **discolouration of the lips and fingertips from lack of oxygen.**

The patient's blood pressure at 80 mm Hg (systolic)/40 mm Hg (diastolic) was **dangerously below its normal measure of 130/70.** A pulse rate of 140/minute was **almost twice the normal rate of 60–80.** Respiration at 35/minute was more than **twice the normal rate of 12–16.**

Laboratory blood tests yielded a white blood cell count of 20 000/cu mm (normal value: 5000–10 000), **indicating a severe inflammatory response by the heart muscle.** The elevated serum transaminase enzymes **(produced in quantity only when the heart muscle fails)** confirmed the earlier diagnosis. A blood urea nitrogen level of 60 mg% (normal value: 12–16 mg%) indicated **that the kidneys had ceased to filter out metabolic waste products.** The 4+ protein and casts reported from the urinalysis (normal value: 0) **revealed that the kidney tubules were degenerating as a result of the lowered blood pressure.**

The patient immediately received morphine **to ease the chest pain,** followed by oxygen **to relieve strain on the cardiopulmonary system,** and an intravenous solution of dextrose and water **to prevent shock.**

The version explains (in boldface) the raw data. Exact dosages are not mentioned because the readers are not treating the patient. Normal values of lab tests and vital signs, however, make interpretation easier. (Expert readers would know these values.) Knowing what medications the patient received would be especially important to the lab technician because some medications affect test results. For a non-technical audience, however, the message needs further translation.

The Non-technical Document

Readers with no specialized training expect technical data to be translated into terms they understand. Non-technical readers are impatient with abstract theories but want enough background to help them make the right decision or take the right action. They are bored by long explanations but frustrated by bare facts not explained or interpreted. They expect a report that is clear on first reading, not one that requires review or study.

The following is a non-technical version of our medical report. The physician might write this version for the patient's spouse who is overseas on business, or as part of a script for a documentary film about emergency room treatment.

A Non-technical Version

General readers need everything translated into terms they understand

Heart sounds and electrical impulses both were abnormal, **indicating a massive heart attack caused by failure of a large part of the heart muscle**. The lungs were swollen with fluid and the lips and fingertips showed a bluish discolouration from **lack of oxygen**.

Blood pressure was dangerously low, **creating the risk of shock**. Pulse and respiration were **almost twice the normal rate, indicating that the heart and lungs were being overworked** in keeping oxygenated blood circulating freely.

Blood tests confirmed the heart attack diagnosis and **indicated that waste products usually filtered out by the kidneys were building up in the bloodstream. Urine tests showed that the kidneys were failing as a result of the lowered blood pressure.**

The patient was given **medication to ease the chest pain, oxygen to ease the strain on the heart and lungs**, and **intravenous solution to prevent the blood vessels from collapsing and causing irreversible shock**.

This non-technical version explains (in boldface) the situation using everyday language. It omits any mention of medications, lab tests, or normal values because these have no meaning for the reader. The writer merely summarizes events and explains the causes of the crisis and the reasons for the particular treatment.

In some other situation, however (say, in a jury trial for malpractice), the non-technical audience might need information about specific medication and treatment. Such a report would, of course, be much longer—a short course in emergency coronary treatment.

Each version of the medical report is useful *only* to readers at a specific level. Doctors and nurses have no need for the explanations in the two latter versions, but they do need the specialized data in the first. Beginning medical students and paramedics might be confused by the first version and bored by the third. Non-technical readers would find both the first and second versions meaningless.

Primary and Secondary Readers

Whenever you prepare a single document for multiple readers, classify your readers as *primary* or *secondary.* Primary readers usually are those who requested the document and who will use it as a basis for decisions or actions. Secondary readers are those who will carry out the project, who will advise the primary readers about their decision, or who will somehow be affected by this decision. They will read your document (or perhaps only part of it) for information that will help them get the job done, for educated advice, or to keep up with new developments.

Often these two audiences differ in technical background. Primary readers may require highly technical messages, and secondary readers may need semi-technical or non-technical messages—or vice versa. When you must write for audiences at different levels, follow these guidelines:

How to tailor a single document to multiple readers

1. If the document is short (a letter, memo, or anything under two pages), rewrite it at various levels for various readers.
2. If the document exceeds two pages, address the primary readers. Then provide appendices for secondary readers (technical appendices when secondary readers are technical, or non-technical versions when they are not). Letters of transmittal, informative abstracts, and glossaries are other supplements that help non-specialized audiences understand a highly technical report. (See Chapter 21 for how to use and prepare appendices and other supplements.)

The next scenario shows how some documents must be tailored to both primary and secondary readers.

Tailoring a Document to Different Readers

When Daphne McCrae writes the results of her tests on potentially damaged ski-lift grips, her primary reader will be the client, Trendmark Ski Resort. That audience will include Max Lauder, the maintenance supervisor who has some technical knowledge of metal and metal fatigue. The audience will also include Trendmark's management board and its lawyer, all of whom have little or no technical knowledge.

McCrae's report may eventually have legal implications, so it must be presented in meticulous detail. But her non-specialist readers will need explanations of her testing methods. These readers will also need photos of the test equipment to fully understand the processes involved. The report will have to define specialized terms such as *fractographs* (microscopic photographs of fractured surfaces) and *HSLA* (high-strength, low-alloy) steel, such as ASTM grade A 242 (which has 0.4% copper alloyed to the steel to provide greater weathering resistance).

The report's secondary readers will include Daphne McCrae's supervisor and outside consulting engineers who may evaluate McCrae's test procedures and assess the validity of her findings. Consultants will focus on various parts of the report to verify that McCrae's procedure has been exact and faultless. For these readers, she will have to include appendices spelling out the technical details of her analysis: *how* light-microscopic fractographs revealed the presence and direction of fractures, and *how* the pattern of these fractures indicates a casting flaw in the original grip, not torsional fatigue. Finally, McCrae must present the technical details of her finding that only one grip has the casting flaw and that the other grips are safe for operation.

In McCrae's situation, primary readers need to know *what her findings mean*, whereas secondary readers need to know *how she arrived at her conclusions.* If she serves each group's needs, her information will be worthwhile.

DEVELOP AN AUDIENCE/PURPOSE PROFILE

When you write for a particular reader or defined group of readers, you can focus sharply on your audience by using an analytical tool like the Audience/Purpose Profile Sheet in Figure 2.2. This form can also be used to identify and analyze a variety of *secondary* audiences, whose varied roles, self-perceptions, attitudes toward you and your role, attitudes toward the document's subject matter, and emotional states could produce diverse reactions to your document.

Reader Characteristics

Identify the primary readers by name, job title, and specialty (e.g., Martha Jones, Director of Quality Control, B.S. and M.S. in mechanical engineering). Are they superiors, colleagues, or subordinates? Are they inside or outside your organization? What is their likely attitude toward this topic? Are they apt to accept or reject your conclusions and recommendations? Will you present good or bad news? How might their cultural backgrounds affect their expectations and interpretations?

Also identify secondary readers who are interested in or affected by your document or who might affect the primary readers' perceptions or use of your document.

Purpose of the Document

Learn why readers want the document and how they will use it. Do they merely want a record of activities or progress? Do they expect only raw data, or conclusions and recommendations as well? Will readers act immediately on the information? Do they need step-by-step instructions? Will the document be read and discarded, filed, published, or distributed electronically? In your audience's view, *what* is most important? What purpose should this document achieve?

Readers' Technical Background

Colleagues who speak your technical language will understand raw data. Supervisors responsible for several technical areas may want interpretations and recommendations. Managers who have limited technical knowledge expect definitions and explanations. Clients with no technical background expect versions that spell out what the facts mean to *them* (to their health, pocketbook, or business prospects).

ON THE JOB...

Varying Technical Knowledge

"One of the cases I was involved in had seven engineers and seven insurance companies with their lawyers and adjusters. Our moderator was an engineer. We engineers understood each other, but the other people in the room were very frustrated. We could have simplified for their benefit, but some of the analysis had to be explained through engineering math. The nuances of the failure analysis would have been lost if expressed in lay terms. Also, we had to go into detail when challenged by another engineer..."

—Tom Guenther, consulting structural engineer

AUDIENCE/PURPOSE PROFILE

Audience Identity and Needs

Primary reader(s): ______________________ *(name, title)*

Secondary reader(s): ______________________

Relationship: ______________________ *(client, employer, other)*

Intended use of document: ______________________ *(perform a task, solve a problem, other)*

Prior knowledge about this topic: ______________________ *(knows nothing, a few details, other)*

Additional information needed: ______________________ *(background, only bare facts, other)*

Probable questions: ______________________

____

____

____

____

____

Audience's Probable Attitude and Personality

Attitude toward topic: ______________________ *(indifferent, skeptical, other)*

Probable objections: ______________________ *(cost, time, none, other)*

Probable attitude toward this writer: ______________________ *(intimidated, hostile, receptive, other)*

Persons most affected by this document: ______________________

Temperament: ______________________ *(cautious, impatient, other)*

Probable reaction to document: ______________________ *(resistance, approval, anger, guilt, other)*

Risk of alienating anyone: ______________________

____

Audience Expectations about the Document

Reason document originated: ______________________ *(audience request, my idea, other)*

Scope: ______________________ *(comprehensive, concise, other)*

Material important to this audience: ______________________ *(interpretations, costs, conclusions, other)*

____

Most useful arrangement: ______________________ *(problem-causes-solutions, other)*

Tone: ______________________ *(businesslike, apologetic, enthusiastic, other)*

Intended effect on this audience: ______________________ *(win support, change behaviour, other)*

Due date: ______________________

Figure 2.2 Audience/Purpose Profile Sheet (see **www.pearsoned.ca/lannon** for an online version of this form)

Readers' Knowledge of the Subject

Do not waste time rehashing information readers already have. Readers expect something *new* and *significant.* Writing has informative value[1] when it (1) conveys knowledge that will be new *and* worthwhile to the intended audience; (2) reminds the audience about something they know but ignore; or (3) offers fresh insight about something familiar.

The informative value of any document is measured by its relevancy to the writer's purpose and the audience's needs. As a member of this book's audience, for instance, you expect to learn about technical writing, and our purpose is to help you do so. In this situation, which of these statements would you find useful?

1. Technical writing is hard work.
2. Technical writing responds to a specific situation. In the writing process, you carefully choose and present information, analysis, and supporting material that meet your reader's needs *and* serve your own purpose.

Statement 1 offers no news to anyone who has ever picked up a pencil, and so it has no informative value for you. But statement 2 offers a new perspective on something familiar. No matter how much you might have struggled through decisions about punctuation, organization, and grammar, chances are you haven't viewed writing as entailing the critical thinking discussed in this book. Because statement 2 provides new insight, you can say it has informative value.

The more non-essential information readers receive, the more they are likely to overlook or misinterpret the important material. Take the time to determine what your readers need, and try to give them just that.

Appropriate Details and Format

The amount of detail in your document *(How much is enough?)* will depend on what you have learned about your readers' needs. Were you asked to "keep it short" or to "be comprehensive"? Can you summarize, or does everything need spelling out? What length will they tolerate? Are the primary readers most interested in conclusions and recommendations, or do they want all of the details? Have they requested a letter, a memo, a short report, or a long, formal report with supplements (title page, table of contents, appendices, and so on)? What kinds of visuals (charts, graphs, drawings, photographs) make this material more accessible? What level of technicality will connect with primary readers?

For example, which level of technicality in the following example means more to you? Which level would be more appropriate for an automotive sales brochure?

High Technicality	The diesel engine generates 10 BTUs per gallon of fuel as opposed to the conventional gas engine's 8 BTUs.
Low Technicality	The diesel engine yields 25 percent better fuel mileage than its gas-burning counterpart.

---

1. Adapted from James L. Kinneavy's assertion that discourse ought to be unpredictable, in *A Theory of Discourse* (Englewood Cliffs, NJ: Prentice Hall, 1971).

Due Date

Does your document have a deadline? Workplace documents almost always do. Allow plenty of time to collect data, to write, and to revise. Whenever possible, ask primary readers to review an early draft and to suggest improvements.

Readers' Cultural Background

Some information needs can be culturally determined. For example, readers in certain cultures might value thoroughness and complexity above all: lists of data, with every relevant detail included and explained. Readers in other cultures might prefer an overview of the material, with multiple perspectives and liberal use of graphics (Hein 125–26).

North American business culture generally values plain talk that spells out the meaning directly, but some cultures prefer indirect and somewhat ambiguous messages, which leave explanations and interpretation for readers to decipher (Leki 151; Martin and Chaney 276–77). To avoid seeming impolite, some readers might hesitate to request clarification or additional information. Even disagreement or refusal might be expressed as "We will do our best" or "This is very difficult," instead of "No"—to avoid offending and to preserve harmony (D. Rowland 47).

Correspondence practices vary from culture to culture. In British business letters, for example, the salutation is followed by a comma (Dear Ms. Morrison,); in North America, it is followed by a colon (Dear Ms. Morrison:). Also, European data formats vary from North American practices, as Table 2.1 illustrates.

Table 2.1 Typical Data Formats

	Canada/U.S.	United Kingdom	France	Germany	Portugal
Date	May 15, 2004 15/5/04 (Can.) 5/15/04 (U.S.)	15th May, 2004 15/5/04	15 mai 2004 15.05.04	15. Mai 2004 15.5.04	15/5/04
Time	10:32 p.m.	10:32 p.m.	22.32 22 h 32	22.32 Uhr Uhr 22.32	22H32m
Currency	$123.45 C$123.45 Can$123.45 US$123.45	£123.45 GB£123.45	€123,45	€123,45	€123.45
Large Number	1,234,567.89	1,234,567.89	1. 234 .567,89	1.234.567,89	1.234.567,89
Phone Number	(905) 555-1234	(081) 987 1234 0255 876543	(15) 61-87-34-02 (15) 61.87.34.02	(089) 2 61 39 12	056-244 33 056 45 45 45

Source: Adapted from Mary Ellen Guffey, et al. *Business Communication.* 4th Canadian ed. Toronto: Nelson, 2005, p. 114.

GUIDELINES for Intercultural Communication

The following advice may help with intercultural communication. Although it seems aimed at our encounters with people outside North America, our own culture is not homogeneous, so it also applies to Canada and the United States.

1. Where feasible, hire a translator to convert your proposal or report to the *buyer's* language. Where that's not feasible, or where your reader prefers to receive your document in English, keep your sentences and paragraphs short. Use direct, simple, precise words. Use relative pronouns such as *that*, *which*, and *who* to introduce clauses. Avoid technical jargon and North American idioms ("hit the ceiling," "A-OK," "par for the course").
2. Pay special attention to the openings of letters and memos, and to the introductions of reports—North Americans like to get straight to the point; Asians and Latin Americans like to build relationships first.
3. When writing recommendations, consider whether your client's culture favours careful, deliberate team consultation or quick individual action.
4. Look at the physical format of reports produced in the reader's culture, and incorporate some aspects of that format in your report.
5. In oral communication, use perception-checking to learn whether your message has been interpreted the way you hoped: (1) pay attention to the receiver's reaction as you see and hear it (e.g., is there silence and little facial expression?); (2) what does this tell you? (e.g., has the receiver understood and assented?); and (3) confirm your perception (it may well be inaccurate if your receiver comes from a culture that values silence or is reluctant to admit a lack of understanding).

Certain factors affect each method of communication

6. Remember that much of what we communicate orally is conveyed non-verbally, and interpretations of non-verbal cues vary widely from culture to culture, even within the same nation. For example, European-Canadians see eye contact as an indicator of openness and friendliness, but Cree-Canadians and many other Native North Americans do not like to make eye contact with authority figures, such as teachers, supervisors, or coaches.

Consider the meaning of non-verbal cues

7. In both writing and speaking, remember Edward T. Hall's differentiation of "low-context cultures" and "high-context cultures"—North American, German, and Scandinavian cultures are at the low-context end, and Arab, Chinese, Japanese, and Mexican cultures are at the high-context end. British and French cultures are placed in the middle of the continuum. People from low-context cultures value individualism and direct, explicit communication, while high-context cultures prefer collectivist approaches and indirect, implicit communication that relies on shared understandings and non-verbal cues.

   Individualists tend to prefer linear, analytical thinking that shows how various parts relate to each other. However, collectivists from high-context cultures like to use synthetic thinking, which favours holistic approaches—elements are seen as part of the larger whole (E.T. Hall; Gudykunst).

(continued)

GUIDELINES for Intercultural Communication

(continued)

8. In dealing with people from other cultures, avoid *ethnocentrism*—the tendency to believe that the cultural practices, standards, and values of one culture are superior to other cultures. Ethnocentrism often leads to misunderstandings and conflict, especially when all communicators believe their culture is superior.

WEB CONNECT

For useful discussions of audience analysis, visit

www.io.com/~hcexres/textbook/
http://owl.english.purdue.edu/workshops/hypertext/reportW/audience.html

For advice on cross-cultural studies and intercultural communication, see

www.immi.se/intercultural/
www.beyondintractability.org/essay/cross-cultural_communication/
www.stephweb.com/forum/index.htm
www.stephweb.com/capstone/
www.techscribe.co.uk/techw/international_english.htm

For general advice on communicating in various specific countries, visit

www.communicaid.com

EXERCISES

1. Using internet or print sources, choose a piece written at the highest level of technicality you understand and then translate the piece for a layperson, as in the example on page 32. Exchange translations with a colleague from a different major. Read your colleague's translation and write a paragraph evaluating its level of technicality. Submit to your instructor a copy of the original, your translated version, and your evaluation of your colleague's translation.
2. Assume that a new employee is taking over your job because you have been promoted. Identify a specific problem in the job that could cause difficulty for the new employee. Write for the employee instructions for avoiding or dealing with the problem. Before writing, create an audience/purpose profile by answering (on paper) the questions on page 35. Then brainstorm for details. Submit to your instructor your audience/purpose analysis, brainstorming list, and instructions.

COLLABORATIVE PROJECT

Write a student survival guide aimed at students coming to your college or university from a specific country. Discuss housing, food, campus student resources, how to get the most from one's professors, local entertainment, aspects of campus life, and healthy living choices, among other topics. Note that the internet has plenty of sites that give advice that seems aimed at Canadians. You will need to adapt this advice to consider your readers' knowledge of your city, knowledge of Canadian customs, food preferences, attitudes toward study and the professor/student role set, and familiarity with Canadian idioms and the English language itself.

CHAPTER 3

Writing Efficiently

LEARNING OBJECTIVES

After reading this chapter, you should be able to

- **Understand that an organized writing process leads to quickly produced, effective documents.**
- **Identify and use the stages of an efficient writing process.**
- **Write first drafts that require minimal editing.**
- **Apply these efficiencies to collaborative writing projects.**

At work, writers need to produce effective documents quickly. Most employers will not tolerate inefficient work habits, including writing habits. Here are three scenarios that illustrate that it's just as important to write efficiently as it is to create effective documents.

Bill, a Halifax civil engineering technologist, returns to his office from a site inspection. As Bill sits down at his desk, his office manager tells him that he must write a proposal that afternoon for a soil-testing contract. Bill checks his watch; he has two hours to gather relevant data from company files and produce a two-page proposal before he has to catch a plane for a company meeting in Toronto.

Bill spends 20 minutes gathering, choosing, and arranging the data and supporting arguments. Then, working from a standard proposal structure for soil-testing contracts, he composes a 550-word proposal on his personal computer in 35 minutes. He spends another 15 minutes polishing the document and sends it to two colleagues for proofreading. They find four mechanical errors and two minor errors in logic. Bill corrects the errors and prints three copies of the proposal; he takes two copies to the office manager. In total, Bill produces the proposal in 90 minutes.

George works for a national research organization in Saskatoon. He has a master's degree in chemistry and a doctorate in biology. His company bills his services for $85 an hour, a rate that his company's clients are glad to pay because George's research methods, data, and analyses are thorough and accurate. His reports feature clear structures and phrasing.

However, George is required to take a three-day technical writing course because typically it takes him a full work week (plus his own time in the evenings) to produce a project-completion report that other researchers could produce in half the time.

Rita has a background in electronics and computers; she has a 10-month contract to write software documentation manuals for an Ottawa-based software development company. The company is very pleased with the quality of Rita's work, but its director of development, Martin Lefebvre, has told Rita that her contract will be renewed only if she can decrease the time it takes her to produce a manual. Martin suggests a minimum improvement of 25 percent in writing efficiency.

Bill is an efficient writer. George and Rita are not, partly because both have perfectionist tendencies, but more because each has learned bad writing and time-wasting habits. Rita, for example, writes through a discovery method that requires several complete rewrites of each document. George's main problem is that he frequently reorganizes his reports as he composes drafts and thus wastes time rewriting whole sections in order to make the material read smoothly.

Bill writes more efficiently than Rita and George because Bill has learned to

- identify several related but separate writing tasks
- focus on one task at a time and perform each task well
- identify the best sequence for completing the various writing tasks
- reduce writing time by starting quickly and by writing a first draft that requires relatively little revision

Efficient writers such as Bill have learned, primarily through trial and error, to use a writing process that is broken down into the stages shown in Figure 3.1.

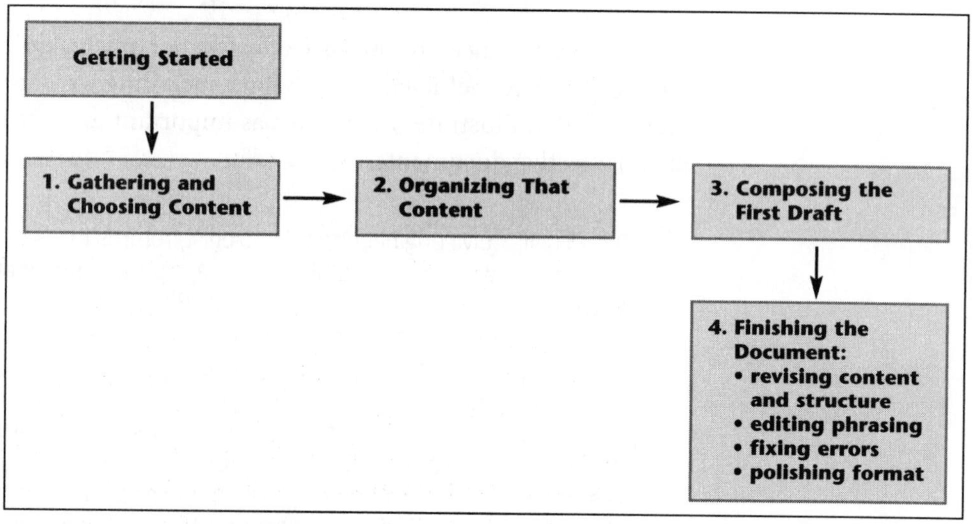

Figure 3.1 An Efficient Writing Process

GETTING STARTED

Figure 3.1 shows the first section, "Getting Started," as preliminary to the other four stages. Technical and business writers benefit from immediately asking: *What does my reader need and expect?* and *What purpose am I trying to fulfill?* (The audience/purpose profile described in Chapter 2 provides an excellent starting point for people who write business correspondence and technical documents.)

Technical writing differs from essay writing. Essayists often have to discover their subject as they progress. This process of writing until the writer discovers what she or he really wants to say is called *free-writing;* it may be necessary, but it results in many crumpled pages and in lengthy writing sessions.

Rewriting draft after draft is simply not necessary for most business and technical writing projects. Nor do you have to wait for that first "golden phrase" to start the river of words flowing. As a technical/business writer, you can be productive within 30 seconds of sitting down to write. Here's how:

ON THE JOB...

A Productive Writing Process

"I usually start with a written goal, based on my understanding of the reader's needs. I never assume that readers know what I'm 'talking about,' so I research what the reader already knows. I use an evolving detailed outline, a draft table of contents, and a draft introduction to start writing longer documents. I write first drafts in longhand and edit as I key in those drafts. . . ."

—Marilyn Riley Nault, freelance writer and editor

- *Use an audience/purpose profile* to determine the types of information and analysis to include. List the types of questions that your reader would ask (or that your reader has already asked).
- *Choose an appropriate, proven structure* and then "fill in the blanks." Several of this book's chapters suggest structures for frequently written documents; progress reports, proposals, feasibility reports, and application letters are among those described. Then, use elements of an audience/purpose profile to modify the suggested structure to meet your readers' needs and preferences.

The foregoing two methods will help you start writing almost any job-related document. However, occasionally you'll tackle a subject that is not clearly defined, or perhaps your readers' needs and priorities will be difficult to pin down. For "open-ended" situations, here are two methods for getting your mind in gear:

1. *Brainstorm a list of ideas and topics.* A random listing of possible topics and ideas works precisely because it takes advantage of the natural chaos that exists in our minds. Often, we are most creative when we allow free thought association to generate a series of loosely related points and topics. It's important to simply record these points as they come, and not to edit them. Later, when the creative frenzy has abated, you can discard the points that don't seem relevant. Then, you can organize the material that remains.

   Now let's look at a list of topics and ideas that might be generated by the writer of an in-house product description of a new camera-style scanner. (The writer is part of a design team at GlobeTech that has recently developed the device in response to a request from GlobeTech's general manager to produce a new consumer product. GlobeTech is seeking to diversify.)

   The writer, Thanh Pham, hasn't previously written such a product description. Also, the product is quite different from the industrial controls manu-factured by his company, so he doesn't have a model to emulate. Here's Thanh's list:

- limitation of previous scanners—why inadequate for scanning images
- solution: appearance and size; weight; features and controls
- how the new device works (just an overview): (1) the optical process and (2) storage of images—floppy disk; on-board storage
- downloading images to a PC
- performance specs: resolution; size of scanned images; storage capacity

Notice that Thanh's thoughts contain some order and "connections," even though he was just letting the ideas "flow." The first items in the list reflect a problem–solution sequence, and the last three items a chronological pattern.

2. *Brainstorm ideas in a cluster diagram.* Cluster diagramming suits people who think visually. It also suits those who are used to following hypertext links through the internet. Here's how Thanh could use clustering to generate ideas for his product description. He could

- circle the main topic ("Cam Scan") in the centre of a clean page
- record any ideas that pop into his mind and circle those ideas
- avoid censoring ideas, but simply record them
- join related ideas with lines, but do not focus on these connections—instead, keep on recording ideas until the flow stops

The resulting diagram might look like Figure 3.2:

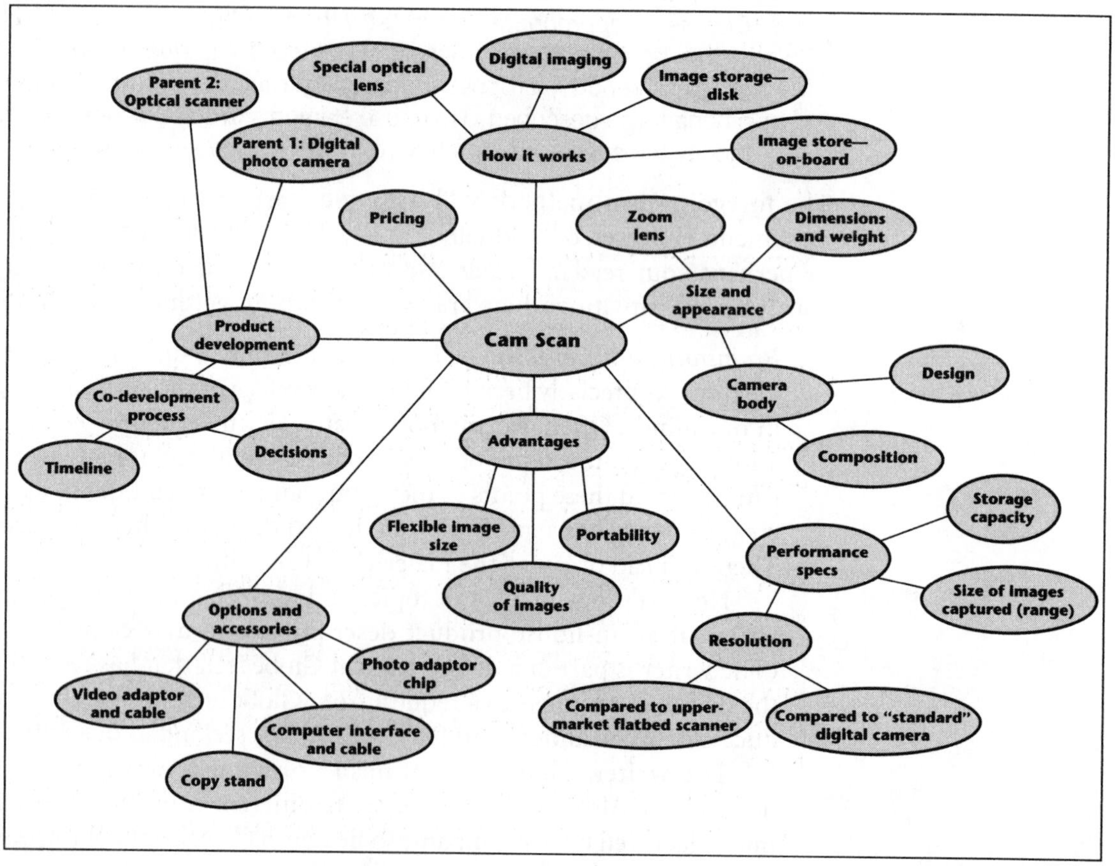

Figure 3.2 Sample Cluster Diagram

HOW TO SAVE WRITING TIME

Whether you have generated ideas by brainstorming or by one of the more structured approaches described earlier, you are now well underway and you can complete these four writing tasks in turn:

1. *Choose the content*, based on
   - technical or research notes
   - personal observations
   - arguments and evidence
   - deductions and conclusions
   - available illustrations

   Then, check to see if anything has been omitted, or if any material should be deleted. Revising content at this point takes less time than revising material later in the process.

2. *Organize the blocks of material.* If you're writing a letter, decide what goes in each paragraph. If you're writing a longer document, start with larger blocks of material and work your way to the paragraph level. Next, organize the ideas and information *within* each block.

   Again, determine whether any material should be added, rearranged, or omitted; **such changes take much more time after a draft's been phrased.**

3. *Write the first draft.* Since you know what to include and where to place it, you will be able to concentrate on the best way to phrase each sentence, and you will understand where to inject transitional statements. If you have done steps 1 and 2 properly, this draft will be close to a finished product. The very act of phrasing sentences can sometimes change your perception of your message, so you might have to modify your writing plan as you go.

   By working from an outline, you will save composition time. After all, you only have to think of *how* to phrase things; you've already chosen the content and arranged it. Your mind is free to concentrate on phrasing; you're not burdened by three writing tasks at once.

4. *Evaluate, revise, edit, proofread, and correct.* Wait as long as possible before polishing the writing. You may gain a new perspective on the best way to structure and express parts of the document. Also, you'll proofread more effectively if you distance yourself from the material.

   Use objective indexes, such as the Fog Index (Chapter 4) to help evaluate your writing and to make it more readable. Finally, proofread the material at least three times to locate errors. Ideally, you should use at least two other proofreaders in addition to yourself.

   Compared to a process of writing and rewriting (and more rewriting), this four-stage writing process will save you a great deal of revision and editing. **Investing a little time early in the process pays large dividends later in the process!**

   Writing efficiently in the manner just described also will help you produce more *effective* writing; concentrating on one task at a time allows you to better perform each of those tasks.

COMPOSING WITH A WORD PROCESSOR

If you type as fast as you handwrite and if you're accustomed to reading a computer screen, consider using a word processor to plan and compose the first draft of a document. Composing with a computer has several advantages:

- *Brainstorming* lists of ideas suits word processing, especially if you type quickly.
- Choosing content is easy to do—you can add, delete, or move points with little effort.
- Today's sophisticated word-processing software makes it easy to arrange the *chosen content into an outline.* Most software includes an outliner function that helps you divide topics into main headings and levels of subheadings. The computer tracks levels in the outline so that you can easily add, subtract, or rearrange parts of the outline. The outliner functions are especially useful for long, complicated reports.
- *Key phrases* can be placed within the outline to represent paragraphs. Later, when you compose each paragraph, each key phrase gets expanded into a topic sentence for its corresponding paragraph. Essentially, then, the computer eliminates the drudgery of retyping headings and key phrases. You simply fill in the paragraphs under each heading or key phrase. (Some writers type several key notes for each intended paragraph and then expand the notes into a series of closely linked sentences. They find that a premeditated list of points for each paragraph helps them write tight, clear paragraphs that require little subsequent revision.)
- Word processors help *identify and correct errors in spelling, punctuation, and grammar.* However, automated checkers have many limitations: a synonym offered by an electronic thesaurus may not accurately convey your intended meaning; the spell checker cannot differentiate between incorrectly used words such as "they're," "their," and "there," or "it's" and "its." And although spell and grammar checkers help, they cannot evaluate those subtle choices of phrasing that can be very important—no automated checker will tell you whether "you can reach me at..." or "call me at..." is more appropriate in a given situation.

THE PROCESS IN ACTION

The following situation illustrates how a busy person, who must balance the technical and management components of the job, uses time efficiently to write a proposal to his or her supervisor.

Process to Write a Proposal

The company is MMT Consulting, an engineering firm with its headquarters in Calgary and with branch offices in Sudbury, Winnipeg, Edmonton, Kelowna, and Prince George. MMT specializes in feasibility studies, design projects, and construction management for the mining and petroleum sectors.

Art Basran manages MMT's Kelowna branch. He is responsible for MMT's contract to help the Jackson Mining Company choose a method of hauling coal from Jackson Mining's projected new mine site in the mountains north of Grand Forks, British Columbia. As Art and his staff start to investigate the project, they learn that they need to use specialized accounting methods to evaluate four alternatives for hauling the coal to the railhead.

Art's team, at Jackson Mining's request, examines the proposed route and calculates grade resistances and energy requirements along the route. The team then researches capital costs for constructing road beds and a railroad. Capital costs are also calculated for purchasing diesel trucks, a diesel train, an electric train, and a fleet of electric trains. Finally, annual operating costs are computed for the four options.

After gathering all of the data, Art realizes that he does not have a uniform method of applying the three main evaluation criteria (capital costs, annual operating costs, and potential for expanding the delivery system) to all four transportation options. He consults Brendan Winters, a chartered accountant who works with mining companies. Brendan recommends an accounting vehicle called Equivalent Uniform Annual Costs (EUAC), which combines all the variables and thus allows a uniform comparison of the four haul methods.

Now, Art faces the task of convincing his regional manager, Brenda Backstrom, to accept the EUAC method. Backstrom, a conservative thinker, tends to resist new ways of doing things. However, she has accepted her company's newly developed business strategy—MMT presents itself as an innovative, advanced engineering firm.

Art gets started by

- checking notes of his meeting with Brendan Winters
- jotting questions that Brenda Backstrom will have
- brainstorming a list of points to make in explaining EUAC

Time to get started: 10 minutes.

Art's next step is to choose **an approach.** He decides to write a direct proposal because he knows that his reader prefers direct communication, not a lengthy analysis that eventually leads to a recommendation. Art also knows that his reader prefers short messages, so Art chooses a memo that will not exceed two pages.

With the format decision made, Art turns to the **choice of content**. His word-processed list includes

- situation more complex than usual—financial considerations
- *solution:* EUAC (Brendan's idea)
- process of preparing EUAC (see my notes)
- *note:* we already do 5 of the 6 steps
- advantages of EUAC
  (1) relatively easy—Brendan's software
  (2) qualitative and quantitative
- our qualifications: Peter, John, Brendan
- why our "normal" method won't work: too complex, not reliable, too diffuse
- request authorization

Before thinking about the order of his material, Art **edits the content** he's listed. He decides that discussing the inadequacies of the "normal" method could be too negative and that it would take the memo beyond two pages, so he deletes that part. He also thinks of a third EUAC advantage (using the EUAC method makes MMT look good), and he adds that point, so his list now includes

- situation more complex than usual—financial considerations
- *solution:* EUAC (Brendan's idea)

- process of preparing EUAC (see my notes)
- *note:* we already do 5 of the 6 steps
- advantages of EUAC
  (1) relatively easy—Brendan's software
  (2) qualitative and quantitative
  (3) using this innovative method gives us a competitive advantage
- our qualifications: Peter, John, Brendan
- request authorization

Time to choose and edit content: 8 minutes.

At this point, Art's writing is interrupted by a phone call, which leads to other conversations between Art and two technologists in the office. After 40 minutes, Art returns to organize the content of his proposal. As he looks at his edited contents list, Art realizes that he has jotted down his points in the order he has successfully used for proposals in the past:

1. reader connection and statement of problem
2. proposed solution
3. description of proposal
4. supporting arguments
5. request for authorization

However, Art also realizes that it would be better to place his team's qualifications *before* his supporting arguments, to establish that his Kelowna team can handle the proposed approach. Using the cut-and-paste function on his word processor, Art places his list of points as follows:

- situation more complex than usual—financial considerations
- *solution:* EUAC (Brendan's idea)
- process of preparing EUAC (see my notes)
- *note:* we already do 5 of the 6 steps
- our qualifications: Peter, John, Brendan
- advantages of EUAC
  (1) relatively easy—Brendan's software
  (2) merges qualitative *and* quantitative methods
  (3) using this innovative method gives us a competitive advantage
- request authorization

Before using this outline to compose his memo, Art **reviews its structure**. He realizes that he should start his supporting arguments with his strongest point, so he rearranges the EUAC advantages as follows: (1) merges qualitative and quantitative methods; (2) gives us a competitive advantage; (3) Brendan's software—easy to use and inexpensive.

Time to organize content: 3 minutes.

Feeling in control of the writing process, Art **composes the first draft**, working quickly from his outline and detailed notes. He composes the 754-word document in 33 minutes. At that point, Art has to leave for a meeting, which takes the rest of the afternoon. Following is Art's draft (Figure 3.3).

Re: Recommending a Coal-Haul Method to Jackson Mining

As you requested, I have begun to prepare a recommendation for Jackson Mining's consideration. Its situation, however, is considerably much more complex than other transportation issues we have analyzed in the past. In this case, we must consider the factor of fluctuating interest rates as well as varying amortization periods for carrying the capital debt. This problem is additionally compounded by not knowing how long Jackson Mining expects to operate the proposed Othello mine and haul coal from it.

After consulting with Brendan Winters, a Penticton C.A. who has a special interest in mining projects, I propose we should use Equivalent Uniform Annual Costs (EUAC) as the main method of comparing Jackson Mining's four alternative transportation methods. EUAC provides a comprehensive, as well as a clear, way of comparing the four alternatives.

The Process

Preparing a comprehensive set of EUAC requires a six-step process. You will note from the following list of steps that we would normally preform the first five steps in this kind of analysis, the sixth step, the actual EUAC calculations, uses data generated during the first five steps of the process. These, then, are the steps:

1. Gather field data about the proposed road and railroad routes. This step will require doing our own surveys as well as gathering data from existing maps and surveys.
2. Research specifications of the diesel trucks and train options that are suitable for the type of terrain found on the proposed routes. We will need physical and mechanical specifications as well as the capital costs for this equipment.
3. Determine the fuel consumption figures for each of the four options. This set of calculations will be quite extensive, particularly in this case, because of the length of the haul road and because of the grade variances on that road.
4. Combine the fuel costs with projected labour and maintenance costs to determine the annual operating costs for each alternative.
5. Determine the capital costs for the four alternatives.
6. Combine the annual operating costs and the capital costs with varying interest rates to produce an EUAC for each of the study periods of one to 20 years. Please see the attached sample table and sample figure, which show the results for three of the 20 years that could be considered. These samples are based on roughly estimated data.

Figure 3.3 Draft Document

(continued)

Qualifications

I believe our team is well equipped to handle this innovative method of assessing Jackson Mining's transportation needs. Peter Bondra, the engineer who will lead the research team, has degrees in both civil and mechanical engineering, and useful experience in railbed construction. His main assistant will be John Housley who graduated two years ago from the Civil Engineering Technology program here in Kelowna. John has 15 years' experience in road construction and knows the area north of Grand Forks because of his frequent hunting trips in that area. In addition, John is well versed in a variety of surveying techniques. He'll be able to deal with the area's rough terrain.

After the data have been collected, Brendan Winters has indicated his willingness to be available to direct the cost analysis. He has particular expertise in calculating and presenting EUAC data.

Advantages of Using the EUAC Comparisons

The main advantage of using EUAC comparisons is that it provides qualitative comparisons as well as quantitative data. In effect, an EUAC creatively merges enginerring analysis with the maximal kind of accounting techniques to help our client see what the data really mean.

Providing this kind of inovative analysis will position our firm as a creative, advanced engineering firm. Brendan Winters and I have recently surveyed a variety of resource-based companies, and not one of them had used the EUAC method. I believe its use will give us a competitive advantage in this bid and in others.

Furthermore, the complicated EUAC caclations will only take an extra day of work on this project because Brendan Winters has modified an accounting software program to help do the computations. His contribution will cost our firm an additional $1,200.00, a relatively small part of our budget for this project.

Conclusion

I need to talk to you about using Equivalent Uniform Annual Costs in the Jackson Mining project before the end of this week. If I'm out of the office when you call, call me at my new cellular phone number, (250) 863-2999. If you would like a more comprehensive view of how EUAC can be used, I can prepare such a document in three hours and email it to you immediately.

Art Basran

Figure 3.3 Draft Document

Paragraph	Phrasing	Concern/problem	Improvements
1	Its situation, however, is *considerably much* more complex than other transportation issues we have analyzed in the past. . . . This problem is *additionally compounded by not knowing* . . . operate the proposed Othello mine *and haul coal from it.*	wordy, pompous wordy, pompous	Its situation, however, is more complex than other transport issues we have analyzed. Also, we don't know . . . operate the proposed Othello mine.
2	EUAC provides a comprehensive, *as well as* a clear, way of comparing the four alternatives.	wordy	EUAC provides a complete, clear comparison of the four options.
5	. . . Brendan Winters has indicated his willingness to be available . . .	wordy	. . . Brendan Winters will be available . . .
7	. . . surveyed a variety of resource-based companies . . .	inexact and therefore not persuasive	. . . surveyed 12 mining and forestry companies . . .
9	I need to talk to you about using Equivalent Uniform Annual Costs . . . before the end of this week.	the tone is too aggressive for addressing one's supervisor	May we discuss using EUAC … by this Friday?

His evaluation leaves him satisfied with the content of the proposal, but he sees wordy phrases and some phrases whose tone needs changing. Some of these are shown in the table above.

Art's paring of unnecessary words reduces the word count from 754 to 663 and makes several sentences easier to read. Then, confident that he has established the right tone in the memo, Art puts the document through his software's spell checker, which detects several errors ("preform," "enginerring," "inovative," "caclations"). But, not trusting either his own proofreading or the spell checker, Art gives the document to a colleague, who finds a comma splice in paragraph 3 and a pronoun agreement error ("... advantage of using EUAC comparisons is that *it* provides...") in paragraph 6.

Art's revision, editing, and proofreading time: 18 minutes.

Finally, Art takes four minutes to apply some final touch-ups and print the proposal.

Art's finished document is shown in Figure 3.4. **His time to produce the memo, including discussions with colleagues, totals 84 minutes.** Every minute of that time has been productive.

MMT Consulting Inter-office MEMORANDUM

To: Brenda Backstrom
Western Regional Manager

Date: December 3, 2008

From: Art Basran
Kelowna Branch Manager

Re: Method of Comparing Transportation Alternatives for Jackson Mining's Proposed Othello Mine

As you requested, I'm preparing a proposal for Jackson Mining's consideration. Its situation, however, is more complex than other transport issues we have analyzed. In this case, we must consider fluctuating interest rates and varying amortization periods for carrying the capital debt. Also, we don't know how long Jackson Mining expects to operate the proposed Othello mine.

After consulting with Brendan Winters, a Penticton C.A. who has a special interest in mining projects, I propose that we use Equivalent Uniform Annual Costs (EUAC) as the main method of comparing Jackson Mining's four alternative transportation methods. EUAC provides a complete, clear comparison of the four options.

The Process

Preparing a comprehensive set of EUAC requires a six-step process, the first five of which we would normally perform in this kind of analysis; the sixth step, the actual EUAC calculations, uses data generated during the first five steps of the process. Here are the steps:

1. Gather field data about the proposed road and railroad routes. This step will require doing our own surveys as well as gathering data from existing maps and surveys.
2. Research specifications of the diesel trucks and train options that are suitable for the type of terrain found on the proposed routes. We will need physical and mechanical specifications as well as the capital costs of this equipment.
3. Determine the fuel consumption figures for each of the four options. This set of calculations will be quite extensive for the Othello Mine road, which is about 80 kilometres and which has many grade variances.
4. Combine the fuel costs with projected labour and maintenance costs to determine the annual operating costs for each alternative.
5. Determine the capital costs for the four alternatives.
6. Combine the annual operating costs and the capital costs with varying interest rates to produce an EUAC for each of the study periods of one to 20 years. Please see the attached sample table and figure that show the results for three of the 20 years that could be considered. These samples are based on estimated data.

Qualifications

Our team is well equipped to handle this innovative method of assessing Jackson Mining's transportation needs. Peter Bondra, the engineer who will lead the research team, has degrees in both civil and mechanical engineering and useful experience in railbed construction. His main assistant will be

Figure 3.4 An Efficiently Produced Document *(continued)*

Brenda Backstrom
December 3, 2008
Page 2

John Housley who graduated two years ago from the Civil Engineering Technology program here in Kelowna. John has 15 years' experience in road construction and knows the area north of Grand Forks because of his frequent hunting trips in that area. He'll be able to deal with the area's rough terrain. In addition, John is well versed in a variety of surveying techniques.

After the data have been collected, Brendan Winters will be available to direct the cost analysis. He's an expert in calculating and presenting EUAC data.

Advantages of Using the EUAC Comparisons

The main advantage of using EUAC comparisons is that they provide qualitative comparisons as well as quantitative data. EUAC combines engineering and accounting ideas to help our client see what the data really mean. Our competitors have not yet realized the value of EUAC analysis, so I believe its use will give us a competitive advantage in this and future bids.

This kind of innovative analysis helps position MMT as a creative, advanced engineering firm, a strategy that matches the positioning objective established at our recent management summit.

Furthermore, the complicated EUAC calculations will take only one day of work on this project because Brendan Winters has modified some accounting software to do the computations. His work will cost our firm $1,200.00, which is just 2.5 percent of our project budget.

Conclusion

May we discuss using EUAC for Jackson Mining by this Friday? If I'm out of the office when you call, please call my new cellular phone, (250) 863-2999. If you would like a fuller explanation of how EUAC can be used, I could email you.

Art Basran

Attachments: Sample Calculations

Figure 3.4 An Efficiently Produced Document

ON THE JOB...
Collaborative Writing

"Most of our writing happens in teams. Typically, our project teams (or sometimes just the Project Director) develop a detailed outline for a written product. The team then goes over it together and writing assignments are made (intentional use of the passive voice there). The assignments usually match the content areas for which team members have been responsible. The Project Director (generally me) is responsible for the introduction that describes the purpose of the work and for the conclusions/implications. The middle part is 'technical' and I usually review those sections without getting into the details. We have a writing style that is consistent across most of our products. It takes about six months for team members to learn to write in that style. One of the biggest team writing challenges we have is the tendency for recent graduates to overwrite. They have learned in their academic programs to write very formally, with ponderous vocabulary and lots of passive voice. Our stuff has to get to the point in a hurry...."

—Paul Harder, president of a mid-sized consulting company

PRODUCTIVE COLLABORATIVE WRITING

The challenges of writing efficiently as a solitary writer are magnified when a group produces a document (or prepares a collaborative oral presentation). As Chapter 1 shows, many sources of misunderstanding and disagreement can arise, which will interfere with the timely completion of a project. The pressure of deadlines can exacerbate friction caused by differing levels of commitment, varying degrees of liking and respect that group members have for each other, and varying work habits.

In any group, then, members have to find ways of persuasively expressing their views, of accepting criticism, and of working with others who hold different views. The following guidelines aim to provide a context for productive group work.

Reviewing and Editing Others' Work

Documents produced collaboratively are reviewed and edited extensively. *Reviewing* means evaluating how well a document connects with its intended audience and meets its intended purpose with these qualities:

- accurate, appropriate, useful, and legal content
- material organized for the reader's understanding
- clear, easy to read, and engaging style
- effective visuals and page design
- a document that is safe, dependable, and easy to use

GUIDELINES for Managing a Collaborative Project[1]

These guidelines focus on projects in which people meet face to face, but they can apply as well to electronically mediated collaboration.

1. *Appoint a project or group manager.* This person assigns tasks, enforces deadlines, conducts meetings, and consults with supervisors.
2. *Define a clear and definite goal.* Compose a purpose statement that spells out the project's goal and the group's plan for achieving it. Be sure each member understands the goal.

(continued)

1. Adapted from Debs, "Collaborative Writing" 38–41; Hill-Duin 45–46; Hulbert, "Developing" 53–54; McGuire 467–68; Morgan 540–41.

GUIDELINES for Managing a Collaborative Project

(continued)

Group structures

3. *Decide how the group will be organized.* Here are two possibilities:
   - The group researches and plans together, but each person writes a different part of the document.
   - Some members plan and research; one person writes a complete draft; others review, edit, revise, and produce the final version.

   Whatever the arrangement, the final revision should display a consistent style throughout—as if written by one person only.
4. *Divide the task.* Who will be responsible for which parts of the document or which phases of the project? Should one person alone do the final revision? Which jobs are the most difficult? Who is best at doing what (writing, editing, layout, graphics, oral presentation)? Who will make final decisions?
5. *Establish a timetable.* Specific completion dates for each phase will keep everyone focused on what is due and when.
6. *Decide on a meeting schedule and format.* How often will the group meet, and for how long? In or out of the office? Who will take notes (or minutes)? Will the supervisor attend or participate?

Group processes

7. *Establish a procedure for responding to the work of other members.* Will reviewing and editing be done in writing, face to face, as a group, one on one, or via computer? Will the project manager supervise this process?
8. *Establish procedures for dealing with group problems.* How will gripes and disagreements be aired (to the manager, the whole group, the offending individual)? How will disputes be resolved (by vote, the manager)? How will irrelevant discussion be avoided or curtailed? Expect some conflict, but try to use it positively, and try to identify a natural peacemaker in the group.
9. *Decide how to evaluate each member's contribution.* Will the manager assess each member's performance and, in turn, be evaluated by each member? Will members evaluate each other? What are the criteria? Figure 3.5 on the following page depicts one possible form for a manager's evaluation of members. Equivalent criteria for evaluating the manager include open-mindedness, ability to organize the team, fairness in assigning tasks, ability to resolve conflicts, or ability to motivate. (Members might keep a journal of personal observations, for overall evaluation of the project.)
10. *Prepare a project management plan.* Figure 3.6 on the following page has a sample plan sheet.
11. *Submit progress reports regularly.* Progress reports enable everyone to track activities, problems, and rate of progress.

Beyond these guidelines, respect for other people's views and willingness to listen are essential ingredients for successful collaboration.

Performance appraisal for ______________________

(After each item, place an X in the column that applies.)

	Superior	Acceptable	Unacceptable
Dependability			
Cooperation			
Effort			
Quality of work			
Ability to meet deadlines			

____
Project manager's signature

Figure 3.5 Sample Form for Evaluating Team Members

Management Plan Sheet

Project title:
Audience:
Project manager:
Team members:
Purpose statement:

Specific Assignments	**Due Dates**
Research:	Research due:
Planning:	Plan and outline due:
Drafting:	First draft due:
Revising:	Reviews due:
Preparing final documents:	Revisions due:
Presenting oral briefing:	Final document due:
	Progress report(s) due:

Work Schedule

Group meetings:	Date	Place	Time	Note-taker
#1				
#2				
#3				
etc.				
Mtgs. w/manager:				
#1				
#2				
etc.				

Miscellaneous

How will disputes and grievances be resolved?
How will performances be evaluated?
Other matters (internet searches, email routing, computer conferences, etc.)?

Figure 3.6 Sample Plan Sheet for Managing a Collaborative Project

In reviewing, you explain how you respond as a reader, which helps writers to think about ways of revising. Criteria for reviewing various documents appear in checklists throughout this book.

Ways in which editors improve writing

Editing makes copy more precise and readable. Editors typically suggest improvements like these:

- rephrasing or reorganizing sentences
- clarifying a topic sentence
- choosing a better word or phrase
- correcting spelling, usage, or punctuation, and so on

Editing criteria appear in Chapter 4, and inside the rear cover.

ON THE JOB...

Collaborative Writing

"My work in preparing user manuals is almost entirely collaborative. The actual process of writing takes maybe 30 percent of my time. More time is spent consulting with my information sources such as the software designers and field support people. I then meet with the publication and graphics departments to plan the manual's structure and format. As I prepare various drafts, I have to keep track of which reviewer has which draft. Because I rely on others' feedback, I circulate materials often. And so I write email messages on a regular basis. One major challenge is getting everyone involved to agree on a specific plan of action and then to stay on schedule so we can meet our publication deadlines..."

—Pam Herbert, technical writer, software firm

GUIDELINES for Peer Reviewing and Editing

1. *Read the entire piece at least twice before you comment.* Develop a clear sense of the document's purpose and its intended audience. Try to visualize the document as a whole before you evaluate specific parts or features.
2. *Remember that correctness does not guarantee effectiveness.* Poor usage, punctuation, or mechanics do distract readers and harm the writer's credibility. However, "correct" writing might still contain faulty rhetorical elements (inappropriate content, confusing organization, wordy style, etc.).
3. *Understand the acceptable limits of editing.* In the workplace, editing can range from cleaning up and fine-tuning to an in-depth rewrite (in which case editors are cited prominently as consulting editors or co-authors). In school, however, rewriting someone else's piece to the extent that it ceases to belong to that writer may constitute plagiarism.
4. *Be honest but diplomatic.* Most of us are sensitive to criticism—even when it is constructive—and we all respond more favourably to encouragement. Be supportive instead of judgmental.

(continued)

GUIDELINES for Peer Reviewing and Editing *(continued)*

5. *Explain why something doesn't work.* Instead of "this paragraph is confusing," say "this paragraph lacks a clear topic sentence, so I had trouble discovering the main idea." Help the writer identify the cause of the problem.
6. *Make specific recommendations for improvements.* Write out suggestions in enough detail for the writer to know what to do.
7. *Be aware that not all feedback has equal value.* Even professional reviewers and editors can disagree. Your job as a reviewer or editor is to help clarify and enhance a document—without altering its original meaning.

Face-to-Face Versus Electronically Mediated Collaboration

Benefits of face-to-face meetings

Should groups meet in the same physical space or in virtual space? Face-to-face collaboration seems preferable when people don't know each other, when the issue is sensitive or controversial, or when people need to interact on a personal level (Munter 81).

Advantages of electronic collaboration

Electronically mediated (virtual) collaboration might be better when people are in different locations or have different schedules. For example, this edition of *Technical Communication* was written in British Columbia, California, and Arizona while being responded to by editors based in southern Ontario. Virtual collaboration might also work when it is important to avoid personality clashes, to encourage shy participants, or to prevent intimidation by dominant participants (Munter 81, 83).

Chapter 1 lists several technologies that erase distance and enable people to work together in the same virtual space.

Research indicates that electronic meetings are more productive than face-to-face meetings (Tullar, Kaiser, and Balthazard 54). Written ideas can be more carefully considered and expressed, and they provide a durable record for feedback and reference. On the negative side, equipment crashes are disruptive. And the lack of personal contact (such as a friendly grin or a handshake) makes it hard for trust to develop (T. Clark 49–50).

NOTE

Many cultures value the social (or relationship) function of communication as much as its informative function (Archee 41). Therefore, a recipient might consider some communications media more appropriate than others, preferring a phone conversation to text messaging or email.

The term "single sourcing" has been coined to refer to a variety of software and related processes that facilitate virtual collaboration. The fourth edition of this book, for example, has been produced with WriteRAP, a proprietary software that Pearson Education Canada has adapted. WriteRAP allows authors, reviewers, editors, and page designers to view and work on the book while it is displayed on a password-protected website.

IN BRIEF SINGLE SOURCING TECHNOLOGY "REWRITES" THE WRITING PROCESS

At one time, technical writers were responsible for researching material, writing it, formatting it, and printing it. And that was it. These days, the "writer" converts paper documents to electronic formats, stores data in multiple formats, creates and manipulates graphics, retrieves documents and lost hyperlinks, and updates data on various media. It's no wonder that technical communicators have turned to *single sourcing* to help manage their work.

Single sourcing may be defined as using "one document source to produce multiple outputs" (Wardin). But what does that mean? Technical marketing writer Marc Arellano talks about "a well of data and images from which [he draws] appropriate material in appropriate formats for the application at hand—a proposal, a brochure, a website page, a magalogue" (Single). Other technical writers think of creating a variety of documents (annual reports, user manuals, online tutorials, technical updates) all from one database that has been planned in such a way that "certain types of information can be presented or omitted without affecting the presentation of other types of information" (Davidovic).

Single sourcing can actually be quite simple. You might convert a Word file to a PDF document and then plug that PDF file into a website and onto a CD-ROM. Or, you might create modules or "chunks" of information for your base résumé, and then use cut-and-paste to select and place those chunks that suit the résumé for a particular job application. Milan Davidovic, a member of the Toronto chapter of the Society for Technical Communication (STC), believes that planning one's résumé as a series of related chunks is a good way to learn the basic principles of single sourcing.

The trick is in the planning, says Davidovic, who lists three types of tools for single sourcing a résumé:

1. "create your source content as a word processor template and delete unneeded information from each document you create based on that template";
2. "put the content into a database, and then use the report function of the database to output your résumé"; and
3. "Use help-authoring tools or...online résumé tools found at job search sites such as Monster.ca."

So, how do you know when to use single sourcing methods? Speaking at the March 2003 meeting of the Toronto chapter of the STC, Rob Hanna suggested one should ask questions such as the following:

- Is this a valuable document, perhaps one tied to a product?
- Will this document require updating?
- Will this document have a long life span?
- Will parts of this document be used elsewhere?

Here are some other tools that facilitate single sourcing, at various levels of complexity:

1. Screen capture tools, says Carla Wardin, "are specifically designed to save time due to their systematic and automatic features." Wardin points to other advantages of using screen capture programs:

- They eliminate editing time.
- They allow the user to capture objects such as toolbar buttons and icons.
- Programs such as SnagIt set up a catalogue of items that's easy to access.
- Some screen capture software programs have batch conversion features.
- Most screen capture programs have a multiple output feature to "simultaneously send captured material...to the printer, email, and the web."

2. Microsoft Word has features that make single sourcing in Word possible: main and subdocuments, mail merge, database links, search and replace, templates, and others.
3. More technically complex projects can, for example, "convert FrameMaker source files to HTML Help *.chm files," which can also be "the source of a printed user guide and the hyperlinked PDF of the user guide placed on the distribution CD" (Finger). Michele Marques has an excellent introduction to using FrameMaker for producing multiple versions of a manual with conversion to online versions (see **www.techwr-1.com/node/66**). Mif2Go is one tool that converts FrameMaker to HTML, XML, Word RTF, and Help formats.
4. Still more complex single-sourcing models employ various combinations of markup

(continued)

language (HTML, XML, XSL, XSLT, XSL-FO, and/or CSS) to build architectures that transform and format information for simultaneous applications—print, website, e-newsletter, online help, and so on.

5. "Dynamic customized content" sets up documentation to meet users' needs, in three main modes:
   - a user profile is assigned to each login name so that when the user logs in, he or she sees only that part of the information package that has been defined as relevant for that user
   - user selection modes allow users to select from a form
   - pattern recognition software "learns" the user's preferences and then provides that kind of data or provides selectable links (Rockley 191).
6. The highest level of single sourcing uses electronic performance system software (EPSS) to provide the right information (training, stock quotes, data updates, answers to user questions, reference material) when users *need* the information, "often before they know they need it" (Rockley 191).

   Whatever the level of single-sourcing tech-nology, its use will grow because of its advantages:
   - Reusing content saves time and money—Sean Brierley describes how a software manufacturer reduced its production time for an online version of its printed manual from 80 hours to three hours (Brierley 16).
   - Single sourcing reduces errors.
   - Coded single sourcing simplifies the document creation processes (once the code is set).
   - Single sourcing suits the needs of e-commerce, especially when information can be customized for individual consumers, and automatically sent to them as the information becomes available. (For example, an airline can alert a customer about special flights and fares from that customer's "home" airport.)
   - Single sourcing can automatically update documents as new information becomes available.
   - Some single sourcing tools can do more than reproduce content in different formats; they can be programmed to reduce the amount of detail and change the appearance or size of illustrations *automatically* for such applications as online quick reference guides.

Looking at single sourcing from the point of view of a small firm that writes proposals and contracts for clients, communications consultant Stan Chung says, "an intranet can be used to make sure that a company's profile, projects, clients, and résumés are always current. For a large client, say a bridge builder or engineering firm, it is really important to have all the specs, photos, and reports in one place."

Ann Rockley, a Toronto-based expert in single sourcing applications, predicts a fundamental paradigm shift in the way writers will function, as single sourcing becomes prevalent. More and more, *writers* will focus on creating the content (researching, organizing, composing), while *information designers* will set up the structures required for effective communication in various media. Meanwhile, *editors* will regain an important role as they ensure standards and consistency from platform to platform. And *information technologists* will take care of the technical aspects of delivering information to users, says Rockley (192–93). In this scenario, writers will go back to what they used to do—researching, thinking, and writing!

A variety of documents describing single sourcing can be accessed through the STC's Single Sourcing Special Interest Group, at **www.stcsig.org/ss/linksss.htm**.

WEB CONNECT

Colorado State's department has comprehensive advice on writing processes:

http://writing.colostate.edu/guides

Documents describing single sourcing can be found at these sites:

www.stcsig.org/ss/linksss.htm
http://cherryleaf.com/single_sourcing_part1.htm
www.techwr-l.com/node/66

EXERCISES

1. Use the efficient writing process described on page 45 to complete your next writing assignments. Adapt that process to suit your skills and preferences. For example, you may prefer to complete all stages of the process on a computer. Or, if you type very slowly, you may prefer to handwrite the content list, the outline, and the first draft. Then, you could edit and correct that draft as you key it into the computer.
2. In a one-page memo or email to your writing instructor, describe your writing habits and outline your plans for becoming a more efficient writer. Use your own version of the writing process described on page 41 to create this memo. You should produce a printed memo within 60 minutes!
3. Use the following form (Figure 3.7) to audit your writing habits as you complete your next few writing assignments. The time log should give you an idea of how efficiently you write and where you could begin to save time in the writing process.

Stage of Writing Process	Time Spent	Methods and Results
Getting started		
1. Gathering/choosing content: information, ideas, and analysis		
2. Organizing content		
3. Phrasing first draft		
4. Revising content and structure Editing style and paragraphs Finding and correcting errors		

Figure 3.7 Time Audit

COLLABORATIVE PROJECT

See this book's accompanying website for a collaborative writing exercise. Go to **www.pearsoned.ca/lannon**, "Writing Exercises," and then "Collaborative Project."

CHAPTER 4

Editing for Readable Style

LEARNING OBJECTIVES

After reading this chapter, you should be able to

- Understand the components of effective and appropriate technical writing style.
- Edit documents to make them clear, concise, fluent, exact, and appropriate in tone.
- Employ a combination of subjective and objective tools to evaluate your writing.

You might write for a diverse or specific audience, or for experts or non-experts. But no matter how technically appropriate your document, audience needs are not served unless your style is *readable*.

A definition of style

Writing style influences reader response to a document. Your writing style is the product of

- the words you choose
- the way in which you put a sentence together
- the length of your sentences
- the way in which you connect sentences
- the tone you convey

Readable sentences require correct grammar, punctuation, and spelling. However, correctness alone is no guarantee of readability. For example, this response to a job applicant is mechanically correct but inefficient:

Inefficient style

> We are in receipt of your recent correspondence indicating your interest in securing the advertised position. Your correspondence has been duly forwarded for consideration by the personnel office, which has employment candidate selection responsibility. You may expect to hear from us relative to your application as the selection process progresses. Your interest in the position is appreciated.

Notice how hard you have worked to extract information that could be expressed this simply:

More efficient

Your application for the advertised position has been forwarded to our personnel office. As the selection process moves forward, we will be in touch. Thank you for your interest.

Inefficient style makes readers work harder than they should. Style can be inefficient for many reasons, but it is especially inept when it

- makes the writing impossible to interpret
- takes too long to make the point
- reads like a Dick-and-Jane story from primary school
- uses imprecise or needlessly long words
- sounds stuffy and impersonal

Regardless of its cause, inefficient style results in writing that is less informative and less persuasive. Moreover, inefficient style can be unethical—by confusing or misleading readers.

To help your audience spend less time reading, you must spend more time editing for a style that is *clear, concise, fluent, exact,* and *likeable.*

EDITING FOR CLARITY

A clear sentence requires no more than a single reading. It avoids ambiguous constructions, signals relationships among its parts, and emphasizes the main idea. The following guidelines will help you edit for clarity.

Avoid Ambiguous Phrasing

Workplace writing ideally has *one* meaning only and allows for *one* interpretation. Does one's "suspicious attitude" mean that one is "suspicious" or "suspect"?

Ambiguous phrasing All managers are not required to submit reports. (*Are some or none required?*)

Revised Managers are **not all required** to submit reports.

or

Managers are *not required* to submit reports.

Ambiguous phrasing Most city workers strike on Friday.

Revised Most city workers **are planning to strike** Friday.

or

Most city workers **typically strike** on Friday.

Avoid Ambiguous Pronoun References

Each pronoun you use (*he, she, it, their,* etc.) must refer to one clearly identified noun. If the pronoun's referent (or antecedent) is ambiguous, readers will be confused.

Ambiguous referent	Our patients enjoy the warm days while they last. (*Are the patients or the warm days on the way out?*)

Depending on whether the referent for *they* is patients or warm days, the sentence can be clarified.

Clear referent	While these warm days last, our patients enjoy them.
	or
	Our terminal patients enjoy the warm days.
Ambiguous referent	Jack resents his assistant because he is competitive. (*Who's the competitive one—Jack or his assistant?*)
Clear referent	Because his assistant is competitive, Jack resents him.
	or
	Because Jack is competitive, he resents his assistant.

Avoid Ambiguous Punctuation

A missing hyphen, comma, or other punctuation mark can obscure your meaning.

Missing hyphen	Replace the trailer's inner wheel bearings. (*The inner-wheel bearings or the inner wheel-bearings?*)
Missing comma	Does your company produce liquid hydrogen? If so, how[,] and where do you store it? (*Notice how the meaning changes with a comma after "how."*)
	Police surrounded the crowd[,] attacking the strikers. *(Without the comma, the crowd appears to be attacking the strikers.)*

Although missing hyphens and commas are prime culprits, other omissions can cause ambiguity as well. A missing colon after *kill* yields the headline "Moose Kill 200." A missing *'s* after *Mills* creates this gem: "Mills Remains Buried in Saskatoon." Punctuation *does* affect meaning.

Exercise 1

Revise the following sentences to eliminate ambiguities in phrasing, pronoun reference, or punctuation.

a. Call me any evening except Tuesday after 7 o'clock.
b. I cannot recommend this candidate too highly.
c. Visiting colleagues can be tiring.
d. Janice dislikes working with Claire because she's impatient.
e. Despite his efforts, Joe misinterpreted Sam's message.
f. Our division needs more effective writers.
g. Tell the reactor operator to evacuate and sound a general alarm.

Avoid Telegraphic Writing

Function words show relationships between the *content words* (nouns, adjectives, verbs, and adverbs) in a sentence. Some examples of function words:

- articles (*a, an, the*)
- prepositions (*in, of, to*)
- linking verbs (*is, seems, looks*)
- relative pronouns (*who, which, that*)

Some writers mistakenly try to compress their writing by eliminating these function words.

Ambiguous	Proposal to employ retirees almost dead.
Revised	The proposal to employ retirees **is** almost dead.
Ambiguous	Uninsulated end pipe ruptured. (*What ruptured? The pipe or the end of the pipe?*)
Revised	**The** uninsulated end **of the** pipe ruptured.
	or
	The uninsulated pipe **on the** end ruptured.
Ambiguous	The reactor operator told management several times she expected an accident. (*Did she tell them once or several times?*)
Revised	The reactor operator told management several times **that** she expected an accident.
	or
	The reactor operator told management **that** several times she expected an accident.

Avoid Ambiguous Modifiers

Modifiers explain, define, or add detail to other words or ideas. If a modifier is too far from the words it modifies, the message can be ambiguous.

Misplaced modifier	**Only** press the red button in an emergency. (*Does* **only** *modify* **press** *or* **emergency***?*)
Revised	Press **only** the red button in an emergency.
	or
	Press the red button in an emergency **only**.

Another problem with ambiguity occurs when a modifying phrase has no word to modify.

Dangling modifier	**Being so well known in the computer industry**, I would appreciate your advice.

The writer meant to say that the *reader* is well known, but with no word to join itself to, the modifying phrase dangles. Eliminate the confusion by adding a subject:

Revised	Because **you** are so well known in the computer industry, I would appreciate your advice.

Exercise 2

Revise the following sentences to repair telegraphic writing or to clarify ambiguous modifiers.

a. The manager claimed repeatedly she reported the danger.
b. I want the final Amex report written by your division.
c. The president refused to believe any internal report was inaccurate.
d. After offending our best client, I am deeply annoyed with the new manager.
e. Send memo to programmer requesting explanation.
f. Do not enter test area while contaminated.

Unstack Modifying Nouns

One noun can modify another noun (as in "software development"). But when two or more nouns modify a noun, the string of densely packed words becomes hard to read and ambiguous.

Stacked Be sure to leave enough time for a **training session participant** evaluation. (*Evaluation of the session or of the participants?*)

With no function words (articles, prepositions, verbs, relative pronouns) to break up the string of nouns, readers cannot see the relationships among the nouns. What modifies what?

Stacked nouns also deaden your style. Bring your style *and* your reader to life by using action verbs (*complete, prepare, reduce*) and prepositional phrases.

Revised Be sure to leave enough time **for** participants **to evaluate** the training session.

or

Be sure to leave enough time **to evaluate** participants **in the** training session.

No such problem with ambiguity occurs when adjectives are stacked in front of a noun:

Clear He was a nervous, angry, confused, but dedicated employee.

Readers can readily see that the adjectives modify *employee.*

Exercise 3

Revise the following sentences to unstack modifying nouns.

a. Develop online editing system documentation.
b. We need to develop a unified construction automation design.
c. Install a hazardous materials dispersion monitor system.
d. I recommend these management performance improvement incentives.
e. Sarah's job involves fault analysis systems troubleshooting handbook preparation.

Arrange Word Order for Coherence

In coherent writing, everything sticks together; each sentence builds on the preceding sentence and looks ahead to the following sentence. Sentences generally work best when the beginning looks back at familiar information and the end provides the new (or unfamiliar) information:

Familiar		**Unfamiliar**
My dog	has	fleas.
Our supervisor	just won	the lottery.
This company	is planning	a merger.

Use Active Voice Often

A verb's *voice* signals whether a sentence's subject acts or is acted upon. The active voice ("I did it") is more direct, concise, and persuasive than the passive voice ("It was done by me"). In the active voice, the agent performing the action serves as the subject:

Active	***Agent***	***Action***	***Recipient***
	Joe	lost	your report.
	Subject	***Verb***	***Object***

The passive voice reverses the pattern, making the recipient of an action serve as subject.

Passive	***Recipient***	***Action***	***Agent***
	Your report	was lost	by Joe.
	Subject	***Verb***	***Prepositional phrase***

Sometimes the passive eliminates the agent altogether:

Passive	Your report was lost. *(Who lost it?)*

Some writers mistakenly rely on the passive voice because they think it sounds more objective and important. But the passive voice often makes writing wordy, indecisive, evasive, and unethical.

Concise and direct (active)	I underestimated labour costs for this project. (*7 words*)
Wordy and indirect (passive)	Labour costs for this project were underestimated by me. (*9 words*)
Evasive (passive)	Labour costs for this project were underestimated. (*7 words*)

Do not evade responsibility by hiding behind the passive voice:

Passive (not responsible)	A **mistake** was made in your shipment.
	It was decided not to hire you.
	A **layoff** is recommended.

Use the active voice when reporting errors or bad news. Readers appreciate clarity and sincerity.

The passive voice creates a weak and impersonal tone.

Weak and impersonal	An offer will be made by us next week.
Strong and personal	We will make an offer next week.

Use the active voice when you want action. Otherwise, your statement will have no power.

Weak passive	If my claim is not settled by May 15, the Better Business Bureau will be contacted, and their advice on legal action will be taken.
Strong active	If you do not settle my claim by May 15, I will contact the Better Business Bureau for advice on legal action.

Notice how this active version emphasizes the new and significant information by placing it at the end.

Use the active voice for giving instructions.

Faulty passive	The bid should be sealed.
	Care should be taken with the dynamite.
Correct active	**Seal** the bid.
	Be careful with the dynamite.

Avoid shifts from active to passive voice in the same sentence.

Faulty shift	During the meeting, project members spoke and presentations were given.
Correct	During the meeting, project members spoke and **gave** presentations.

Unless you have a deliberate reason for choosing the passive voice, use the *active* voice for making forceful connections.

Exercise 4

The following sentences are wordy, weak, or evasive because they are in the passive voice. Revise each sentence as a concise, forceful, and direct expression in the active voice, to identify the person or agent performing the action.

a. The evaluation was performed by us.
b. The report was written by our group.
c. Unless you pay me within three days, my lawyer will be contacted.
d. Hard hats should be worn at all times.
e. It was decided to reject your offer.
f. It is believed by us that this contract is faulty.
g. The decision was made that your request for promotion should be denied.

Use Passive Voice Selectively

Passive voice is appropriate in lab reports and other documents in which the agent's identity is immaterial to the message.

Use the passive voice when your audience does not need to know the agent.

Correct passive Mr. Jones **was brought** to the emergency room.
The bank failure **was publicized** provincewide.

Use the passive voice to focus on events or results when the agent is unknown, unapparent, or unimportant.

Correct passive All memos in the firm **are filed** in a database.
Josef's article **was published** last week.

Use the passive voice when you want to be indirect or inoffensive (as in requesting the customer's payment or the employee's cooperation, or to avoid blaming someone—such as your supervisor) (Ornatowski 94).

Active but offensive **You** have not paid your bill.
You need to overhaul our filing system.

Inoffensive passive **This bill** not been paid.
Our filing system needs to be overhauled.

Use the passive voice if the person behind the action has reason for being protected.

Correct passive The criminal **was identified**.
The embezzlement scheme **was exposed**.

Exercise 5

The following sentences lack proper emphasis because of an improper use of the active voice. Revise each ineffective active voice as an appropriate passive voice to emphasize the recipient rather than the actor.

a. Joe's company fired him.
b. Someone on the maintenance crew has just discovered a crack in the nuclear-core containment unit.
c. The tornado destroyed the barn.
d. You did a poor job editing this report.

Avoid Overstuffed Sentences

A sentence crammed with ideas makes details hard to remember and relationships hard to identify:

Overstuffed Publicizing the records of a private meeting that took place three weeks ago to reveal the identity of a manager who criticized our company's promotion policy would be unethical.

Clear things up by sorting out the relationships.

Revised In a private meeting three weeks ago, a manager criticized our company's policy on promotion. It would be unethical to reveal the manager's identity by publicizing the records of that meeting. (*Other versions are possible here, depending on the writer's intended meaning.*)

Give your readers no more information than they can retain in one sentence.

Exercise 6

Unscramble this overstuffed sentence by making shorter, clearer sentences:

A smoke-filled room causes not only teary eyes and runny noses but also can alter people's hearing and vision, as well as creating dangerous levels of carbon monoxide, especially for people with heart and lung ailments, whose health is particularly threatened by second-hand smoke.

EDITING FOR CONCISENESS

Writing can suffer from two kinds of wordiness: one kind occurs when readers receive information they don't need (think of an overly detailed weather report during local television news). The other kind of wordiness occurs when too many words are used to convey information readers *do* need (as in saying "a great deal of potential for the future" instead of "great potential").

Every word in the document should advance your meaning. Concise writing conveys the most information in the fewest words. But it includes the details necessary for clarity.

Use fewer words whenever fewer will do. But remember the difference between *clear writing* and *compressed writing* that is impossible to decipher.

First drafts rarely are concise. The following strategies will help you "trim the fat."

Avoid Wordy Phrases

Each phrase here can be reduced to one word:

Wordy		Concise
at a rapid rate	=	rapidly
due to the fact that	=	because
the majority of	=	most
on a personal basis	=	personally
give instruction to	=	instruct
would be able to	=	could
readily apparent	=	obvious
a large number	=	many
prior to	=	before
aware of the fact that	=	know
conduct an inspection of	=	inspect
in close proximity	=	near

Eliminate Redundancy

A redundant expression says the same thing twice, in different words, as in *fellow colleagues.*

a **dead** corpse	**end** result
completely eliminate	cancel **out**
basic essentials	consensus **of opinion**
blue **in colour**	**utter** devastation
mental awareness	**the month of** August
mutual cooperation	**utmost** perfection

Avoid Needless Repetition

Unnecessary repetition clutters writing and dilutes meaning.

Repetitious In trauma victims, breathing is restored by **artificial respiration.** Techniques of **artificial respiration** include mouth-to-mouth **respiration** and mouth-to-nose **respiration**.

Repetition in the above passage disappears when sentences are combined.

Concise In trauma victims, breathing is restored by artificial respiration, **either mouth-to-mouth or mouth-to-nose.**

Repetition can be useful. Don't hesitate to repeat, or at least rephrase, material (even whole paragraphs in a longer document) if you feel that readers need reminders.

Exercise 7

Revise the following wordy sentences to eliminate needless phrases, needless repetition, and redundancy.

a. I have admiration for Professor Singh.
b. Due to the fact that we made the lowest bid, we won the contract.
c. On previous occasions we have worked together.
d. She is a person who works hard.
e. We have completely eliminated the bugs from this program.
f. This report is the most informative report on the project.

Avoid *There is* and *There are* Sentence Openers

Weak	**There is** a coaxial cable connecting the antenna to the receiver.
Revised	A coaxial cable connects the antenna to the receiver.
Weak	**There is** a danger of explosion in Number 2 mineshaft.
Revised	Number 2 mineshaft is in danger of exploding.

In some contexts, however, proper emphasis would call for a *There* opener.

Correct	People often have wondered about the rationale behind Boris's sudden decision. Actually, **there are** several good reasons for his dropping out of the program.

Avoid Some *It* Sentence Openers

Avoid beginning a sentence with *It*—unless the *It* clearly points to a specific referent in the preceding sentence: "This document is excellent. It deserves special recognition."

Weak	**It** was his bad attitude that got him fired.
Revised	His bad attitude got him fired.
Weak	**It** is necessary to complete both sides of the form.
Revised	Please complete both sides of the form.

Delete Needless Prefaces

Instead of delaying the new information in your sentence, get right to the point.

Wordy	**I am writing this letter because** I wish to apply for the position of copy editor.
Concise	Please consider me for the position of copy editor.
Wordy	As far as artificial intelligence is concerned, the technology is only in its infancy.
Concise	Artificial-intelligence technology is only in its infancy.

Exercise 8

Revise the following sentences to eliminate *There* and *It* openers and needless prefaces.

a. There was severe fire damage to the reactor.
b. There are several reasons why Jenna left the company.
c. It is essential that we act immediately.
d. It has been reported by Clayton that several safety violations have occurred.
e. This letter is to inform you that I am pleased to accept your job offer.

Avoid Weak Verbs

Use verbs that express a definite action: *open, close, move, continue, begin.* Avoid weak verbs that express no specific action: *is, was, are, has, give, make, come, take.* In some cases, such verbs are essential to your meaning: "Dr. Yang is operating at 7:00 a.m." "Take me to the laboratory." But in other cases, weak verbs add words without advancing meaning. All forms of the linking verb *to be* (*am, are, is, was, were, will, have been, might have been*) generally are weak. This next sentence achieves conciseness because of the strong verb *consider:*

Concise	Please **consider** my offer.
Weak and wordy	Please **take into consideration** my offer.

Don't disappear behind weak linking verbs and their baggage of needless nouns and prepositions.

Weak	My recommendation **is** for a larger budget.
Strong	I **recommend** a larger budget.

Strong verbs, or action verbs, suggest an assertive, positive, and confident writer. Here are some weak verbs converted to strong:

Weak		**Strong**
is in conflict with	=	conflicts
has the ability to	=	can
give a summary of	=	summarize
make an assumption	=	assume
come to the conclusion	=	conclude
take action	=	act
make a decision	=	decide

Exercise 9

Revise the following wordy and vague sentences to eliminate weak verbs.

a. Our disposal procedure is in conformity with federal standards.
b. Please make a decision today.
c. We need to have a discussion about the problem.
d. Your conclusion is in agreement with mine.
e. This manual gives instructions to end users.

Delete Needless *To Be* Constructions

The preceding section showed that forms of *to be* (*is, was, are,* etc.) are weak. Sometimes the *to be* form itself mistakenly appears behind such verbs as *appears, seems,* and *finds.*

Wordy	Your product seems **to be** superior. I consider this employee **to be** highly competent.

Avoid Excessive Prepositions

Needless prepositions make wordy sentences.

Wordy	The recommendation first appeared **in** the report written **by** the supervisor **in** January **about** that month's productivity.
Concise	The recommendation first appeared in the supervisor's productivity report for January.

The following prepositional phrases can be reduced.

Excessive		**Reduced**
with the exception of	=	except for
in reference to	=	about (or regarding)
in order that	=	so
in the near future	=	soon
in the event that	=	if
at the present time	=	now
in the course of	=	during
in the process of	=	during (or in)

Fight Noun Addiction

Nouns manufactured from verbs (nominalizations) often accompany weak verbs and needless prepositions.

Weak and wordy	We ask for the **cooperation** of all employees.
Strong and concise	We ask that all employees **cooperate.**
Weak and wordy	Give **consideration** to the possibility of a career change.
Strong and concise	**Consider** a career change.

Besides causing wordiness, a nominalization can be vague—by hiding the agent of an action.

Wordy and vague	**A valid requirement** for immediate action exists. (*Who should take the action? We can't tell.*)
Precise	We **must act** immediately.

Here are nominalizations restored to their verb forms:

Vague		Precise
conduct an investigation of	=	investigate
provide a description of	=	describe
conduct a test of	=	test
make a discovery of	=	discover

Nominalizations drain the life from your style. So, write as you would speak, but avoid slang or overuse of colloquialisms. Also avoid excessive economy. For example, "Employees must cooperate" would not be a desirable alternative to "We ask for the cooperation of all employees."

Exercise 10

Revise the following sentences to eliminate needless prepositions and *to be* constructions, and to cure noun addiction.

a. Igor seems to be ready for a vacation.
b. In the event of system failure, your sounding of the alarm is essential.
c. These are the recommendations of the chairperson of the committee.
d. Our acceptance of the offer is a necessity.
e. Please perform an analysis and make an evaluation of our new system.
f. A need for your caution exists.

Make Negatives Positive

A positive expression is easier to understand than a negative one.

Indirect and wordy	Please do not be late in submitting your report.
Direct and concise	Please submit your report on time.

Readers work even harder to translate sentences with multiple negative expressions:

Confusing and wordy	Do **not** distribute this memo to employees who have **not** received a security clearance.
Clear and concise	Distribute this memo only to employees who have received a security clearance.

Besides the directly negative words (*no, not, never*), some words are indirectly negative (*except, forget, mistake, lose,* uncooperative).

Confusing and wordy	**Do not neglect** to activate the alarm system. My diagnosis was **not inaccurate**.
Clear and concise	**Be sure** to activate the alarm system. My diagnosis was **accurate**.

The positive versions are more straightforward *and* persuasive.

Some negative expressions, of course, are perfectly correct, as in expressing disagreement.

Correct negatives	This is **not** the best plan. Your offer is **unacceptable**. This project **never** will succeed.

Select positives over negatives whenever your meaning allows:

Negatives		**Positives**
did not succeed	=	failed
does not have	=	lacks
did not prevent	=	allowed
not unless	=	only if

Clean Out Clutter Words

Clutter words stretch a message without adding meaning. Here are some of the commonest: *very*, *definitely*, *quite*, *extremely*, *rather*, *somewhat*, *really*, *actually*, *currently*, *situation*, *aspect*, *factor*.

Cluttered	**Actually,** one **aspect** of a business **situation** that could **definitely** make me **quite** happy would be to have a **somewhat** adventurous partner who **really** shared my **extreme** attraction to risks.
Concise	I seek an adventurous business partner who enjoys risks.

Delete Needless Qualifiers

Qualifiers such as *I feel, it seems, I believe, in my opinion,* and *I think* soften the tone and impact of a statement. Use qualifiers to express uncertainty or to avoid seeming arrogant or overconfident.

Appropriate qualifiers	Despite Frank's poor grades last year he will, **I think,** do well in college. Your product **seems** to be what we need.

But when you are certain, eliminate the qualifier so as not to seem tentative or evasive.

Needless qualifiers	**It seems** that I've made an error. We **appear to** have exceeded our budget. **In my opinion,** this candidate is outstanding.

In communicating across cultures, keep in mind that a direct, forceful style might be considered offensive.

Exercise 11

Revise the following sentences to eliminate inappropriate negatives, clutter words, and needless qualifiers.

a. Our design must avoid non-conformity with building codes.
b. Never fail to wear protective clothing.
c. Do not accept any bids unless they arrive before May 1.
d. I am not unappreciative of your help.
e. I appear to have misplaced the contract.

EDITING FOR FLUENCY

Fluent sentences are easy to read because of clear connections, variety, and emphasis. Their varied length and word order eliminate choppiness and monotony. Fluent sentences enhance *clarity*, allowing readers to see the most important ideas. Fluent sentences enhance *conciseness*, often replacing several short, repetitious sentences with one longer, economical sentence. The following strategies will help you write fluent sentences.

Combine Related Ideas

A choppy, wordy series of short, disconnected sentences is also unclear.

Disconnected Jogging can be healthful. You need the right equipment. Most necessary are well-fitting shoes. Without this equipment you take the chance of injuring your legs. Your knees are especially prone to injury. (*5 sentences*)

Clear, concise, and fluent Jogging can be healthful if you have the right equipment. Shoes that fit well are most necessary because they prevent injury to your legs, especially your knees. (*2 sentences*)

Most sets of information can be combined in different relationships, depending on what you want to emphasize. Imagine that this set of facts describes an applicant for a junior-management position with your company.

- Roy Dupuis graduated from an excellent engineering school.
- He has no experience.
- He is highly recommended.

Assume you are stating your impression of this candidate to your firm's managing partner. To convey a negative impression, you might combine the facts in this way:

Strongly negative emphasis Although Roy Dupuis graduated from an excellent management school and is highly recommended, **he has no experience.**

The *independent* idea (in boldface) receives the emphasis. To continue with our example, if you are undecided but leaning in a negative direction, you might write

Slightly negative emphasis Roy Dupuis graduated from an excellent engineering school and is highly recommended, **but** he has no experience.

In the sentence above, the ideas before and after *but* are both independent. These independent ideas are joined by the coordinating word *but,* which suggests that both sides of the issue are equally important (or "coordinate"). Placing the negative idea last, however, gives it slight emphasis.

Finally, to emphasize strong support for the candidate, you could say:

Strongly positive emphasis	Although Roy Dupuis has no experience, he graduated from an excellent management school and is highly recommended.

In the above version the earlier idea is subordinated by *although,* leaving the two final ideas independent.

Caution: Combine sentences only to advance your meaning and to ease the reader's task. A sentence with too much information and too many connections can be difficult for readers to sort out.

Overstuffed	Our night supervisor's oral order from upper management to repair the overheated circuit was misunderstood by Leslie Kidd, who gave the wrong instructions to the emergency crew, thereby causing the fire within 30 minutes.
Clearer	Upper management issued an oral order to repair the overheated circuit. Our night supervisor transmitted the order to Leslie Kidd, who misunderstood. Kidd incorrectly instructed the emergency crew, and the fire began within 30 minutes.

Vary Sentence Construction and Length

We have just seen how related ideas often need to be linked in one sentence, so that readers can grasp the connections:

Disconnected	The nuclear core reached critical temperature. The loss-of-coolant alarm was triggered. The operator shut down the reactor.
Connected	As the nuclear core reached critical temperature, triggering the loss-of-coolant alarm, the operator shut down the reactor.

But an idea that should stand alone for emphasis needs a sentence of its own:

Correct	Core meltdown seemed inevitable.

However, an unbroken string of long or short sentences can bore and confuse readers, as can a series with identical openings:

Dreary	There are some drawbacks about diesel engines. **They** are difficult to start in cold weather. **They** cause vibration. **They** also give off an unpleasant odour. **They** cause sulphur dioxide pollution.
Varied	Diesel engines have some drawbacks. Most obvious are their noisiness, cold-weather starting difficulties, vibration, odour, and sulphur dioxide emission.

Similarly, when you write in the first person, overusing *I* makes you appear self-centred. (Some organizations require use of the third person, avoiding the first person completely, for all manuals, lab reports, specifications, product descriptions, etc.)

Do not avoid personal pronouns if they make the writing more readable (by eliminating passive constructions).

Use Short Sentences for Special Emphasis

All this talk about combining ideas might suggest that short sentences have no place in good writing. Wrong. Short sentences show connections and clarify relationships; short sentences (even one-word sentences) provide vivid emphasis. They stick in a reader's mind.

Exercise 12

Combine each set of sentences into one fluent sentence that provides the requested emphasis. For example,

Sentence set	John is a loyal employee. John is a motivated employee. John is short-tempered with his colleagues.
Combined for positive emphasis	Even though John is short-tempered with his colleagues, he is a loyal and motivated employee.
Sentence set	This word processor has many features. It includes a spelling checker. It includes a thesaurus. It includes a grammar checker.
Combined to emphasize thesaurus	Among its many features, such as spelling and grammar checkers, this word processor includes a thesaurus.

a. The job offers an attractive salary.
It demands long work hours.
Promotions are rapid.
(*Combine for negative emphasis.*)

b. The job offers an attractive salary.
It demands long work hours.
Promotions are rapid.
(*Combine for positive emphasis.*)

FINDING THE EXACT WORDS

Too often, language can be a vehicle for *camouflage* rather than communication. People see many reasons to hide behind language, as when they

- speak for their company but not for themselves
- fear the consequences of giving bad news
- are afraid to disagree with company policy
- recommend an action some readers will resent

- worry about making a bad impression
- worry about being wrong
- pretend to know more than they do
- avoid admitting a mistake or ignorance

Inflated and unfamiliar words, borrowed expressions, and needlessly technical terms camouflage meaning. Whether intentional or accidental, poor word choices have only one result: inefficient and often unethical writing that resists interpretation and frustrates the reader.

Following are strategies for finding words that are *convincing, precise,* and *informative.*

Use Simple and Familiar Words

Don't replace technically precise words with vague, imprecise non-technical words. Don't write *a part that makes the computer run* when you mean *central processing unit.* Use the precise term, and define it in a glossary:

Correct	Central processing unit: the part of the computer that controls information transfer and carries out arithmetic and logical instructions.

Certain technical words may be indispensable in certain contexts, but the non-technical words usually can be simplified. Instead of *answering in the affirmative, say yes;* or instead of *endeavouring to promulgate* a new policy, *try to announce* it.

Unfamiliar words	Acoustically attenuate the food-consumption area.
Revised	Soundproof the cafeteria.

Don't use three syllables when one or two will do. Generally, trade for fewer:

Three Syllables		One or Two Syllables
aggregate	=	total
demonstrate	=	show
endeavour	=	effort, try
frequently	=	often
initiate	=	begin
is contingent upon	=	depends on
multiplicity of	=	many
optimum	=	best
subsequent to	=	after
utilize	=	use

Trim wherever you can. Most important, choose words you hear and use in everyday speaking—words that are universally familiar.

Don't write *I deem* when you mean *I think*, or *keep me apprised* instead of *keep me informed*, or *I concur* instead of *I agree*, or *securing employment* instead of *finding a job*, or *it is cost prohibitive* instead of *we can't* afford it.

Don't write like the author of a report from the U.S. Federal Aviation Administration, who recommended that manufacturers of the DC–10 re-evaluate *the design of the entire pylon assembly to minimize design factors which are resulting in sensitive and/or critical maintenance and inspection procedures* (23 words, 54 syllables). A plain English translation: *Redesign the pylons so they are easier to maintain and inspect* (11 words, 18 syllables).

Besides the annoyance they cause, needlessly long or unfamiliar words can be *ambiguous.*

Ambiguous Make an improvement in the clerical situation.

Should we hire more clerical personnel or better personnel or should we train the personnel we have? Words chosen to impress readers too often confuse them instead. A plain style is more persuasive because "it leaves no one out" (Cross 6).

Of course, now and then the complex or more elaborate word best expresses your meaning. For instance, we would not substitute *end* for *terminate* in referring to something with an established time limit.

Correct Our trade agreement terminates this month.

If a complex word can replace a handful of simpler words—and can sharpen your meaning—use the complex word.

Weak	Six rectangular grooves **around the outside edge** of the steel plate are needed for the pressure clamps to fit into.
Informative and precise	Six rectangular grooves on the steel plate **perimeter accommodate** the pressure clamps.
Weak	We need a **one-to-one exchange of ideas and opinions**.
Informative and precise	We need a **dialogue**.
Weak	Sexist language **contributes to the ongoing prevalence** of gender stereotypes.
Informative and precise	Sexist language **perpetuates** gender stereotypes.

Exercise 13

Revise the following sentences for straightforward, familiar language.

a. May you find luck and success in all endeavours.
b. I suggest you reduce the number of cigarettes you consume.
c. A good writer is cognizant of how to utilize grammar in a correct fashion.
d. I will endeavour to ascertain the best candidate.

Avoid Useless Jargon

Every profession has its own "shorthand." Among specialists, technical terms are a precise and economical way to communicate. For example, *stat* (from the Latin *statim* or "immediately") is medical jargon for *drop everything and deal with this emergency.* For computer buffs, a *glitch* is a momentary power surge that can erase the contents of internal memory; a *bug* is an error that causes a program to run incorrectly. Such useful jargon conveys clear meaning to a knowledgeable audience.

Technical language, however, can be used appropriately or inappropriately. The latter is useless jargon, meaningless to insiders as well as outsiders. In the world of useless jargon, people don't *cooperate* on a project; instead, they *interface* or *contiguously optimize their efforts.* Rather than *designing a model,* they *formulate a paradigm.* Instead of *observing limits or boundaries,* they *function within specific parameters.*

A popular form of useless jargon is adding *-wise* to nouns, as shorthand for *in reference to* or *in terms of.*

Useless jargon	Expensewise and schedulewise, this plan is unacceptable.
Revised	In terms of expense and scheduling, this plan is unacceptable.

Another form of jargon creates verbs from nouns or adjectives by adding an *-ize* ending: don't invent *prioritize* from *priority;* instead use *to rank priorities.*

At its worst, jargon makes its user seem stuffy and pretentious:

Pretentious	Unless all parties interface synchronously within given parameters, the project will be rendered inoperative.
Possible translation	Unless we coordinate our efforts, the project will fail.

Beyond reacting with frustration, readers often conclude that useless jargon is camouflage for a writer with something to hide. So, think about your readers and ask yourself: "Can I more easily say exactly what I mean?" Use jargon only if it *improves* your communication.

Use Acronyms Selectively

Acronyms are another form of specialized shorthand, or jargon. They are formed from the first letters of words in a phrase (as in *LOCA* from *l*oss *o*f *c*oolant *a*ccident) or from a combination of first letters and parts of words (as in *bit* from *b*inary dig*it*).

Computer technology has spawned countless acronyms, including:

Acronym		**Meaning**
LAN	=	local area network
Telnet	=	telephone network
RAM	=	random access memory

Acronyms *can* communicate concisely—but only when the audience knows their meaning, and only when you use the term often in your document. Whenever you first use an acronym, spell out the words from which it is derived.

An acronym defined

> **Modem** ("modulator + demodulator"): a device that converts, or "modulates," computer data in electronic form into a sound signal that can be transmitted via phone line and then reconverted, or "demodulated," into electronic form for the receiving computer.

For lay audiences, try to avoid acronyms altogether or be sure to define the terms that make up the acronym.

Avoid Triteness

Writers who rely on tired old phrases (clichés) like the following seem too lazy or too careless to find exact ways to say what they mean.

make the grade	the chips are down
in the final analysis	not by a long shot
close the deal	last but not least
hard as a rock	welcome aboard
water under the bridge	over the hill

Exercise 14

Revise the following sentences to eliminate useless jargon and triteness.

a. For the obtaining of the X-33 printer, our firm will have to accomplish the disbursement of funds to the amount of $3000.
b. To optimize your financial return, prioritize your investment goals.
c. The use of this product engenders a 50 percent repeat consumer encounter.
d. We wish to welcome all new managers aboard.
e. Intercom utilization will be employed to initiate substitute employee operative involvement.

Avoid Misleading Euphemisms

Euphemisms try to be polite or to make unpleasant subjects seem less offensive. Thus, we *powder our nose* or *use the boys' room* instead of *using the toilet;* we *pass away* instead of *dying.* Euphemisms make the truth seem less painful.

When euphemisms avoid offending or embarrassing our audience, they are perfectly legitimate. Instead of telling a job applicant he or she is *unqualified,* we might say, *your background doesn't meet our needs.* In addition, there are times when friendliness and inter-office harmony are more likely to be preserved with writing that is not too abrupt, bold, blunt, or emphatic (MacKenzie 2).

Euphemisms are unethical if they understate the truth when only the truth will serve. In the sugar-coated world of misleading euphemisms, bad news disappears:

- Instead of being *laid off* or *fired,* workers are *surplused* or *deselected,* or the company is *downsized.*
- Instead of *lying* to the public, the government *engages in a policy of disinformation.*

- Instead of *wars* and *civilian casualties,* we have *conflicts* and *collateral damage.*

Language loses impact when *criminals* become *offenders,* when *rape* becomes *sexual assault,* and when people who are just plain *lazy* become *underachievers.* Plain talk is always better than deception. If someone offers you a job *with limited opportunity for promotion,* expect a *dead-end* job.

Avoid Overstatement and Unsupported Generalizations

Exaggerating destroys credibility. Be cautious when using words such as *best, biggest, brightest, most,* and *worst.*

Overstated	**Most** businesses have no loyalty toward their employees.
Revised	**Some** businesses have little loyalty toward their employees.
Overstated	You will find our product to be the **best.**
Revised	You will **appreciate the high quality** of our product.

Unsupported generalizations harm your credibility. Be aware of the vast differences in meaning among these words:

few	never	most	all	many
some	rarely	often	always	sometimes

Unless you specify *few, some, many,* or *most,* readers can interpret your statement to mean *all.*

Misleading Assembly-line employees are doing shabby work.

Unless you mean *all,* qualify your generalization with *some, most*—or even better, specify *20 percent.*

Exercise 15

Revise the following sentences to eliminate euphemism, overstatement, or unsupported generalizations.

a. I finally must admit that I am an abuser of intoxicating beverages.
b. I was less than candid.
c. This employee is poorly motivated.
d. Most entry-level jobs are boring and dehumanizing.
e. Clerical jobs offer no opportunity for advancement.

Avoid Imprecise Words

Even words listed as synonyms carry different shades of meaning. Do you mean to say *I'm slender, you're slim, she's lean,* or *he's scrawny?* The wrong choice could be disastrous.

A single wrong word can offend readers, as in this statement by a job applicant:

Offensive	Another attractive feature of your company is its **adequate** training program.

While *adequate* might convey honestly the writer's intended meaning, the word seems inappropriate in this context (an applicant expressing a judgment about a program). Although the program may not have been highly ranked, the writer could have used any of several alternatives (*solid, respectable, growing*—or no modifier at all).

Be especially aware of similar words with dissimilar meanings, as in these examples:

affect/effect	ensure/insure
all ready/already	imply/infer
among/between	invariably/inevitably
continual/continuous	obtain/attain
eager/anxious	uninterested/disinterested

Be on the lookout for imprecisely phrased (and therefore illogical) comparisons.

Imprecise	Your bank's interest rate is higher than Central Bank. *(Can a rate be higher than a bank?)*
Precise	Your bank's interest rate is higher than Central Bank's.

Imprecise language can create ambiguity: *send us more personal information* might request *more* information that is personal or information that is *more* personal.

Precision ultimately enhances conciseness, when one exact word replaces multiple inexact words.

Wordy and less exact	I have **put together** all the financial information. **Keep doing** this exercise for 10 seconds.
Concise and more exact	I have **assembled** all the. . . **Continue** this exercise. . .

Be Specific and Concrete

General words name broad classes of things, such as *job, computer,* or *person.* Such terms usually need to be clarified by more specific ones.

General		**Specific**
job	=	senior accountant for Softbyte Press
computer	=	Acer 9000
person	=	Sarah Chu, production manager

The more specific your words, the sharper your meaning.

General	structure
	dwelling
	vacation home
	log cabin
↓	log cabin in Ontario
Specific	a three-room log cabin on the banks of Green Lake

Notice how the picture becomes more vivid as we move to lower levels of generality.

Abstract words name qualities, concepts, or feelings (*beauty, luxury, depression*) whose exact meaning has to be nailed down by *concrete* words—words that name things we can know through our five senses.

Abstract		**Concrete**
a **beautiful** view	=	snowcapped mountains, a wilderness lake, pink granite ledge, 25-metre birch trees
a **luxurious** condominium	=	imported tiles, glass walls, oriental rugs
a **depressed** worker	=	suicidal urge, insomnia, feelings of worthlessness, no hope for improvement

Choose informative words that express exactly what you mean. Don't write *thing* when you mean *lever, switch, micrometer,* or *disk.* Instead of evaluating an employee as *good, great, disappointing,* or *terrible,* use terms that are more concrete, such as *reliable, skillful, dishonest,* or *incompetent*—further clarified by examples.

When you can, provide solid numbers and statistics that make your point:

General Transport Canada's 2005 statistics show that traffic fatalities were lower than in 2004. Indeed, the 2005 total was the lowest in years. However, deaths caused by rollovers (mostly in SUVs) increased.

Specific Transport Canada's 2005 statistics show 2851 traffic fatalities; that figure is down 4.7 percent from 2004's total of 2992 and is the lowest total of traffic deaths since 1955. However, deaths caused by rollovers increased from 519 to 665. By contrast, before 1991 rollover deaths did not exceed 200 in any year. (The increase can be attributed to the growing popularity of SUVs—the U.S. National Highway Safety Administration reports that the rollover rate for SUVs is 98 per 1 000 000, double that of all vehicles, which is 47 per 1 000 000.)

Exercise 16

Revise the following sentences to make them more precise or informative.

a. Our outlet does more business than Montreal.
b. Anaerobic fermentation is used in this report.
c. Confusion is in control of this office.
d. Your crew damaged a piece of office equipment.

One version of specific, concrete, and controlled phrasing is found in ASD Simplified Technical English's specification ASD-STE100™. It was developed by people in the aerospace industry, but it has commercial and industrial applications in helping people write clear documentation.

The specification provides a dictionary of words and their meanings and a set of writing rules. The dictionary specifies words that can be used. To accommodate each industry's specialist vocabulary, ASD Simplified Technical English allows one to create one's own dictionary of approved verbs and nouns.

Each word is assigned to just one part of speech and each word has just one meaning. The writing rules specify the structure of the text and tenses are strictly controlled (Unwalla).

TechScribe's Dr. Mike Unwalla supports the Plain English movement, but he sees some limitations in ASD Simplified Technical English:

> Should we be using ASD Simplified Technical English (or some other simplified English) in commercial and industrial environments? If you have looked at other pages on the TechScribe web site, you may have noticed that we do not conform to the rules of ASD-STE100. . . . That's because the site is (in part) a marketing tool. If someone searches for "technical communication consultancy," and if our term is "technical writing consultancy," then we won't be found. That's not good. Clearly, a simplified English is of no use in the marketing field. We want flexibility of expression and the ability to play on words to entice people into purchasing our products and services.
>
> On the other hand, with safety-critical systems, the last thing we need is ambiguity. Every instruction, every description, must be clear. ASD Simplified Technical English can help us to achieve that requirement. There are limitations to ASD Simplified Technical English, but it goes a long way to ensuring that communications are not ambiguous. . . .

Use Analogies to Sharpen the Image

Ordinary *comparison* shows similarities between two things *of the same class* (two computer keyboards, two methods of cleaning dioxin-contaminated sites). *Analogy* shows some essential similarity between two things of *different classes* (report writing and computer programming, computer memory and post office boxes).

Analogies are good for emphasizing a point *(Some rain is now as acidic as vinegar)*. They are especially useful in translating something abstract, complex, or unfamiliar, as long as the easier subject is broadly familiar to readers. Analogy therefore calls for a particularly careful analysis of audience.

Analogies can save words and convey vivid images. The following sentence from a description of a trout feeder mechanism uses an analogy to clarify the positional relationship between two working parts:

Analogy	The metal rod is inserted (and centred, **crosslike**) between the inner and outer sections of the clip.

Without the analogy *crosslike*, we would need something like this to visualize the relationship:

Missing analogy	The metal rod is inserted, **perpendicular to the long plane and parallel to the flat plane**, between the inner and outer sections of the clip.

This second version is doubly inefficient: more words are needed to communicate, and more work is needed to understand the meaning.

Besides naming things vividly, analogies help *explain* things. The following analogy from the *Congressional Research Report* helps us understand something unfamiliar (dangerous levels of a toxic chemical) by comparing it to something more familiar (human hair).

> **Analogy** A dioxin concentration of 500 parts per trillion is lethal to guinea pigs. One part per trillion is roughly equal to the thickness of a human hair compared to the distance across North America.

ADJUSTING THE TONE

Your tone is your personal stamp—the personality that takes shape between the lines. The tone you create depends on (1) the distance you impose between yourself and the reader, and (2) the attitude you show toward the subject.

Assume that a friend is going to take over a job you've held. You've decided to write your friend instructions for parts of the job. Here is your first sentence:

Informal

> Now that you've arrived in the glamorous world of office work, put on your track shoes; this is no ordinary manager-trainee job.

First, we notice that the sentence imposes little distance between the writer and the reader (it uses the direct address, *you*, and the humorous suggestion to "put on your track shoes"). The ironic use of *glamorous* suggests that the writer means just the opposite: that the job holds little glamour.

For a different reader (the recipient of a company training manual, for example), the writer would have chosen some other opening:

Semi-formal

> As a manager trainee at GlobalTech, you will work for many managers. In short, you will spend little of your day seated at your desk.

The tone now is serious, no longer intimate, and the writer expresses no distinct attitude toward the job. For yet another audience (those who will read an annual report for clients or investors), the writer again might alter the tone:

Formal

> Manager trainees at GlobalTech are responsible for duties that extend far beyond desk work.

Here the businesslike shift from second- to third-person address makes the tone too impersonal for any document addressed to the trainees themselves.

We already know how tone works in speaking. When you meet someone new, for example, you respond in a tone that defines your relationship:

Tone announces interpersonal distance

> Honoured to make your acquaintance. *(formal tone—greatest distance)*
> How do you do? *(formal)*
> Nice to meet you. *(semi-formal—medium distance)*
> Hello. *(semi-formal)*

Hi. *(informal—least distance)*
What's happening? *(informal—slang)*

Each of these greetings is appropriate in some situations, inappropriate in others.

To decide on an appropriate distance from which to address a particular audience, follow these guidelines:

- Use a formal or semi-formal tone in writing for superiors, professionals, or academics (depending on what you think the reader expects).
- Use a semi-formal or informal tone in writing for colleagues and subordinates (depending on how close you feel to your readers).
- Use an informal tone when you want your writing to be conversational, or when you want it to sound like a person talking.
- Above all, find out what the preferences are in your organization.

> **ON THE JOB...**
>
> **Proofreading for Tone**
>
> *"Tone and timing are critical in my documents. Proposals, progress reports, invoices, collection letters—they all have to be sent at exactly the right time. And they must have the right tone. Of course, we proofread for errors and for technical accuracy, but we also check the tone, which must be respectful and businesslike. Every once in a while, I have to use a firm tone with a client who wants to cut corners or is slow to pay, but even then I don't want a judgmental or angry tone to creep in...."*
>
> **—Ken Langedyk, consulting civil engineer**

Whichever tone you select, be consistent throughout your document.

Inconsistent tone	My office isn't fit for a pig [*too informal*]; it is ungraciously unattractive [*too formal*].
Revised	The shabbiness of my office makes it an unfit place to work.

In general, lean toward an informal tone without falling into slang.

In addition to setting the distance between writer and reader, your tone implies your *attitude* toward the subject and the reader:

Tone announces attitude

We dine at seven.
Dinner is at seven.
Let's eat at seven.
Let's chow down at seven.
Let's strap on the feedbag at seven.
Let's pig out at seven.

The words we choose tell readers a great deal about where we stand.

If readers expect an impartial report, try to keep your own biases out of it. But for situations in which your opinion is expected, or in which you perceive some danger or ethics violation, let readers know where you stand.

Say "I enjoyed the fibre optics seminar" instead of "My attitude toward the fibre optics seminar was one of high approval." Say "Let's liven up our dull relationship" instead of "We should inject some rejuvenation into our lifeless liaison."

Use the following strategies for making your tone conversational and appropriate.

Use an Occasional Contraction

Unless you have reason to be formal, use (but do not overuse) contractions. Balance an *I am* with an *I'm*, a *you are* with a *you're*, an *it is* with an *it's* (as we've done throughout this book). Write, "Don't be wordy and vague." However, if you really want to stress the negative command, write "Do not be wordy and vague."

Generally, use contractions only with pronouns, not with nouns or names.

Awkward contractions	Barbara'll be here soon. Health's important.
Ambiguous contractions	The dog's barking. Bill's skiing.

These ambiguous contractions could be confused with possessive constructions.

Address Readers Directly

Use the personal pronouns *you* and *your* to connect with readers.

Impersonal tone	Students at our university will find the faculty always willing to help.
Personal tone	As a student at our university, **you** will find the faculty always willing to help.

Research shows that readers relate better to something addressed directly to them.

Caution: Use *you* and *your* only to correspond *directly* with the reader, as in a letter, memo, instructions, or some form of advice, encouragement, or persuasion. By using *you* and *your* when your subject and purpose call for first or third person, you might write something wordy and awkward like this:

Wordy and awkward	**When you** are in northern Ontario, you can see wilderness lakes everywhere around **you.**
Appropriate	Wilderness lakes are everywhere in northern Ontario.

Formal reports and proposals do not lend themselves to personal pronouns such as *I* and *you.* Although it is natural, perhaps, to write "we conclude," it is better to write "this report's findings suggest" or "the evidence points to."

Exceptions might occur when (1) you need to specify that you performed a task ("I tested the brake system three times") or when (2) you wish to emphasize a report recommendation ("We recommend four solutions"). Still, that recommendation could be phrased, "This report has shown that four solutions are required."

Exercise 17

The following sentences contain pretentious language, unclear expression of attitude, missing contractions, or indirect address. Adjust the tone.

a. Further interviews are a necessity to our ascertaining the most viable candidate.
b. This project is beginning to exhibit the characteristics of a loser.
c. We are pleased to tell you that you are a finalist.
d. Do not submit the proposal if it is not complete.
e. Employees must submit travel vouchers by May 1.

Use *I* and *We* When Appropriate

Instead of disappearing behind your writing, use *I* or *We* when referring to yourself or your organization.

Distant	The writer would like a refund.
Revised	**I** would like a refund.

A message becomes doubly impersonal when both the writer and the reader disappear.

Impersonal	The requested report will be sent next week.
Personal	**We** will send the report **you** requested next week.

Use the Active Voice

Because the active voice is more direct and economical than the passive voice, it generally creates a less formal tone.

Passive and impersonal	Travel expenses cannot be reimbursed unless receipts are submitted.
Active and personal	We cannot reimburse your travel expenses unless you submit receipts.

Exercise 18

The following sentences have too few *I* or *We* constructions or too many passive constructions. Adjust the tone.

a. Payment will be made as soon as an itemized bill is received.
b. You will be notified.
c. Your help is appreciated.
d. Your request will be given our consideration.
e. This writer would like to be considered for your opening.

Emphasize the Positive

Whenever you offer advice, suggestions, or recommendations, try to emphasize benefits rather than flaws.

Critical tone	Because of your division's lagging productivity, a management review may be needed.
Encouraging tone	A management review might help boost productivity in your division.

Avoid an Overly Informal Tone

We generally do not write in the same way we would speak to friends at the local burger joint or street corner. Achieving a conversational tone does not mean lapsing into substandard usage, slang, profanity, or excessive colloquialisms. *Substandard usage* ("He ain't got none," "I seen it today," "She brang the book") fails to meet standards of educated expression. *Slang* ("hurling," "belted," "bogus," "bummed") usually has specific meaning only for members of a particular in-group. *Profanity* ("This idea sucks," "What the hell") not only displays contempt for the audience but often earns contempt for the person using it. *Colloquialisms* ("okay," "a lot," "snooze," "in the bag") are understood more widely than slang, but tend to appear more in speaking than in writing.

Slang and profanity are almost always inappropriate in school or workplace writing. The occasional colloquial expression, however, helps soften the tone of any writing—as long as the situation calls for a measure of informality. Tone is considered offensive when it violates the reader's expectations: when it seems disrespectful, tasteless, distant and aloof, too chummy, casual, or otherwise inappropriate for the topic, the reader, and the situation.

A formal, or academic, tone is perfectly appropriate in countless writing situations: a research paper, a job application, a report for the company president.

Avoid Bias

Even controversial subjects deserve unbiased treatment, as in the following description of a management–employee confrontation.

A factual account

> At 9:00 a.m. on Tuesday, January 21, 80 women employees set up picket lines around the executive offices of our Orillia branch, bringing business to a halt. The group issued a formal protest, claiming that their working conditions were repressive, their salary scale unfair, and their promotional opportunities limited. The women demanded affirmative action, insisting that the company's hiring and promotional policies and wage scales be revised. The demonstration ended when Garvin Tate, vice president in charge of personnel, promised to appoint a committee to investigate the group's claims and to correct any inequities.

Notice the absence of implied judgments; the facts are presented objectively. A less impartial version of the event, from a protestor's point of view, might read:

> Last Tuesday, sisters struck another blow against male supremacy when 80 women employees paralyzed the company's repressive and sexist administration for more

> than six hours. The timely and articulate protest was aimed against degrading working conditions, unfair salary scales, and lack of promotional opportunities for women. Stunned executives watched helplessly as the group organized their picket lines, determined to continue their protest until their demands for equal rights were addressed. An embarrassed vice president quickly agreed to study the group's demands and to revise the company's discriminatory policies. The success of this long-overdue confrontation serves as an inspiration to oppressed women employees everywhere.

Judgmental words (*male supremacy, degrading, paralyzed, articulate, stunned, discriminatory*) inject the writer's attitude, even though it isn't called for. In contrast to this bias, the following version patronizingly defends the status quo:

A biased version

> Our Orillia branch was the scene of an amusing battle of the sexes last Tuesday, when a group of irate feminists, 80 strong, set up picket lines for six hours at the company's executive offices. The protest was lodged against supposed inequities in hiring, wages, working conditions, and promotion for women in our company. The radicals threatened to surround the building until their demands for "equal rights" were met. A bemused vice president responded to this carnival demonstration with patience and dignity, assuring the militants that their claims and demands—however inaccurate and immoderate—would receive just consideration.

Again, qualifying adjectives and superlatives slant the tone.

Being unbiased, of course, doesn't mean burying your head—and your values—in the sand. Remaining neutral about something you know to be wrong or dangerous is unethical (Kremers 59). If, for instance, you conclude that the Orillia protest was clearly justified, say so.

Avoid Sexist Usage

When we refer to doctors, lawyers, and other professionals as *he* or *him*, while we refer to nurses, administrative assistants, and homemakers as *she* or *her*, we use sexist phrasing. In this traditional stereotype, males do the jobs that "really matter" and that pay higher wages, whereas females serve only as support and decoration. When females do "invade" traditional "male" roles, we might express our surprise at their boldness by calling them *female executives, female sportscasters, female surgeons,* or *female hockey players.* Likewise, to demean males who have settled for "female" roles, we sometimes refer to *male secretaries, male nurses, male flight attendants,* or *male models.*

The following are guidelines for non-sexist usage:

1. Use neutral expressions:

Guidelines for non-sexist usage

chair or chairperson	rather than	chairman
businessperson	rather than	businessman
supervisor	rather than	foreman
police officer	rather than	policeman
letter carrier	rather than	postman

2. Rephrase to eliminate the pronoun, if you can do so without altering your original meaning.

Sexist	A writer will succeed if **he** revises.
Revised	A writer who revises succeeds.

3. Use plural forms.

Sexist	A writer will succeed if **he** revises.
Revised	Writers will succeed if **they** revise (but *not* A writer will succeed if **they** revise.)

When using a plural form, avoid creating an error in pronoun-referent agreement by having the *plural* pronoun *they* or *their* refer to a *singular* referent (as in *Each writer should do their best*). Note: the *Oxford English Dictionary* committee now approves this "error," but it is not yet widely accepted.

4. When possible (as in direct address) use *you: You will succeed if you revise.* But use this form only when addressing someone directly. (See page 89 for discussion.)
5. Use occasional pairings (him or her, she or he, his or hers): A writer will succeed if *she or he* revises.

   But note that overuse of such pairings can be awkward: *A writer should do his or her best to make sure that he or she connects with his or her readers.* Most handbooks now encourage alternating use between the two pronouns, and discourage pairings and *he/she: An effective writer always focuses on her audience; the writer strives to connect with all his readers.*
6. Drop diminutive endings such as *-ess* and *-ette* used to denote females (*poetess, drum majorette, actress,* etc.).
7. Use *Ms.* instead of *Mrs.* or *Miss,* unless you know that person prefers one of the traditional titles.

Avoid Offensive Usages of All Types

Enlightened communication respects all people in reference to their specific cultural, racial, ethnic, and national background; sexual and religious orientation; age or physical condition. References to individuals and groups should be as neutral as possible; no matter how inadvertent, any expression that seems condescending or judgmental or that violates the reader's sense of appropriateness is offensive. Detailed guidelines for reducing biased usage appear in these two works, among others:

Schwartz, Marilyn, et al. *Guidelines for Bias-Free Writing.* Bloomington, IN: Indiana UP, 1995.

American Psychological Association. *Publication Manual of the American Psychological Association.* 4th ed. Washington: 1994.

Below is a sampling of suggestions adapted from these works:

- When referring to members of a particular culture, be as specific as possible about that culture's identity: instead of *Asian* or *Hispanic,* for instance, use *Korean* or *Nicaraguan.*
- Avoid judgmental expressions: instead of *Third-World* or *undeveloped nations* or the *Far East,* use *developing* or *newly industrialized nations* or *East Asia.*
- When referring to someone who has a disability, avoid terms that could be considered pitying or overly euphemistic, such as *victims, unfortunates, challenged,* or *differently abled.* Focus on the individual instead of the disability: instead of *blind person* or *amputee,* refer to *a person who is blind* or *a person who has lost an arm.*
- When referring to members of a particular age group, use *girl* or *boy* for people of age 14 or under; *young person, young adult, young man,* or *young woman* for those of high school age; and *woman* or *man* for those of university age.

Exercise 19

The following sentences contain negative emphasis, excessive informality, biased expressions, or offensive usage. Adjust the tone.

a. If you want your workers to like you, show sensitivity to their needs.
b. By not hesitating to act, you prevented my death.
c. The union has won its struggle for a decent wage.
d. The group's spokesman demanded salary increases.
e. Each employee should submit his vacation preferences this week.

CONSIDERING THE CULTURAL CONTEXT

The style guidelines in this chapter apply specifically to standard English in North America. But practices and preferences can differ widely in different cultural contexts. Certain cultures might prefer long sentences and technical language to convey an idea's full complexity. Other cultures value expressions of respect, politeness, praise, and gratitude more than clarity or directness (Hein 125–26; Mackin 349–50).

Some documents in other languages tend to be more formal than in English, and some rely heavily on passive voice (Weymouth 144). French readers, for example, may prefer an elaborate style that reflects sophisticated and complex modes of thinking. In contrast, our "plain English," conversational style might connote simple-mindedness, disrespect, or incompetence (Thrush 277).

In translation or in a different cultural context, certain words carry offensive or unfavourable connotations. A few notable disasters (Gesteland 20; Victor 44):

- The Chevrolet *Nova*—meaning "doesn't go" in Spanish
- Colgate's *Cue* toothpaste—pronounced like an obscenity in French
- A brand of bicycle named *Flying Pigeon*—imported for a North American market

Idioms ("strike out," "ground rules") hold no logical meaning for other cultures. Slang ("bogus," "fat city") and colloquialisms ("you bet," "gotcha") can strike readers as too informal and crude.

USING AUTOMATED TOOLS WISELY

Many of the strategies in this chapter could be executed rapidly with word-processing software. By using the *global search and replace function* in some programs, you can command the computer to search for ambiguous pronoun references. The computer will also detect overuse of passive voice, *to be* verbs, *There* and *It* sentence openers, negative constructions, clutter words, needless prefaces and qualifiers, overly technical language, jargon, sexist language, and so on. With an online dictionary or thesaurus, you can check definitions or see a list of synonyms for a word you have used in your document.

But these editing aids can be extremely imprecise. No amount of automation is likely to eliminate the writer's burden of *choice.* None of the rules or advice offered in this chapter applies universally. Ultimately, the informed writer's sensitivity to meaning, emphasis, and tone—the human contact—determines the effectiveness of any document.

USING OBJECTIVE SELF-EVALUATION TOOLS

Indexes for evaluating the readability of your phrasing

This chapter presents many tools for polishing writing, but you may not know where to start, or even if much editing is needed. Moreover, you may have to evaluate the readability of your own writing, a difficult task at best. If so, you will find the following objective indexes useful.

1. *Calculate the percentage of SVO and SVC sentences.* Most clear writing features a high percentage (75 percent or better) of basic sentence patterns: **subject-verb-object** (SVO) and **subject-verb-complement** (SVC).

Do you write simple sentences?

Hockey players need skating skills. *(SVO)*
Hockey players take risks on the ice. *(SVO + complementary prepositional phrase)*
Hockey players are resilient. *(SVC)*
Pro hockey players are reluctant to play in Canada. *(SVC + complementary prepositional phrase)*
In most cases, pro hockey players hire player agents. (*Adverbial opening + SVO*)
Consequently, they seldom participate in contract negotiations. *(Adverbial opening + SVC)*

Quick index: Examine a passage of 10 sentences or more. Confirm that 75 percent or more of the sentences use an SVO or SVC sentence pattern.

NOTE *More complicated patterns include compound sentences (two or more independent clauses), complex sentences (one independent clause and one or more dependent clauses), and compound-complex sentences (two or more independent clauses and at least one dependent clause).*

Do you restrict the number of words before the subject?

2. *Count the words before the subject.* Readable sentences quickly get to the point, even though many sentences start with transition words.

   Quick index: In a passage of 10 or more sentences, calculate the average number of words before the sentences' subjects. **That average should be three words or fewer.**

Do you control the number of words between the subject and verb?

3. *Count the words between subject and verb.* Occasionally, you can afford to place words between the subject and verb (John, *a large, ungainly man with a pronounced limp,* slowly walked home). But you should **restrict the average number of intervening words to three or fewer.**

Do you control sentence length and the number of "big" words?

4. *Calculate the percentage of linking verbs.* Forms of the verb *to be* (*is, are, has been, will be, would have been*) and words like *seems, appears,* and *looks* link subjects and predicates. In most cases, linking verbs contribute to wordy phrasing and weaker phrasing than do active verbs. (Compare "he is a trainer of dogs" with "he trains dogs.")

   Quick index: Count all the verbs in a passage of at least 100 words. Then calculate the percentage of linking verbs; **these less efficient verbs should make up 30 percent or less of the total number of verbs** in the passage.
5. *Calculate a Fog Index.* During World War II, Robert Gunning devised a readability index based on these main principles:

- The longer the sentence, the harder it is to understand.
- "Big" words (of three or more syllables) contribute to reading difficulty.
- A document's readability can be gauged by taking random samples.
- Each sample passage needs to be about 100 words (or more) to give an accurate measurement of readability.
- Each sample passage must consist of complete sentences.
- Proper nouns of three or more syllables (*Saskatchewan*) and words that become three syllables by adding *es* (*excesses*) or *ed* (*exceeded*) should not be counted as "big" words. (Gunning 32–40)

A Fog Index calculation includes several steps. The following calculation is for the two paragraphs in point number 4, above. (A sentence is defined as ending with a period. "30 percent" is counted as two words. Numerals are not counted among the "big" words.)

1. No. of sentences	6
2. No. of words	100
3. Avg. sentence length	16.67
4. No. of "big" words	7
5. Percentage of "big" words	7
6. Subtotal (16.67 + 7)	23.67
7. Multiply by 0.4, a constant (23.67 x 0.4)	**9.47**
	Fog Index

A Fog Index reading may be misleading

A Fog Index of 9.47 roughly translates to a Grade 10 reading level. But the bottom line index tells only part of the story. The examined passage has a low rating primarily because only 7 of the 100 words have three or more syllables. By contrast, the paragraph on page 95 ("Many of the strategies. . . have used in your document") has an index of 18.4, mainly because 22.5 percent of the words have three or more syllables. Literally interpreted, that index says the passage requires a Ph.D. candidate's reading level. But is the paragraph really that difficult to follow? Probably not—words such as strategies, executed, rapidly, and word-processing should not pose a problem for the readers of this textbook.

This text tries to maintain a Fog Index of 11 to 13. Most of your business and technical writing should have an index of 10 to 12. Remember, though, not to panic if the index is higher; the high reading may result from a high percentage of three-syllable words, most of which your readers know very well. If a high reading results from a high average sentence length, then you should edit to correct that problem.

NOTE *Many word-processing programs contain objective evaluation tools. Refer to your user's manual for more details.*

WEB CONNECT

Many websites provide advice about writing clear prose and exercises to improve editing techniques. Here is a representative sampling, starting with the Plain English Network site:

www.blm.gov/nhp/NPR/pe_toc.html
www.sheridanc.on.ca/~sherman/rap.dir/weeks1to4/Cutfog.html
http://andromeda.rutgers.edu/~jlynch/Writing/
www.io.com/~hcexres/textbook
http://europa.eu.int/comm/translation/en/ftfog/index.htm
www.sec.gov/pdf/handbook.pdf

Note: Probably the most useful of the above sites are the last two: a site sponsored by the European Commission's Translation Service, and the U.S. Securities and Exchange Commission's Plain Language Handbook.

EXERCISES

1. Calculate Fog Index readings for various passages in this text. For each reading, consider:
   - Does that reading reflect the degree of difficulty?
   - Does the reading match the reading levels for anticipated readers of this book?
2. Use the five objective self-evaluation tools to assess the readability of a document important to you (application letter, progress report, class term-project report).
3. Find a passage that you find very difficult to read. Determine some of the causes of that difficulty by using the five objective indexes on pages 95-96 of this chapter.

COLLABORATIVE PROJECT (ONGOING)

Form a proofreading/editing group of three to four people. Evaluate and proofread each other's assignments. Use the editing advice in this chapter to improve conciseness, clarity, and naturalness. Compare the objective readability ratings for your writing to those of other writers in your group.

CHAPTER 5

Summarizing Information

LEARNING OBJECTIVES

After reading this chapter, you should be able to

- Understand the applications and value of summarizing documents.
- Recognize and include the elements of a useful summary.
- Employ the suggested stages of effectively and efficiently summarizing a document.
- Distinguish among "closing summary," "informative abstract," and "descriptive abstract."

A summary is a short version of a longer document. An economical way to communicate, a summary saves time, space, and energy.

PURPOSE OF SUMMARIES

ON THE JOB...

The Importance of Summaries

"Every time I run a training session in corporate communication, participants tell horror stories about working weeks or months on a report, only to have it disappear somewhere up the management chain. We use copies of those 'invisible' reports as case studies, and invariably the summary turns out to have been poorly written, providing readers few or no clues as to the report's significance...."

—**Frank Sousa, communications consultant**

Chapter 15 will show that as we record our research findings, we summarize and paraphrase to capture and compress the main ideas. In addition to this role as a research aid, summarized information is vital in day-to-day workplace transactions.

On the job, you have to write concisely about your work. You might report on meetings or conferences, describe your progress on a project, or propose a money-saving idea. Many new employees provide superiors (decision makers) with summaries of the latest developments in their field.

Given today's pace and volume of information, summaries are more vital than ever. Some reports and proposals can be hundreds of pages long. Those who must act on this information need to rapidly identify what is most important in a document. From a good summary, busy readers can get enough information to decide whether they should read the entire document, parts of it, or none of it.

Whether you summarize someone else's document or your own, your job is to communicate the *essential message* accurately and in the fewest words, as in the following passage and summary:

The original passage

> The lack of technical knowledge among owners of television sets leads to their suspicion about the honesty of television repair technicians. Although television owners might be fairly knowledgeable about most repairs made to their automobiles, they rarely understand the nature and extent of specialized electronic repairs. For instance, the function and importance of an automatic transmission in an automobile are generally well known; however, the average television owner knows nothing about the flyback transformer in a television set. The repair charge for a flyback transformer failure is roughly \$150—a large amount to a consumer who lacks even a simple understanding of what the repairs will accomplish. In contrast, a \$450 repair charge for the transmission on the family car, though distressing, is more readily understood and accepted.

Three significant ideas make up the essential message: (1) television owners lack technical knowledge and are suspicious of repair technicians; (2) an owner usually understands even the most expensive automobile repairs; and (3) owners do not understand or accept expenses for television repairs. Here's a possible summary:

A summarized version

> Because television owners lack technical knowledge about their sets, they are often suspicious of repair technicians. Although consumers may understand expensive automobile repairs, they rarely understand or accept repair and parts expenses for their television sets.

This summary is almost 30 percent of the original length because the original itself is short. With a longer original, a summary might be 5 percent or less. But length is less important than informative value: an effective summary gives readers only what they need. For short documents that can be read quickly, the only summary needed is usually an *opening thesis* or *topic sentence* that previews the contents.

ELEMENTS OF A SUMMARY

All effective summaries display the following elements:

- *The essential message:* The essential message is the significant material from the original: controlling ideas (thesis and topic sentences); major findings; important names, dates, statistics, and measurements; and conclusions or recommendations. Significant material does not include background; the author's personal comments or conjectures; introductions; long explanations, examples, or definitions; visuals; or data of questionable accuracy.
- *Non-technical style:* More people generally read the summary than any other part of a document. So write at the lowest level of technicality. Translate technical data into plain English. "The patient's serum glucose measured 240 mg%" can be translated as "The patient's blood sugar remained critically high." But if you know all your readers are experts, you don't need to simplify.
- *Independent meaning:* In meaning as well as style, your summary should stand alone as a self-contained message. Readers should have to read the original only for more detail—not to make sense of the basic ideas.

- *No personal assessment:* Avoid personal comments ("This interesting report" or "The author is correct in assuming").
- *Conciseness:* Conciseness is vital, but never at the expense of clarity and accuracy. Make the summary economical but clear and comprehensive.

CRITICAL THINKING IN THE SUMMARY PROCESS

Follow these guidelines for summarizing your own writing or another's.

1. *Read the entire original.* When summarizing another's work, get a complete picture before writing a word.
2. *Reread and underline.* Reread the original, underlining essential material. Focus on the thesis and topic sentences.
3. *Edit the underlined information.* Reread the underlined material and cross out whatever does not advance the meaning.
4. *Rewrite in your own words.* Include all essential material in the first draft, even if it's too long; you can trim later.
5. *Edit your own version.* When you have everything readers need, edit for conciseness.
   a. Cross out all needless words without harming clarity or grammar. Use complete sentences.
   b. Cross out needless prefaces, such as "The writer argues" or "Also discussed is."
   c. Use numerals for numbers, except to begin a sentence.
   d. Combine related ideas in order to emphasize relationships.
6. *Check your version against the original.* Verify that you have preserved the essential message and added no comments.
7. *Rewrite your edited version.* Add transitional expressions to reinforce the connection between related ideas.
8. *Document your source.* If summarizing another's work, cite the source immediately below the summary, and place directly quoted statements within quotation marks. (See Chapter 19 for documentation formats.)

A SAMPLE SITUATION

Imagine that you work in the information office of your province's ministry of the environment. In a coming election, citizens will vote on a referendum proposal for constructing municipal trash incinerators. Referendum supporters argue that incinerators would help solve the growing problem of waste disposal in highly populated parts of the province. Opponents argue that incinerators cause air pollution.

To clarify the issues for voters, the ministry will mail a newsletter to each registered voter. You have been assigned the task of researching the recent data and summarizing it. Here is one of the articles. You have underlined key phrases. (The margin notes reflect your critical thinking as you prepare to summarize the article.)

INCINERATING TRASH: A HOT ISSUE GETTING HOTTER

Combine as orienting sentence (controlling idea)

Alarmed by the tendency of landfills to contaminate the environment, both public officials and citizens are vocally seeking alternatives. The most commonly discussed alternative is something called a resource recovery facility. Nearly 40 Canadian cities have built such in the last 15 years, and another 50 or so are in various stages of planning.

Include definition

These recovery facilities are a new form of an old technology. Basically, they're incinerators. But, unlike the incinerators of old, they don't just burn waste. They also recover energy. The energy is sold as steam to an industrial customer, or it is converted to electricity and sold to the local utility. (A few facilities, but not many, also recover metals or other materials before using the waste as fuel.)

Include major fact

Include major statistics

A ton of trash possesses the energy content of a barrel and a half of oil. This is not a trivial amount. Canada discards 50 million tonnes of municipal refuse a year. If all of it were converted to energy, we could replace the equivalent of 12 percent of our oil imports.

Include major fact

At the local level, selling energy or materials not only replaces non-renewable resources, it also provides a source of income that partly offsets the cost of operating the facility.

Include major fact

Delete explanation

The new facilities are, on average, much cleaner than the municipal incinerators of old. Many have two-stage combustion units, in which the second stage burns exhaust gases at high temperature, converting many potential organic pollutants to less harmful emissions, such as carbon dioxide. Some, especially the larger and newer facilities, also come equipped with the latest in pollution-control devices.

Delete questionable point

The environmental community is uneasy with this new technology. Environmentalists have argued for many years that the best method of handling municipal trash is to recycle it—i.e., to separate the glass, metal, paper, and other materials and use them again, either without reprocessing or as raw materials in producing new products. The thought of the potential resources in municipal solid waste simply being burned, even with energy recovery, has made many environmentalists opponents of resource recovery.

Include key finding and explanation

More recently, opponents have found a stronger reason to oppose burning waste: dioxin in the plants' emissions. The amounts present are extremely small, measured in trillionths of a gram per cubic metre of air. But dioxin can be deadly, at least to animals, at very low levels.

What Is Dioxin?

Delete technical details

Dioxin is a generic term for any of 75 chemical compounds, the technical name for which is poly-chlorinated dibenzo-p-dioxins (PCDDs). A related group of 135 chemicals, the PCDFs, or furans, are often found in association with PCDDs.

Delete long explanation

The most infamous of these substances, 2,3,7,8-TCDD, is often referred to as the "most toxic chemical known." This judgment is based on animal test data. In laboratory tests, 2,3,7,8-TCDD is lethal to guinea pigs at a concentration of *500 parts per trillion*. A part per trillion is roughly equivalent to the thickness of a human hair compared to the distance across Canada.

Include major point

The effects on humans are less certain, for many reasons: it is difficult to measure the amounts to which humans have been exposed and difficult to isolate the effects of dioxin from the effects of other toxic substances on the same population; and the latency period for many potential effects, such as cancer, may be as long as 20 to 30 years.

Include continuation of major point

Nevertheless, because of the extreme effects of this substance on animals, known releases of dioxin have generated considerable public alarm. One of the most publicized releases occurred at Seveso, Italy, in July 1976, where a pharmaceutical plant explosion resulted in the contamination of at least 700 acres of fields and affected more than 5000 people. Dioxin was found in the soil in concentrations of 20 to 55 parts per billion.

Delete long example

The immediate effects on humans were nausea, headaches, dizziness, diarrhea, and an acute skin condition called chloracne, which causes burn-like sores. The effects on animals were more severe: birds, rabbits, mice, chickens, and cats died by the hundreds, within days of the explosion. In response to the explosion, the Italian provincial authorities evacuated 730 people from the zone nearest the plant, and sealed off an area containing another 5000 people from contact with non-residents.

Delete long example

In North America, perhaps the best known dioxin contamination incident occurred at Times Beach, Missouri, where used oil, contaminated with dioxin, was sprayed on roads as a dust suppressant. Soil samples showed dioxin at levels exceeding 100 parts per billion. While no human health effects were documented at Times Beach, a flood in December 1982 led to widespread dispersal of the contamination, as a result of which the entire town was condemned, the population evacuated, and over $30 million of the U.S.'s Superfund money used to purchase the condemned property.

Include the most striking and familiar example

Dioxin was among the substances of concern at Love Canal. And it was the major contaminant in the chemical defoliant Agent Orange, the subject of a lawsuit by 15 000 Vietnam veterans and dependants and an out-of-court settlement of those complaints valued at $180 million.

Include key findings

As early as 1978, trace amounts of dioxin were found in the routine emissions of a municipal incinerator. Virtually every incinerator tested since that date has shown traces of dioxin.

Adapted from James E. McCarthy, *Congressional Research Service Review*, Apr. 1986: 19–21.

Assume that in two early drafts of your summary, you rewrote and edited; for coherence and emphasis, you then inserted transitions and combined related ideas. Here is your final draft.

INCINERATING TRASH: A HOT ISSUE GETTING HOTTER

(A Summary)

Because landfills often contaminate the environment, trash incinerators (resource recovery facilities) are becoming a popular alternative. Nearly 40 are operating in Canadian cities, and 50 more are planned. Besides their relatively clean burning of waste, these incinerators recover energy, which can be sold to offset operating costs. One ton of trash has roughly the energy content of 1.5 barrels of oil. Converting all Canadian refuse to energy could reduce oil imports by 12 percent.

However, incinerator emissions contain very small amounts of dioxin (a generic name for any of 75 related chemicals). Even low dioxin levels can be deadly to animals. In fact, animal tests have helped label one dioxin substance "the most toxic chemical known." Although effects on human beings are less certain, news of dioxin in the environment creates public alarm, as evidenced at Love Canal and by the successful Agent Orange lawsuit by 15 000 Vietnam veterans and dependants. Almost every municipal incinerator tested since 1978 has shown traces of dioxin.

The version above is trimmed, tightened, and edited: word count is reduced to roughly 20 percent of the original. A summary this long serves well in many situations, but other audiences might want a briefer and more compressed summary—say, 10 to 15 percent of the original:

A More Compressed Summary

Because landfills often contaminate the environment, trash incinerators (resource recovery facilities) are becoming a popular alternative across Canada. Besides their relatively clean burning of waste, these incinerators recover energy, which can be sold to offset operating costs.

However, incinerator emissions contain very small amounts of dioxin, a chemical proven so deadly to animals, even at low levels, that it has been labelled the most toxic chemical known. Although its effects on human beings are less certain, news of dioxin in the environment creates public alarm. Almost every municipal incinerator tested since 1978 has shown traces of dioxin.

Notice that the essential message is still intact; related ideas are again combined and fewer supporting details are included. Clearly, length is adjustable according to your audience and purpose.

FORMS OF SUMMARIZED INFORMATION

In preparing a report, proposal, or other document, you might summarize others' material as part of your presentation. But you will often summarize your own material as well. For instance, if your document extends to several pages, it might include three forms of summary, in different locations, with different levels of detail: *closing summary, informative abstract,* or *descriptive abstract.*[1] Figure 5.1 depicts these forms.

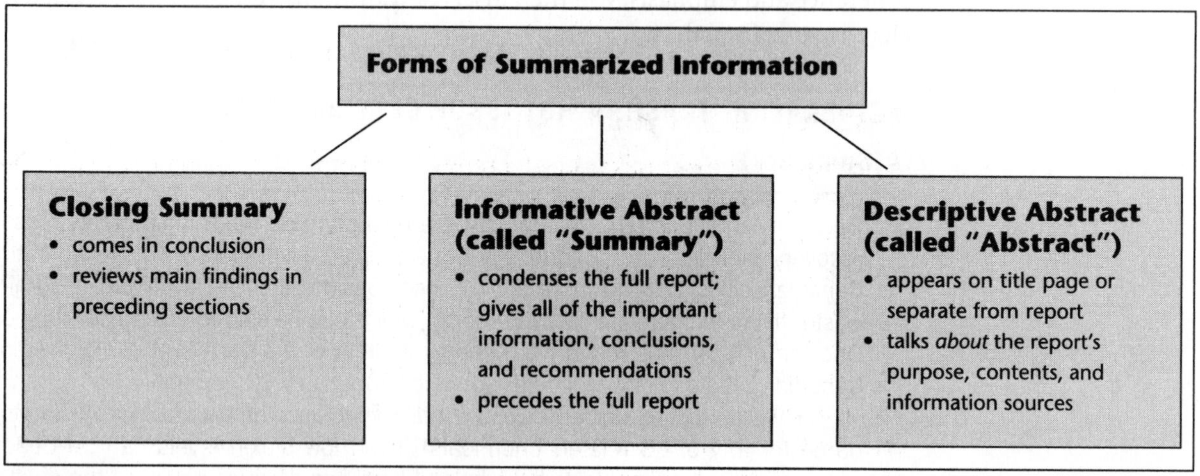

Figure 5.1 Summarized Information Assumes Various Forms

1. Adapted from Vaughan. Although we take liberties with his classification, Vaughan's insightful article helped clarify our thinking about the overlapping terminology that perennially seems to confound discussions of these distinctions.

Closing Summary

A *closing summary* refers to summarized information at the beginning of a conclusion section or at the end of a report's central body sections. It helps readers review and remember the preceding major findings. This look back at the "big picture" helps readers appreciate the conclusions and recommendations that follow.

Informative Abstract ("Summary")

Many report readers appreciate condensed versions of reports. Some of these readers like to see a capsule version of a report before reading the complete document; others simply want to know basically what a report says without having to read the full document.

In order to meet reader needs, the *informative abstract* appears just after the title page. This summary tells the reader essentially what the full version says: it identifies the need or issue that has prompted the report; it describes the report's analytical method; it reviews the main facts and findings; and it condenses the report's conclusions and recommendations.

Actually, the term *informative abstract* is not used much these days. You are more likely to encounter *summary* or *synopsis*. The heading "executive summary" is used for material summarized for managers who may not understand all the technical jargon a report might contain. By contrast, a "technical summary" is written for readers at the same technical level as the author of the report. You may need two or three levels of summary for report readers who have different levels of technical expertise.

> **ON THE JOB...**
>
> **Value of Summaries**
>
> *"There's so much information in our field, which makes summaries that much more valuable. Some reports can be expected to have a relatively long shelf life, to remain useful and relevant for some time; these reports especially need a well-written technical or executive summary (or both) that a reader can use to get a good grasp of the subject and what needed to be done...."*
>
> **—Jan Bath, civil engineering technologist**

See Chapter 21 for more discussion of the summary section in a report.

Descriptive Abstract ("Abstract")

A *descriptive abstract* talks about a report; it doesn't give the report's main points. It just helps potential readers decide whether to read the report. Thus, a descriptive abstract conveys only the nature and extent of a document. It presents the broadest view and offers no major facts from the original. It indicates whether conclusions and recommendations are included, but doesn't list them.

Descriptive abstracts usually appear in special publications or in electronic databases, both of which name and briefly describe hundreds of reports. One such publication is the widely used *Fisheries Abstracts*. However, some reports place a one- to three-sentence abstract on the report's title page. In all these placements, the term *abstract* will signal a brief description, not all of the report's highlights.

CHECKLIST FOR SUMMARIES

Use this checklist to refine your summaries.

Content

- Does the summary contain only the essential message?
- Does the summary make sense as an independent piece?
- Is the summary accurate when checked against the original?
- Is the summary free of any additions to the original?
- Is the summary free of needless details?
- Is the summary economical yet clear and comprehensive?
- Is the source documented?
- Does the descriptive abstract tell what the original is about?

Organization

- Is the summary coherent?
- Are there enough transitions to reveal the line of thought

Style

- Is the summary's level of technicality appropriate for its audience?
- Is the summary free of needless words?
- Are all sentences clear, concise, and fluent?
- Is the summary written in correct English?

WEB CONNECT

These three sites discuss summary writing.

http://web.uvic.ca/wguide/Pages/MasterToc.html#Summaries
http://users.drew.edu/~sjamieso/Summary.html
www.garage.com/resources/writingexecsum.shtml

EXERCISES

1. Read each of these two paragraphs, and then list the significant ideas contained in each essential message. Write a summary of each paragraph.

    In recent years, ski-binding manufacturers, in line with consumer demand, have redesigned their bindings several times in an effort to achieve a noncompromising synthesis between performance and safety. Such a synthesis depends on what appear to be divergent goals. Performance, in essence, is a function of the binding's ability to hold the boot firmly to the ski, thus enabling the skier to change rapidly the position of his or her skis without being hampered by a loose or wobbling connection. Safety, on the other hand, is a function of the binding's ability both to release the boot when the skier falls, and to retain the boot when subjected to the normal shocks of skiing. If achieved, this synthesis of performance and safety will greatly increase skiing pleasure while decreasing accidents.

    Contrary to public belief, sewage-treatment plants do not fully purify sewage. The product that leaves the plant to be dumped into the leaching (sievelike drainage) fields is secondary sewage containing toxic contaminants such as phosphates, nitrates, chloride, and heavy metals. As the secondary sewage filters into the ground, this conglomeration is carried along. Under the leaching area develops a contaminated mound through which groundwater flows, spreading the waste products over great distances. If this leachate reaches the outer limits of a well's drawing radius, the water supply becomes polluted. And because all water flows essentially toward the sea, more pollution is added to the coastal regions by this secondary sewage.

2. Attend a campus lecture on a topic of interest and take notes on the significant points. Write a summary of the lecture's essential message.

3. Find an article about your major field or area of interest and write both an informative abstract and a descriptive abstract of the article.

COLLABORATIVE PROJECT

Select a long paper that you have written for one of your courses; write an informative abstract and a descriptive abstract of the paper.

CHAPTER 6

Organizing for Readers

LEARNING OBJECTIVES

After reading this chapter, you should be able to

- Create an outline that best organizes a given document according to its content, purpose, and intended audience.
- Distinguish among standard paragraphs and paragraphs that place the topic sentence in an alternate position.
- Choose appropriate paragraph structures, from among general-to-specific, specific-to-general, and chronological patterns.

One of your biggest writing challenges is to transform your material into manageable form. First, you need to unscramble information to make sense of it for yourself; then you need to shape it for the reader's understanding.

In order to follow your thinking, readers need a message organized in a way that makes sense to *them.* But data rarely materialize or thinking rarely occurs in neat, predictable sequences. So you must *shape* random ideas and data into an organized pattern of meaning. In trying to organize, you will face questions like these:

TYPICAL QUESTIONS IN ORGANIZING FOR READERS

- What major question am I answering for my reader(s)?
- What secondary questions will help answer the main question?
- What relationships and answers do the gathered data suggest?
- What should I emphasize?
- What belongs where?
- What do I place first? Why?
- What comes next?
- How do I end?

Writers rely on the following strategies for organizing material: topical arrangement, outlining, paragraphing, and sequencing.

TOPICAL ARRANGEMENT

Whenever you analyze something, you break it down to discover constituents, connections, similarities, trends, associations, correlations, relationships, and perspectives. You break the topic into subtopics (that's commonly called *partition*). You also see which things share similarities and should therefore be discussed at the same level in a certain category (that's called *classification*). The following example explains how this can be achieved.

An example of partition

A discussion of Olympic Games events could be initially divided (*partitioned*) into two main types: Summer and Winter Games. Then, for example, the Summer events could be listed as the 38 "sports" at the 2008 Beijing Games (aquatics, archery, athletics, etc.). "Aquatics" could be further subdivided into diving and swimming. "Athletics" encompasses several track and field events: distance races, middle distance, sprints, hurdles, javelin, triple jump, and so on. And these events are further differentiated by gender.

Classifying according to purpose

However, someone might use a different approach by classifying the 38 official events. For example, baseball, softball, volleyball, team handball, field hockey, and basketball might be grouped together as "team games." Or a Canadian reporter might focus on the games in which the Canadian teams are participating. Rowing, canoe/kayak, cycling, and sailing might be classified as "race" events, while a "race event" such as triathlon might be lumped together with the track and field events. The classification depends on the writer's purpose.

The following case study illustrates how authors arrange and develop topics for a report.

The reason for the report

In March 2001, Ducks Unlimited submitted a "State of the Science" report to the Walkerton Inquiry. *Beyond the Pipe* reviewed studies of the "link between watershed features, water quality, and water quantity" ("International Scientific Review").

The information in the report came from 165 articles and reports, based on studies conducted in Canada, the U.S., and elsewhere. After reviewing that literature, Ducks Unlimited and University of Toronto researchers concluded that wetlands and riparian buffer zones

The report's conclusions

- "can significantly reduce contaminants in surface and groundwater,"
- "can reduce the variability in the quality and quantity of water sources," and
- "can improve source water quality for drinking water treatment."

The researchers also determined that current policies "do not sufficiently protect wetlands and riparian areas" and that protection and restoration costs are "small compared to the costs of in-pipe treatment." However, where land costs are high, restoration may not be economically feasible (Gabor et al. 40–41).

The report's recommendations

The report recommended that the province should

1. create integrated, comprehensive water management policy
2. enhance wetland protection
3. encourage and enhance wetland restoration
4. encourage riparian area protection programs
5. improve its understanding of watershed management (Gabor et al. 41–43)

The authors' main challenge

Beyond the Pipe's purpose was to persuade the inquiry that the Ducks Unlimited goal of preserving wetlands is consistent with the need to protect drinking water sources. The gathered evidence supports that contention, but the report could fulfill its persuasive purpose *only* if it used a clear, logical structure. After a $1^1/_2$ page introduction that provides a context and describes the report's four main objectives, the report's 31 pages of findings are organized into five smoothly integrated sections.

Table 6.1 shows the full set of relationships among the report's three levels of topics and subtopics.

Table 6.1 Relationships within a Raptor's Topical Arrangement (based on a Ducks Unlimited report)

Wetlands	Permanent Cover	Buffer Strips	Wetland Loss	Policy

Wetlands of Southern Ontario
Hydrological Functions
  Water storage and flood reduction
  Groundwater recharge
Water Quality Functions
  Nutrient assimilation
  Sediments
  Pathogens
  Contaminants
Summary
	Upland Conservation Programs	Sediment Removal and Erosion Control
		Nutrient Assimilation
		  Nitrogen
		  Phosphorus
		Pathogens
		Pesticides
		Contaminants
				Wetland Protection in Ontario
				  Federal policies
				  Provincial policies
				  Other instruments
				Riparian Area Management
				  Why Protect and Restore?
				  Water quality
				  Costs of natural vs. in-pipe treatment

OUTLINING

The value of outlining

The arrangement of related topics and subtopics in Table 6.1 illustrates the technique of outlining, an important skill developed by efficient and effective technical writers. Outlines use partition and classification to guide readers through the material in a pattern that readers find logical (and, ultimately, persuasive).

How should you organize the document to make it logical for your audience? Begin with the basics. Useful writing of any length—a book, report, chapter, letter, or memo—typically has an introduction, body, and conclusion.

- The *introduction* provides orientation by doing any of these things: explaining the topic's origin and significance and the document's purpose; identifying briefly your intended audience and your information sources; defining specialized terms or general terms that have special meanings in your document; accounting for limitations such as incomplete or questionable data; previewing the major topics to be discussed in the body section.

  Some introductions need to be long and involved; others, short and to the point. Reports too often waste readers' time with needless background information. If you don't know your readers well enough to give them only what they need, use subheadings so that they can choose what they want to read.

- The *body* delivers on the promise implied in your introduction ("Show me!"). Here you present your data, discuss your evidence, lay out your case, or tell readers what to do and how to do it. Body sections come in all different sizes, depending on how much readers need and expect.

  Body sections are titled to reflect their specific purpose: "Description and Function of Parts," for a mechanical description; "Required Steps," for a set of instructions; "Collected Data," for a feasibility analysis; "Operating Instructions," for a user's manual.
- The *conclusion* of a document has assorted purposes: it might evaluate the significance of the report, re-emphasize key points, take a position, predict an outcome, offer a solution, or suggest further study. If the issue is straightforward, the conclusion might be brief and definite. If the issue is complex or controversial, the conclusion might be lengthy and open ended. Whatever the conclusion's specific purpose, readers expect a clear perspective on the whole document.

  Conclusions vary with the document. You might conclude a mechanical description by reviewing the mechanism's major parts and then briefly describing one operating cycle. You might conclude a comparison or feasibility report by offering judgments about the facts you've presented and then recommending a course of action.

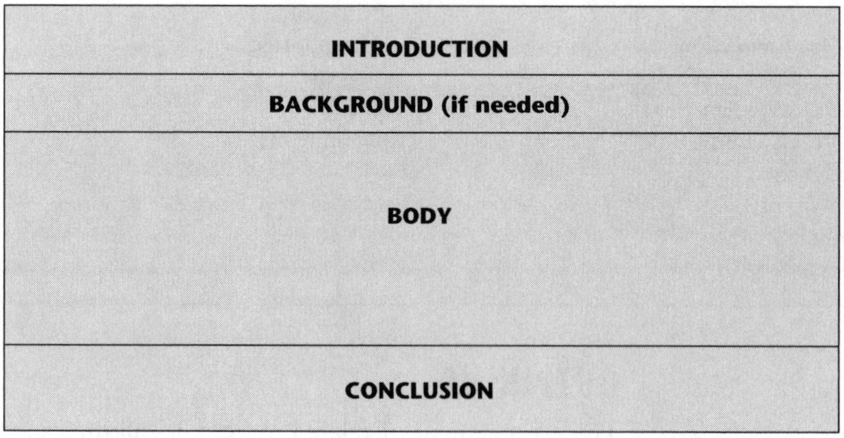

A suitable beginning, middle, and ending are essential, but alter your outline as you see fit. No single form of outline should be followed exactly by any writer. **The organization of any document ultimately is determined by its audience's needs and expectations**. In many cases, specific requirements about a document's organization and style are spelled out in a company's style guide. Structures for specific types of documents are provided in various sections of this text. In particular, see the action structure for short reports, in Chapter 17.

The computer is especially useful for rearranging outlines until they reflect the sequence in which you expect readers to approach your message.

The Formal Outline

A simple list usually suffices for organizing short documents. However, long or complex documents call for a systematic, formal outline, to mark divisions and to show how categories relate. Here, for example, is a formal outline for the report illustrated in Table 6.1.

A formal outline whose topical arrangement uses an appropriate pattern:

- nature of need (problem)
- nature of wetlands and their restorative functions (solution)
- nature of natural cover (solution)
- riparian buffer strips (solution)
- wetland loss (a reminder of the extent of the problem)
- inadequate protection policies (cause of problem)
- conclusions and recommendations (why and how to implement a solution)

BEYOND THE PIPE—WETLANDS, RIPARIAN BUFFER STRIPS, AND WATER QUALITY

INTRODUCTION

- The need for fresh water
- Wetlands and watershed management

Objectives

WETLANDS

- Wetlands of Southern Ontario
- Hydrological Functions of Wetlands
    - Water storage and flood reduction
    - Groundwater recharge
- Water Quality Functions
    - Nutrient assimilation
        - Nitrogen
        - Phosphorus
    - Sediments
    - Pathogens
    - Contaminants
- Summary

PERMANENT COVER

- Upland Conservation Programs

BUFFER STRIPS

- Sediment Removal and Erosion Control
- Nutrient Assimilation
    - Nitrogen
    - Phosphorus
- Pathogens
- Pesticides
- Summary

WETLAND LOSS

- Percentage of loss in Ontario

POLICY

- Wetland Protection in Ontario
    - Federal policies and legislation
    - Provincial policies
    - Other instruments for protection
- Riparian Area Management
- A Case for the Protection and Restoration of Wetlands and Riparian Areas
    - Wetlands and riparian areas as water quality support systems
    - Funding natural versus in-pipe water treatment—a comparison

CONCLUSIONS AND RECOMMENDATIONS

Technical documents often use decimal notation:

Decimal notation in a technical document

2.0 WETLANDS
 2.1 Wetlands of Southern Ontario
 2.2 Hydrological Functions of Wetlands
  2.2.1 Water storage and flood reduction
  2.2.2 Groundwater recharge
 2.3 Water Quality Functions
  2.3.1 Nutrient assimilation
   2.3.1.1 Nitrogen
   2.3.1.2 Phosphorus

Decimal notation makes it easier to refer readers to specific sections of a document ("See section 2.3.1.2"), and is usually preferred in engineering, government, and industry.

The section in Chapter 18 on writing formal reports shows three levels of outlines: *planning outline*, which guides the writer's research and initial organization; *working outline*, a lengthy formal device that acts as a blueprint for a document; and *paragraph outline*, which is a short, informal overview of the structure of a paragraph or series of related paragraphs.

The Importance of Being Organized

The neat and ordered outline shown earlier represents the *product* of outlining, not the *process*. Beneath any finished outline (or document) lies *planning*. Whether you work alone or as part of a team, planning is an essential element of the writing process. Initially, planning may take the form of general discussions and brainstorming. The ideas generated are often written on a whiteboard or displayed on a computer screen as notes or flow charts (see "Getting Started," pages 42–44).

The second stage of planning involves *organizing* the ideas into specific topics. Ideas may be discarded because they are not within the scope of the project; other ideas may be generated as the topics are being identified. When you know the main topics you need to cover for your project, you are ready to put them into an outline. If you have used a computer during your planning and organizing, you already have a draft outline. The next step is to rearrange your outline so that it flows logically (has a sequence). Various types of sequencing are covered later in this chapter.

Two rules of effective and efficient writing follow:

1. **Never** start writing until you have thoroughly planned the topics to be included in your document and created an organized, logical outline.
2. When you start writing, follow your outline closely; don't start planning again!

Outlining and Reorganizing on a Computer

Most word-processing programs enable you to work on your document and your outline simultaneously. As shown in Figure 6.1, an "outline view" of the

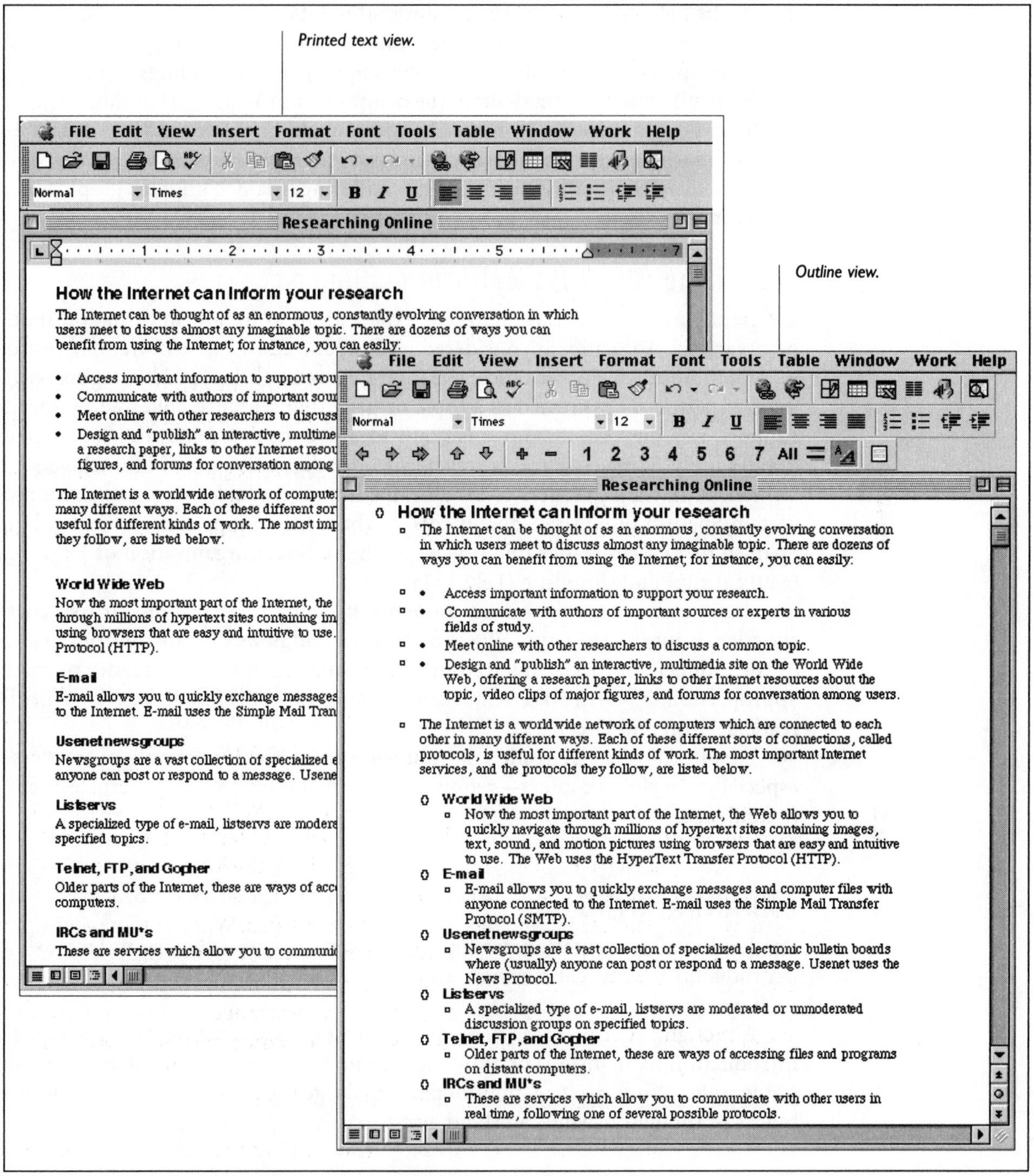

Figure 6.1 Using a Computer's Outline Features

Source: Munger, David, et al. *Researching Online,* 2nd ed. New York: Longman, 1998:2.

document helps you to see relationships among ideas at various levels, to create new headings, to add text beneath headings, and to move headings and their subtext. You also can *collapse* the outline view to display the headings only.

Switch between "normal view" (to compose your text) and "outline view" (to examine the arrangement of material). You can add or delete headings or text and reorganize whole sections of your document (*Microsoft Word* 504–05).

As a visual alternative to traditional outlining, many computer graphics programs enable you to display prose outlines as tree charts.

Organizing for Cross-cultural Audiences

Different cultures often have different expectations as to how information should be organized. A document considered well organized by one culture may confuse or offend another. For instance, a paragraph in English typically begins with a main idea directly expressed as a topic or orienting sentence, followed by specific support; any digression from this main idea is considered harmful to the paragraph's *unity.* Some cultures, however, consider digression a sign of intelligence or politeness. To native readers of English, the long introductions and digressions in certain Spanish or Russian documents might seem tedious and confusing, but a Spanish or Russian reader might view the more direct organization of English as overly abrupt and simplistic (Leki 151).

Expectations can differ even among same-language cultures. British correspondence, for instance, typically expresses the bad news directly up front, instead of the indirect approach preferred in North America. A bad-news letter or memo appropriate for North American readers could be considered evasive by British readers (Scott and Green 19).

Despite all our electronic communication tools, connecting with readers—especially in a global context—requires, above all, human sensitivity and awareness of audience.

PARAGRAPHING

Readers look for orientation, for shapes they can recognize. Beyond its larger shape (introduction, body, conclusion), a document depends on the smaller shapes of each paragraph.

Although paragraphs can have various structures and purposes (paragraphs of introduction, conclusion, or transition), our focus here is on *standard support paragraphs.* While part of the document's larger design, each of these middle blocks of thought usually can stand alone in meaning and emphasis.

The Standard Paragraph

All the sentences in a standard paragraph relate to the main point, which is expressed as the *topic sentence:*

Topic sentences

> Computer literacy has become a requirement for all "educated" people.
> A video display terminal can endanger the operator's health.
> Chemical pesticides and herbicides are both ineffective and hazardous.

Each topic sentence introduces an idea, judgment, or opinion. But in order to grasp the writer's exact meaning, readers need explanation. Consider the third statement:

> Chemical pesticides and herbicides are both ineffective and hazardous.

Imagine you are a researcher for the Eastern power utility and have been asked to determine whether the company should (1) begin spraying pesticides and herbicides under its power lines, or (2) continue with its manual (and non-polluting) ways of minimizing foliage and insect damage to lines and poles. If you simply responded with the preceding assertion, your employer would have questions:

- Why, exactly, are these methods ineffective and hazardous?
- What are the problems?
- Can you explain?

To answer these questions and to support your assertion, you need a fully developed paragraph:

Introduction (topic sentence)

Body (2–6)

Conclusion (7–8)

> [1]**Chemical pesticides and herbicides are both ineffective and hazardous.** [2]Because none of these chemicals has permanent effects, pest populations invariably recover and need to be resprayed. [3]Repeated applications cause pests to develop immunity to the chemicals. [4]Furthermore, most of these products attack species other than the intended pest, killing off its natural predators, thus actually increasing the pest population.[5] Above all, chemical residues survive in the environment (and living tissue) for years, often carried hundreds of kilometres by wind and water. [6]This toxic legacy includes such biological effects as birth deformities, reproductive failures, brain damage, and cancer. [7]Although intended to control pest populations, these chemicals ironically threaten to make the human population their ultimate victims. [8]We therefore recommend continuing our present control methods.

Most standard paragraphs in technical writing have an introduction-body-conclusion structure. They begin with a clear topic (or orienting) sentence, stating a generalization. Details in the body support the generalization.

THE TOPIC SENTENCE

Readers look to a paragraph's opening sentences for a framework. When they don't know exactly what the paragraph is about, readers struggle to grasp your meaning. Read this next paragraph once only, and then try answering the questions that follow.

A paragraph with its topic sentence omitted

> Besides containing several toxic metals, it percolates through the soil, leaching out naturally present metals. Pollutants such as mercury invade surface water, accumulating in fish tissues. Any organism eating the fish—or drinking the water—in turn faces the risk of heavy metal poisoning. Moreover, acidified water can release heavy concentrations of lead, copper, and aluminum from metal plumbing, making ordinary tap water hazardous.

Can you identify the paragraph's main idea? Probably not. Without the topic sentence, you have no framework for understanding this information in its larger meaning. And you don't know where to place the emphasis: on polluted fish? on metal poisoning? on tap water?

Now, insert the following opening sentence and reread the paragraph:

The missing topic sentence

Acid rain indirectly threatens human health.

With this orientation, the exact meaning becomes obvious.

The topic sentence should appear *first* in the paragraph, unless you have a good reason to place it elsewhere. In some instances, a paragraph's main idea may require a "topic statement" consisting of two or more sentences:

A topic statement can have two or more sentences

The most common strip-mining methods are open-pit mining, contour mining, and auger mining. The specific method employed will depend on the type of terrain that covers the coal.

The topic sentence or topic statement should immediately tell readers what to expect. Don't write *Some pesticides are less hazardous and often more effective than others* when you mean *Organic pesticides are less hazardous and often more effective than their chemical counterparts.* The first topic sentence leads everywhere and nowhere; the second helps focus the reader on what to expect from the paragraph. Don't write *Acid rain poses a danger*, leaving readers to decipher your meaning of *danger*. If you mean that *Acid rain is killing our lakes and polluting our water supplies*, say so. Uninformative topic sentences keep readers guessing.

Alternative Topic Sentence Placement

Nearly all paragraphs in technical and business writing open with a topic sentence, but sometimes the opening sentence will provide a transition, which is followed by the topic in the second sentence and then by the rest of the paragraph. Here's an effective paragraph in a report's conclusion section:

Transition sentence (1)
Topic sentence (2)
Supporting reasons (3–5)

1As this report has demonstrated, erosion control blankets have a wide range of uses. 2**Therefore, these blankets should be considered for controlling run-offs on the Summit Highway.** 3The blankets provide a warm, moist environment for the hydro-seeded wild grass to germinate. 4Also, the blankets prevent erosion until the grass can provide a stable sub-soil-root system to prevent erosion. 5Finally, the straw and the coconut fibre in the blankets gradually decay into the soil to make the soil more fibrous and resistant to run-off erosion.

Some paragraphs open with a transition that continues the direction established by the previous paragraph(s), and then switch to the real topic of the new paragraph.

Transition sentence (1)
Switch to the real topic (2)
Descriptive explanation (3–5)

1We recommend erosion control blankets for the majority of road banks on the Summit Highway. 2**However, for banks that are 2:1 or steeper, we recommend heavy-duty geogrid.** 3Skalned Engineering's studies have shown that steep banks require geogrids of 10-centimetre side wall mesh that can be filled with small-scale blast rock (Appendix 2). 4The geogrid can also be partially filled with soil, which can be hydro-seeded. 5Skalned's study revealed that geogrid covers of this type prevent erosion of banks as steep as 1.5 to 1.

Other paragraphs, such as the following, effectively place the main idea at the end of the paragraph.

Sentence 1 introduces the topic area, but not the paragraph's main idea
List of details (2 and 3)

1Worried about heavy erosion, we used Gabion baskets to retain the 2:1 banks of Tumbledown Creek below LeBihan Falls. 2We observed that the baskets retained their

Main idea (4)

geometric shapes despite the heavy aggregate that filled them. [3]Also, because we placed geotextile fabric beneath the Gabion structure, the strong 2007 spring run-off didn't scour or undercut the Gabion system. [4]**Overall, the entire system remained intact and stable despite the powerful erosive conditions that ran from early March to late May.**

Paragraph Unity

A paragraph is unified when all its material belongs there—when every word, phrase, and sentence directly support the topic sentence.

A unified paragraph

> **Solar power offers an efficient, economical, and safe solution to Eastern Canada's energy problems.** To begin with, solar power is highly efficient. Solar collectors installed on fewer than 30 percent of roofs in the East would provide more than 70 percent of the area's heating and air-conditioning needs. Moreover, solar heat collectors are economical, operating for up to 20 years with little or no maintenance. These savings recoup the initial cost of installation in only 10 years. Most important, solar power is safe. It can be transformed into electricity through photovoltaic cells (a type of storage battery) in a noiseless process that produces no air pollution—unlike coal, oil, and wood combustion. In sharp contrast to its nuclear counterpart, solar power produces no toxic waste and poses no catastrophic danger of meltdown. Thus, massive conversion to solar power would ensure abundant energy and a safe, clean environment for future generations.

One way to damage unity in the paragraph above would be to discuss the differences between active and passive solar heating, or manufacturers of solar technology, or the advantages of solar power over wind power. Although these matters do broadly relate to the general issue of solar energy, none directly advances the meaning of *efficient, economical,* or *safe.*

Every topic sentence has a keyword or phrase that carries the meaning. In the pesticide-herbicide paragraph (page 117), the keywords are *ineffective* and *hazardous.* Anything that fails to advance their meaning throws the paragraph—and the reader—off track.

Paragraph Coherence

In a unified paragraph, everything belongs. In a coherent paragraph, everything sticks together: topic sentence and support form a connected line of thought, like the links in a chain. To convey precise meaning, a paragraph must be unified. To be readable, a paragraph must also be coherent.

Paragraph coherence can be damaged by (1) short, choppy sentences, (2) sentences in the wrong sequence, or (3) insufficient transitions and connectors (see the Appendix) for linking related ideas. Here is how the solar energy paragraph might become incoherent:

An incoherent paragraph

> Solar power offers an efficient, economical, and safe solution to Eastern Canada's energy problems. Unlike nuclear power, solar power produces no toxic waste and poses no danger of meltdown. Solar power is efficient. Solar collectors could be installed on fewer than 30 percent of roofs in the East. These collectors would provide more than 70 percent of the area's heating and air-conditioning needs. Solar power is safe. It can be transformed into electricity. This transformation is made possible by photovoltaic cells (a type of storage battery). Solar heat collectors are economical. The photovoltaic process produces no air pollution.

Here, in contrast, is the original, coherent paragraph with sentences numbered for later discussion and with transitions and connectors shown in boldface. Notice how this version reveals a clear line of thought:

A coherent paragraph

> [1]Solar power offers an efficient, economical, and safe solution to Eastern Canada's energy problems. [2]**To begin with**, solar power is highly efficient. [3]Solar collectors installed on fewer than 30 percent of roofs in the East would provide more than 70 percent of the area's heating and air-conditioning needs. [4]**Moreover**, solar heat collectors are economical, operating for up to 20 years with little or no maintenance. [5]**These savings** recoup the initial cost of installation within only 10 years. [6]**Most important**, solar power is safe. [7]**It** can be transformed into electricity through photovoltaic cells (a type of storage battery) in a noiseless process that produces no air pollution—unlike coal, oil, and wood combustion. [8]**In sharp contrast** to its nuclear counterpart, solar power produces no toxic waste and poses no danger of catastrophic meltdown. [9]**Thus,** massive conversion to solar power would ensure abundant energy and a safe, clean environment for future generations.

We can easily trace the sequence of thoughts in this paragraph.

1. The topic sentence establishes a clear direction.
2–3. The first reason is given and then explained.
4–5. The second reason is given and explained.
6–8. The third and major reason is given and explained.
9. The conclusion sums up and re-emphasizes the main point.

Within this line of thinking, each sentence follows logically from the one before it. Readers know where they are at any place in the paragraph. To reinforce the logical sequence, related ideas are combined in individual sentences, and transitions and connectors signal clear relationships. The whole paragraph sticks together.

Paragraph Length

Paragraph length depends on the writer's purpose and the reader's capacity for understanding. Actual word count is less important than how thoroughly the paragraph makes your point. Consider these guidelines:

- In writing that carries highly technical information or complex instructions, short paragraphs (perhaps in a vertically displayed list) give the reader plenty of breathing space. A clump of short paragraphs, however, can make a document seem choppy and poorly organized.
- In writing that explains concepts, attitudes, or viewpoints, support paragraphs generally run from 100 to 300 words. But long paragraphs can be tiring and hard to follow, especially if important ideas get buried in the middle. On average, report paragraphs should be kept to 100 words, while paragraphs in letters and memos should average about 60 words.
- Long paragraphs can be broken into parts—using bullets, for example—to make the information more accessible to the reader.
- In letters, memos, or news articles, paragraphs of only one or two sentences focus the reader's attention. A short paragraph (even a single-sentence paragraph) can highlight an important idea in any document.
- Avoid long paragraphs at the beginning or end of a document because they can discourage the reader or obscure the emphasis.

SEQUENCING

Research demonstrates that readers more easily understand and remember material that is organized in a logical sequence (Felker et al. 11). In practice, these logical sequences tend to be one of three main types: *general to specific, specific to general*, and *chronological* (see Figure 6.2). A single paragraph usually follows one particular sequence. A longer document may use one particular sequence or a combination of sequences.

General to Specific

Most technical and business writing relies heavily on general-to-specific patterns, such as

- descriptive sequence
- statement plus illustration
- emphatic sequence (statement plus detailed evidence or arguments)
- extended definition
- classification
- comparison and contrast

Spatial Sequence. The most common *descriptive* pattern uses a spatial sequence, which begins at one location and ends at another. Such a sequence is most useful in describing a physical item or a mechanism; its parts appear in the sequence in which readers would actually view the parts or in the order in which each part functions (left to right, inside to outside, top to bottom). This description of a hypodermic needle proceeds from the needle's base (hub) to its point:

"What does it look like?"

A hypodermic needle is a slender, hollow steel instrument used to inject medication into the body (usually through a vein or muscle). The instrument has three parts, all considered sterile: the hub, the cannula, and the point. The hub is the lower, larger part of the needle that attaches to the necklike opening on the syringe barrel. Next is the cannula (stem), the smooth and slender central portion. Last is the point, which consists of a bevelled (slanted) opening, ending in a sharp tip. The diameter of a needle's cannula is indicated by a gauge number; commonly, a 24–25 gauge needle is used for subcutaneous injections. Needle lengths are varied to suit individual needs. Common lengths used for subcutaneous injections include 0.85 cm, 1.25 cm, 1.5 cm, and

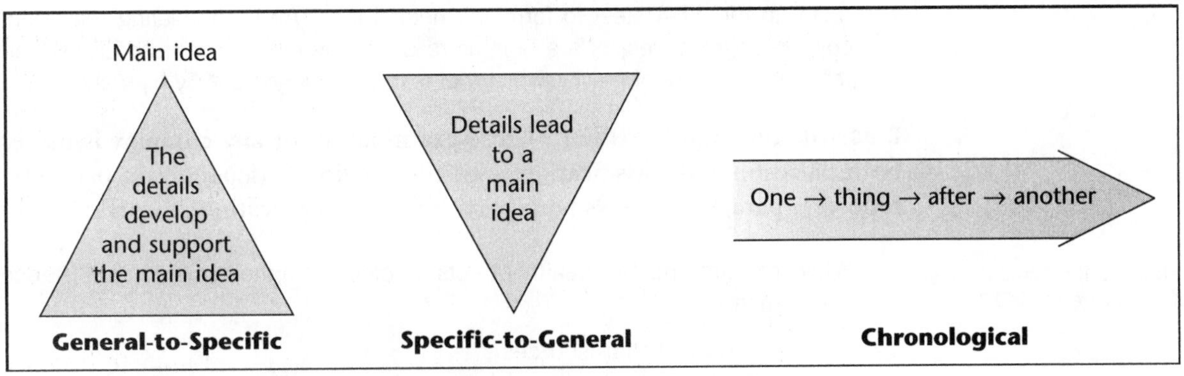

Figure 6.2 Three Main Types of Paragraph Patterns

1.85 cm. Regardless of length and diameter, all needles have the same functional design.

Product and mechanism descriptions almost always have some type of visual to support or amplify the verbal description.

Statement Plus Illustration. Often, the best way to prove a point is to illustrate it with an example or story. The main point appears in the topic sentence and the illustration forms the remainder of the paragraph, as in the following example:

"Why should I believe you?"

Sometimes, steep erosion-prone slopes can be stabilized simply and inexpensively. For example, our client at 458 Summit Road was unwilling to spend an estimated $38 000 for a recommended reinforced concrete retaining wall at the rear of his property. Our low-budget solution involved C350 erosion control blankets, hydro-seeded wild grass cover, and multi-flow drainage pipe, all for only $8546. For 27 months, the slope has withstood erosion.

Statement Plus Evidence or Arguments (Emphatic Sequence). Reasons offered in support of a specific viewpoint or recommendation often appear in workplace writing, as in the pesticide-herbicide paragraph on (page 117) or the solar energy paragraph on page 119. For emphasis, the reasons or examples usually are arranged in decreasing or increasing order of importance.

"What should I remember about this?"

Although strip mining is safer and cheaper than conventional mining, it damages the surrounding landscape. Among its effects are scarred mountains, ruined land, and polluted waterways. Strip operations are altering our country's land at the rate of 506 hectares (1250 acres) per week. An estimated 7085 kilometres (4400 miles) of streams have been poisoned by silt drainage in British Columbia alone. If strip mining continues at its present rate, 14 900 square kilometres (5750 square miles) of Canadian land eventually will be stripped barren.

Extended Definition. Another descriptive pattern used to organize a paragraph is found in an extended definition (or "expanded definition"—see Chapter 7). Such a paragraph piles up the details to help a reader understand a term.

"What does this term really mean?"

Orlimar's Trimetal fairway woods incorporate the multi-metal technology found in all the Trimetal clubs: a steel shell, an alpha Maraging face, and copper-tungsten weights. The head's shell features stainless steel's high strength-to-weight ratio; to finish the hitting surface, Carpenter Metals has developed a way to merge ultra-hard alpha Maraging metal to the 17-4 steel to form the head's face. And, completing the technology, copper-tungsten weights are built as rails into the sole of the head. These rails promote a low centre of gravity, which helps the struck golf ball fly high and long.

Classification and Partition. Close examination of any complex issue requires both partition and classification. (See the previous discussion on page 110) The following paragraph shows both partition and classification at work.

"How are the components of the issue related?"

While researching the health effects of electromagnetic fields, you'll encounter information about

- various radiation sources
- the ratio of the level of risk to the level of exposure
- workplace studies of effects on workers

- lab studies of cell physiology, biochemistry, and behaviour
- statistical studies of disease in certain populations
- conflicting expert views, and
- local authorities' views

Comparison-Contrast Sequence. Evaluation of two or more items on the basis of their similarities or differences often appears in job-related writing.

"How do these items compare?"

Point-by-point comparison

The ski industry's quest for a binding that ensures good performance as well as safety has led to development of two basic types. **Although both bindings improve performance and increase the safety margin, they have different release and retention mechanisms.** The first type consists of two units (one at the toe, another at the heel) that are spring-loaded. These units apply their retention forces directly to the boot sole. Thus the friction of boot against ski allows for the kind of ankle movement needed at high speeds over rough terrain, without causing the boot to release. In contrast, the second type has one spring-loaded unit at either the toe or the heel. From this unit extends a boot plate that travels the length of the boot to a fixed receptacle on its opposite end. With this plate binding, the boot has no part in release or retention. Instead, retention force is applied directly to the boot plate, providing more stability for the recreational skier, but allowing for less ankle and boot movement before releasing. Overall, the double-unit binding performs better in racing, but the plate binding is safer.

For comparing and contrasting more specific data on these bindings, two lists would be more effective.

Block comparison

The **Rossignol Axium 100 X** plate binding offers the following features:

1. lightweight strength and control for carving skis
2. an elastomer built into the back of the plate to help maintain the ski's natural flex while eliminating vibration
3. a DIN setting range of 3 to 10, with an adjustable range for skiers 30 to 108 kilograms
4. 45 mm of lateral elastic travel, 12 mm of vertical elastic travel in the heel piece, and 24 mm of adjustment

The **Salomon A912 PS** offers the following features:

1. a beefy interface for enhanced stability
2. simultaneous wing adjustment
3. a DIN setting range of 4 to 12, with an adjustable range for skiers 41 to 120 kilograms
4. a diagonal pivot shock-absorption system that provides protection in forward and backward twisting falls
5. an adjustment range of 24 mm

Instead of this block structure (in which one binding is discussed and then the other), the writer might have chosen a point-by-point structure in which points common to both items are listed together (such as release methods in the above combined paragraph). The point-by-point comparison is favoured in feasibility and recommendation reports because it offers readers a meaningful comparison between common points.

Specific-to-General Sequence

Much less common than the general-to-specific sequences just described, *specific-to-general* sequences finish with the paragraph's main point. One such paragraph, the Gabion basket example on page 118-119, builds to a climax. The following paragraph leaves its main point until the end because the writer wants the reader to first see the writer's justification for an unpopular bottom line:

The unpopular bottom line needs preceding justification

> Gendron Road Services has attempted several unsuccessful methods to repair the deteriorating approach apron at the north end of the LaSalle Bridge. First, Gendron tried four types of standard surface repair methods, but in each case, potholes reappeared within two months. Then, Gendron engineers tried deep surface patch techniques, but the patched pieces broke up during the spring thaw. Gendron has even experimented with a sub-surface heating grid, with poor results. **Gendron therefore recommends that the city authorize a complete reconstruction of the bridge approach, at a cost of $1.9 million above Gendron's annual maintenance contract.**

In the next specific-to-general paragraph, several examples lead to a logical bottom-line conclusion:

The bottom line

> Integrating a shop area's radiant heating system with an office area's forced air system appeals to fabrication shops and garages. Other enthusiastic users include nursing homes, hotels, and motels. In all these settings, radiant exchange systems can heat one area of a building while they cool another, with increased efficiency and economy. **Thus, these systems are becoming more popular.**

Chronological Patterns

Time-based patterns include past-tense narration, process description, instructions, and causal analysis patterns.

Narrative Sequence. Past-tense narration is easy to read in the following brief description of how a golf putting green was prepared before it was contoured and seeded. Notice that the paragraph uses transitions to keep the progression of events clear. (The transitions are bolded.)

"What happened?"

> In preparing the sub-base soil for the new fifth green, the crew **first** removed all soil and rock to a depth of 1.5 metres. **At that level,** they discovered a small seeping spring, so they **then** established the green's subterranean catch basin at the spring's rocky exit point. **Next**, with excavation complete, the crew laid a cross pattern of drainage pipe leading from the catch basin, and they covered the drain piping with 0.5 metres of pea gravel and 0.75 metres of fine sand. The green's surface **was thus ready** to be contoured.

Instructions. Explanations of how to do something or how something happened generally are arranged according to a strict time sequence: first step, second step, and so on.

"How is it done?"

> **Instead of breaking into a jog too quickly and risking injury, take a relaxed and deliberate approach.** Before taking a step, spend at least 10 minutes stretching and warming up, using any exercises you find comfortable. (Consult a jogging book for specialized exercises.) When you've completed your warm-up, set a brisk walking

pace. Exaggerate the distance between steps, taking long strides and swinging your arms briskly and loosely. After roughly 100 metres at this brisk pace, you should feel ready to jog. So break into a very slow trot: lean your torso forward and let one foot fall in front of the other (one foot barely leaving the ground while the other is on the pavement). Keep the slowest pace possible, just above a walk. *Do not bolt out like a sprinter!* While jogging, relax your body. Keep your shoulders straight and your head up, and enjoy the scenery.

Process Description. Chapter 9 contains a sample of a complete process description, told in present tense. The same descriptive method can be used to organize a single paragraph, as in the following explanation of a vapour compression cycle in a geothermal heating system.

"How does this process work?"

All heat pumps use a vapour compression cycle to transport heat from one location to another. In heating mode, the cycle starts as the cold liquid refrigerant within the heat pump passes through a heat exchanger (evaporator) and absorbs heat from the low temperature source (fluid circulated through the earth connection). The refrigerant evaporates into a gas as heat is absorbed. The gaseous refrigerant then passes through a compressor, where it is pressurized, raising its temperature to over 80°C. The hot gas then circulates through a refrigerant-to-air heat exchanger, where the heat is removed and sent through the air ducts. When the refrigerant loses the heat, it changes back to a liquid. The liquid refrigerant cools as it passes through an expansion valve, and the process begins again (Groundloop 2001).

Problem-Causes-Solution Sequence. Another form of chronological development is used to explain how a problem was solved. The problem-solving sequence proceeds from description of the problem, through diagnosis, to solution. After outlining the cause of the problem, this next paragraph explains how the problem has been solved:

"How was the problem solved?"

On all waterfront buildings, the unpainted wood exteriors had been severely damaged by the previous winter's high winds and sandstorms. **After repairing the damage, we took protective steps against further storms.** First, all joints, edges, and sashes were treated with water-repellent preservative to protect against water damage. Next, three coats of non-porous primer were applied to all exterior surfaces to prevent paint from blistering and peeling. Finally, two coats of wood-quality latex paint were applied over the non-porous primer. To prevent coats of paint separating, we applied the first coat within two weeks of the priming coats, and the second within two weeks of the first. Now, 14 months later, no blistering, peeling, or separation has occurred.

Cause–Effect Analysis. Cause–effect analyses represent a useful variation of *chronological* paragraph sequencing. The direct version starts with causes and proceeds to effects—the sequence follows an action to its results. Below, the topic sentence identifies the causes, and the remainder of the paragraph discusses its effects.

"What will happen if I do this?"

Some of the most serious accidents involving gas water heaters occur when a flammable liquid is used in the vicinity. The heavier-than-air vapours of a flammable liquid such as gasoline can flow along the floor—even the length of a basement—and be explosively ignited by the flame of the water heater's pilot light or burner. Because the victim's clothing frequently ignites, the resulting burn injuries are commonly serious and extremely painful. They may require long hospitalization, and can result in disfigurement or death. *Never, under any circumstances, use a flammable liquid near a gas heater or any other open flame* (Consumer Product Safety Commission).

Effect-to-Cause Sequence. The indirect version starts with the effects and traces back to the cause(s). This sequence identifies the main "effect" (the problem) in the topic sentence.

"How did this happen?"

Modern whaling techniques have brought the whale population to the threshold of extinction. In the 19th century, invention of the steamboat increased hunters' speed and mobility. Shortly afterward, the grenade harpoon was invented so whales could be killed quickly and easily from the ship's deck. In 1904, a whaling station opened on Georgia Island, in South America. This station became the gateway to Antarctic whaling for the nations of the world. In 1924, factory ships were designed that enabled round-the-clock whale tracking and processing. These ships could reduce a 30-metre-long whale to its by-products in roughly 30 minutes. After World War II, more powerful boats with remote sensing devices gave a final boost to the whaling industry. The number of kills had now increased far beyond the whales' capacity to reproduce.

WEB CONNECT

The University of Toronto's Engineering Communication Centre has useful advice on using outlines and other aspects of effective writing. (Click on the appropriate subtopic.)
www.ecf.utoronto.ca/~writing/handbook.html

Here are two other potentially helpful resources:
http://writing.colostate.edu/guides/processes/organize/
www.plainlanguagenetwork.org/plaintrain/ClearAndEffectiveParagraphs.html

EXERCISES

1. Locate, copy, and bring to class a paragraph that has the following features:
   - an orienting topic sentence
   - adequate development
   - unity
   - coherence
   - a recognizable sequence
   - appropriate length for its purpose and audience

   Be prepared to identify and explain each of these features in a class discussion.
2. For each of the following documents, indicate the most logical sequence. (For example, a description of a proposed computer lab would follow a spatial sequence.)
   - a set of instructions for operating a power tool
   - a report analyzing the weakest parts in a piece of industrial machinery
   - a report analyzing the desirability of a proposed oil refinery in your area
   - a detailed breakdown of your monthly budget to trim excess spending
   - a report investigating the reasons for student apathy on your campus
   - a report evaluating the effects of the ban on DDT in insect control
   - a report on any highly technical subject, written for the general reader
   - a report investigating the success of a no-grade policy at other universities and colleges
   - a proposal for a no-grade policy at your university or college

COLLABORATIVE PROJECT

Organize into small groups. Choose *one* of these topics, or one your group settles on, and then brainstorm to develop a formal outline for the body section of a report. One representative from your group can write the final draft outline and display it (using a data projection unit, overhead projector, or similar equipment) for class revision.

- job opportunities in your career field
- a physical description of the ideal classroom
- how to organize an effective job search
- how the quality of your higher educational experience can be improved
- arguments for and against a formal grading system
- an argument for an improvement you think your university or college needs most

CHAPTER 7

Definitions

LEARNING OBJECTIVES

After reading this chapter, you should be able to

- Identify situations where definitions are useful.
- Use (and recognize when to use) parenthetical definitions, sentence definitions, and expanded definitions.
- Distinguish between categorical and operational definitions.
- Apply techniques for expanding and developing technical definitions.

When you define a term, you explain the precise meaning you intend by using that term. Clear writing depends on definitions that both reader and writer understand. Unless you are sure readers know the exact meaning you intend, always define the term upon first use.

PURPOSE OF DEFINITIONS

Every specialty has its own technical language. Engineers, architects, or programmers talk about *torque*, *tolerances*, or *microprocessors*; lawyers, real estate brokers, and investment counsellors discuss *easements*, *liens*, *amortization*, or *escrow accounts*. Whenever such terms are unfamiliar to an audience, they need defining.

Most of the specialized terms previously mentioned are concrete and specific. Once *microprocessor* has been defined for the reader, its meaning will not differ appreciably in another context. When a term is highly technical, a writer can figure out that it should be defined for some readers. However, familiar terms like *disability*, *guarantee*, *tenant*, *lease*, or *mortgage* acquire very specialized meanings in specialized contexts. Here definition becomes crucial. What *guarantee* means in one situation is not necessarily what it means in another. Contracts are detailed (and legal) definitions of the specific terms of an agreement.

Assume you're shopping for disability insurance to protect your income in case of injury or illness. Besides comparing prices, you want each company to define *physical disability*. Although company A offers the cheapest policy, it might define *physical disability* as inability to work at *any* job. Therefore, if a neurological disorder prevents you from continuing work as a designer of electronic devices, without disabling you for some menial job, you might not qualify as "disabled." In contrast, company B's policy, although more expensive, might define *physical disability* as inability to work at your *specific* job. Both companies use the term *physical disability*, but each defines it differently. Because they are legally responsible for the documents they prepare, all communicators rely on the technique of clear definition.

ELEMENTS OF DEFINITIONS

For all definitions, use an appropriate level of English, list each defined term's basic properties, and remain objective.

Plain English

Clarify meaning by using language readers understand.

Unclear A tumour is a neoplasm.

Better A tumour is a growth of cells that occurs independently of surrounding tissue and serves no useful function.

Unclear A solenoid is an inductance coil that serves as a tractive electromagnet. *(A definition appropriate for an engineering manual, but too specialized for general readers.)*

Better A solenoid is an electrically energized coil that converts electrical energy to magnetic energy capable of performing mechanical functions.

Basic Properties

Convey the properties of an item that differentiate it from all others. A thermometer has a singular function: it measures temperature. Without this essential information, a definition would have no real meaning for uninformed readers. Any other data about thermometers (types, special uses, materials used in construction) are secondary. A book, on the other hand, cannot be defined according to functional properties because books have multiple functions. A book can be used to write in or to display pictures, to record financial transactions, to read, and so on. Also, other items (individual sheets of paper, posters, newspapers, picture frames) serve the same functions. The basic property of a book is physical: it is a bound volume of pages. Readers would have to know this *first*, to understand what a book is.

Objectivity

Unless readers understand that your purpose is to persuade, omit your opinions from a definition. *Bomb* is defined as "an explosive weapon detonated by impact, proximity to an object, a timing mechanism, or other predetermined means." If you define a bomb as "an explosive weapon devised and perfected by hawkish idiots to blow up the world," you are editorializing, *and* ignoring a bomb's basic property.

TYPES OF DEFINITIONS

Definitions vary greatly in length and detail: from a few words in parentheses, to one or more complete sentences, to multiple paragraphs or pages.

Your choice of definition type depends on what information readers need, and that, in turn, depends on why they need it. *Carburetor*, for instance, could be defined in one sentence, briefly telling readers what it is and how it works. But this definition would be expanded for the student mechanic who needs to know the origin of the term, how the device was developed, what it looks like, how it is used, and how its parts interact. Audience needs should guide your choice.

Parenthetical Definition

A parenthetical definition explains the term in a word or phrase, often as a synonym in parentheses following the term:

Parenthetical definitions

> The effervescent (bubbling) mixture is highly toxic.
> The leaching field (sievelike drainage area) requires crushed stone.

Clarifying Definition

Another option is to express your definition as a clarifying phrase:

Clarifying definition

> The trees on the site are mostly deciduous; that is, they shed their foliage at season's end.

Use parenthetical and clarifying definitions to convey the general meaning of specialized terms so that readers can follow the discussion where these terms are used.

Sentence Definition

Elements of sentence definitions

A definition may require one or more sentences with this structure: (1) the item or term being defined, (2) the class (specific group) to which the term belongs, and (3) the features that differentiate the term from all others in its class.

Term	Class	Distinguishing Features
carburetor	a mixing device	in gasoline engines; blends air and fuel into a vapour for combustion within the cylinders
transit	a surveying instrument	measures horizontal and vertical angles
diabetes	a metabolic disease	caused by a disorder of the pituitary gland or pancreas and characterized by excessive urination, persistent thirst, and decreased ability to metabolize sugar
stress	an applied force	strains or deforms a body
laser	an electronic device	converts electrical energy to light energy, producing a bright, intensely hot, and narrow beam of light

fibre optics	a technology	uses light energy to transmit voices, video images, and data through hair-thin glass fibres

These elements can be combined into one or more sentences.

A complete sentence definition

Diabetes is a metabolic disease caused by a disorder of the pituitary gland or pancreas. This disease is characterized by excessive urination, persistent thirst, and decreased ability to metabolize sugar.

Sentence definition is especially useful for stipulating the precise working meaning of a term that has several possible meanings. State your working definitions at the beginning of your report:

A working definition

Throughout this report, the term *disadvantaged student* means...

Classifying the Term. Be specific and precise in your classification. The narrower your class, the more specific your meaning. *Transit* is correctly classified as a "surveying instrument," not as a "thing" or an "instrument." *Stress* is classified as "an applied force"; to say it "takes place when..." or "is something that. . ." fails to reflect a specific classification. Be sure to select precise terms of classification: *diabetes* is precisely classified as "a metabolic disease," not as "a medical term."

Differentiating the Term. Differentiate the term by separating the item it names from every other item in its class. Make these distinguishing features narrow enough to pinpoint the item's unique identity and meaning, yet broad enough to be inclusive. A definition of *brief* as "a legal document introduced in a courtroom" is too broad because the definition doesn't differentiate *brief* from all other legal documents (wills, written confessions, etc.). Conversely, differentiating *carburetor* as "a mixing device used in automobile engines" is too narrow because it ignores the carburetor's use in all other gasoline engines.

ON THE JOB...

Clarity in the Construction Industry

"When we build a custom-designed home, we draw up a contract that essentially defines the project and our respective responsibilities. Then we prepare a complete flow chart that lists the details of work to be completed and relevant timelines. That chart also provides for notes about each stage of the project. We discuss this description with the client at the beginning and at weekly on-site meetings. At the meetings, we write site notes that we later send by email to the client. The client has to make thousands of decisions during the building process, and we're careful to record them all. Everything goes into a project binder that can be reviewed. At the lock-up stage, we can usually submit a "Cost to Complete" report. All of this communication serves to define and quantify what's happening. Also, our emails to the client frequently ask if there's anything else we need to explain or quantify. Clarity is what I'm after, every step of the way!"

—Ken Dahlen, Keith Construction

Also, avoid circular definitions (repeating, as part of the distinguishing features, the word you are defining). Thus, *stress* should not be defined as "an applied force that places stress on a body." The class and distinguishing features must express the item's basic property ("an applied force that strains or deforms a body").

Categorical versus Operational Definitions. So far, our sample definitions have placed the defined term in a category; we could use the term *categorical definition* for this common method of defining things in sentences. Categorical definitions are static, but a second type of sentence definition, *operational definition,* defines things in active terms. Here's an example:

Operational definition

> **Technologists** translate engineering designs into working plans and then see that these plans are carried out.

In the example, technologists are defined in terms of *what they do,* rather than in terms of *what they are.*

Operational definitions work best in proposals, progress reports, and résumés because the active verbs contribute to the sense of an active and successful person, plan, or activity. Also, operational definitions use fewer words to convey meaning. Compare the above example to its categorical equivalent:

Categorical definition

> A technologist **is someone who** translates engineering designs into working plans and then sees that these plans are carried out.

EXPANDED DEFINITIONS

Every day, technologists must communicate their ideas, work processes, or product information to people outside of their area of expertise. One of the biggest problems facing a technologist is making his or her ideas clear to someone with little or no understanding of these ideas. The expanded definition is one of the most important document types that allows you to practice this skill.

The word "definition" comes from a Latin word meaning "boundary." Thus, definitions put boundaries around an idea so that someone with no understanding of it may see what it looks like, what its component parts are, how it works, how it is similar or different to other things, and what specific examples of its use are. By putting these boundaries around an idea, we put limits around it and are able to see it in isolation from all other ideas. Explaining your ideas, whether to upper management or clients, will often involve isolating them and translating them into non-technical terms.

The Reading-Based Expanded Definition

A second, and just as important, purpose for writing an expanded definition is that it allows you to continue to practice your reading comprehension and paraphrasing skills. By writing an expanded definition that is based on an article, you develop important skills:

- You practice careful and close reading.
- You develop the critical thinking skills of analysis and classification through understanding and reorganizing the content of the article.

- You develop comprehension skills by practicing the skill of paraphrasing another's ideas, which reinforces your understanding.
- You improve your communicating abilities through a process of reading and writing aimed at a particular audience (non-technical) who has specific needs for understanding new information.

In summary, the reading-based expanded definition both helps you practice your writing skills and improves your comprehension and analytical abilities.

The expanded definitions you will write will have a four-paragraph structure beginning with an introduction and followed by three paragraphs that give the reader more detail about the term being defined. There are five ways to give the reader more detail, and you will choose three of the following five expansion methods for your expanded definition:

- Operating Principle
- Analysis of Parts
- Required Materials or Conditions
- Comparison or Contrast
- Examples

Introduction

Begin your expanded definition with an introduction that starts with a formal sentence definition. In addition to this sentence, the introduction may contain any or all of the following elements, depending on what the article you have read contains for appropriate paraphrasing:

- The etymology (word origin) of the term
- The term's purpose, history and background, including
    - Why it is used and/or what it is used for
    - When and where it was first used, discovered, or invented and how its use has changed over time
    - Who invented or discovered it
    - Any other background information that will help a reader get an overview of the technology or technological concept that the term represents.

Avoid giving details about the term's parts or operation in this opening paragraph: an introduction should only give a reader general information necessary to understand these details. Moreover, in addition to discussing a term's history and background, discussing the purpose of the term will allow you to "lead" a non-technical reader gradually into the more technical aspects of your definition.

Here is an example of an introduction that emphasizes the purpose of acid rain:

> Acid rain is environmentally damaging rainfall that occurs after fossil fuels burn, releasing nitrogen and sulphur oxides into the atmosphere. Acid rain, simply stated, increases the acidity level of waterways because these nitrogen and sulphur oxides combine with the air's normal moisture. The resulting rainfall is far more acidic than normal rainfall. Acid rain is a silent threat because its effects, although slow, are cumulative.

History and Background. The meaning of specialized terms such as *radar*, *bacteriophage*, *silicon chips*, or *X-ray* often can be clarified through a background discussion: discovery or history of the concept, development, method of production, applications, and so on.

> The idea of lasers...dates back as far as 212 B.C., when Archimedes used a [magnifying] glass to set fire to Roman ships during the siege of Syracuse. (Gartiganis 22)

> The early researchers in fibre optic communications were hampered by two principal difficulties—the lack of a sufficiently intense source of light and the absence of a medium which could transmit this light free from interference and with a minimum signal loss. Lasers emit a narrow beam of intense light, so their invention in 1960 solved the first problem. The development of a means to convey this signal was longer in coming, but scientists succeeded in developing the first communications-grade optical fibre of almost pure silica glass in 1970. (Stanton 28)

Etymology. A word's origin (its development and changing meanings) can clarify its definition. *Biological control* of insects is derived from the Greek *bio*, meaning "life" or "living organism," and the Latin *contra*, meaning "against" or "opposite." Biological control, then, is the use of living organisms against insects.

Some technical terms are acronyms, derived from the first letters or parts of several words. *Laser* is an acronym for "light amplification by stimulated emission of radiation."

Sometimes a term's origin can be colourful as well as informative. *Bug* (jargon for "programming error") is said to derive from an early computer at Harvard that malfunctioned because of a dead bug blocking the contacts of an electrical relay. Because programmers, like many of us, were reluctant to acknowledge error, the term became a euphemism for *error*. Correspondingly, *debugging* is the correcting of errors in a program.

The paragraph below was written by a student as an introduction for an expanded definition of the term "modem." See if you can find the components of an introduction in the paragraph:

> A modem is a device that uses telephone lines to transmit and receive computer information, allowing remote computers to exchange information with each other. The word modem is a shortened form of the term modulator-demodulator. Modems send data in "bits", binary digits of ones and zeros. The sending modem "modulates" data into a signal that is compatible with the phone line, and the receiving modem "demodulates" the signal back into digital data. While the earliest modems had a speed of about 300 bits per second, modem technology improved over time so that by the late 1990s, modems could transmit data at almost 56 kilobits per second. However, conventional modem technology has reached its theoretical maximum data rate and has been surpassed by newer technologies.

The following paragraph functions as an introduction that provides background information for an expanded definition of the term "Bunsen burner":

> The Bunsen burner is a basic piece of laboratory equipment used to produce a continuous flame at relatively low temperatures. Originally designed by Robert W. Bunsen in the late 1800s, the "Bunsen burner" has become a generic term for basic lab burners made by many firms.
>
> Most burners look and perform alike, though burners from different companies do include slightly different features.

Body

Develop the body of your expanded definition based on how the article reveals information that can be paraphrased according to three of the following five expansion methods.

Operating Principle

If the article that you are paraphrasing contains sufficient details about how the term operates according to a sequence of events, you should use this expansion method in your expanded definition.

Explaining how a term works requires understanding how specific operations or processes occur in a chronological and logical sequence. The word "chronological" comes from the root "chronos," a Greek word meaning "time." The word "logical" comes from the root "logos," another Greek word meaning "reason." Therefore, all operations take place in time and follow a reasonable order of events.

When you read an article to paraphrase information about a technology's operating principles, you must understand the details that represent the linked causes and effects of distinct events that happen in specific places and at particular times. In other words, you must explain why these events occur and what happens as a result of these events.

In describing a solar home-heating system, you would begin with the heat collectors on the roof, moving through the pipes, pumping system, and tanks for the heated water, to the heating vents in the floors and walls—from source to outlet. After this functional sequence of operating parts, you could describe each part in a spatial sequence.

The following is an "Operating Principle" paragraph for the term "Acid rain":

> Most research shows that power plants burning oil or coal are the primary cause of acid rain. The burnt fuel is not completely expended, and some residue enters the atmosphere. Although this residue contains several potentially toxic elements, sulphur oxide and, to a lesser extent, nitrogen oxide are the major problem, because they are transformed when they combine with moisture. This chemical reaction forms sulphur dioxide and nitric acid, which then rain down to earth.

The term "stethoscope" can be defined by how it completes one operating cycle, as shown in the following paragraph that is organized according to a functional sequence—the organization of parts through which sound travels:

> In an operating cycle, the diaphragm contact piece, placed against the skin, picks up sound impulses from the body surface. These impulses cause the plastic diaphragm to vibrate. The amplified vibrations, in turn, are carried through a tube to a dividing point. From here, the amplified sound is carried through two separate but identical series of tubes to hollow ear plugs.

Analysis of Parts

The article that you are paraphrasing may contain information that allows you to provide detailed descriptions of the components that make up the term, whether the term is defined as a technology, process, or concept. The article's content may allow you to explain what the parts look like based on what they are made of, how they are measured, and where they are located in relation to the other components.

Within the expanded definition, a paragraph that focuses on describing the term's parts should follow an organizational pattern that reflects how the parts are logically connected. In other words, you should paraphrase information so that each part is described according to a spatial sequence.

Part of all physical descriptions, a spatial sequence answers these questions: *What is it? What does it do? What does it look like? What parts and material is it made of?* Use this sequence when you want readers to visualize the item as a static object or mechanism at rest (a house interior, a document, the CN Tower, a plot of land, a chainsaw, or a computer keyboard). Can readers best visualize this item from front to rear, left to right, top to bottom? (What logical path do the parts create?) A retractable pen would logically be viewed from outside to inside.

When your subject can be divided into parts, identify and explain them:

> The standard frame of a pitched-roof wooden dwelling consists of floor joists, wall studs, roof rafters, and collarties.

In discussing each part, of course, you would further define specialized terms, such as *floor joists*.

The term "stethoscope" can also be defined according to an analysis of parts. Note how the following paragraphs use a spatial sequence and then emphasize a description of the diaphragm contact piece.

Remember that although these examples include multiple paragraphs and visuals, your expanded definition will develop only <u>one</u> paragraph for each expansion method and will <u>not</u> include visuals.

> The standard stethoscope is roughly 61 cm long and weighs about 140 grams. The instrument consists of a sensitive sound-detecting and amplifying device whose flat surface is pressed against a bodily area. This amplifying device is attached to rubber and metal tubing that transmits the body sound to a listening device inserted in the ear.
>
> Seven interlocking pieces contribute to the stethoscope's Y-shaped appearance: (1) diaphragm contact piece, (2) lower tubing, (3) Y-shaped metal piece, (4) upper tubing, (5) U-shaped metal strip, (6) curved metal tubing, and (7) hollow ear plugs. These parts form a continuous unit.

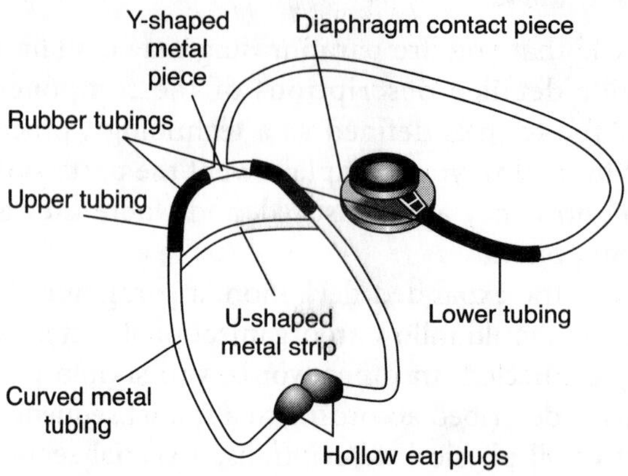

FIGURE 1 Stethoscope with Diaphragm Contact Piece (Front View)

Diaphragm Contact Piece

Definition, size, shape, and material

The diaphragm contact piece is a shallow metal bowl, about the size of a dollar coin (and twice its thickness), which is caused to vibrate by various body sounds.

Three separate parts make up the piece: hollow steel bowl, plastic diaphragm, and metal frame, as shown in Figure 2.

Sub-parts

The stainless steel metal bowl has a concave inner surface, with concentric ridges that funnel sound toward an opening in the tapered base, then out through the hollow appendage. Lateral threads ring the outer circumference of the bowl to accommodate the interlocking metal frame. A fitted diaphragm covers the bowl's upper opening.

The diaphragm is a plastic disk, 2 mm thick, 10.2 cm in circumference, with a moulded lip around the edge. It fits flush over the metal bowl and vibrates sound toward the ridges. A metal frame that screws onto the bowl holds the diaphragm in place.

Function and relation to adjoining parts

The stainless steel frame fits over the disk and metal bowl. A 0.75 cm ridge between the inner and outer edge accommodates threads for screwing the frame to the bowl. The frame's outside circumference is notched with equally spaced, perpendicular grooves—like those on the edge of a dime—to provide a gripping surface.

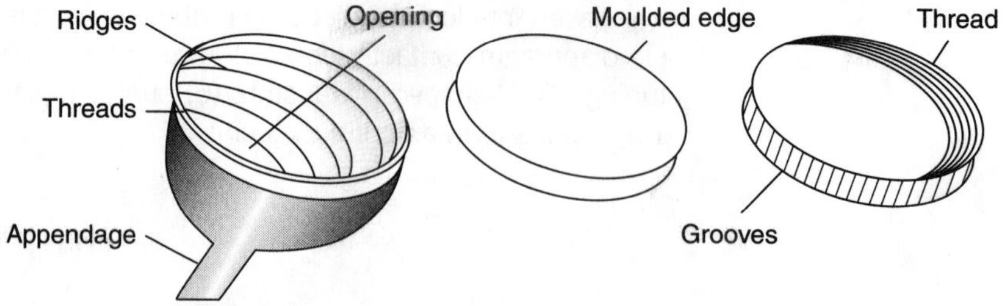

FIGURE 2 Exploded View of a Diaphragm Contact Piece

Mode of attachment

The diaphragm contact piece is the heart of the stethoscope that receives, amplifies, and transmits sound through the system of attached tubing. The piece attaches to the lower tubing by an appendage on its apex (narrow end), which fits inside the tubing.

Each part of the stethoscope, in turn, is described according to its own logic of organization.

An analysis of parts can focus on the most important components, as shown in the following example of the term "Bunsen burner" being defined according to a description of its main parts.

Remember that your analysis of parts will be developed in <u>one</u> paragraph.

Base The heavy die-cast base of the Fisher burner is very stable. It is made from non-ferrous metal and has a nickel finish. Here are its main features and dimensions:

- Hexagonal-shaped foundation that is 7 cm in diameter and 5 cm high
- A 1.9 cm diameter threaded cylinder at the top of the base
- A 1.25 cm diameter hexagonal brass nut at the top of the cylinder, with a small hole in the centre from which gas is emitted into the pipe

A valve is threaded vertically up into the bottom centre of the base of the burner. It allows the user to adjust the volume of gas that flows from the gas inlet up through the base cylinder.

Gas Valve Jutting out from the side of the cylinder, parallel to the surface on which the base of the burner rests, is a tapered gas inlet 6.35 cm long. The inlet has serrated edges that hold the gas tube securely to the burner.

The valve looks like a car axle with only one wheel attached. The 5.1 cm stem, or "axle," rests on a round 1.9 cm diameter base, or "wheel." Actually, this base is about the diameter and thickness of a 5-cent piece. It has serrated edges so that it can be twisted with ease. The 0.32 cm diameter stem is threaded and screws vertically into the base of the burner. When twisted clockwise, it closes and decreases gas flow. When twisted counterclockwise, it opens and increases gas flow.

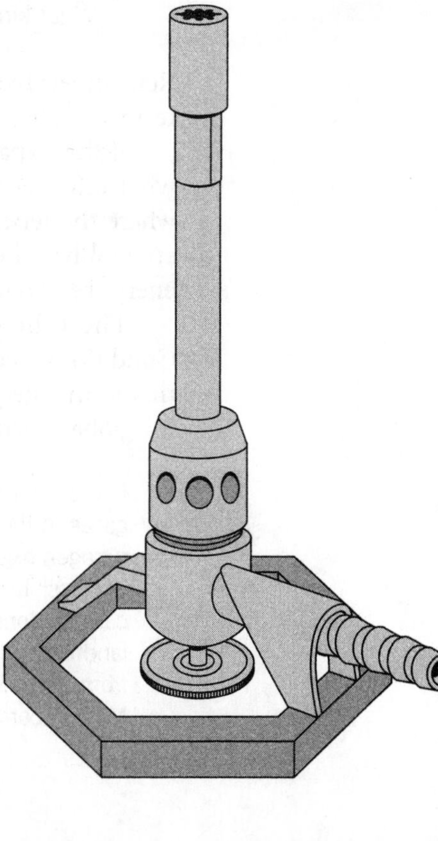

Pipe An 11.5 cm long pipe extends straight up from the top of the base of the burner. Except for its flared ends, the pipe is 1.25 cm in diameter. The combining of gas and air at the bottom of the pipe produces a flame that emerges at the top.

The pipe threads onto the cylinder at the top of the burner base. The bottom of the pipe flares out to form an end piece with eight 0.48 cm holes drilled around its circumference. The holes let in air that mixes with gas entering from the base. When the pipe is turned clockwise, the amount of air entering the holes is reduced and the temperature of the flame is lowered. When the pipe is turned counterclockwise, the amount of air entering the holes is increased and the temperature of the flame is raised.

The flared top end of the pipe looks much like a socket piece for a socket wrench. Called a "flame retainer" by the manufacturer, it helps keep the flame from going out. Viewed vertically from above the burner, the top of the retainer is shaped like a wagon wheel with short spokes. The "spokes" are actually eight ports that open to the pipe hole but close off before they reach the circumference of the pipe. Spaced evenly on the circumference, these ports help control the flame.

Required Materials or Conditions

An article may present information that allows you to understand what materials or conditions are needed within the environment surrounding the term. With this expansion method, you must distinguish the *parts* of the term you are defining from the necessary items or circumstances that allow these parts to function properly. Requirements allow the term's operation to be effective. Materials are physical items whereas conditions are environmental (temperature, weather, location, time).

The following questions are examples of the ways in which you can avoid confusing required materials or conditions with an analysis of parts:

- What are the required materials for an iPod to work?
- What are the required materials for an air conditioner to work?
- What kinds of conditions are necessary before a cell phone will work?

Remember: required materials or conditions are things <u>external</u> to the parts of the term.

If this expansion method can be developed, then read the article to determine what information represents things existing or activities occurring in the places where the term is used. For example, a paragraph that develops the definition of ethanol based on required materials or conditions might focus on describing the energy requirements and cost considerations for cultivating the corn used in ethanol.

The following paragraph is a student-written example of a "Required Conditions" section for an expanded definition of "Global warming." Note that for this term, "Required Conditions" means causes; that is, the conditions necessary for global warming to occur are the same as the causes of global warming:

> In order for global warming to occur, there must be high concentrations of greenhouse gases in the atmosphere. Greenhouse gases consist of carbon dioxide, methane, and nitrogen oxide; these gases are all carbon based. Carbon dioxide is produced by burning fossil fuels, such as gasoline and coal. The main contributors of carbon dioxide are cars, factories, and power plants. Methane is a by-product of waste decomposing in landfills and from the belching of large herds of cattle. Finally, nitrogen oxide comes from using fertilizers, which are used in large quantities on commercially-grown crops. Most importantly, global warming would not be possible without the Sun and its energy.

Comparison or Contrast

A comparison or a contrast requires a discussion of at least two technologies, processes, or concepts. Make sure you are comparing or contrasting the term you are defining with another type. For example, a document that discusses the differences between solar and gas heating is a contrast between two types of heating technology.

A comparison means explaining the similarities between the term you are defining and something else. A contrast means explaining the differences between the term you are defining and something else. Whether you choose to develop a comparison or a contrast paragraph, you must explain what the term means by showing how it shares qualities with something that may be more familiar to the reader.

When you are paraphrasing information for comparison or contrast, items being compared or contrasted must have something essential in common and be from the same category: comparing a computer to a coniferous tree will yield very little meaningful information. Those shared features should then be described in order to clarify the term's meaning based on specific similarities or differences, which could relate to physical, functional, or conceptual properties.

Also, try to establish three key points of similarity or difference: any fewer and there will be no basis for comparison. Finally, there must be a purpose for the comparison or contrast. In other words, ask the following questions:

- What will be learned about your term as a result of the comparison or contrast?
- What feature of the term you are defining is highlighted by the comparison or contrast?

Note that discussing advantages and disadvantages of one thing is not the same as comparing two different things. For example, would a document that discusses the advantages and disadvantages of solar heating be a comparison? Or would a document discussing the benefits and drawbacks of driving a hybrid vehicle be a comparison? In order to compare or contrast, there must be something other than your term that you are comparing it to.

The following examples illustrate how the expansion methods of comparison and contrast can be used to define a term.

Even though the "Contrast" example has two paragraphs, you will develop only one paragraph.

Here is a contrast between optical fibre and conventional copper cable:

> Beams of laser light coursing through optical fibres of the purest glass can transmit many times more information than the present communications systems. . . . A pair of optical fibres has the capacity to carry more than 10 000 times as many signals as conventional copper cable. A 1.25 cm ($^1/_2$") optical cable can carry as much information as a copper cable as thick as a person's arm. . . .
>
> Not only does fibre optics produce a better signal, [but] the signal travels farther as well. All communications signals experience a loss of power, or attenuation, as they move along a cable. This power loss necessitates placement of repeaters at 1.5- or 3.0-kilometre intervals of copper cable in order to regenerate the signal. With fibre, repeaters are necessary about every 50 or 65 kilometres, and this distance is increasing with every generation of fibre. (Stanton 27–28)

Here is a combined comparison and contrast:

> Fibre optics technology results from the superior capacity of light waves to carry a communications signal. Sound waves, radio waves, and light waves can all carry signals; their capacity increases with their frequency. Voice frequencies carried by telephone operate at 1000 cycles per second, or hertz. Television signals transmit at about 50 million hertz. Light waves, however, operate at frequencies in the hundreds of trillions of hertz. (Stanton 28)

Here is an example of how two kinds of heating can be contrasted. Remember that you will develop only one paragraph for either a comparison, contrast, or a combination of comparison and contrast.

> **Radiant Heating vs Traditional Heating** A traditional heating system warms air directly, which we feel on our skin as immediate heat, but its impact is transitory. Turn off the source of the heat, and the space being warmed immediately starts to cool. On a winter's day, for example, a residential furnace pumps hot air into the rooms until a preset temperature is reached, then the thermostat switches off the furnace. The warming effect stops immediately and the air temperature, influenced by cooler windows and walls, begins to drop.
>
> A radiant heating system, rather than warming air directly, radiates heat outwards in all directions until the rays contact another surface. If the surface is cooler than the radiant panel, the surface begins to warm up and the air near to it also warms, but gently, and so our skin feels the warmth as a gentle, comfortable heating. On a cool winter's day, a furnace pumps heat into the radiant panels as hot water or they are heated electrically until a preset room temperature is reached, when the source of the heat is switched off. The warming effect, however, does not stop immediately because the radiant panel continues to radiate residual heat for a considerable time. Consequently, the air in the room cools much more slowly than with hot air heating.

Examples

Once a term's parts and/or operation have been explained, the term may also be defined according to particular types or specific uses. The following examples illustrate how the term "robot" may be defined by how it is classified or used:

Specific types of robots:

- NASA's Mars Rover
- Sony's AIBO
- Honda's ASIMO

Specific uses for robots:

- To defuse bombs
- To build machine parts on factory assembly lines
- To mow lawns

In the same way that you could understand the expansion method "Required Conditions" as causes, you may also see "Examples" as outcomes or effects.

Therefore, if the article you are reading contains such information, answer the following question: *What happens as a result of the term's operation or usage?*

Note also that a reader will not understand what the term means if your paragraph is just a list of examples with no details about each one. Instead of listing, choose only one or two of the most interesting examples, and discuss each in detail. A good example highlights a significant aspect of the term.

Sometimes the article's author will discuss the "pros" and "cons" of a technology, process, or concept. These may be advantages and disadvantages or benefits and problems. However, paraphrase information that represents advantages and disadvantages only as examples of use, never as a comparison, because, as previously stated, a comparison requires that the term being defined is looked at in relation to something else. Below is a paragraph from an expanded definition of "E-mail" giving examples of the benefits and the drawbacks of using this communication tool:

> E-mail has both advantages and disadvantages. People can save time when they correspond using e-mail since messages can be sent instantly. Also, if people are physically distant from one another, e-mail can allow them to have meetings without actually getting together in person. However, a drawback to the efficiency of e-mail is that people often don't read or write messages carefully, which can result in misleading or inaccurate communication. Also, unwanted messages can distract people from their work, or worse, transmit programs that can cause computers to malfunction.

Below is a student-written paragraph taken from an expanded definition of "Recycling" that gives examples of different materials that can be recycled:

> Recyclable materials are sorted into groups, and each group goes through a different process where it will be transformed into raw materials. For example, plastics are melted down and moulded into pellets that can be used to make new plastic materials. Glass is also melted down and made into pellets that are used to make other glass products. Furthermore, paper products are ground into a pulp that can be reformed into many types of products. Finally, organic waste goes through an anaerobic composting process which allows it to be used to fertilize farmers' fields.

The paragraphs below could be used in an expanded definition of the term "Laser." The first gives examples of how lasers are used to treat health problems, and the second gives different ways lasers are used to store and transmit information.

> Lasers are increasingly used to treat health problems. Thousands of eye operations involving cataracts and detached retinas are performed every year by ophthalmologists. . . . Dermatologists treat skin problems. . . . Gynecologists treat problems of the reproductive system, and neurosurgeons even perform brain surgery—all using lasers transmitted through optical fibres. (Gartiganis 24–25)

> Using lasers in the calculating and memory units of computers, for example, permits storage and rapid manipulation of large amounts of data. And audiodisc players use lasers to improve the quality of the sound they reproduce. The use of optical cable to transmit data also relies on lasers. (Gartiganis 25).

Choosing the Best Expansion Methods and Order

When paraphrasing information from an article to define a term, you should understand the difference between describing a technology or concept and exploring the relationships it has with other things or with specific instances of its use.

Here are the expansion methods used to describe something:

- Parts Analysis
- Operating Principles
- Required Materials and/or Conditions

Here are the expansion methods used to explore relationships of similarity, difference, or specificity:

- Comparison and/or Contrast
- Examples

Here are some general rules when choosing which expansion methods to use and what order to present them in:

- Use the "describing" methods **before** discussing the "relationship" methods since a reader will understand the relationships only after he or she has been given a clear picture of what it is you are defining, with paragraphs that discuss the fundamentals, like what its parts are or how it works.
- Choose three methods that allow you to define your term as effectively as you can. Usually, the Parts Analysis or Operating Principles paragraphs will be necessary to give the audience a clear idea of how the term looks or functions.
- Use a comparison or examples only **after** clearly defining the parts or operation of a term.

CHAPTER 8

Descriptions and Specifications

LEARNING OBJECTIVES

After reading this chapter, you should be able to

- Incorporate the elements of clear, objective descriptions of mechanisms, places, or objects.
- Appreciate the range of uses for technical specifications.
- Apply the principles of effective mechanism description and specifications to technical marketing documents.

Description (creating a picture with words) is part of all writing. But technical descriptions convey information about a product or mechanism to someone who will use it, buy it, operate it, assemble it, or manufacture it, or to someone who has to know more about it. Any item can be visualized from countless different perspectives. Therefore, *how* you describe—your perspective—depends on your purpose and the needs of your audience.

Two kinds of descriptions are featured in this chapter: mechanism description and specifications. We start with a mechanism description (see Figure 8.1 on the following page).

PURPOSE OF DESCRIPTION

Manufacturers use descriptions to sell products; banks require detailed descriptions of any business or construction venture before approving a loan; and medical personnel maintain daily or hourly descriptions of a patient's condition and treatment.

No matter what the subject of description, readers expect answers to as many of these questions as are applicable: *What is it? What does it do? What does it look like? What is it made of? How does it work? How was it put together?* The description in Figure 8.1 on the following page, part of an installation and operation manual, answers applicable questions for do-it-yourself homeowners.

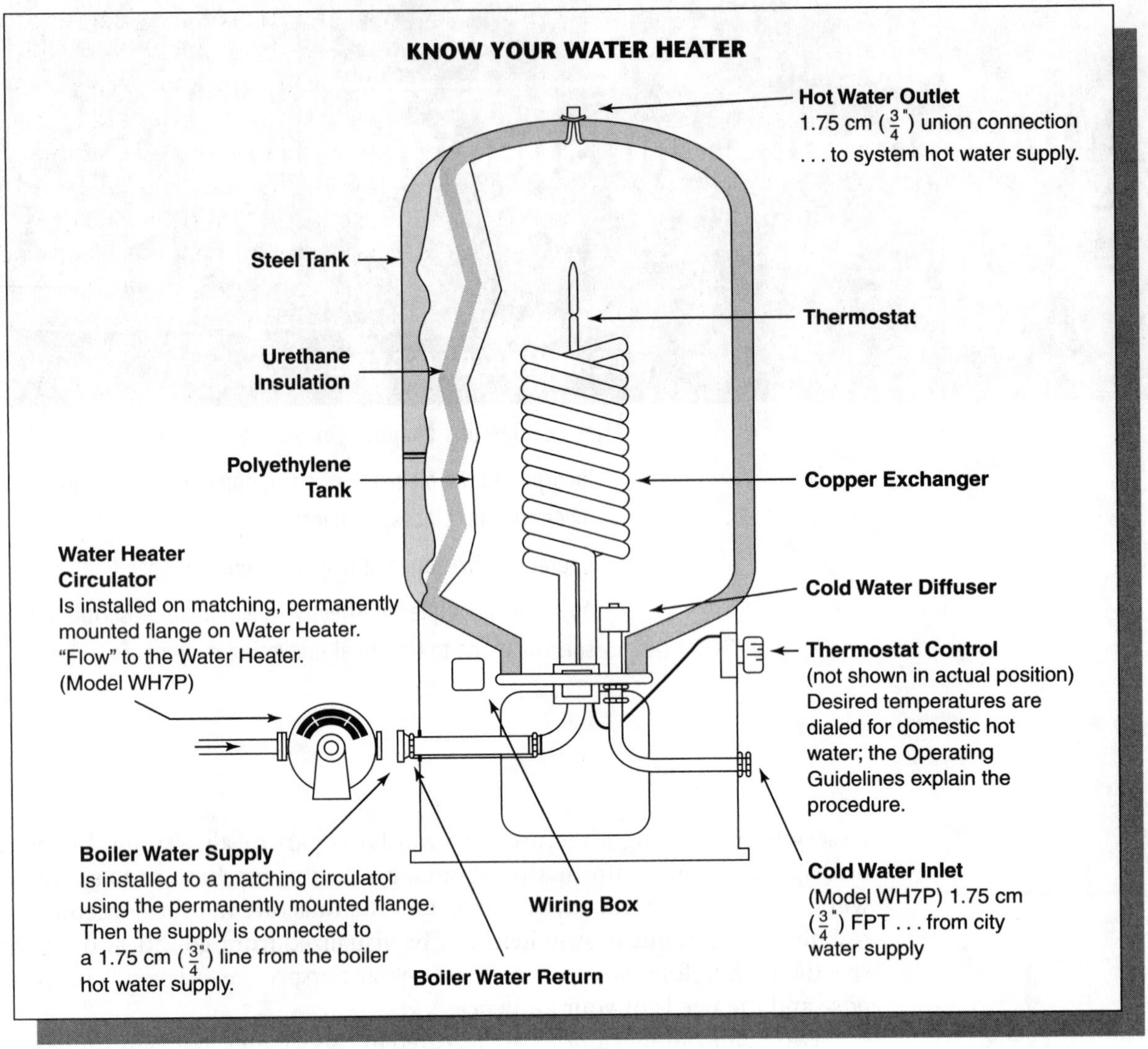

Figure 8.1 A Mechanism Description

Source: Courtesy of AMTROL Inc.

OBJECTIVITY IN DESCRIPTION

Each description is mainly *subjective* or *objective:* based on feelings or fact. Subjective description emphasizes the writer's attitude toward the thing, whereas objective description emphasizes the thing itself.

Essays describing "An Unforgettable Person" or "A Beautiful Moment" express opinions, a personal point of view. Subjective description aims at expressing feelings, attitudes, and moods. You create an *impression* of your subject ("The weather was miserable"), more than communicating factual information about it ("All day, we had freezing rain and gale-force winds").

Objective description shows an impartial view, filtering out personal impressions and focusing on observable details.

Except for promotional writing, descriptions on the job should be impartial, if they are to be ethical. Pure objectivity is, of course, humanly impossible. Each writer filters the facts and their meaning through her or his own perspective. Nonetheless, we are expected to communicate the facts as we know them and understand them. One writer offers this useful distinction: "All communication requires us to leave something out, but we must be sure that what is left out is not essential to our [reader's] understanding of what is put in" (Coletta 65).

An ethical writer "is obligated to express her or his opinions of products, as long as these opinions are based on objective and responsible research and observation" (MacKenzie 3). Being "objective" does not mean forsaking personal evaluation in cases in which a product may be unsafe or unsound. Even positive claims made in promotional writing (for example, "reliable," "rugged") should be based on objective and verifiable evidence.

Here are guidelines for remaining impartial.

Record the Details That Enable Readers to Visualize the Item. Ask these questions: *What could any observer recognize? What would a camera record?*

Subjective His office has an *awful* view, *terrible* furniture, and a *depressing* atmosphere.

The italicized words only *tell;* they do not *show.*

Objective His office has broken windows looking out on a brick wall, a rug with a 15 cm hole in the centre, chairs with bottoms falling out, missing floorboards, and a ceiling with plaster missing in three or four places.

Use Precise and Informative Language. Use high-information words that enable readers to visualize. Name specific parts without calling them "things," "gadgets," or "doohickeys." Avoid judgmental words (*impressive, poor*), unless your judgment is requested and can be supported by facts. Instead of "large," "long," and "near," give exact measurements, weights, dimensions, and ingredients.

Use words that specify location and spatial relationships: *above, oblique, behind, tangential, adjacent, interlocking, abutting,* and *overlapping.* Use position words: *horizontal,vertical, lateral, longitudinal, in cross-section, parallel.*

Indefinite	**Precise**
a late-model car	a 2007 Acura TL sedan
an inside view	a cross-sectional, cutaway, or exploded view
next to the foundation	adjacent to the right side
a small red thing	a red activator button with a 2.5 cm diameter and a concave surface

Do not confuse precise language, however, with overly complicated technical terms or needless jargon. Don't say "phlebotomy specimen" instead of "blood," or "thermal attenuation" instead of "insulation," or "proactive neutralization" instead of "damage control." The clearest writing uses precise but plain language. General readers prefer non-technical language, as long as the simpler words do the job. Always think about your specific readers' needs.

ELEMENTS OF MECHANISM DESCRIPTION

Clear and Limiting Title

Promise exactly what you will deliver—no more and no less. "A Description of a Norco Freeride Shore One Mountain Bicycle" promises a complete description, down to the smallest part. If you intend to describe the brakeset only, be sure your title so indicates: "A Description of the Avid Juicy 7 Hydraulic Disc Brakes."

Overall Appearance and Component Parts

Let readers see the big picture before you describe each part.

> The standard stethoscope is roughly 61 cm long and weighs about 140 grams. The instrument consists of a sensitive sound-detecting and amplifying device whose flat surface is pressed against a bodily area. This amplifying device is attached to rubber and metal tubing that transmits the body sound to a listening device inserted in the ear.
>
> Seven interlocking pieces contribute to the stethoscope's Y-shaped appearance: (1) diaphragm contact piece, (2) lower tubing, (3) Y-shaped metal piece, (4) upper tubing, (5) U-shaped metal strip, (6) curved metal tubing, and (7) hollow ear plugs. These parts form a continuous unit.

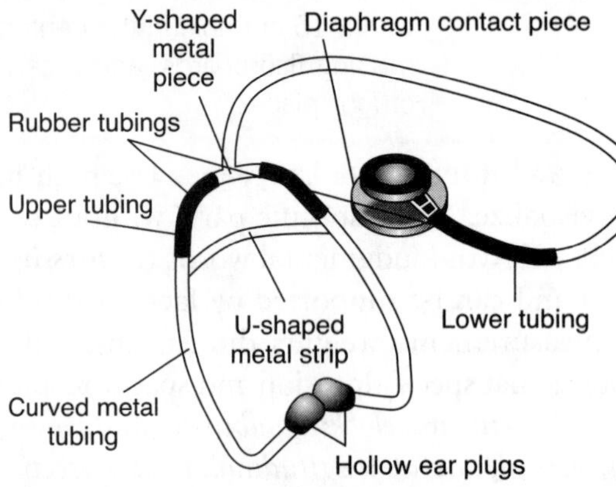

FIGURE 1 Stethoscope with Diaphragm Contact Piece (Front View)

Visuals

Use drawings, diagrams, or photographs generously. Our overall description of the stethoscope is greatly clarified by Figure 1.

Function of Each Part

Explain what each part does and how it relates to the whole.

> The diaphragm contact piece is caused to vibrate by body sounds. This part is the heart of the stethoscope that receives, amplifies, and transmits the sound impulse.

Appropriate Details

Give enough detail for a clear picture, but do not burden readers needlessly. Identify your readers and their reasons for reading your description.

The description of the water heater in Figure 8.1 focuses on what this model looks like and what it's made of. Its intended audience of do-it-yourselfers will know already what a hot-water maker is and what it does. That audience needs no background. A description of how it was put together appears with the installation and maintenance instructions later in the manual.

Specifications for readers who will manufacture the water heater would describe each part in exact detail (e.g., the steel tank's required thickness and pressure rating as well as required percentages of iron, carbon, and other constituents in the steel alloy).

Clearest Descriptive Sequence

Any item usually has its own logic of organization, based on (1) the way it appears as a static object, (2) the way its parts operate in order, or (3) the way its parts are assembled. We describe these relationships, respectively, in a spatial, functional, or chronological sequence.

Spatial Sequence. Part of all physical descriptions, a spatial sequence answers these questions: *What is it? What does it do? What does it look like? What parts and material is it made of?* Use this sequence when you want readers to visualize the item as a static object or mechanism at rest (a house interior, a document, the CN Tower, a plot of land, a chainsaw, or a computer keyboard). Can readers best visualize this item from front to rear, left to right, top to bottom? (What logical path do the parts create?) A retractable pen would logically be viewed from outside to inside. The specifications in Figure 8.2 proceed from the ground upward.

Functional Sequence. The functional sequence answers: *How does it work?* It is best used in describing a mechanism in action, such as an SLR digital camera, a nuclear warhead, a smoke detector, or a car's cruise-control system. The logic of the item is reflected by the order in which its parts function. Like the hot-water heater in Figure 8.1, a mechanism usually has only one functional sequence.

In describing a solar home-heating system, you would begin with the heat collectors on the roof, moving through the pipes, pumping system, and tanks for the heated water, to the heating vents in the floors and walls—from source to outlet. After this functional sequence of operating parts, you could describe each part in a spatial sequence.

Chronological Sequence. A chronological sequence answers: *How has it been put together?* The chronology follows the sequence in which the parts are assembled.

Use the chronological sequence for an item that is best visualized by its assembly (such as a piece of furniture, an umbrella tent, or a pre-hung window or door unit). Architects might find a spatial sequence best for describing a proposed beach house to clients; however, they would use a chronological sequence (of blueprints) for specifying to the builder the prescribed dimensions, materials, and construction methods at each stage.

Ruger, Filstone, and Grant Architects

SPECIFICATIONS FOR THE POWNAL CLINIC BUILDING

Foundation

Footings: 8" x 16" concrete (load-bearing capacity: 3000 lb. per sq. in.)
Frost walls: 8" x 4' @ 3000 psi
Slab: 4" @ 3000 psi, reinforced with wire mesh over vapour barrier

Exterior Walls

Frame: eastern pine #2 timber frame with exterior partitions set inside posts
Exterior partitions: 2" x 4" kiln-dried spruce set at 16" on centre
Sheathing: 1/4" exterior-grade plywood
Siding: #1 red cedar with a 1/2" x 6' bevel
Trim: finished-pine boards ranging from 1" x 4" to 1" x 10"
Painting: 2 coats of Clear Wood Finish on siding; trim primed and finished with one coat of bone-white, oil base paint

Roof System

Framing: 2" x 12" kiln-dried spruce set at 24" on centre
Sheathing: 5/8" exterior-grade plywood
Finish: 240 Celotex 20-year fibreglass shingles over #15 impregnated felt roofing paper
Flashing: copper

Windows

Anderson casement and fixed-over-awning models, with white exterior cladding, insulating glass and screens, and wood interior frames

Landscape

Driveway: gravel base, with 3" traprock surface
Walks: timber defined, with traprock surface
Cleared areas: to be rough graded and covered with wood chips
Plantings: 10 assorted lawn plants along the road side of the building

Figure 8.2 Specifications for a Building Project (Partial)

Combined Sequences. The description of a bumper jack on pages 152–154 alternates among all three sequences: a spatial sequence (bottom to top) for describing the overall mechanism at rest, a chronological sequence for explaining the order in which the parts are assembled, and a functional sequence for describing the order in which the parts operate.

A GENERAL MODEL FOR DESCRIPTION

Description of a complex mechanism almost invariably calls for an outline. This model is adaptable to any description.

I. Introduction: General Description
   A. Definition, Function, and Background of the Item
   B. Purpose (and Audience—where applicable)
   C. Overall Description (with general visuals, if applicable)
   D. Principle of Operation (if applicable)
   E. List of Major Parts

II. Description and Function of Parts
   A. Part One in Your Descriptive Sequence
      1. Definition
      2. Shape, dimensions, material (with specific visuals)
      3. Sub-parts (if applicable)
      4. Function
      5. Relation to adjoining parts
      6. Mode of attachment (if applicable)
   B. Part Two in Your Descriptive Sequence (and so on)

III. Summary and Operating Description
   A. Summary (used only in a long, complex description)
   B. Interrelation of Parts
   C. One Complete Operating Cycle

This outline is tentative, because you might modify, delete, or combine certain parts to suit your subject, purpose, and reader.

Introduction: General Description

Give readers only as much background as they need to get the picture.

A Description of the Standard Stethoscope

Introduction

Definition and function

The stethoscope is a listening device that amplifies and transmits body sounds to aid in detecting physical abnormalities.

History and background

This instrument has evolved from the original wooden, funnel-shaped instrument invented by a French physician, R.T. Lennaec, in 1819. Because of his female patients' modesty, he found it necessary to develop a device, other than his ear, for auscultation (listening to body sounds).

Purpose and audience

This report explains to the beginning paramedical or nursing student the structure, assembly, and operating principle of the stethoscope. [*Omit this section if you submit to your instructor an audience/purpose profile or if you write for a workplace audience.*]

Finally, give a brief, overall description of the item, discuss its principle of operation, and list its major parts, as in the overall stethoscope description on page 146.

Description and Function of Parts

The body of your text describes each major part. After arranging the parts in sequence, follow the logic of each part. Provide only as much detail as your readers need.

Readers of this description will use a stethoscope daily, so they need to know how it works, how to take it apart for cleaning, and how to replace worn or broken parts. (Specifications for the manufacturer would require many more technical details—dimensions, alloys, curvatures, tolerances, etc.)

Diaphragm Contact Piece

Definition, size, shape, and material

The diaphragm contact piece is a shallow metal bowl, about the size of a dollar coin (and twice its thickness), which is caused to vibrate by various body sounds.

Sub-parts

Three separate parts make up the piece: hollow steel bowl, plastic diaphragm, and metal frame, as shown in Figure 2.

The stainless steel metal bowl has a concave inner surface, with concentric ridges that funnel sound toward an opening in the tapered base, then out through the hollow appendage. Lateral threads ring the outer circumference of the bowl to accommodate the interlocking metal frame. A fitted diaphragm covers the bowl's upper opening.

The diaphragm is a plastic disk, 2 mm thick, 10.2 cm in circumference, with a moulded lip around the edge. It fits flush over the metal bowl and vibrates sound toward the ridges. A metal frame that screws onto the bowl holds the diaphragm in place.

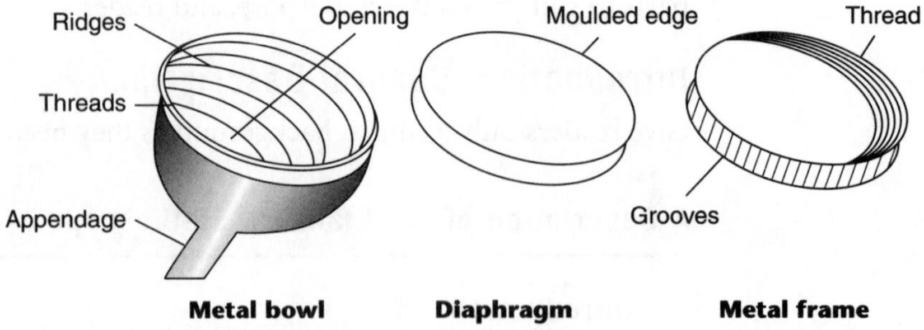

FIGURE 2 Exploded View of a Diaphragm Contact Piece

Function and relation to adjoining parts

The stainless steel frame fits over the disk and metal bowl. A 0.75 cm ridge between the inner and outer edge accommodates threads for screwing the frame to the bowl. The frame's outside circumference is notched with equally spaced, perpendicular grooves—like those on the edge of a dime—to provide a gripping surface.

Mode of attachment

The diaphragm contact piece is the heart of the stethoscope that receives, amplifies, and transmits sound through the system of attached tubing. The piece attaches to the lower tubing by an appendage on its apex (narrow end), which fits inside the tubing.

Each part of the stethoscope, in turn, is described according to its own logic of organization.

Summary and Operating Description

Conclude by explaining how the parts work together to make the whole item function.

Summary and Operating Description

How parts interrelate

The seven major parts of the stethoscope provide support for the instrument, flexibility of movement for the operator, and ease in auscultation.

One complete operating cycle

In an operating cycle, the diaphragm contact piece, placed against the skin, picks up sound impulses from the body surface. These impulses cause the plastic diaphragm to vibrate. The amplified vibrations, in turn, are carried through a tube to a dividing point. From here, the amplified sound is carried through two separate but identical series of tubes to hollow ear plugs.

A SAMPLE SITUATION

The following description of an automobile jack, aimed toward a general audience, follows our outline model.

A Mechanism Description for Non-technical Readers

AUDIENCE/PURPOSE PROFILE. Some readers of this description (written for an owner's manual) will have no mechanical background. Before they can follow instructions for using the jack safely, they will have to learn what it is, what it looks like, what its parts are, and how, generally, it works. They will not need precise dimensions (e.g., "The rectangular base is 20.25 cm long and 16.5 cm wide, sloping upward 3.75 cm from the front outer edge to form a secondary platform 2.5 cm high and 7.5 cm square"). The engineer who designed the jack might include such data in specifications for the manufacturer. Laypeople, however, need only the dimensions that will help them recognize specific parts and understand their function, for safe use and assembly.

Also, this audience will need only the broadest explanation of how the leverage mechanism operates. Although the physical principles (torque, fulcrum) would interest engineers, they would be of little use to readers who simply need to operate the jack safely.

Description of a Standard Bumper Jack

INTRODUCTION—GENERAL DESCRIPTION

Definition, purpose, and function

The standard bumper jack is a portable mechanism for raising the front or rear of a car through force applied with a lever. This jack enables even a frail person to lift one corner of a two-ton automobile.

Overall description (spatial sequence)

The jack consists of a moulded steel base supporting a free-standing, perpendicular, notched shaft (Figure 1). Attached to the shaft are a leverage mechanism, a bumper catch, and a cylinder for insertion of the jack handle. Except for the main shaft and leverage mechanism, the jack is made to be dismantled and to fit neatly in the car's trunk.

Operating principle

The jack operates on a leverage principle, with a human hand travelling 46 cm and the car only 1 cm during a normal jacking stroke. Such a device requires many strokes to raise the car off the ground but may prove a lifesaver to a motorist on some deserted road.

List of major parts

Five main parts make up the jack: base, notched shaft, leverage mechanism, bumper catch, and handle.

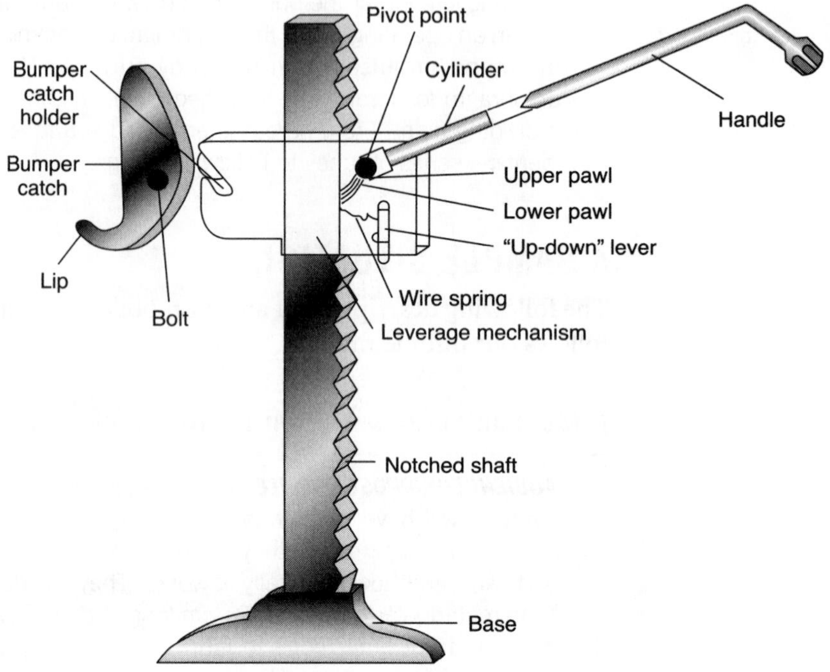

FIGURE 1 A Side View of the Standard Bumper Jack

DESCRIPTION OF PARTS AND THEIR FUNCTION

(Chronological sequence) First major part

BASE The rectangular base is a moulded steel plate that provides support and a point of insertion for the shaft (Figure 2). The base slopes upward to form a platform containing a 1.25 cm depression that provides a stabilizing well for the shaft. Stability is

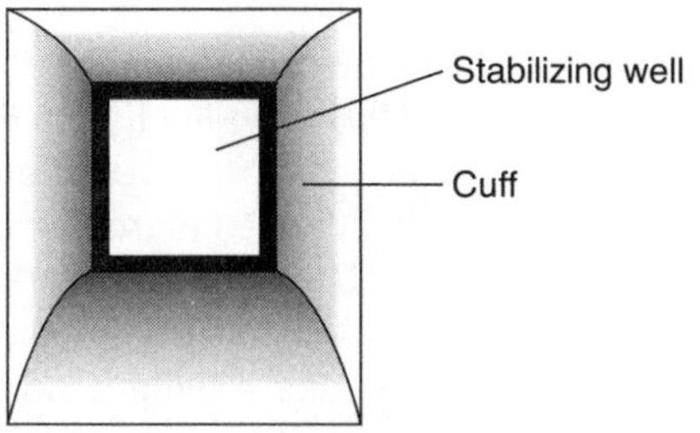

FIGURE 2 A Top View of the Jack Base

Definition, shape, and size
Function and mode of attachment

Second major part, etc.

increased by a 1.25 cm cuff around the well. As the base rests on its flat surface, the bottom end of the shaft is inserted into its stabilizing well.

NOTCHED SHAFT The notched shaft is a steel bar (80 cm long) that provides a vertical track for the leverage mechanism. The notches, which hold the mechanism in its position on the shaft, face the operator.

The shaft vertically supports the raised automobile, and attached to it is the leverage mechanism, which rests on individual notches.

LEVERAGE MECHANISM The leverage mechanism provides the mechanical advantage needed for its operator to raise the car. It is made to slide up and down the notched shaft. The main body of this pressed-steel mechanism contains two units: one for transferring the leverage and one for holding the bumper catch.

The leverage unit has four major parts: the cylinder, connecting the handle and a pivot point; a lower pawl (a device that fits into the notches to allow forward and prevent backward motion), connected directly to the cylinder; an upper pawl, connected at the pivot point; and an "up-down" lever, which applies or releases pressure on the upper pawl by means of a spring (Figure 1). Moving the cylinder up and down with the handle causes the alternate release of the pawls, and thus movement up or down the shaft—depending on the setting of the "up-down" lever. The movement is transferred by the metal body of the unit to the bumper-catch holder.

The holder consists of a downsloping groove, partially blocked by a wire spring (Figure 1). The spring is mounted in such a way as to keep the bumper catch in place during operation.

BUMPER CATCH The bumper catch is a steel device that attaches the leverage mechanism to the bumper. This 23 cm moulded plate is bent to fit the shape of the bumper. Its outer 0.5 cm is bent up to form a lip (Figure 1), which hooks behind the bumper to hold the catch in place. The two sides of the plate are bent back 90 degrees to leave a 5.0 cm bumper-contact surface, and a bolt is riveted between them. This bolt slips into the groove in the leverage mechanism and provides the attachment between the leverage unit and the car.

HANDLE The jack handle is a steel bar that serves both as lever and lug-bolt remover. This round bar is 56 cm long, 1.5 cm in diameter, and is bent 135 degrees roughly 13 cm from its outer end. Its outer end is a wrench made to fit the wheel's lug bolts. Its inner end is bevelled to form a bladelike point for prying the wheel covers and for insertion into the cylinder on the leverage mechanism.

CONCLUSION AND OPERATING DESCRIPTION

Assembly

One quickly assembles the jack by inserting the bottom of the notched shaft into the stabilizing well in the base, the bumper catch into the groove on the leverage mechanism, and the bevelled end of the jack handle into the cylinder. The bumper catch is then attached to the bumper, with the lever set in the "up" position.

One complete operating cycle (functional sequence)

As the operator exerts an up-down pumping motion on the jack handle, the leverage mechanism gradually climbs the vertical notched shaft until the car's wheel is raised above the ground. When the lever is in the "down" position, the same pumping motion causes the leverage mechanism to descend the shaft.

SPECIFICATIONS

Airplanes, bridges, smoke detectors, and countless other items are produced according to certain specifications. A particularly exacting type of description, specifications (or "specs") prescribe standards for performance, safety, and quality. For almost any product, specifications spell out

- the methods for manufacturing, building, or installing the product
- the materials and equipment to be used
- the size, shape, and weight of the product

Because these requirements define an acceptable level of quality, specifications have ethical and legal implications. Any product "below" specifications provides grounds for a lawsuit. When injury or death results (as in a bridge collapse caused by inferior reinforcement), the contractor, subcontractor, or supplier who cut corners is criminally liable.

Federal and provincial regulatory agencies routinely issue specifications to ensure safety. Health Canada specifies standards for a wide variety of materials and devices, from the operation of seat belts to the fire-retardant qualities of cloth used for infant pyjamas. Meanwhile, the Canadian Standards Association designates safety and operating specifications for nearly every product sold in this country. Further, provincial and local agencies issue specifications in the form of building codes, electrical codes, and property development requirements, to name just a few.

Government departments (Defence, Environment, etc.) issue specifications for all types of military hardware and other equipment. A set of NASA specifications for spacecraft parts can be hundreds of pages long, prescribing the standards for even the smallest nuts and bolts, down to screw-thread depth and width in millimetres.

The private sector issues specifications for countless products or projects, to help ensure that customers get exactly what they want. Figure 8.2 shows partial specifications drawn up by an architect for a building that will house a small medical clinic. This section of the specs covers only the structure's "shell." Other sections detail the requirements for plumbing, wiring, and interior finish work.

ON THE JOB...

Changing Specifications on the Job

"When the client specifies changes in a project, I can cost those changes and send them in an email. For example, in a site meeting yesterday, my site superintendent noted 19 items to be changed, half of which will result in extra costs. This morning, my email to the client listed them all, including the ones I was able to estimate right away. The email also told him how long it would take to cost the remaining items and asked him if he wanted us to delay them until we can learn what they'll cost...."

—Ken Dahlen, Keith Construction (March 14, 2007)

The detailed building specifications partially shown in Figure 8.2 provide the basis for the comprehensive agreement between the builder and the client. In addition, the specifications (along with properly drawn building plans) are important in convincing the municipal authority to issue a building permit. Subsequently, building inspectors will use the plans and specifications as part of their criteria when they inspect the clinic in various stages of the building process.

Specifications like those in Figure 8.2 must be clear enough for *identical* interpretation by the widest possible range of readers (Glidden 258–59):

- *The customer,* who has the big picture of what is needed and who wants the best product at the best price
- *The designer* (architect, engineer, computer scientist, etc.), who must translate the customer's wishes into the actual specifications
- *The contractor or manufacturer,* who won the job by making the lowest bid and so must preserve profit by doing only what is prescribed
- *The supplier,* who must provide the exact materials and equipment
- *The workforce,* who will do the actual assembly, construction, or installation (managers, supervisors, subcontractors, and workers—some working on only one part of the product, such as plumbing or electrical)
- *The inspectors* (such as building, plumbing, or electrical inspectors), who evaluate how well the product conforms to the specifications

Each of these parties has to understand and agree on exactly *what* is to be done and *how* it is to be done. In the case of a lawsuit over failure to meet specifications, the readership broadens to include judges, lawyers, and jury. Figure 8.3 depicts how a clear set of specifications unifies all readers (their various viewpoints, motives, and levels of expertise) in a shared understanding.

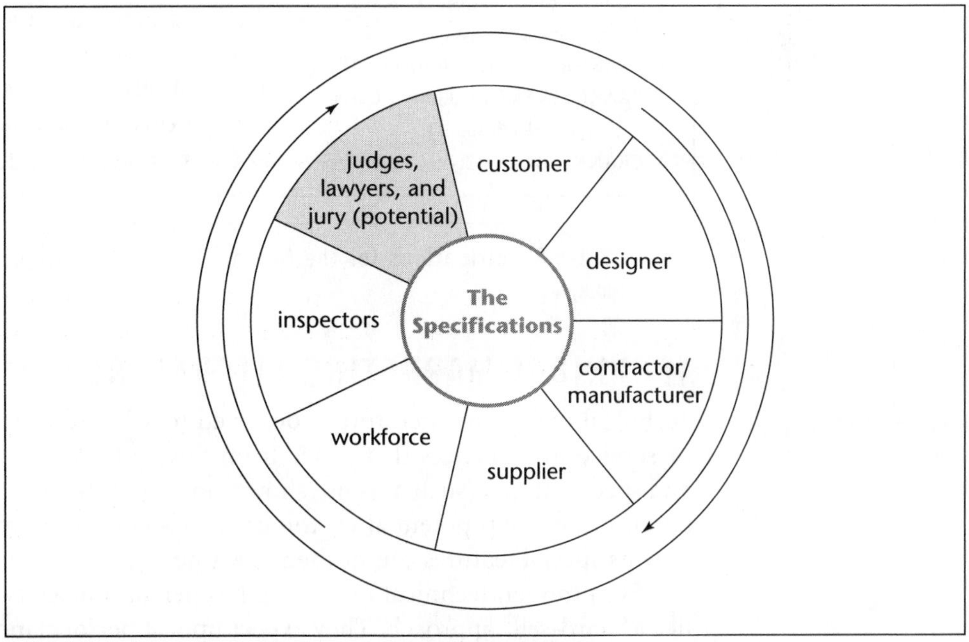

Figure 8.3 Users and Potential Users of Specifications

In addition to guiding a product's design and construction, specifications can facilitate the product's use and maintenance. For instance, specifications in a computer manual include the product's performance limits, or *ratings*: its power requirements, work or processing or storage capacity, environment requirements, the make-up of key parts, and so on. Product support literature for appliances, power tools, and other items routinely contains ratings to help readers select a good operating environment or replace worn or defective parts (Riney 186). The ratings in Figure 8.4 are taken from a manufacturer's website.

Key Features: full suspension; all lightweight components; SRAM XO & Shimano XTR drivetrain

FRAME: Hyfraformed aluminum, Horst Link 4-bar linkage, 145-165mm travel, Fox DHX 5.0 AIR w/boost valve
FORK: FOX 36 TALAS RC2, QR-20, 100-160mm travel, external air spring pressure, rebound, compression, and travel
HUBS: Mavic Crossmax SX Wheelset
RIMS: Mavic Crossmax SX Wheelset
SPOKES: Mavic Crossmax SX Wheelset
TIRES: Kenda Nevegal, 2.35 kevlar
BRAKES: Avid Juicy 7 hydraulic, 7" rotor
BRAKE LEVERS: Avid Juicy 7 Carbon (Speed dial adjustable)
CRANKS: Truvativ Stylo GXP, 2 piece, hollow axle, 24/36/bash guard, Black Spire Stinger dual guide pulley
PEDALS: DMR V-12 magnesium, sealed bearings
CHAIN: Sram PC 971
FREEWHEEL: Sram 9.0 11-34T 9 sp
FRONT DERAILLEUR: Shimano XTR, 31.8
REAR DERAILLEUR: Sram XO 9 speed, medium cage
SHIFTERS: Sram X-0 trigger, 9 speed
COLOUR: Champagne Silver
SUGGESTED RETAIL: $5850 Cdn

Figure 8.4 Specifications for the Norco 2007 Six SE "All Mountain" Bike
Source: Courtesy Norco.

TECHNICAL MARKETING LITERATURE

Technical marketing audiences expect a factual presentation

Technical marketing literature is designed to sell a technical or scientific product or service to audiences that range from novice to highly informed. Descriptions and specifications (such as those shown on page 148) are essential marketing tools because they help potential customers to visualize the product and to recognize how its special features can fit their exact needs.

Even though technical marketing has persuasion as its main goal, readers dislike a "hard-sell" approach. They expect upbeat performance claims such as "high-performance components" to be backed up by solid evidence—results of objective product testing, performance ratings, and specific technical data that indicate how the product meets or exceeds industry specifications.

Unlike proposals, which are also used to sell a product or service, technical marketing materials tend to be less formal and more dynamic, colourful, and varied. A typical proposal is tailored to one specific client's needs and follows a fairly standard format. Marketing literature, on the other hand, uses a wide variety of formats for a broad array of audiences and needs:

Common forms of technical marketing documents

- *Business letters* are the most personal type of marketing document. See, for example, how Manson Harding's sales letter on pages 222–223 creates a human connection with a potential customer.
- *Fact sheets* offer basic data about the product or service in a straightforward, unadorned format, usually on a single $8^1/_2$" by 11" page, sometimes using both sides of the page. Fact sheets provide reams of technical information, but they are designed to be inviting and navigable, with engaging, easily "read" visuals; concise, readable paragraphs; clear headings; and complex data chunked into clearly labelled lists (Hilligoss 63).
- *Webpages* are especially effective for technical marketing. A visitor can explore the links of particular interest, read or download the material, and easily return to the homepage. Webpages offer several advantages: information is easily updated; customers can interact to ask questions or place orders; and, through animation, the product can be shown in operation (Gurak and Lannon 238). Figure 8.5 on the following page shows a Norco Performance Bikes webpage, which opens to hyperlinked specifications and product descriptions, "news" stories, and a "community" of video clips, podcasts, photos, and stories by and about people who ride Norco bikes. This site reaches its audience of hardcore riders and "wannabes" by combining specs, tech talk, and human-interest stories.
- *Brochures* have been a popular marketing medium. Good brochures feature panels that provide a logical sequence, with each panel offering its own discrete chunk of information about the product (Hilligoss 63). That strategy works equally well for online brochures. The Norco website, for example, provides hyperlinks to descriptions and specifications for its 125+ bicycles.
- *E-newsletters*, easily sent via email to consenting, often enthusiastic, consumers, are a recent addition to direct marketing strategy. These newsletters, which can be quickly produced, include human-interest stories and technical product features and usage (Arellano).
- *Magalogues*, "a hybrid of magazine and catalogue formats, represent the latest trend in presenting product brochures" (Arellano, Email). Part of Norco's 2007 magalogue is shown in Figure 8.6 on the following page. The featured photo and some of the copy from pages 3 and 4 of the magalogue also appear on Norco's website.

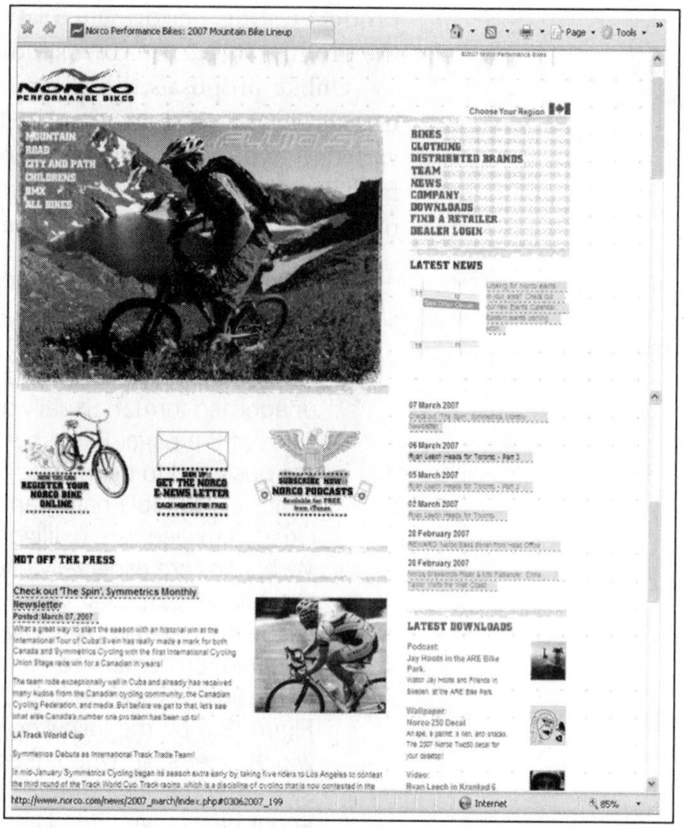

Figure 8.5 Sample Technical Marketing Website
Source: Courtesy Norco.

DH Norco's VPS Team DH, A-Line, and Atomik downhill mountain bikes were designed for two purposes: - to tackle the toughest freeride lines, – and to get riders on the downhill mountain bike World Cup podium. After being awarded the first ever 5-Star rating from NSMB.com for the 2006 Team DH, the downhill race designers had to work extra hard this year to improve this year's model.

For 2007, we've chosen to keep our Horst link 4-bar linkage design, as it is still the bestrear suspension system for isolating both the pedaling and braking forces...

CATEGORY FEATURES

1. Rear suspension travel: 199-232 mm (Atomik: 180-205 mm)
2. 150 X 12 mm rear wheel over locknut
3. Horst link 4-bar linkage (FSR Patented)

Figure 8.6 Magalogue Excerpt
Source: Courtesy Norco.

CHECKLIST FOR REVISING AND EDITING DESCRIPTIONS

Use this checklist to refine the content, arrangement, and style of your description.

Content

- Does the title promise exactly what the description delivers?
- Are the item's overall features described, as well as each part?
- Is each part defined before it is discussed?
- Is the function of each part explained?
- Do visuals appear whenever they can provide clarification?
- Will readers be able to visualize the item?
- Are any details missing, needless, or confusing for this audience?
- Is the description ethically acceptable?

Arrangement

- Does the description follow the clearest possible sequence?
- Are relationships among the parts clearly explained?

Style and Page Design

- Is the description sufficiently impartial?
- Is the language informative and precise?
- Will the level of technicality connect with the audience?
- Is the description written in plain English?
- Is each sentence clear, concise, and fluent?
- Is the page design inviting and accessible?

WEB CONNECT

This product description of a "Tourist" Swiss Army Knife simply provides a photo and a list of the knife's basic features:

www.swissarmy.com/MultiTools/Product.htm?category=originalswissarmyknives&product=53131&

These two sites advise how to write effective descriptions of mechanisms:

http://jerz.setonhill.edu/writing/technical/mechanism.htm
www.ecf.utoronto.ca/~writing/handbook-rhetoric.html

EXERCISES

1. Select an item from the following list or a device used in your major field. Using the general outline as a model, develop an objective description. Include (a) all necessary visuals; (b) a rough diagram for each visual; or (c) a "reference visual" (a copy of a visual published elsewhere) with instructions for adapting your visual from that one. (If you borrow visuals from other sources, provide full documentation.) Write for a specific use by a specified audience. Attach your written audience/purpose profile (based on the worksheet, page 35) to your document.

Breathalyzer	Skinner box
sphygmomanometer	radio
transit	distilling apparatus
sabre saw	bodily organ
hazardous waste site	brand of woodstove
photovoltaic panel	catalytic converter

Remember, you are simply describing the item, its parts, and its function: *do not* provide directions for its assembly or operation.

As an optional assignment, describe a place you know well. You are trying to convey a visual image, not a mood; therefore, your description should be impartial, discussing only the observable details.

2. The bumper-jack description in this chapter is aimed toward a general reading audience. Evaluate it by using the revision checklist. In one or two paragraphs, discuss your evaluation, and suggest revisions.

3. Locate a description and specifications for a particular brand of automobile or some other consumer product. Evaluate this material for promotional and descriptive value and ethical appropriateness.

COLLABORATIVE PROJECT

Assume your group is an architectural firm designing buildings at your university or college. Develop a set of specifications for duplicating the interior of the classroom in which this course is held. Focus only on materials, dimensions, and equipment (whiteboard, desk, etc.) and use visuals as appropriate. Your audience includes teachers, school administrators, and the firm that will construct the classroom. Use the same format as in Figure 8.2 (page 148), or design a better one. Appoint one member to present the completed specifications in class. Compare versions from each group for accuracy and clarity.

CHAPTER 9

Process Analyses, Instructions, and Procedures

LEARNING OBJECTIVES

After reading this chapter, you should be able to

- Understand the similarities and important differences between instructions and process analysis, and between instructions and procedures.
- Research, plan, and write an effective process analysis.
- Demonstrate the elements of readable, useful instructions.
- Apply principles of effective instruction to print and online tutorials.

A process is a series of actions or changes leading to a product or result. *Instructions* and *tutorials* describe how to carry out a "process"; a *procedure* is a special kind of instructional set. *Process analysis* identifies, describes, and explains the sequence of events in a repeatable process. This chapter discusses all four types of process-related description.

Although process analysis and instructions both present chronological steps leading to a predicted result, that's where the similarity ends. The reasons for writing and reading a process analysis are quite different from the motivations for writing and reading instructions. These fundamental differences lead to the differences in content, structure, voice, mood, appearance, and style summarized in Table 9.1.

PROCESS ANALYSIS

Why readers read process analyses

Readers of process analyses want to know *how* and *why* the processes occur, so a writer's first order of business is to divide the process into its parts or principles. Usually, those parts occur in chronological order. Moreover, the first part or step of the process usually leads to the second step and often creates the conditions that allow that second step to occur. Then, the second step leads to the third step, and so on.

This chronological development of dependent steps is particularly noticeable to writers who analyze mechanical processes (operation of a piston-driven engine), geological processes (formation of icebergs), or chemical processes (chemical hydration within concrete). Even electronic processes, which occur at blinding speed, can be understood as a series of causative actions: it's possible to know the exact order, duration, and effect caused by each sub-process within an electronic circuit.

The electronic example raises another very interesting point about most processes. They depend on the "conditions" that cause them. The process of an electronic circuit's operation depends on the design of the circuit itself. In a less confining way, perhaps, the process by which a road is washed by heavy spring run-off depends on the physical conditions of water volumes, soil composition, and terrain.

As Table 9.1 illustrates, a process analysis must include enough detail to enable readers to follow the process step by step. That level of detail depends on the reader's needs. For example, a back-country skier who wants to avoid avalanches will be satisfied with a basic description of the forces and conditions that affect the slab-avalanche process. However, a civil engineer studying avalanches will need to know much more about snow compaction forces, changes in crystalline structures, and the forces that cause snow layers to shear apart.

Because it emphasizes the process itself, rather than the reader's role, process analysis is written in the third person. Indeed, all aspects of a process analysis resemble a technical essay:

- It uses standard paragraphs, most of which use chronological patterns.
- It employs serious, reflective phrasing.
- It employs precise, accurate vocabulary.
- It presents a formal appearance, usually with headings, formal illustration format, and formal documentation of sources.

To help the reader fully understand the process, the writer must carefully plan the structure of a process analysis. The writer's first step is to analyze the process itself, at the level of the reader's interests and needs. This analysis will help the writer produce a detailed outline.

For an idea of the components of such an outline, see the structure for process analysis summarized in Table 9.1.

The following process analysis has used a structure like the one outlined in Table 9.1. The document's writer, Bill Kelly, belongs to an environmental group studying the problems of acid rain in its southern Ontario community. To gain community support, the environmentalists must educate citizens about the problem. Bill's group is publishing and mailing a series of brochures. The first brochure explains how acid rain is formed.

Here is Bill's audience/purpose profile for the document.

A Process Analysis for Non-technical Readers

AUDIENCE/PURPOSE PROFILE. My audience will consist of general readers. Some already will be interested in the problem; others will have no awareness (or interest). Therefore, I'll keep my explanation at the lowest level of technicality (no chemical formulas, equations). But my explanation needs to be vivid enough to appeal to less aware or less interested readers. I'll use visuals to create interest and to illustrate simply. To give an explanation thorough enough for broad understanding, I'll divide the process into three chronological steps: how acid rain develops, spreads, and destroys.

This is the document resulting from Bill's analysis of both his subject and his audience.

Table 9.1 Process Analysis and Instructions Compared

Process Analysis Compared to Instructions

Purpose	Helps the reader understand how and why the process occurs
Audience	Aimed at interested persons who want to understand how something works or how it happens
Content	Explanations are essential, in addition to straight chronological description of the stages of the process. Description of the physical environment is part of some descriptions. Illustrations are often very useful. Descriptions are specific and detailed.
Structure	*General idea (lead-in)* ◆ names and defines process and its special features ◆ where, when, why, how often the process occurs ◆ where necessary, gives background theory ◆ lists the main stages or actions of the process *Individual stages (chronological)* ◆ each stage is described in detail and related to the stages that precede and follow; the importance of particular stages is noted ◆ each stage includes applicable measurements of time, distance, direction, density, volume, etc. *Conclusion (lead out to practical considerations)* ◆ where applicable, comments about time needed for overall process, cost, process applications, special problems, immediate and long-term results
Voice/Mood	Uses indicative mood: e.g., "the next stage takes three hours. . ." Stays detached, in third person: e.g., "the skier's first move. . ." Active or passive voice: e.g., "the signal travels. . ." or "the signal is next transferred to the filtering stage. . ."
Appearance and Style	Usually looks formal (headings, paragraphs, standard spacing) Reads like a "serious" discussion Uses a mixture of sentence types and lengths Uses precise, accurate vocabulary

Table 9.1 Process Analysis and Instructions Compared

Instructions Compared to Process Analysis

Helps the reader perform the process that is described	**Purpose**
Aimed at persons who need to complete a task or want to improve performance	**Audience**
Provides no more detail than is necessary (**Note:** Analysis and explanations *may* be necessary.) Features a very careful *chronological listing of steps* Very carefully describes *exact steps* to take Includes *frequent visual illustration*	**Content**
Introduction ◆ concisely explains the overall actions to be performed ◆ in some cases, provides background information and, where necessary, lists materials/equipment to be used or the conditions necessary for successful action ◆ in some cases, cautions reader about safety factors *Chronological list of steps* (plus necessary explanations) ◆ where appropriate, combines groups of steps together under subheadings: e.g., "Setting the Timer," "Selecting Programs" ◆ shows the interrelations and sequence of actions by using numbered steps and sequence transitions: e.g., "next," "then," "10 minutes later," "after the liquid cools" ◆ gives reasons for performing certain actions in a specific way or at a specific time ◆ uses illustrations to show the *results* of performed actions, not just the techniques for performing the actions *Brief practical conclusion* ◆ reminds the reader of expected results/performance times	**Structure**
Uses imperative mood: e.g., "Set the timer by choosing..." Directly addresses reader: e.g., "Your first task will be to..." Uses active voice: e.g., "Choose one of three settings..."	**Voice/Mood**
Uses some paragraphs, but mostly uses numbered point form Looks "user friendly" Writes in phrases or short sentences Features direct, straightforward vocabulary Employs lots of open space	**Appearance and Style**

How Acid Rain Develops, Spreads, and Destroys

INTRODUCTION

Definition

Acid rain is environmentally damaging rainfall that occurs after fossil fuels burn, releasing nitrogen and sulphur oxides into the atmosphere. Acid rain, simply stated, increases the acidity level of waterways because these nitrogen and sulphur oxides combine with the air's normal moisture. The resulting rainfall is far more acidic than normal rainfall. Acid rain is a silent threat because its effects, although slow, are cumulative. This analysis explains the cause, the distribution cycle, and the effects of acid rain.

Purpose

Brief description of the process

Most research shows that power plants burning oil or coal are the primary cause of acid rain. The burnt fuel is not completely expended, and some residue enters the atmosphere. Although this residue contains several potentially toxic elements, sulphur oxide and, to a lesser extent, nitrogen oxide are the major problem, because they are transformed when they combine with moisture. This chemical reaction forms sulphur dioxide and nitric acid, which then rain down to earth.

Preview of stages

The major steps explained here are (1) how acid rain develops, (2) how acid rain spreads, and (3) how acid rain destroys.

THE PROCESS

First stage

How Acid Rain Develops Once fossil fuels have been burned, their usefulness is over. Unfortunately, it is here that the acid rain problem begins.

Fossil fuels contain a number of elements that are released during combustion. Two of these, sulphur oxide and nitrogen oxide, combine with normal moisture to produce sulphuric acid and nitric acid. (Figure 1 illustrates how acid rain develops.) The released gases undergo a chemical change as they combine with atmospheric ozone and water vapour. The resulting rain or snowfall is more acid than normal precipitation.

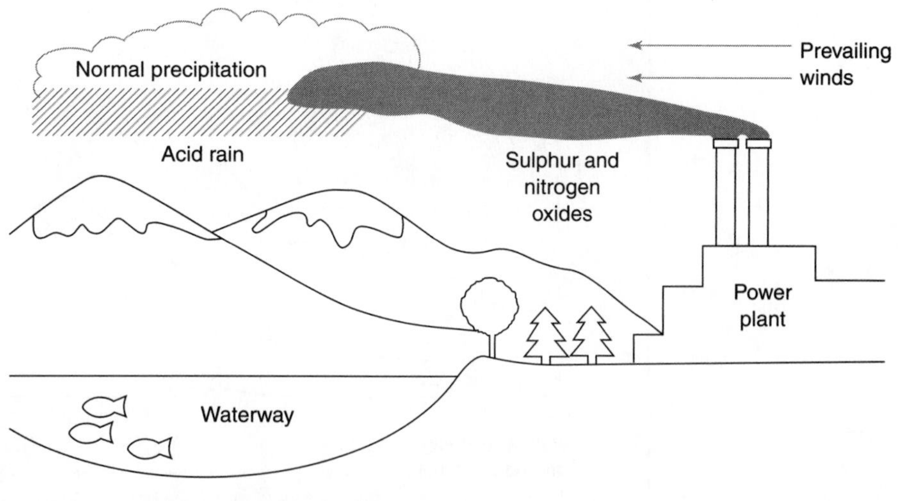

FIGURE 1 How Acid Rain Develops

Definition

Acid level is measured by pH readings. The pH scale runs from 0 through 14—a pH of 7 is considered neutral. (Distilled water has a pH of 7.) Numbers above 7 indicate increasing degrees of alkalinity. (Household ammonia has a pH of 11.) Numbers below 7 indicate increasing acidity. Movement in either direction on the pH scale, however, means multiplying by 10. Lemon juice, which has a pH value of 2, is 10 times more acidic than apples, which have a pH of 3, and is 1000 times more acidic than carrots, which have a pH of 5.

Because of carbon dioxide (an acid substance) normally present in air, unaffected rainfall has a pH of 5.6. At this time, the pH of precipitation in the northeastern United States and Canada is between 4.5 and 4. In Massachusetts, rain and snowfall have an average pH reading of 4.1. A pH reading below 5 is considered to be abnormally acidic, and therefore a threat to aquatic populations.

Second stage

How Acid Rain Spreads Although it might seem that areas containing power plants would be most severely affected, acid rain can in fact travel thousands of kilometres from its source. Stack gases escape and drift with the wind currents. The sulphur and nitrogen oxides are thus able to travel great distances before they return to earth as acid rain.

For an average of two to five days after emission, the gases follow the prevailing winds far from the point of origin. Estimates show that about 50 percent of the acid rain that affects Canada originates in the United States; at the same time, 15 to 25 percent of the U.S. acid rain problem originates in Canada.

The tendency of stack gases to drift makes acid rain a widespread menace. More than 200 lakes in the Adirondacks, hundreds of kilometres from any industrial centre, are unable to support life because their water has become so acidic.

Third stage

How Acid Rain Destroys Acid rain causes damage wherever it falls. It erodes various types of building rock such as limestone, marble, and mortar, which are gradually eaten away by the constant bathing in acid. Damage to buildings, houses, monuments, statues, and cars is widespread. Some priceless monuments and carvings already have been destroyed, and even trees of some varieties are dying in large numbers.

Sub-stage

More important, however, is acid rain damage to waterways in the affected areas. (Figure 2 illustrates how a typical waterway is infiltrated.)

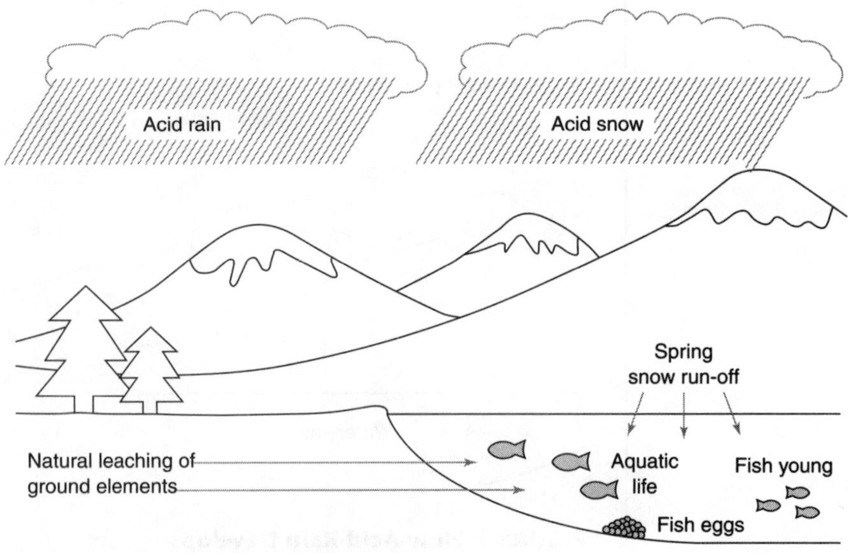

FIGURE 2 How Acid Rain Destroys

Because of its high acidity, acid rain dramatically lowers the pH in lakes and streams. Although its effect is not immediate, acid rain eventually can make a waterway so acidic it dies. In areas with natural acid-buffering elements such as limestone, the dilute acid has less effect. The northeastern United States and Canada, however, lack this natural protection, and so are continually vulnerable.

The pH level in an affected waterway drops so low that some species cease to reproduce. In fact, a pH level of 5.1 to 5.4 means that fisheries are threatened; once a waterway reaches a pH level of 4.5, no fish reproduction occurs. Because each creature is part of the overall food chain, loss of one element in the chain disrupts the whole cycle.

In the northeastern United States and Canada, the acidity problem is compounded by the run-off from acid snow. During the cold winter months, acid snow sits with little melting, so that by spring thaw, the acid released is greatly concentrated. Aluminum and other heavy metals normally present in soil are also released by acid rain and run-off. These toxic substances leach into waterways in heavy concentrations, affecting fish in all stages of development.

SUMMARY

One complete cycle

Acid rain develops from nitrogen and sulphur oxides emitted by industrial and power plants burning fossil fuels. In the atmosphere, these oxides combine with ozone and water to form acid rain: precipitation with a lower-than-average pH. This acid precipitation returns to earth many kilometres from its source, severely damaging waterways that lack natural buffering agents. The northeastern United States and Canada are the most severely affected areas in North America.

ELEMENTS OF INSTRUCTIONS

Why readers need to read instructions

As consumers, we need instructions to learn how to operate everything from automobiles to VCRs. But we also seek instruction on topics that we know reasonably well. For instance, we may read instructional magazine articles on how to ski steep slopes or how to hit a particular golf shot or how to perform an aerobics sequence, even though we might already be able to perform the activity. Why? To perform the activity better!

Almost anyone with a responsible job writes and reads instructions. The new employee uses instructions for operating office equipment or industrial machinery; the employee going on vacation writes instructions for the replacement person. The person who buys a computer reads the manuals (or documentation) for instructions on connecting a printer or running a program.

Instructions carry profound ethical and legal implications. Each year, as many as 10 percent of workers are injured on the job (Clement 149). Countless injuries also result from misuse of consumer products such as power tools and car jacks—misuse often caused by defective instructions.

A reader injured because of inaccurate, incomplete, or misleading instructions can sue the writer. Courts have ruled that a writing defect in product support literature carries liability, as would a design or manufacturing defect in the product itself (Girill, *Technical Communication and Law* 37). Some legal experts argue that writing defects carry even greater liability than product defects because they are more easily demonstrated to a non-technical jury (Bedford and Stearns 128).

To ensure that your own instructions meet professional and legal requirements for accuracy, completeness, and clarity, observe the following guidelines.

ON THE JOB...

The Value of Instructions

"You may have the greatest software on the planet, but if your on-screen help and user guides are not clear, then your customers will struggle with the software. They'll call your help desk and they'll complain. I help software companies to reduce their customer support costs. How? By writing clear instructions for their software. The result is that customers don't call the help desk as often as they used to. There's a case study on ***www.techscribe.co.uk/techw/cssdl.htm....***"

—Mike Unwalla, principal writer, TechScribe

Clear and Limiting Title

Make your title promise exactly what your instructions deliver—no more and no less. The title "Instructions for Cleaning the Drive Head of a Laptop Computer" tells readers what to expect: instructions for a specific procedure on a selected part. But the title "The Laptop Computer" gives no forecast. A reader of a document so titled might think the document contains a history of the laptop, or a description of each part, or a wide range of related information.

Informed Content

Make sure that you know exactly what you're talking about. Ignorance on your part makes you no less liable for instructions that are faulty or inaccurate:

Never count on ignorance as an excuse

> If the author of [a car repair] manual had no experience with cars, yet provided faulty instructions on the repair of the car's brakes, the home mechanic who was injured when the brakes failed may recover [damages] from the author. (Walter and Marsteller 165)

Do not write instructions unless you know the procedure in detail and unless you actually have performed it.

Visuals

In addition to showing what to do, instructional visuals attract the attention of today's graphics-oriented readers and help keep words to a minimum. Instructions also often include a persuasive dimension: to motivate interest, commitment, or action.

Types of visuals especially suited to instructions include icons, representational and schematic diagrams, flow charts, photographs, and prose tables.

Illustrate any step that might be difficult for readers to visualize. Show the same angle of vision the reader will have when doing the activity or using the equipment—and name the angle (*side view, top view*) if you think readers will have trouble figuring it out for themselves.

The less specialized your audience, the more visuals they are likely to need. But do not illustrate any action simple enough for readers to visualize on their own, such as "Press ENTER" for any user familiar with a keyboard.

Figure 9.1 depicts an array of visuals and their specific instructional functions. Virtually each of these visuals is easily constructed and some could be further

How to Locate Something

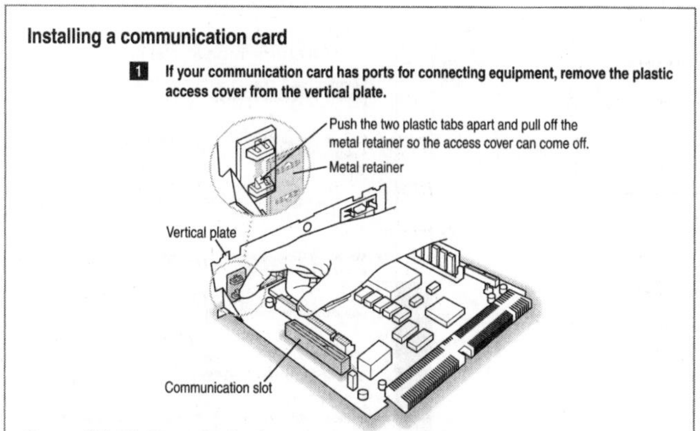

Source: © Apple Computer, Inc.*

How to Operate Something

Source: SuperStock.

How to Handle Something

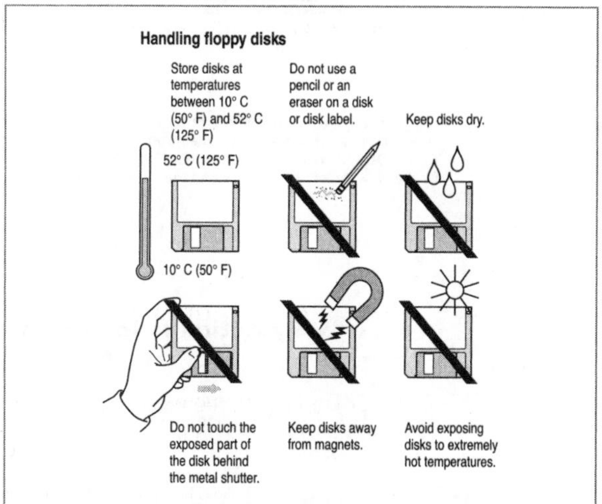

Adapted: © Apple Computer, Inc.*

How to Assemble Something

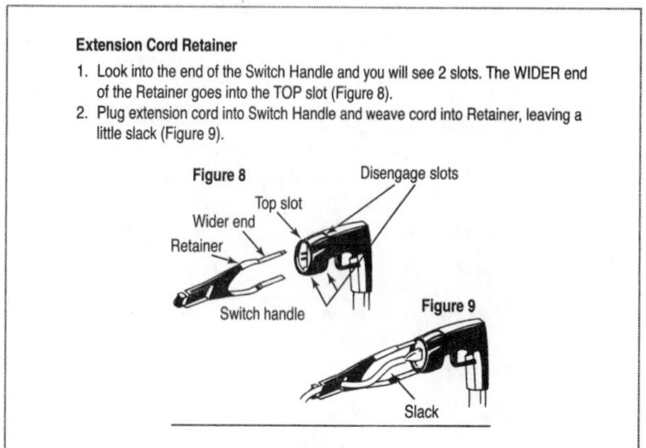

Source: Courtesy of Black & Decker® (U.S.), Inc.

How to Position Something

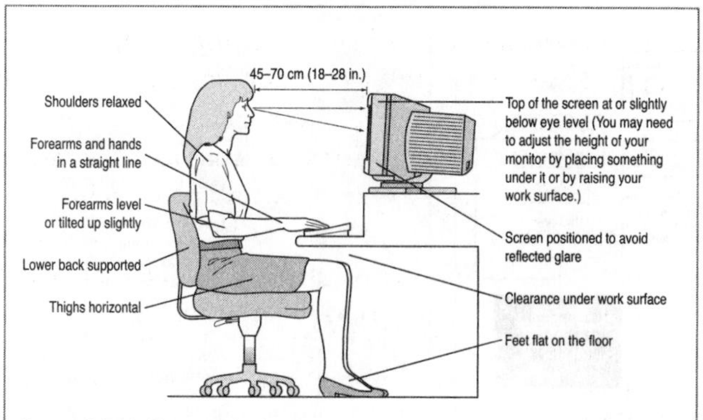

Source: © Apple Computer, Inc.*

How to Avoid Damage or Injury

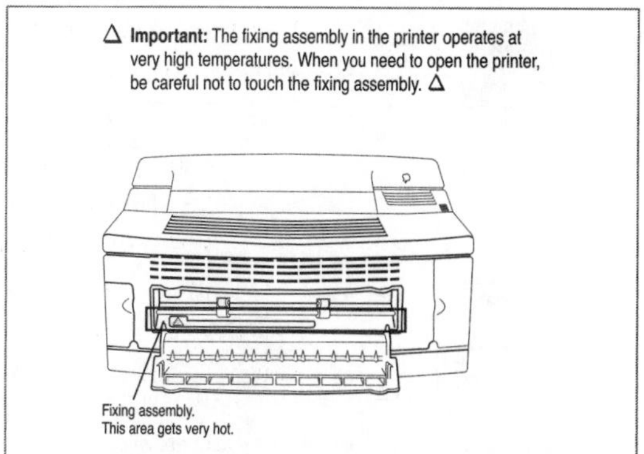

Source: © Apple Computer, Inc.*

Figure 9.1 Common Types of Instructional Visuals and Their Functions

*Illustrations © Apple Computer, Inc. 1993. Used with permission. Apple, the Apple logo, and Power Macintosh are registered trademarks™ of Apple Computer, Inc. All rights reserved. All sources Apple unless otherwise indicated.

How to Diagnose and Solve Problems

GENERAL TROUBLESHOOTING CHART

If the amplifier is otherwise operating satisfactorily the more common causes of trouble may generally be attributed to the following:

1. Incorrect connections or loose terminal contacts. Check the speakers, record player, tape deck, antenna and line cord.
2. Improper operation. Before operating any audio component, be sure to read the instructions.
3. Improper location of audio components. The proper positioning of components, such as speakers and turntable, is vital to stereo.
4. Defective audio components.

Following are some other common causes of mal-function and what to do about them.If the amplifier is

PROGRAM	SYMPTOM	PROBABLE CAUSE	WHAT TO DO
AM, FM or MPX reception	a. Constant or intermit-tent noise heard at certain times or in a certain area	* Discharge or oscillation caused by electrical appli-ances, such as fluorescent lamps, TV sets, D.C. mo-tors, rectifier and oscillator * Natural phenomena, such as atmospherics, static, and thunderbolt * Insufficient antenna input due to reinforced concrete walls or long distance from the station * Wave interterence from other electrical appliances	* Attach a noise limiter to the elec-trical appliance that causes the noise, or attach it to the power source of the amplifier. * Install an outdoor antenna and ground the amplifier to raise the signal-to-noise ratio. * Reverse the power cord plug-receptacle connections. * If the noise occurs at a certain frequency. attach a wave trap to the ANT. input. * Place the set away from other electrical appliances.

Source: Courtesy of Sansui Electronic Co. Ltd.

How to Identify Safe or Acceptable

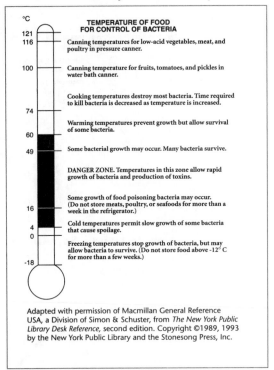

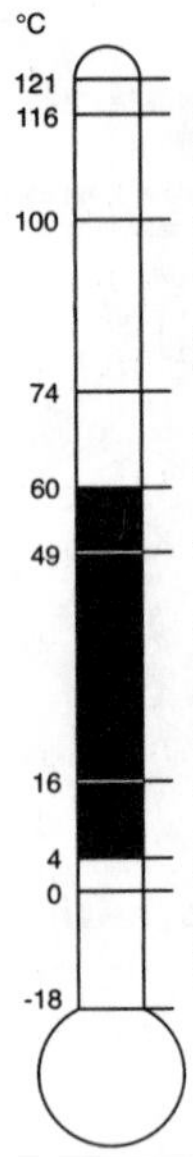

Adapted with permission of Macmillan General Reference USA, a Division of Simon & Schuster, from *The New York Public Library Desk Reference,* second edition. Copyright ©1989, 1993 by the New York Public Library and the Stonesong Press, Inc.

How to Proceed Systematically

CHECK ALL WALL OUTLETS AND SWITCHES

- Do all unused outlets have safety covers placed in receptacle openings? — Shock hazard can result if children insert objects into outlets.
  - ☐ Yes ☐ No → Purchase inexpensive safety covers for all unused outlets.
- Are all outlets and switches working properly? — Improperly operating outlets or switches indicate an unsafe wiring condition may exist.
  - ☐ Yes ☐ No → Have an electrician check them.
- Are all outlets and switches cool to the touch? — Unusually warm outlet or switch may indicate an unsafe wiring condition exists.
  - ☐ Yes ☐ No → Unplug any cord or stop using the switch and have an electrician check.
- Do electrical plugs fit snugly into all outlets? — Loose-fitting plugs can cause overheating.
  - ☐ Yes ☐ No → Have the outlet replaced.

Source: U.S. Consumer Product Safety Commission

Why Action Is Important

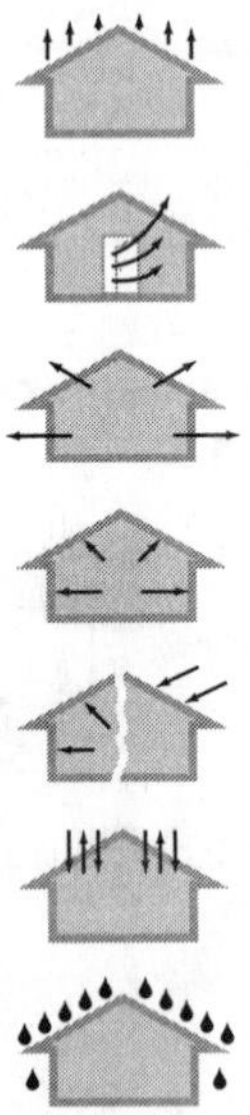

Hidden air leaks can account for up to 50 percent of a typical home's heat loss.

Total area of all air leaks can add up to 0.9 to 1.9 square metres (20 square feet); that's like leaving a door open all winter.

Insulation alone does not seal air leaks.

Sealing air leaks helps insulation do its job.

Insulation not only keeps heat inside the house in winter but also keeps heat out in the summer.

The greatest heat loss or gain occurs through the attic. Sealing attic air leaks and installing attic insulation reduces energy costs and increases comfort.

Insufficient attic ventilation can cause moisture buildup that ruins attic insulation and rots wood.

Adapted with permission of Mass-Save, Inc., Waltham, MA. Copyright ©1993.

How to Make the Right Decisions

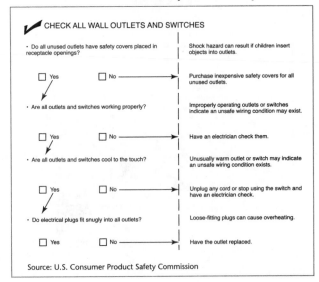

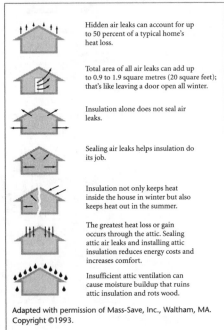

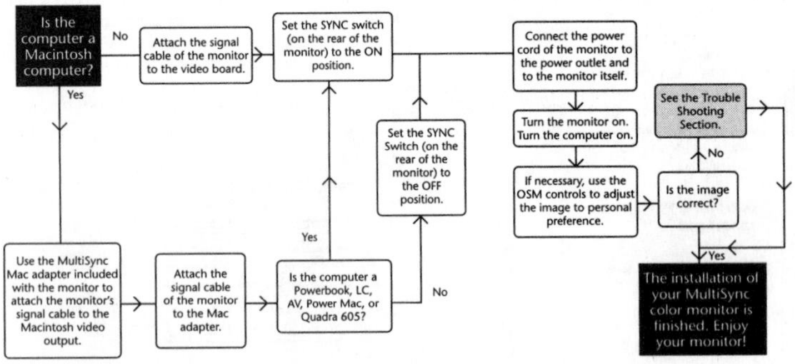

Adapted from Flow chart: "Installation," p.12 of *NEC Enterprise Series MultiSync® XE User's Manual.* Copyright ©1995 NEC Technologies, Inc. Reprinted with permission.

Figure 9.1 Common Types of Instructional Visuals and Their Functions *(Continued)*

*Illustrations © Apple Computer, Inc. 1993. Used with permission. Apple, the Apple logo, and Power Macintosh are registered trademarks™ of Apple Computer, Inc. All rights reserved. All sources Apple unless otherwise indicated.

enhanced, depending on your production budget and graphics capability. Writers and editors often provide an *art brief* and a rough sketch describing the visual and its purpose for the graphic designer or art department.

Appropriate Level of Technicality

Unless you know your readers have the relevant background and skills, write for general readers, and do three things:

1. Give them enough background to understand why they need your instructions.
2. Give them enough detail to understand *what* to do.
3. Give them enough examples to visualize the procedure clearly.

Background Information. Begin by explaining the purpose of the procedure.

Tell readers why they are doing this

> You might easily lose information stored on a floppy disk if:
>
> 1. The disk is damaged by direct sunlight, extreme temperature, or moisture.
> 2. The disk is erased by a faulty disk drive, a power surge, or a user error.
> 3. The stored information is scrambled by a nearby magnet (telephone, computer terminal, or the like).
>
> Always make a back-up copy of any important material.

Also, state your assumptions about your reader's level of technical understanding.

Tell them what they should know already

> To follow these instructions, you should be able to identify these parts of a Macintosh system: computer, monitor, keyboard, mouse, disk drive, and a 3.5-inch floppy disk.

Define any specialized terms that appear in your instructions.

Tell them what each key term means

> *Initialize:* Before you can store or retrieve information on a disk, you must initialize the blank disk (unless you are using pre-formatted disks). Initializing creates a format the computer can understand—a directory of specific memory spaces (like post office boxes) on the disk, where you can store and retrieve information as needed.

When your reader understands *what* and *why*, you are ready to explain *how* the reader can carry out the procedure.

Adequate Detail. Explain the procedure in enough detail for readers to know exactly what to do. Vague instructions result from the writer's failure to consider the readers' needs, as in these unclear instructions for giving first aid to an electrical shock victim:

> 1. Check vital signs.
> 2. Establish an airway.
> 3. Administer external cardiac massage as needed.
> 4. Ventilate, if cyanosed.
> 5. Treat for shock.

These instructions might be clear to medical experts, but not to general readers. Not only are the details inadequate, but also terms such as *vital signs* and *cyanosed* are too technical for laypeople. Such instructions posted for workers in a high-voltage area would be useless. The instructions need illustrations and explanations, as in the illustrations on the following three pages.

The following instruction for Step 2, establishing an airway, provides another example of the value of providing illustrations and explanations:

Adequate detail for general readers

Step 2: While you maintain the head in a backward tilt position, place your cheek and ear close to the victim's mouth and nose. Look for the chest to rise and fall while you listen and feel for breathing. Check for about 5 seconds.

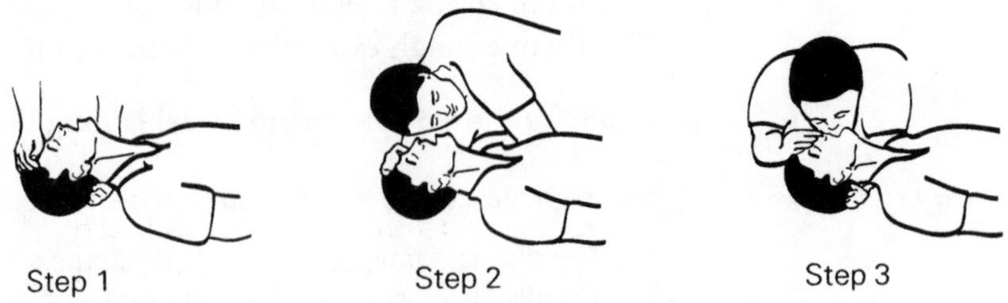

Source: Reprinted with permission from *New York Public Library Desk Reference*, 3rd ed., copyright © 1998, 1993, 1989 by The New York Public Library and the Stonesong Press, Inc.

It's easy to overestimate what people already know, especially when the procedure is almost automatic for you. (Think about when a relative or friend was teaching you to drive a car, or perhaps you tried to teach someone else.) Always assume the reader knows less than you. A colleague will know at least a little less; a layperson will know a good deal less—maybe nothing—about this procedure.

Exactly how much information is enough? These suggestions can help you find an answer:

How to provide adequate detail

- Give everything readers need, so the instructions can stand alone.
- Give only what readers need. Don't tell them how to build a computer when they need to know only how to copy a disk.
- Instead of focusing on the *product* ("How does it work?"), focus on the *task* ("How do I use it?" or "How do I do it?") (Grice, "Focus" 132).
- Omit steps (*"Seat yourself at the computer"*) obvious to readers.
- Adjust the information rate ("the amount of information presented in a given page," Meyer 17) to readers' background and the difficulty of the task. For complex or sensitive steps, slow the information rate. Don't make readers do too much too fast.
- Reinforce the prose with visuals. Don't be afraid to repeat information if it saves readers from flipping pages.
- When writing instructions for consumer products, assume "a barely literate reader" (Clement 151). Simplify.
- Recognize the persuasive dimension of the instructions. You may need to persuade readers that this procedure is necessary or beneficial, or that they can complete this procedure with relative ease and competence.

Examples. Procedures require specific examples (how to load a program, how to order a part), to help readers follow the steps correctly.

Use plenty of examples

To load your program, key this command:

```
Load "Style Editor"
```

Then press ENTER.

Like visuals, examples *show* readers what to do. Examples in fact often appear as visuals.

The examples in Figure 9.1, illustrate these important components of effective instruction:

1. Begin each instruction with an action verb.
2. Let the visual repeat, restate, or reinforce the prose.
3. Place the visual close to the step.

Logically Ordered Steps

Instructions not only divide the procedure into steps; they also guide users through the steps in *chronological order.* They organize the facts and explanations in ways that make sense to readers.

Show how steps are connected

You can splice two wires to make an electrical connection only when you have removed the insulation. To remove the insulation, you will need. . .

Try to keep all information for one step close together.

Warnings, Cautions, and Notes

Here are the only items that should interrupt the steps in a set of instructions (Van Pelt 3):

- A *note* clarifies a point, emphasizes vital information, or describes options or alternatives.

Note: The computer will not initialize a disk that is scratched or imperfect. If your blank disk is rejected, try a new disk.

- A *caution* prevents possible mistakes that could result in injury or equipment damage:

Caution: A momentary electrical surge or power failure will erase the contents of internal memory. To avoid losing your work, every few minutes save on disk what you have just keyed into the computer.

- A *warning* alerts users against potential hazards to life or limb:

Warning: To prevent electrical shock, always disconnect your printer from its power source before cleaning internal parts.

- A *danger* notice identifies an immediate hazard to life or limb:

  Danger: The red canister contains **DEADLY** radioactive material. **Do not break the safety seal** under any circumstances.

In addition to prose warnings, attract readers' attention and help them identify hazards by using symbols or icons such as the following (Bedford and Stearns 128):

Warning **Do not enter** **Radioactivity** **Fire danger**

Preview the warnings, cautions, and notes in your introduction, and place them, *clearly highlighted*, immediately before the respective steps.

NOTE *A recent study found that product users were six times more likely to comply with warnings included in the product usage directions than with a separate warning label ("Notes" 72).*

Use notes, warnings, and cautions only when needed; overuse will dull their effect, and readers may overlook their importance.

Appropriate Words, Sentences, and Paragraphs

Of all communications, instructions have the strictest requirements for clarity, because they lead to *immediate action.* Readers are impatient and often will not read the entire instructions before plunging into the first step. Poorly phrased and misleading instructions can be disastrous.

Like descriptions, instructions name parts, locations and positions, and state exact measurements, weights, and dimensions. Instructions also require your strict attention to phrasing, sentence structure, and paragraph structure.

Transitions to Mark Time and Sequence. Transitional words provide a bridge between related ideas. Some transitions (*in addition*, *next*, *meanwhile*, *finally*, *10 minutes later*, *the next day*, *before*) mark time and sequence. They help readers understand the step-by-step process.

Carefully Shaped Paragraphs and Sentences. Much of the introductory and explanatory material in instructions takes the form of standard prose paragraphs, with enough sentence variety to keep readers interested. But the steps themselves have unique paragraph and sentence requirements. Unless the procedure consists of simple steps, separate the steps by using a numbered list—one step for one activity. If the activity is especially complicated, use a new line (not indented) to begin each sentence in the step.

Instructions ordinarily employ short sentences. But brief is not always best, especially when readers have to fill in the information gaps. Never telegraph your message by omitting articles (*a*, *an*, *the*).

Unlike other documents, instructions call for very little sentence variety. Use similar structures ("Do this. Then do that") to avoid confusing readers. If a single step covers two related actions, follow the sequence of required actions:

Logical sequence	Insert the disk in the drive before switching on the computer.

Make your explanations easy to follow by using a familiar-to-unfamiliar sequence:

Difficult	You must initialize a blank disk before you can store information on it.

This sentence is clearer if the familiar material comes first:

Easier	Before you can store information on a blank disk, you must initialize the disk.

Shape every sentence and every paragraph for the reader's access.

Active Voice and Imperative Mood. Use the active voice and imperative mood ("Insert the disk") to address the reader directly. Otherwise, your instructions can lose authority ("You should insert the disk") or become ambiguous ("The disk is inserted"). In the ambiguous example, we can't tell if the disk is to be inserted or if it already has been inserted.

Indirect or confusing	The user keys in his or her access code. You should key in your access code. It is important to key in the access code. The access code is keyed in.
Direct and clear	Key in your access code.

The imperative makes instructions more definite and easier to understand because the action verb—the crucial word that identifies the next action—comes first. Instead of burying your verb in mid-sentence, *begin* with an action verb (*raise, connect, wash, insert, open*) to give readers an immediate signal.

Affirmative Phrasing. Research shows that readers respond more quickly and efficiently to instructions phrased affirmatively rather than negatively (Spyridakis and Wenger 205).

Weaker	Verify that your disk is not contaminated with dust.
Stronger	Examine your disk for dust contamination.

Parallel Phrasing. Like any items in a series, steps should use identical grammatical form. Parallelism is important in all writing but especially in instructions, because repeating those forms emphasizes the step-by-step organization of the instructions.

Not parallel

To log on to the VAX 950, follow these steps:
1. Switch the terminal to "on."
2. The CONTROL key and C key are pressed simultaneously.
3. Keying LOGON, and pressing the ESCAPE key.
4. Key your user number, and press the ESCAPE key.

Parallel

To log on to the VAX 950, follow these steps:
1. Switch the terminal to "on."
2. Press the CONTROL key and C key simultaneously.
3. Key LOGON, and press the ESCAPE key.
4. Key your user number, and press the ESCAPE key.

Parallelism increases readability and lends continuity to the instructions.

Effective Page Design

Instructions rarely get undivided attention. The reader usually does two things more or less at once: interpreting the instructions and performing the task. Effective instructional design is *accessible* and *inviting*. An effective design conveys the sense that the task is within a qualified user's range of abilities.

Here are suggestions for designing instructions that help users find, recognize, and remember what they need:

How to design your instructions

- Use informative headings that tell readers what to expect, that emphasize what is most important, and that serve as an aid to navigation. A heading such as "How to Initialize Your Blank Disk" is more informative than "Disk Initializing." Also, the second version sounds less like a person speaking and more like a robot!
- Arrange all steps in a numbered list.
- Single-space within steps and double-space between, to separate steps visually. (Use the Spacing Before and After Paragraph feature of your word-processing program for maximum editing flexibility.)
- Double-space to signal a new paragraph, instead of indenting.
- Use white space and highlighting to separate discussion from step.

Set off your discussion on a separate line (like this), indented or highlighted or both. You can highlight with underlining, capitals, dashes, parentheses, and asterisks. Alternatively, you can use **boldface**, *italics*, varying type sizes, and varying typefaces.

- Set off warnings, cautions, and notes in ruled boxes or use highlighting and plenty of white space.
- Keep the visual and the step close together. If room allows, place the visual right beside the step; if not, right after the step. Set off the visual with plenty of white space.
- Strive for format variety that is appealing but not overwhelming or inconsistent. Readers can be overwhelmed by a page with excessive or inconsistent graphic patterns.

The more accessible and inviting the design, the more likely your readers are to follow the instructions. Don't be afraid to experiment until you find a design that works. Then, as with all aspects of effective written instructions, test the usability of your document.

A SAMPLE SET OF INSTRUCTIONS

The instructions for *doing something* (felling a tree) in Figure 9.2 illustrate aspects of our earlier advice. They will appear in a brochure for forestry students about to begin summer jobs with a forestry service.

Instructions for Semi-technical Readers

AUDIENCE/PURPOSE PROFILE. I'm writing these instructions for partially informed readers who know how to use chainsaws, axes, and wedges but who are approaching this dangerous procedure for the first time. Therefore, I'll include no visuals of cutting equipment (chainsaws and so on) because the audience already knows what these items look like. I can omit basic information (such as what happens when a tree binds a chainsaw) because the audience already has this knowledge. Likewise, these readers need no definition of general forestry terms such as *culling* and *thinning*, but they *do* need definitions of terms that relate specifically to tree felling (*undercut, holding wood*, and so on).

To ensure clarity, I will illustrate the final three steps with visuals. The conclusion, for these readers, will be short and to the point—a simple summary of major steps with emphasis on safety.

TUTORIALS

Tutorials emphasize task *learning*, not just performance

Tutorials present instructions placed within a given context and accompanied by appropriate explanations, illustrations, and self-tests. People use instructions primarily to perform tasks or to perform them better. Tutorials not only show how to get things done; they place a greater emphasis on learning the task. So tutorials explain most steps or at least comment on them.

Tutorials employ a distinctive structure

The educational purpose is reflected in the structure of most tutorials—full introductions, a modular breakdown, summaries, and post-tests. Glen Coulthard the lead author and series editor of the *Advantage Series for Computer Education, 2004–2007*, stresses that "each chapter or 'module' in our manuals is conceived as a tutorial. Each module opens with learning objectives and concludes with an assessment mechanism. We provide more than 'how-to' instructions; we educate the reader."

The order in which the modules are presented depends on the topic area:

- Many tutorials use a *sequential* breakdown that mirrors the order in which tasks would be completed. Learn2's tutorial for Group Wise 5.5 Messaging, for example, starts with basics such as "Exploring the toolbar" and "Using the mail functions," before teaching 32 other sequential tasks and concluding with "Utilizing dial sender" and "Converting other conversation place features" (**www.tutorials.com**).
- Another Learn2 online tutorial, Defensive Driving, uses a *lateral topical breakdown*. After an introduction and pre-test, five sessions with titles such as

1

INSTRUCTIONS FOR FELLING A TREE

INTRODUCTION

Forestry Service personnel fell (cut down) trees to cull or thin a forested plot, to eliminate the hazard of dead trees standing near power lines, to clear an area for construction, and the like.

These instructions explain how to remove sizable trees for personnel who know how to use a chainsaw, axe, and wedge safely.

When you set out to fell a tree, expect to spend most of your time planning the operation and preparing the area around the tree. To fell the tree, you will make two chainsaw cuts, severing the stem from the stump. Depending on the direction of the cuts, the weather, and the terrain, the severed tree will fall into a predetermined clearing.

> **WARNING:** Although these instructions cover the basic procedure, felling is very dangerous. Trees, felling equipment, and terrain vary greatly. Even professionals sometimes are killed or injured because of judgment errors or misuse of tools.
>
> Your main concern is safety. Be sure to have an expert demonstrate this procedure before you try it. Also, pay attention to warnings in steps 1 and 4.

To fell sizable trees, you will need this equipment:

—a 3 to 5 horsepower chainsaw with a 51 cm (20-inch) blade
—a single-blade splitting axe
—two or more 31 cm (12-inch) steel wedges

The major steps in felling a tree are (1) choosing the lay, (2) providing an escape path, (3) making the undercut, and (4) making the backcut.

REQUIRED STEPS

1. *How to Choose the Lay*

   The "lay" is where you want the tree to fall. On level ground in an open field, which way you direct the fall makes little difference. But such ideal conditions are rare.

   Consider ground obstacles and topography, surrounding trees, and the condition of the tree to be felled. Plan your escape path and the location of your cuts depending on surrounding houses, electrical wires, and trees. Then follow these steps:

   a. Make sure the tree is still alive.

Figure 9.2 A Set of Instructions

(continued)

b. Determine the direction and amount of lean.

> **WARNING:** If the tree is dead and leaning substantially, do not try to fell it without professional help. Many dead, leaning trees have a tendency to split along their length, causing a massive slab to fall spontaneously.

c. Find an opening into which the tree can fall in the direction of lean or as close to the direction of lean as possible.

Because most trees lean downhill, try to direct the fall downhill. If the tree leans slightly away from your desired direction, use wedges to direct the fall.

2. *How to Provide an Escape Path*
Falling trees are unpredictable. Avoid injury by planning a definite escape path. Follow these steps:

a. Locate the path in the direction opposite of the fall (Figure 1).

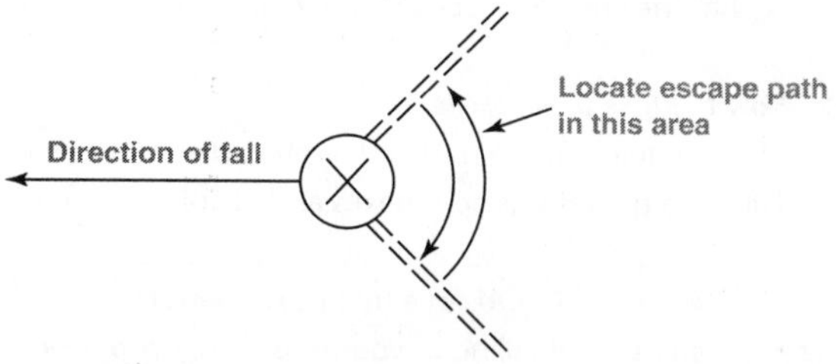

FIGURE 1 Escape-path Location

b. Clear a path 70 cm (2 feet) wide extending beyond where the top of the tree could land.

3. *How to Make the Undercut*
The undercut is a triangular slab of wood cut from the trunk on the side toward which you want the tree to fall. Follow these steps:

a. Start the chainsaw.

b. Holding the saw with blade parallel to the ground, make a first cut 70 to 92 cm (2 to 3 feet) above ground. Cut horizontally, to no more than $\frac{1}{3}$ the tree's diameter (Figure 2).

Figure 9.2 A Set of Instructions *(continued)*

3

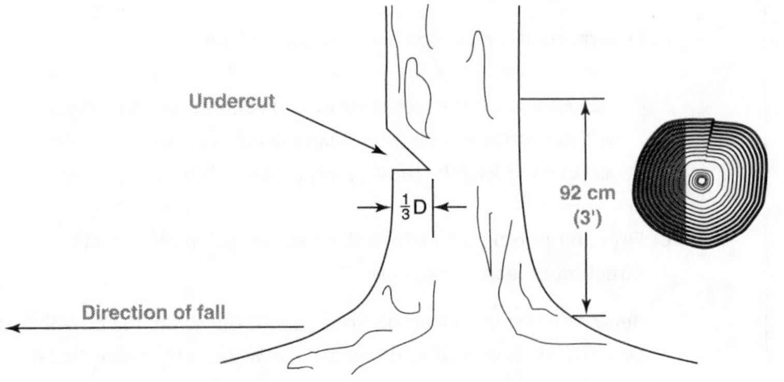

FIGURE 2 Making the Undercut

c. Make a downward-sloping cut, starting 10 to 15 cm (4 to 6 inches) above the first so that the cuts intersect at $\frac{1}{3}$ the diameter (Figure 2).

4. *How to Make the Backcut*

After completing the undercut, you make the backcut to sever the stem from the stump. This step requires good reflexes and absolute concentration.

> **WARNING:** Observe tree movement closely during the backcut. If the tree shows any sign of falling in your direction, drop everything and move out of its way. Also, do not cut completely through to the undercut; instead, leave a narrow strip of "holding wood" as a hinge, to help prevent the butt end of the falling tree from jumping back at you.

To make your backcut, follow these steps:

a. Holding the saw with the blade parallel to the ground, start your cut about 7.5 cm (3 inches) above the undercut, on the opposite side of the trunk. Leave a narrow strip of "holding wood" (Figure 3).

Figure 9.2 A Set of Instructions *(continued)*

4

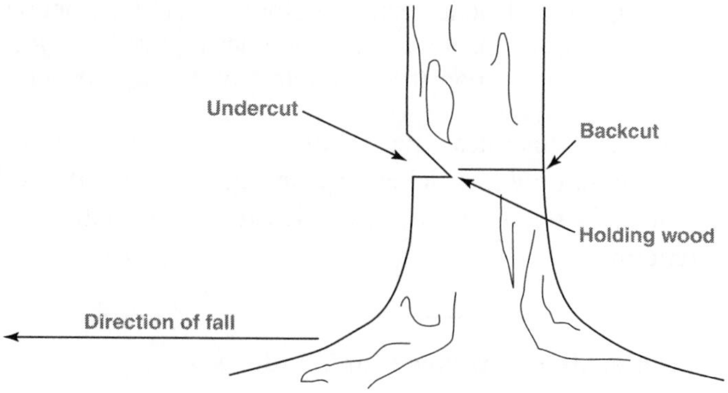

FIGURE 3 Making the Backcut

If the tree begins to bind the chainsaw, hammer a wedge into the backcut with the blunt side of the axe head. Then continue cutting.

b. As soon as the tree begins to fall, turn off the chainsaw, withdraw it, and step back immediately—the butt end of the tree could jump back toward you.

c. Move rapidly down the escape path.

CONCLUSION

Felling is a complex and dangerous procedure. Choosing the lay, providing an escape path, making the undercut, and making the backcut are the basic steps—but trees, terrain, and other circumstances vary greatly.

For the safest operation, seek professional advice and help whenever you foresee *any* complications whatsoever.

Figure 9.2 A Set of Instructions

"What's in it for me?" and "Making choices you can live with" approach the subject from various personal angles. The series ends with a post-test.

- Meanwhile, Learn2's Word 2000 Introduction uses a *hierarchical* approach: Chapter 1 deals with fundamentals such as opening Word, inserting text, and using various keys. Then, after laying this basic groundwork, the tutorial moves on to four specialized chapters at the next level in the hierarchy.

Figure 9.3 illustrates a typical organizational pattern for a tutorial.

The sample tutorial excerpt in Figure 9.4 on the following page shows part of a tutorial's opening module. This excerpt's structure mirrors the tutorial's overall structure.

Figure 9.3 shows the structure within a module

Title: Microsoft Word for Windows 97
Introduction to the tutorial

- general objectives and the main overall task to be accomplished/why important
- intended audience and appropriate level
- required materials, equipment, previous knowledge
- table of contents—modules listed by number and name, often with brief overview

Pre-quiz: users can take the quiz to determine whether they need the tutorial
Module 1: introduction/objective/list of skills/step 1/step 2/step 3, etc./exercise
Module 2, Module 3, etc.
Exercises and/or post-quiz
References (for more information and training)

Figure 9.3 Typical Tutorial Structure

Print versus Online Tutorials

Print's chief advantage is its convenience—users can use the tutorial any time, anywhere, without needing a computer. Users can progress at their own pace, and can easily move back and forth within the tutorial pages. Self-directed tutorials are inexpensive, too; they don't require a trainer and, compared to web-based tutorials, they are cheap to write and require less extensive testing (Price and Korman 190).

Computer-based training (CBT) appeals to many users, however. Online tutorial users don't have to flip from book to monitor when learning computer software, for example. Often, the instructional screen and the corresponding software screen can be open simultaneously, in separate windows. Also, users report that they feel they are actually performing tasks, not just reading about them and imitating them (Price and Korman 191).

CBT tutorials have an additional technical advantage. Although linear structures suit the building of increasingly complex tasks in tutorials, web users often get restless. They would prefer free-flowing hyperlinks through a hierarchical structure. CBT tutorials can offer multi-path structures that, for example, can provide "spur nodes" to digress into related topics and then return to the main tutorial (Farkas

Title

Main objective Audience level

Illustrations are essential for full understanding

Lesson One: Microsoft Word for Windows

This tutorial teaches Microsoft Word basics. Although knowledge of how to navigate in a Windows environment is helpful, this tutorial was created for the computer novice.

To begin, open Microsoft Word. The following screen will appear.

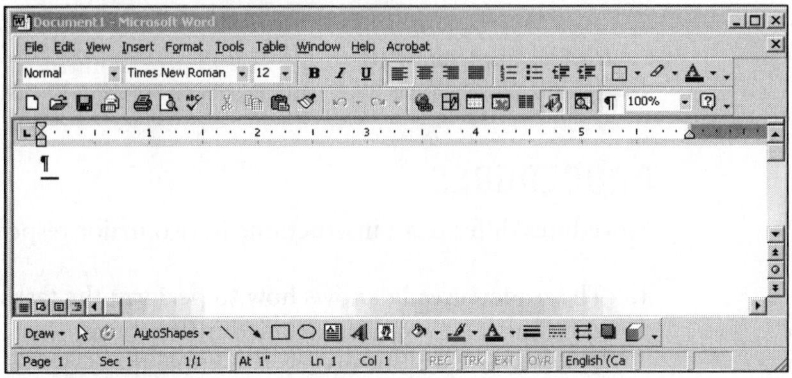

The Menu Bar

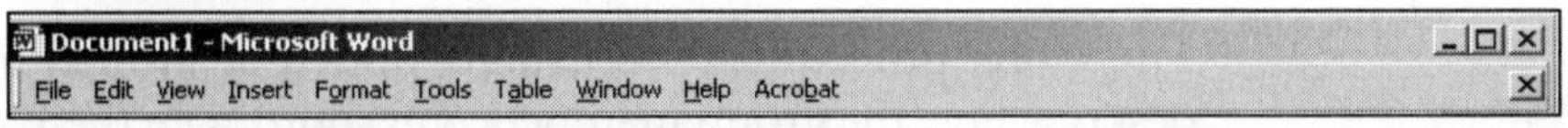

The Menu bar, directly below the Title bar, displays a menu of options: File, Edit, View, Insert, Format, Tools, Table, Window, Help, Acrobat. Here's how to use this menu to instruct the software.

Show only one way of doing a task

1. Point with the mouse to any menu option and click the left mouse button to open a drop-down menu.

   You can then use the left and right arrow keyboard keys to move left and right across the Menu bar options. Also, use the up and down arrow keys to move up and down the drop-down menu.

Separate instructions from explanations

2. To select an option, highlight the item on the drop-down menu and press **Enter**.

   An ellipsis after a menu item signifies additional options; if you select such an option, a dialogue box will appear.

Exercise 1

Give users a chance to practise and learn

Do the following exercise to learn the Microsoft Word menu.

1. Point to the Word **File** on the Menu bar.
2. Click your left mouse button.
3. Press the right arrow key until **Help** is highlighted.
4. Press the left arrow key until **Format** is highlighted.
5. Press the down arrow key until **Style** is highlighted.
6. Press the up arrow key until **Paragraph** is highlighted.
7. Press **Enter** to select the **Paragraph** menu option.
8. Point to Cancel and click the left mouse button to close the dialogue box.

Figure 9.4 Sample Portion of a Module

Source: Based on BayCon Group tutorials.

and Farkas 306, 309–10). "Split-joins," illustrated in Figure 9.5, allow users to choose which path to follow before rejoining the main tutorial.

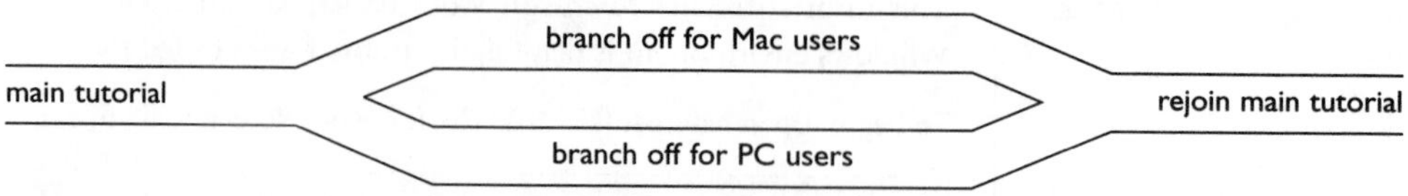

Figure 9.5 Split-join Path

Source: Based on David Farkas and Jean B. Farkas, *Principles of Web Design*, Toronto: Longman, 2002: 310.

PROCEDURES

Procedures differ from instructions in two major respects:

1. The reader already knows how to perform the tasks outlined in the procedure and thus does not need detailed instructions.
2. The reader does not necessarily know the order in which tasks are to be performed, or how and when to coordinate with other members of a work team.

Therefore, procedures are usually aimed at groups of readers; the procedures describe how the group members will coordinate their activities, or when they will perform their particular functions. Examples include evacuation procedures (in case of a fire or toxic spill), maintenance procedures, or installation procedures.

Not all procedures are aimed at groups, however. A software installation will likely be performed by a single technician who has the skills and general knowledge to do the job but who needs to know the specific variations of the procedure required by a given software program. Other procedures such as a union grievance or a procedure for reporting an on-site accident will assume that the reader needs to know whom to contact, when to contact, and what form to use. In these circumstances, the assumption is that the reader doesn't need to be told *how* to grieve the perceived infraction or *how* to phrase the accident report.

The excerpt from a group procedure in Figure 9.6 comes from a Canadian power utility. The procedure demonstrates how workers must coordinate their skills with those of others. In the conductor repair procedure, that coordination is essential in preventing the instant death that could result from a botched manoeuvre.

CONDUCTOR REPAIR ON 72/138 Kv H-FRAME

(INSTALL PRE-FORMED ARMOUR SPLICES USING A SECOND UNIT TO SUPPORT CONDUCTORS)

1. Operate in a crew that has a minimum of four (4) certified Journeymen Power Line Technicians.
2. Conduct a tailboard session to confirm the order in which this procedure is to be performed.
3. Position the aerial device in the best position to maintain safe working clearances while allowing two line technicians to work satisfactorily on the line. Verify safe working clearances with the measuring stick, as outlined in the General Rules.

   NOTE: Position the aerial device directly under the centre phase. Back in with the turret two (2) metres from the centre of the structure. Park the boom truck, which has a wire holder on an insulated jib, on the other side of the structure in such a way that the truck can support each conductor without having to move the truck. Install unit grounding on both vehicles.
4. *Line technicians*—Carry all tools and materials along in the buckets.
5. *Line technicians*—Test the insulators. Install a temporary jumper if it's necessary.
6. *Second unit operator*—Support the outside conductor with the jib and raise the conductor slightly.
7. *Line technician in the insulated aerial bucket*—Move into position while maintaining both phase-to-phase and phase-to-ground clearance. Disconnect the clamp from the insulators with hot sticks.
8. *Second unit operator*—Move the conductor to a position where pre-formed armour rod may be installed without reducing the limits of approach.

   The line technicians may now bond on and complete the repairs.
9. *Line technicians*—Remove the bonds and back away. Move the conductor back to the insulators and use hot line tools to attach a suspension clamp to the insulators again.
10. Repeat this operation on the other outside phase.
11. *Line technicians*—Connect the centre phase and loosen the suspension clamp with hot sticks. The clamp may be slid out on the conductor to a point where the technician in the insulated aerial device can maintain clearances and bond on to the line. After replacing the suspension clamp, you may remove the bonds and move into position to use hot line tools to apply the armour rod.

Figure 9.6 Sample Technical Procedure

CHECKLIST FOR REVISING AND EDITING INSTRUCTIONS

Content

- Does the title promise exactly what the instructions deliver?
- Is the background adequate for the intended audience?
- Do explanations enable readers to understand what to do?
- Do examples enable readers to see how to do it correctly?
- Are the definition and purpose of each step given as needed?
- Is all needless information omitted?
- Are all obvious steps omitted?
- Do notes, cautions, or warnings appear whenever needed, before the step?
- Is the information rate appropriate for readers' abilities and the difficulty of this procedure?
- Do visuals adequately clarify the steps?
- Do visuals repeat prose information whenever necessary?

Page Design

- Does each heading clearly tell readers what to expect?
- Are steps single spaced within, and double spaced between?
- Do white space and highlights set off discussion from steps?
- Is everything accurate?
- Are notes, cautions, or warnings set off or highlighted?
- Are visuals beside or near the step, and set off by white space?

Organization

- Is the introduction adequate without being excessive?
- Do the instructions follow the exact sequence of steps?
- Is all the information for a particular step close together?
- For a complex step, does each sentence begin on a new line?
- Is a conclusion necessary and, if necessary, adequate?

Style

- Do introductory sentences have enough variety to maintain interest?
- Does the familiar material appear first in each sentence?
- Do steps generally have short sentences?
- Does each step begin with the action verb?
- Are all steps in the active voice and imperative mood?
- Do all steps have parallel phrasing?
- Are transitions adequate for marking time and sequence?

WEB CONNECT

The first site contains process description, mechanism description, and instructions. The next site shows a process description of computer software operation (true type fonts). The third site illustrates a set of instructions. The fourth site lists basic, sensible advice on writing instructions.

http://cio.cisco.com/warp/public/707/3.html#intro
www.microsoft.com/opentype/otspec/ttch01.htm
www.fishingnorthwest.com/flypterns.htm
www.techscribe.co.uk/ta/how_to_write_instructions.htm

These sites provide advice and examples of free online tutorials:

www.baycongroup.com/tutorials.htm
www.extropia.com/tutorials.html
www.w3schools.com
www.tutorials.com/
www.good-tutorials.com/

This site includes several short video tutorials:

www.klariti.com/tutorial-videos/index.shtml

EXERCISES

1. Improve the readability of the following instructions by editing them for a more appropriate voice and design. Use the checklist above to evaluate the usability of instructions.

   What to Do Before Jacking Up Your Car

   Whenever the misfortune of a flat tire occurs, some basic procedures should be followed before the car is jacked up. If possible, your car should be positioned on as firm and level a surface as is available. The engine has to be turned off; the parking brake should be set; and the automatic transmission shift lever must be placed in "park," or the manual transmission lever in "reverse." The wheel diagonally opposite the one to be removed should have a piece of wood placed beneath it to prevent the wheel from rolling. The spare wheel, jack, and lug wrench should be removed from the luggage compartment.

2. Select a specialized process that you understand well and that has several distinct steps. Using the process analysis on pages 165–67 as a model, explain this process to colleagues who are unfamiliar with it. Begin by completing an audience/purpose profile (page 35). Some possible topics: how the body metabolizes alcohol, how economic inflation occurs, how the federal deficit affects our future, how a lake or pond becomes a swamp, how a volcanic eruption occurs.
3. Choose a topic from the following list, your major, or an area of interest. Using the general outline in this chapter as a model, outline instructions that require at least three major steps. Address a general reader, and begin by completing an audience/purpose profile. Include (1) all necessary visuals; or (2) a brief (page 479) and a rough diagram for each visual; or (3) a "reference visual" (a copy of a visual published elsewhere) with instructions for adapting your visual from that one. (If you borrow visuals from other sources, provide full references.)

planting a tree	hitting a golf ball
hot-waxing skis	removing the rear wheel of a bicycle
hanging wallpaper	
filleting a fish	avoiding hypothermia

4. Select any one of the instructional visuals in Figure 9.1 pages (169–170) and write a prose version of those instructions—without using visual illustrations or special page design. Bring your version to class and be prepared to discuss the conclusions you've derived from this exercise.
5. Locate an example of five or more visuals from the following list.
   A visual that shows:
   - how to locate something
   - how to operate something
   - how to handle something
   - how to assemble something
   - how to position something
   - how to avoid damage or injury
   - how to diagnose and solve a problem
   - how to identify safe or acceptable limits
   - how to proceed systematically
   - how to make the right decision
   - why an action or procedure is important

   Bring your examples to class for discussion, evaluation, and comparison.

COLLABORATIVE PROJECTS

Any of the exercises may be a collaborative project.

CHAPTER 10

Designing Pages and Documents

LEARNING OBJECTIVES

After reading this chapter, you should be able to

- Learn the basics of effective page design: page balance, open space and textual spacing, graphic highlighting, font choice, headings, headers and footers, and suitable, integrated visuals.
- Master the basics of logical, internally consistent headings systems.
- Adapt design guidelines for varying media, document types, and audiences.

Page design, the layout of words and graphics, determines the look of a page. Well-designed pages attract readers, invite readers in, guide them through the material, and help them understand and remember it. Readers' *first* impressions of documents tend to be purely visual, esthetic judgments.

PAGE DESIGN IN WORKPLACE WRITING

Page design becomes especially significant when we consider these realities about writing and reading in the workplace:

1. *Technical information generally is designed differently from material in novels, news stories, and other forms of writing.* Accessible technical documents require more than just unbroken sequences of paragraphs. Navigating through complex material, readers may need the help of charts, diagrams, lists, various type sizes and typefaces, different headings, and other page-design elements.
2. *Technical documents rarely get readers' undivided attention.* Readers may skim documents while they jot down ideas, talk on the phone, or drink coffee. Or they may refer to sections of the document during a meeting. Following distractions, readers must be able to return easily to documents.
3. *People read work-related documents only because they have to.* Novels, general newspapers, and magazines are read for relaxation, but work-related documents (proposals, reports, newsletters) often require the reader's *labour.* The more complex the document, the harder readers have to work.

4. *As computers generate more and more paper, any document is forced to compete for readers' attention.* Even brilliant writing is useless unless it gets read by its intended audience. Suffering from information overload, today's readers resist documents that appear overwhelming. They want formats that help them find the information they really need. A user-friendly document has an accessible format: at a glance, readers can see the document's organization, where they are in the document, which items matter most, and how items relate.

Reader expectations are high

5. Word processing software contains tools that allow easy production of sophisticated page design. As a result, today's readers are used to seeing high-quality design and they resist reading poorly designed, dense documents.

Notice how the information in Figure 10.1 resists our attention. Without design cues, we have no way of grouping this information into organized units of meaning. Now look at Figure 10.2, which shows the same information after a design overhaul. Notice, also, that the material in Figure 10.2 appears in a slightly different order than in Figure 10.1.

PAGE-DESIGN GUIDELINES

Approach your design decisions from the top down. First, consider the overall look of your pages; next, the shape of each paragraph; and finally, the size and style of individual letters and words (Kirsh 112). Figure 10.3 depicts how design considerations follow a top-down sequence, moving from large matters to small. (All design considerations are influenced by the size of the budget for a publication. For instance, adding a single colour to major heads can double the printing cost.)

If your organization prescribes no specific guidelines, the following design principles should satisfy most readers' expectations.

Shaping the Page

In shaping a page, we consider its look, feel, and overall layout. The following suggestions will help you shape appealing and usable pages.

Use the Right Paper and Ink. For routine documents (memos, letters, in-house reports), key or print in black ink, on 21.5 cm by 28 cm (8 1/2" by 11") low-gloss, white paper. Use rag-bond paper (20 pound or heavier) with a high fibre content (25 percent minimum). Shiny paper produces glare and tires the eyes. Flimsy or waxy paper feels inferior.

For documents that will be published (manuals, marketing literature, etc.), the grade and quality of paper are important considerations. Paper varies in weight, grain, and finish—from low-cost newsprint, with noticeable wood fibre, to wood-free, specially coated paper with custom finishes. Choice of paper finally depends on the artwork to be included, the type of printing, and the intended esthetic effect.

Use High-quality Type or Print. Print hard copy on an inkjet or laser printer. If your inkjet's output is blurry, consider purchasing special inkjet paper for the best output quality.

Types of Geothermal Heat Pump Systems

The energy crisis has intensified research into geothermal heating. As a result, several types of geothermal heat pump (GHP) systems have been developed. This report considers two main types of GHP systems, open loop and closed loop. Each of the types can be installed with vertical or horizontal piping.

In an open loop system, groundwater is drawn from an aquifer through a well and is passed through the pump's heat exchanger. Then, the water is pumped back to the aquifer through a second well, at some distance from the first. An open loop system can therefore present problems—local groundwater chemicals can foul the heat pump's exchanger and distributed water.

Therefore, closed loop systems have become more common; when properly installed, closed loops are economical, efficient, and reliable (Rafferty 10). Such systems circulate a water/anti-freeze solution through a continuous buried pipe. The length of piping depends on ground temperature, the ground's thermal conductivity, soil moisture, and system design.

Variations of vertical and horizontal pipe are used. Horizontal closed loop installations are cost effective for small installations, if sufficient land is available. Pipes are buried in trenches; up to six pipes are placed in each trench, with 3 to 4.5 metres between trenches. By contrast, vertical loops are used for large installations, or for situations where the soil is too shallow for trenching, or for installations where not enough land is available for horizontal trenches. In closed loop systems, a U-tube is installed in a drill hole 30 to 120 metres deep. Most installations require several drill holes; the pipes are joined in parallel or series-parallel patterns.

Two variations of the horizontal type are gaining favour. Pond closed loop systems place loops on the bottom of a pond or stream; others have also appeared in lakes or off shore in the ocean. A special variation is called "slinky" loops—overlapping coils of polyethylene pipe increase the heat exchange per foot of trench. Slinky coil systems can be placed in earth trenches or in water.

Figure 10.1 Ineffective Page Design

TYPES OF GEOTHERMAL HEAT PUMP SYSTEMS

The energy crisis has intensified research into geothermal heating. As a result, several types of geothermal heat pump (GHP) systems have been developed. This report considers two main types of GHP systems, open loop and closed loop. Each of the types can be installed with vertical or horizontal piping.

Open Loop Systems

In an open loop system, groundwater is drawn from an aquifer through a well and is passed through the pump's heat exchanger. Then, the water is pumped back to the aquifer through a second well, at some distance from the first. An open loop system can therefore present problems—local groundwater chemicals can foul the heat pump's exchanger and distributed water.

Closed Loop Systems

The problems with open loops mean that closed loop systems have become more common; when properly installed, closed loops are economical, efficient, and reliable (Rafferty 10). Such systems circulate a water/anti-freeze solution through a continuous buried pipe. The length of piping depends on

- ground temperature,
- the ground's thermal conductivity,
- soil moisture, and
- system design.

Horizontal Closed Loop

Horizontal closed loop installations are cost effective for small installations, if sufficient land is available. Pipes are buried in trenches; up to six pipes are placed in each trench, with 3 to 4.5 metres between trenches.

Two variations of the horizontal type are gaining favour.

1. Pond closed loop systems place loops on the bottom of a pond or stream; others have also appeared in lakes or off shore in the ocean.
2. "Slinky" loops (overlapping coils of polyethylene pipe) increase the heat exchange per foot of trench. Slinky coil systems can be placed in earth trenches or in water.

Vertical Closed Loop

Unlike the horizontal systems, vertical loops are used for large installations, or for situations where the soil is too shallow for trenching, or for installations where not enough land is available for horizontal trenches. In closed loop systems, a U-tube is installed in a drill hole 30 to 120 metres deep. Most installations require several drill holes; the pipes are joined in parallel or series-parallel patterns.

Figure 10.2 Effective Page Design

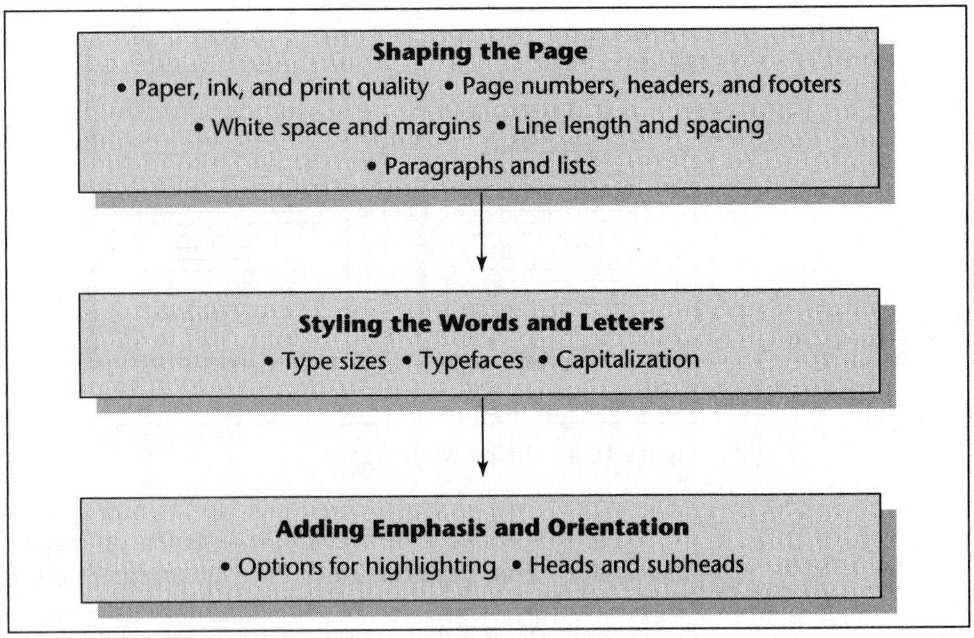

Figure 10.3 A Flow Chart for Decisions in Page Design

Use Consistent Page Numbers, Headers, and Footers. For a long document, count your title page as page i, without numbering it, and number all front-matter pages, including the table of contents and abstract, with lowercase Roman numerals (ii, iii, iv). Number the first text page and subsequent pages with Arabic numerals (1, 2, 3). Along with page numbers, *headers* or *footers* appear in the top or bottom page margins, respectively. These provide chapter or article titles, authors' names, dates, or other publication information. (See, for example, the headers at the top of the pages in this book.)

Use Adequate White Space. White space (all of the space not filled by text and visuals) divides printed areas into small, digestible chunks. It separates sections in a document, headings and visuals from text, and paragraphs from each other (Figure 10.4). White space enhances a document's appearance, clarity, and emphasis.

Well-designed white space imparts a shape to the whole document, a shape that orients readers and lends a distinctive visual form to the printed matter by

1. keeping related elements together
2. isolating and emphasizing important elements
3. providing breathing room between blocks of information

Pages that look uncluttered, inviting, and easy to follow convey an immediate sense of user-friendliness.

Provide Ample and Appropriate Margins. Small margins make a page look crowded and difficult. On your 21.5 cm by 28 cm ($8\frac{1}{2}$" by 11") page, leave margins of at least 2.5 cm (1"). For a document that will be bound, widen the left margin an extra 1.25 cm ($\frac{1}{2}$").

Use white space to orient readers

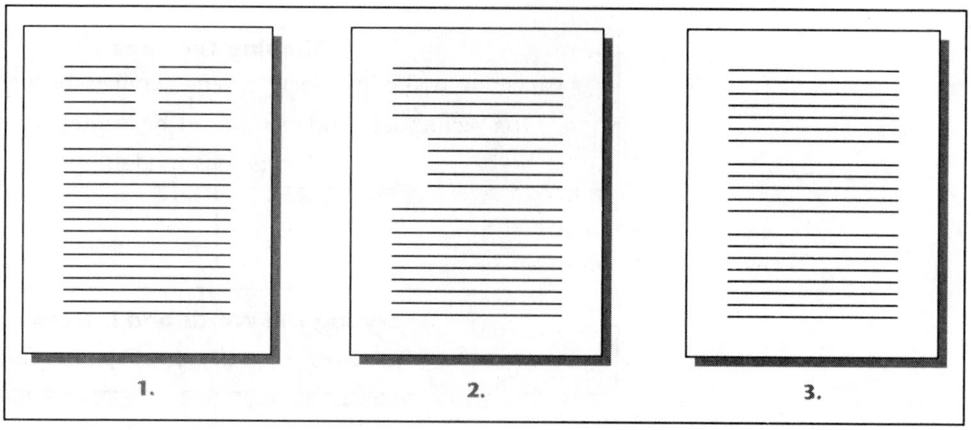

Figure 10.4 Using White Space

Choose between *unjustified* text (uneven or "ragged" right margins) and *justified* text (even right margins). Each arrangement creates its own "feel."

Justified lines

In right-justified text, the spaces vary between words and letters on a line, sometimes creating channels or rivers of white space. The reader's eyes are then forced to adjust continually to these space variations within a line or paragraph. Because each line ends at an identical vertical space, the eyes must work harder to differentiate one line from another (Felker et al. 85). Moreover, to preserve the even margin, words at ends of lines are often hyphenated, and frequently hyphenated line endings can be distracting.

Unjustified lines

Unjustified text, on the other hand, has equal spacing between letters and words on a line, and an uneven right margin. For some readers, a ragged right margin makes reading easier. These differing line lengths can prompt the eye to move from one line to the next line (Pinelli et al. 77). In contrast to justified text, an unjustified page seems to look less formal, less distant, and less official.

Justified text seems preferable for books, or annual reports, or newsletters, or other publications that use two columns. Unjustified text seems preferable for more personal forms of communication such as letters, memos, and in-house reports.

Keep Line Length Reasonable. Long lines tire the eyes. The longer the line, the harder it is for readers' eyes to return to the left margin and locate the next line (White, *Visual Design* 25).

Notice how your eye labours to follow the apparently endless message that here seems to stretch in lines that continue long after your eye was prepared to move down to the next line. After reading more than a few of these lines, you begin to feel tired and bored and annoyed, without hope of ever reaching the end.

Short lines force the eyes to move back and forth (Felker et al. 79). "Too-short lines disrupt the normal horizontal rhythm of reading" (White, *Visual Design* 25).

> Lines that are too
> short cause your eye
> to stumble from one
> fragment to another
> at a pace that too
> soon becomes
> annoying, if not
> nauseating.

A reasonable line length is 70 to 80 characters (or 12 to 15 words) per line for a 21.5 cm by 28 cm ($8^1/_2$" by 11") single-column page. The number of characters will depend on print size. Longer lines call for larger type and wider spacing between them (White, *Great Pages* 70).

Line length, of course, is affected by the number of columns (vertical blocks of print) on your page. Two-column pages often appear in newsletters and brochures, but research indicates that single-column pages work best for complex, specialized information (Hartley 148).

Keep Line Spacing Consistent. For any document likely to be read completely (letters, memos, instructions), single-space within paragraphs and double-space between them. Instead of indenting the first line of single-spaced paragraphs, separate them with a line of space.

Tailor Each Paragraph to Its Purpose. Readers often skim a long document to find what they want. Most paragraphs therefore begin with a topic sentence forecasting the content.

Shape each paragraph

> Use a long paragraph (no more than 15 lines) for clustering material that is closely related (such as history and background, or any body of information best understood in one block).
>
> Use short paragraphs for making complex material more digestible, for giving step-by-step instructions, or for emphasizing vital information.

Avoid *widow* and *orphan* lines. The last line of a paragraph printed at the top of a page is called a *widow.* The first line of a paragraph printed on the bottom of a page is called an *orphan.*

Make Lists for Easy Reading. Readers prefer information in list form rather than in continuous prose paragraphs (Hartley 51).

Types of items you might list include advice or examples, conclusions and recommendations, criteria for evaluation, errors to avoid, materials and equipment for a procedure, parts of a mechanism, or steps or events in a sequence. Notice how the preceding information becomes easier to grasp and remember when displayed in the list below.

Types of items you might list:

- advice or examples
- conclusions and recommendations
- criteria for evaluation

- errors to avoid
- materials and equipment for a procedure
- parts of a mechanism
- steps or events in a sequence

A list of brief items usually needs no punctuation at the end of each line. A list of full sentences or questions requires appropriate punctuation after each item.

Depending on the list's contents, set off each item with some kind of visual or verbal signal. If the items require a strict sequence (as in a series of steps, or parts of a mechanism), use Arabic numbers (1, 2, 3) or the words *First, Second, Third,* and so on. If the items require no strict sequence (as in the bulleted list above), use dashes, asterisks, or bullets. For a checklist, use open boxes. Figure 10.5 illustrates different types of lists.

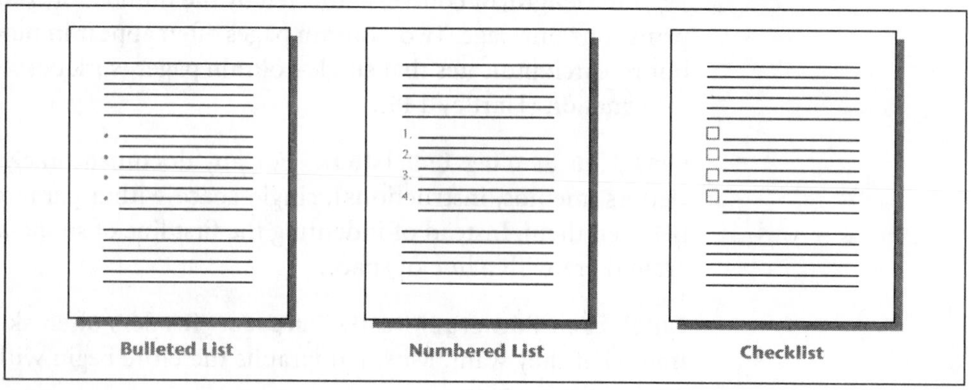

Figure 10.5 Types of Lists

Introduce your list with an explanation. Phrase all listed items in parallel grammatical form. If the items suggest no strict sequence, try to impose some logical ranking (most important to least important, alphabetical, or some such order). Set off the list with extra white space above and below.

Styling the Words and Letters

In styling words and letters, we consider typographic choices that will make the text easy to read.

Use Standard Type Sizes. Word-processing programs offer a wide variety of type sizes:

Select the appropriate type size

9 point

10 point

12 point

14 point

18 point

24 point

The standard type size for most documents is 10 to 12 point. Use larger or smaller sizes for headings, titles, captions (brief explanation of a visual), sidebars (marginal comments), or special emphasis. Use a consistent type size for similar elements throughout the document.

Select Appropriate Fonts. A font (also known as a *typeface*) is the style of individual letters and characters. Each font has its own personality, and thus affects the ways readers respond. Also, particular fonts can influence reading speed by as much as 30 percent (Chauncey 26).

Word-processing programs offer a variety of fonts, such as the ones displayed here in 11-point type:

Select a font for its personality

Times New Roman	Garamond
Brush Script	Palatino
Mistral	Verdana
Impact	**Bondoni MT Black**
Arial	***Script MT Bold***

Can you assign a personality to each of the above fonts? Thousands more fonts are available through the internet—simply key in "fonts" or "free fonts" in a search engine. (But expect to run the gauntlet of advertising!)

For greater visual unity, try to use different sizes and versions (**bold,** *italic,* expanded, condensed) of the same typeface throughout your document—with the possible exception of headings, captions, sidebars, or visuals.

All typefaces divide into two broad categories: *serif* and *sans serif.* Serifs are the fine lines that extend horizontally from the main strokes of a letter.

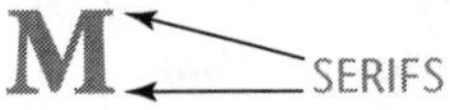

Decide between serif and sans serif type

Serif type makes body copy more readable because the horizontal lines "bind the individual letters" and thereby guide the reader's eyes from letter to letter—as in the type you are now reading (White, *Visual Design* 14).

> In contrast, sans serif type is purely vertical (like this). Clean looking and "businesslike," sans serif is considered ideal for technical material (numbers, equations, etc.), marginal comments, headings, examples, tables, captions to pictures and visuals, and any other material set off from the body copy (White, *Visual Design* 16).

Be aware of cultural variations

European readers generally prefer sans serif type throughout their documents, and other cultures have their own preferences as well. Learn all you can about the design conventions of the culture you are addressing.

Except for special emphasis, stick to the more conservative styles and avoid ornate ones altogether.

Avoid Sentences in Full Caps. Sentences or long passages in full capitals (uppercase letters) are difficult to read because all uppercase letters and words have the same visual outline (Felker 87). The longer the passage, the harder readers work to grasp your emphasis.

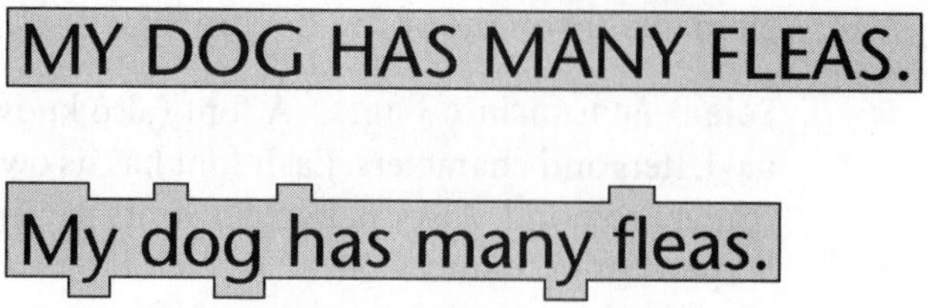
MY DOG HAS MANY FLEAS.
My dog has many fleas.

Full caps are good for emphasis but hard to read

Hard ACCORDING TO THE NATIONAL COUNCIL ON RADIATION PROTECTION, YOUR MAXIMUM ALLOWABLE DOSE OF LOW-LEVEL RADIATION IS 500 MILLIREMS PER YEAR.

Easier According to the National Council on Radiation Protection, your MAXIMUM allowable dose of low-level radiation is 500 millirems per year.

Lowercase letters take up less space, and the distinctive shapes make each word easier to recognize and remember (Benson 37).

Use full caps as section headings (INTRODUCTION) or to highlight a word or phrase (WARNING: NEVER TEASE THE ALLIGATOR). As with other highlighting options discussed below, use full caps sparingly in your document.

Highlighting for Emphasis

Effective highlighting helps readers distinguish the important from the less important elements. Highlighting options include typefaces, type sizes, white space, and other graphic devices that

- emphasize key points
- make headings prominent
- separate sections of a long document
- set off examples, warnings, and notes

You can highlight with underlining, FULL CAPS, dashes, parentheses, and asterisks.

> You can indent to set off examples, explanations, or any material that should be distinguished from other elements in your document.

Using ruled (or keyed) horizontal lines, you can separate sections in a long document:

Using ruled lines, broken lines, or ruled boxes, you can set off crucial information such as a warning or a caution:

Caution: A document with too many highlights can appear confusing, disorienting, and tasteless.

In adding emphasis and orientation, consider design elements that will direct readers' focus and help them navigate the text.

Word-processing software offers highlighting options that might include **boldface,** *italics,* SMALL CAPS, varying type sizes and typefaces, and colour. For specific highlighted items, some options are better than others:

Not all highlighting is equal

Boldface works well for emphasizing a single sentence or brief statement, and is perceived by readers as being "authoritative" (*Aldus Guide* 42).

Italics suggest a more subtle or "refined" emphasis than boldface (Aldus Guide 42). *Italics can highlight words, phrases, book titles, and so on. But multiple lines (like these) of italic type are difficult to read.*

SMALL CAPS WORK FOR HEADINGS AND SHORT PHRASES. BUT ANY LONG STATEMENT ALL IN CAPS IS DIFFICULT TO READ.

Small type sizes (usually sans serif) work well for captions, labels for visuals, or to set off other material from the body copy.

Large type sizes and dramatic typefaces are both difficult to miss and difficult to digest. Be conservative—unless you really need to convey forcefulness.

Colour is appropriate only in some documents, and only when used sparingly. (Pages 484–86 discuss how colour or shading can influence readers' perception and interpretation of a message.)

Whichever highlights you select for a document, be consistent. Make sure that all headings at one level are highlighted identically, that all warnings and cautions are set off identically, and so on. Use the "styles" feature of your word processor to ensure this consistency.

Never combine too many highlights.

Using Headings for Access and Orientation

Readers of long documents often look back or jump ahead to sections that interest them most.

Headings announce how a document is organized, point readers to what they need, and divide the document into accessible blocks or "chunks." An informative heading can help a reader decide whether a section is worth reading (Felker 17). Besides cutting down on reading and retrieval time, headings help readers remember information (Hartley 15).

Make Headings Informative. A heading should be informative but not wordy. Informative headings orient readers, showing them what to expect. Vague or general headings can be more misleading than no headings at all (Redish et al. 144). Whether your heading takes the form of a phrase, a statement, or a question, be sure it advances thought.

Uninformative heading	Document Formatting

What should we expect here: specific instructions, an illustration, a discussion of formatting policy in general? We can't tell.

Informative versions	How to Format Your Document Format Your Document in This Way How Do I Format My Document?

When you use questions as headings, phrase the questions in the same way as readers might ask them.

Make Headings Specific as Well as Comprehensive. Focus the heading on a specific topic. Do not preface a discussion of the effects of acid rain on lake trout with a broad heading, such as "Acid Rain." Use instead "The Effects of Acid Rain on Lake Trout."

Also, provide enough headings to contain each discussion section. If chemical, bacterial, and nuclear wastes are three *separate* discussion items, provide a heading for each. Do not simply lump them under the sweeping heading "Hazardous Wastes." If you have prepared an outline for your document, adapt major and minor headings from it.

Make Headings Grammatically Consistent. All major topics or all minor topics in a document share equal rank; to emphasize this equality, express topics at the same level in identical—or parallel—grammatical form.

Non-parallel headings	How to Avoid Damaging Your Disks: 1. Clean Disk-Drive Heads 2. Keep Disks Away from Magnets 3. Refraining from Exposing the Magnetic Surface 4. It Is Crucial That Disks Be Kept Away from Heat 5. Disks Should Be Kept Out of Direct Sunlight 6. Keep Disks in a Dust-free Environment

In items 3, 4, and 5, the lack of parallelism (no verbs in the imperative mood) obscures the relationship between individual steps and confuses readers. This next version emphasizes the equal rank of these items.

Parallel headings	3. Refrain from Exposing the Magnetic Surface 4. Keep Disks Away from Heat 5. Keep Disks Out of Direct Sunlight

Parallelism helps make a document readable and accessible.

Make Headings Visually Consistent. "Wherever heads are of equal importance, they should be given similar visual expression, because the regularity itself becomes an understandable symbol" (White, *Visual Design* 104). Use identical type size and typeface for all headings at a given rank. (Use the "styles" feature of your word-processing software.)

Lay Out Headings by Rank. Like a road map, your headings should announce clearly the large and small segments in your document. (Use the logical divisions from your outline as a model for heading layout.) Think of each heading at a particular rank as an "event in a sequence" (White, *Visual Design* 95).

Figure 10.6 shows how headings vary in positioning and highlighting, depending on their rank. However, because of space considerations, Figure 10.6 does not show that each higher-level heading yields at least two lower-level headings.

Special authoring software (Adobe FrameMaker or RoboHelp) automatically converts hard-copy documents to various on-screen formats, chunked and linked for easy navigation.

SECTION HEADING

In formal reports, always centre section headings at the top of a new page. Use a type size roughly 4 points larger than body copy (say, 16-point section heads for 12-point body copy). Avoid *overly* large heads, and use no other highlights. Fully capitalize the heading. (Some documents use colour for section headings and capitalize just the first letter of each word.) Leave a full line space above the various headings (as in this example).

Major Topic Heading
Place major topic headings at the left margin (flush left), and begin each word with an uppercase letter. Use a type size roughly 2 points larger than body copy, in boldface. Start the copy immediately below the heading (as shown), or leave one space below the heading.

Minor Topic Heading
Use boldface and the same type size as the body copy, with no other highlights. Start the copy immediately below the heading (as shown), or leave one space below the heading.

Subtopic Heading. Incorporate subtopic headings into the body copy they head. Place subtopic heads flush left and set them off with a period. Use boldface and the same type size as in the body copy, with no other highlights.

1. ***Alternative subtopic heading.*** If numbering is appropriate, place the subtopics in a list, with the numbers flush left and the body copy indented. Use italics *and* boldface if you want to draw particular attention to this fourth level of heading.

- **Bulleted variation.** When the sequence of items in a list is not important, use bullets to precede the indented subtopic headings.

Figure 10.6 Recommended Format for Headings

Provide margins for on-screen pages, so that your text won't bump against (or run off) the edge of the user's screen. Also, avoid using underlines for emphasis because these might be confused with hyperlinks (Munger) and because italicized copy is difficult to read on screen.

Many variations of the above format are used successfully. One such variation is shown in Figure 10.7. Another variation is demonstrated by the report in Figure 18.6, starting on page 420. That report uses decimal notation, which is discussed in Chapter 6.

The layouts in Figures 10.6 and 10.7 embody the following guidelines:

- Ordinarily, use no more than four levels of heading (section, major topic, minor topic, subtopic). Excessive heads and subheads can make a document seem cluttered or fragmented.
- Make sure that the headings system has a consistent, logical progression. Each succeeding heading level in Figure 10.6 and Figure 10.7 has less capitalization than the preceding level.
- Never begin the sentence right after the heading with *this, it,* or some other pronoun referring to the heading. Make the sentence's meaning independent of the heading.
- Use boldface for all headings.
- Never leave a heading floating on the final line of a page. Unless at least two lines of text can fit below the heading, carry it over to the top of the next page.

AUDIENCE CONSIDERATIONS IN PAGE DESIGN

Like any writing decisions, page-design choices are by no means random. An effective writer designs a document for specific use by a specific audience.

In deciding on a format, work from a detailed audience/purpose profile (Wight 11). Know who your readers are and how they will use your information. Design a document to meet their particular needs and expectations, as in these examples:

- If readers will use your document for reference only (as in a repair manual), make sure you have plenty of headings.
- If your relationship with your readers is formal, use *topical headings* ("Advantages of Treated Pipe"); however, if that relationship is more direct and informal, consider using *talking headings* ("We Should Buy Treated Pipe"). For examples of both topical and talking headings, see the sample reports in Chapter 18 and Chapter 17.
- If readers will follow a sequence of steps, show that sequence in a numbered list.
- If readers will need to evaluate something, give them a checklist of criteria (as in this book at the end of most chapters).
- If readers need a warning, highlight the warning so that it cannot possibly be overlooked.
- If readers have asked for your one-page résumé, save space by using a 10-point type size.
- If readers will be facing complex information or difficult steps, widen the margins, increase all white space, and shorten the paragraphs.

1.0 SECTION HEADING

Use a type size roughly 4 points larger than body copy (say, 16-point section heads for 12-point body copy). Use colour to draw attention to the main heading.

1.1 Major Topic Heading

Place major topic headings at the left margin (flush left), and begin each word with an uppercase letter. Use a type size roughly 2 points larger than body copy, in boldface. Start the text on the line below the heading.

1.1.1 Minor Topic Heading

Indent minor topic headings. Use boldface and the same type size as the body copy, with no other highlights. Start the body copy immediately below the heading (as shown).

1.1.1.1 Subtopic heading. Incorporate subtopic headings into the body copy they head. Indent subtopic heads two tabs and set them off with a period. Use boldface and the same type size as in the body copy, with no other highlights.

Figure 10.7 Alternative Format for Headings

Consider cultural variations

Consider also your audience's specific cultural expectations. For instance, Arabic and Persian text is written from right to left instead of left to right (Leki 149). In other cultures, readers move up and down the page, instead of across. Be aware that a particular culture might be offended by certain icons or by a typeface that seems too plain or too fancy (Weymouth 144). Ignoring a culture's design conventions can be interpreted as a sign of disrespect.

DESIGNING ON-SCREEN PAGES

To be read on a computer screen, pages must accommodate small screen size, reduced resolution, and reader resistance to scrolling—among other restrictions. Some special design requirements of on-screen pages are:

Elements of on-screen page design

- Sentences and paragraphs are short and more concise than their hard-copy equivalents.
- The main point usually appears right up front on each screen.
- Each "page" often stands alone as a discrete "module," or unit of meaning. Instead of a traditional introduction-body-conclusion sequence of pages, material is displayed in screen-sized chunks, each linked as hypertext.
- Links, navigation bars, hot buttons, and help options appear on each page.

The following example, Humber College's homepage (Figure 10.8), centres its key information and compelling image on the screen. It uses a relatively simple layout, but provides several pull-down menus of links to important sources of information for current and prospective students and faculty. These menus of links are arranged horizontally above and below the central image and branding message. This screen builds usable complexity into an attractive, accessible design.

Figure 10.9 is another fine example of design in a detailed "technical" document. Figure 10.9 shows the first of six panels of instruction in how to explicate poetry. Notice how visuals, colour, font choices, and other graphics combine to bring out the full potential of the verbal message.

ON THE JOB...

Screen vs. Print Documents

"[For our client, MachineWorks] the print and screen documents serve different purposes. For content that requires extensive reading, print versions are better. On the other hand, when users want to search across several documents or copy sample code from a document, screen versions are better. PDF was chosen over HTML for the screen versions because it is easier to incorporate navigation buttons and multi-document search facilities...."

—Mike Unwalla, principal tech writer, TechScribe (qtd. in Beaumont 18)

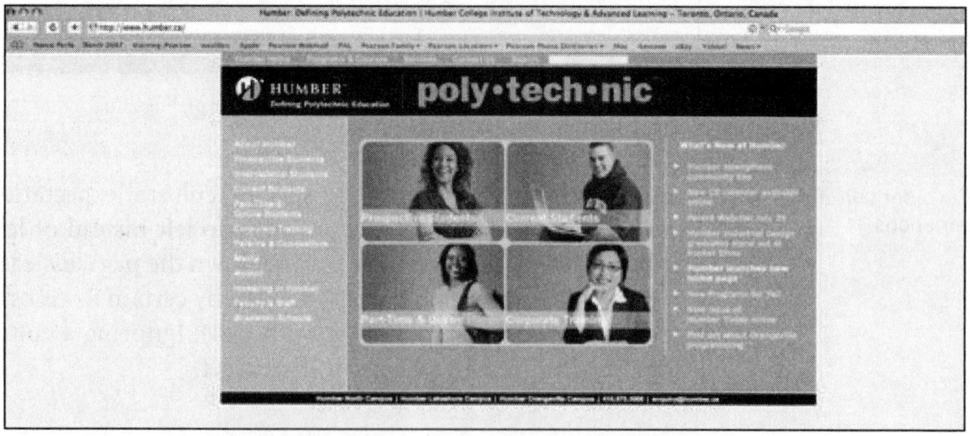

Figure 10.8 A User-friendly Webpage
Source: Courtesy of Humber College.

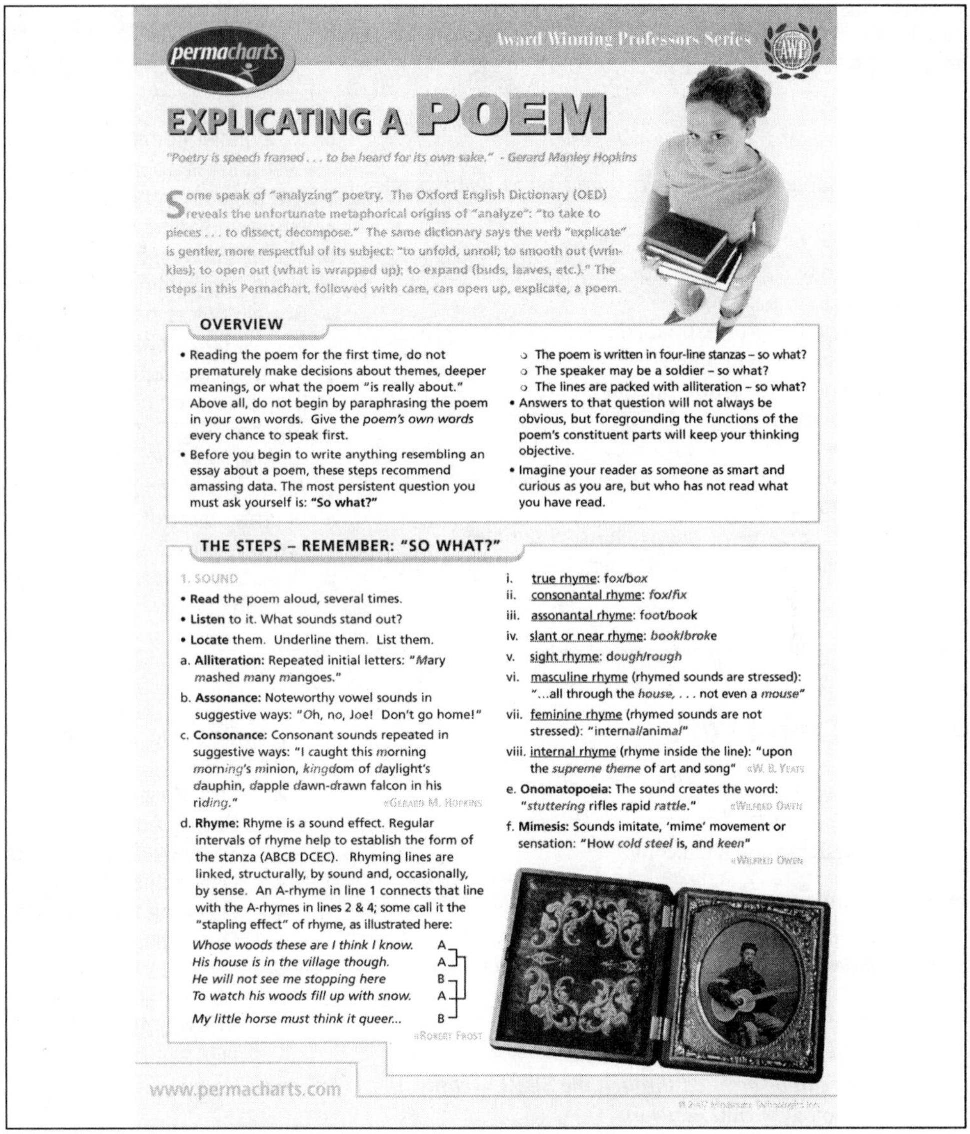

Figure 10.9 Effective Design in an Educational Chart

Source: *Explicating a Poem*, text by Ron Marken, design by Zohra Karim. Content, layout and design © 2007 Mindsource Technologies Inc. Reproduced with permission of Permacharts Inc. *Explicating a Poem* and other Permacharts are available at www.permacharts.com.

CHECKLIST FOR PAGE DESIGN

Use this checklist to revise your page design.

- Is the paper white, low-gloss, rag bond, with black ink?
- Is all type or print neat and legible?
- Does the white space adequately orient the readers?
- Are the margins ample?
- Is the line length reasonable?
- Is the right margin unjustified?
- Is the line spacing appropriate and consistent?
- Does each paragraph begin with a topic sentence? If not, why not?
- Does the length of each paragraph suit its subject and purpose?
- Are all pages free of widow and orphan lines?
- Do parallel items in strict sequence appear in a numbered list?
- Do parallel items of any kind appear in a list whenever a list is appropriate?
- Are pages numbered consistently?
- Is the body type size 10 to 12 points?
- Do full caps highlight only words or short phrases?
- Is the highlighting consistent, tasteful, and subdued?
- Are all format patterns distinct enough so that readers will find what they need?
- Are there enough headings for readers to know where they are in the document?
- Are headings informative, comprehensive, specific, parallel, and visually consistent?
- Are headings clearly differentiated according to rank?
- Is the overall design inviting without being overwhelming?
- Does this design respect the cultural conventions of my audience?

WEB CONNECT

Literally thousands of sites offer advice about webpage design. Here's one of the best:
www.webdesignfromscratch.com/

Ben Hunt, who's responsible for the above site, also updates a list of some of the best current design:
www.webdesignfromscratch.com/current-style.cfm

Wichita State University's Software Usability Research Laboratory (SURL) publishes Usability News, *an online newsletter that can be accessed through the SURL website at*
http://psychology.wichita.edu/surl/

EXERCISES

1. Find an example of effective page design, in a textbook or elsewhere. Photocopy a selection (two or three pages), and attach a memo explaining to your instructor and colleagues why this design is effective. Be specific in your evaluation. Now do the same for an example of poor formatting. Bring your examples and explanations to class, and be prepared to discuss why you chose them.
2. Rewrite the following headings from a set of instructions for listening, to make them parallel.
   - You Must Focus on the Message
   - Paying Attention to Non-verbal Communication
   - Your Biases Should Be Suppressed
   - Listen Critically
   - Listening for Main Ideas
   - Distractions Should Be Avoided
   - Provide Verbal and Non-verbal Feedback
   - Making Use of Silent Periods
   - Are You Allowing the Speaker Time to Make His or Her Point?
   - Keeping an Open Mind Is Important

COLLABORATIVE PROJECT

Working in small groups, redesign a document you select or your instructor provides. Prepare a detailed explanation of your group's revision. Appoint a group member to present your revision to the class, using an opaque or overhead projector, a large-screen computer monitor, data projection unit, or photocopies.

PART II

CHAPTER 11

Writing Persuasively

LEARNING OBJECTIVES

After reading this chapter, you should be able to

- Understand that receivers may resist persuasive messages, and how to overcome that resistance.
- Practise techniques for presenting effective arguments and evidence.
- Consider the cultural and "political" contexts in which messages will be received.

Chapter 1 shows that writers can face persuasion challenges even when their primary goal is to inform. Here are some persuasion challenges:

- A reader might dispute the *facts*: that reader might not agree that all the factual statements are indeed correct, or may believe that key facts have been omitted. Or, the reader might disagree that your information sources are reliable.
- You might have difficulty convincing the reader to accept your *interpretation and evaluation of the facts.*
- Your reader might not accept your *recommended actions.*

Whenever an audience disagrees about what things mean or what is better or worse or what should be done, you have a persuasion challenge to overcome.

As you read this chapter, you will benefit by referring to the audience/purpose profile found on page 35. The profile's categories are explored in the following advice for persuading others.

ASSESS THE POLITICAL REALITIES

If you have worked with others, you already know something about office politics: how some people seek favour, influence, status, or power; how some resent, envy, or intimidate others; how some are easily threatened. Writing consultant Robert Hays sums up the writer's political situation this way: "A writer must labour under political pressures from boss, peers, and subordinates. Any conclusion affecting other people can arouse resistance" (19). Some readers might resist your suggestion for shortening lunch breaks, cutting expenses, or automating the assembly line. Or your document might be seen as an attempt to undermine your supervisor.

EXPECT READER RESISTANCE

People who haven't made up their minds about what to do or think are more likely to be receptive to persuasive influence:

We rely on persuasion to help us make up our minds

> We are all consumers as well as providers of persuasion. Daily, we open OURSELVES to the persuasion of others. We need others' arguments and evidence. We're busy. We can't and don't want to discover and reason out everything for ourselves. We look for help, for short cuts, in making up our minds. (Gilsdorf, "Write Me" 12)

In a world overwhelmed by information, persuasion can help people "process" the information and decide on its meaning.

People who already have decided what to do or think, however, don't like to change their minds without good reason. Sometimes, people refuse to budge. Whenever you question people's stand on an issue or try to change their behaviour, expect resistance. The bigger the readers' stake in the issue, the more personal their involvement will be, and the more resistance you can expect. Research indicates that inducing permanent change in behaviour is especially difficult because people tend to revert to the familiar patterns and activities that are part of their lifestyle or work habits (Perloff 321).

ON THE JOB...

Persuasive Challenges

"Everyone is busy, so you must be very clear about why they need to read your communication and, if appropriate, act on it. You are constantly competing to get the 'mindshare' of your readers..."

—Mary Hoffmann, marketing communications manager for a major computer company

So any document can evoke different reactions—depending on a reader's temperament, preferences, interests, fears, biases, preconceptions, misconceptions, ambitions, or general attitude. Whenever readers feel their views are being challenged, they respond with questions like these:

TYPICAL READER QUESTIONS ABOUT A DOCUMENT THAT ATTEMPTS TO PERSUADE

- Says who?
- So what?
- Why should I?
- What's in it for me?
- What's in it for you?
- What does this really mean?
- Will it mean more work for me?
- Will it make me look bad?

Some ways of yielding to persuasion are better than others

When people do yield to persuasion, they yield either grudgingly, willingly, or eagerly (as in Figure 11.1). Researchers categorize these responses as *compliance, identification,* or *internalization* (Kelman 51–60):

- *Compliance:* "I'm yielding to your demand in order to get a reward or to avoid punishment. I really don't accept it, but I feel pressured and so I'll go along."
- *Identification:* "I'm yielding to your appeal because I like and believe you, I want you to like me, and I feel we have something in common."
- *Internalization:* "I'm yielding because what you're saying makes good sense and it fits my goals and values."

ON THE JOB...

The Key to Persuading Others

"Most writing has a persuasive element. The key to persuasive writing is to be sincere and honest... and to connect on some level with your reader. You must provide something the reader wants...."

—Marilyn Riley Nault, freelance writer and editor

Although compliance is sometimes necessary (as in military orders or workplace safety regulations), nobody likes to be coerced. Effective persuasion relies on identification or internalization. If readers merely comply because they feel they have no choice, then you probably have lost their loyalty and goodwill—and as soon as the threat or reward disappears, you will lose their compliance as well.

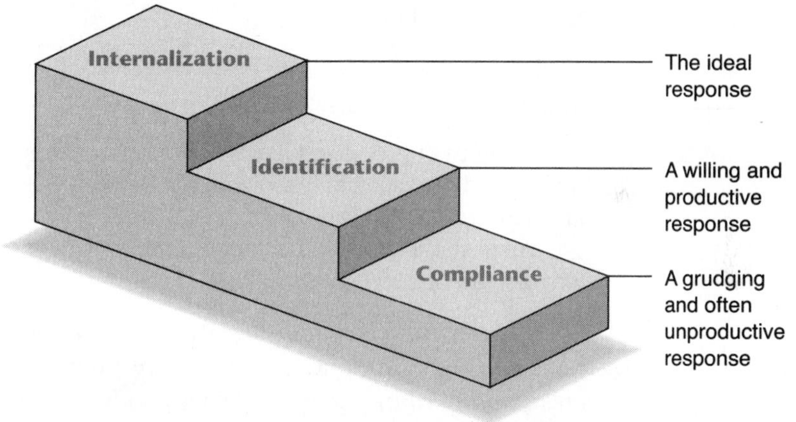

Figure 11.1 The Levels of Response to Persuasion

KNOW HOW TO CONNECT WITH READERS

Persuasive people know when to merely declare what they want, when to reach out and create a relationship, when to appeal to reason—or when to employ some combination of these strategies. Let's call these three connecting strategies the *power connection,* the *relationship connection,* and the *rational connection.*

To illustrate these different connections, picture the following situation:

> Your company has just developed a fitness program, based on findings that healthy employees work better, take fewer sick days, and cost less to insure. This program offers clinics for smoking, stress reduction, and weight loss, along with group exercise. In your second month on the job you receive this notice through email:

Memo

To: All Employees 5/20/08
From: G. Maximus, Human Resources Director
Subject: Physical Fitness

POWER CONNECTION: Orders readers to show up

On Monday, June 10, all employees will report to the company gymnasium at 8:00 a.m. for the purpose of choosing a walking or jogging group. Each group will meet 30 minutes three times weekly during lunchtime.

How would you react to this memo—and to the person who wrote it? Here the writer requires compliance. Although the writer speaks of "choosing," you are given no real choice but simply ordered to show up. This kind of *power connection* is typically used by supervisors and others in power. Although it may or may not achieve its goal, the power connection almost surely will alienate its readers.

Now assume instead that you received the following version of our memo. How would you react to this message and its writer?

Memo

To: All Employees 5/20/08
From: G. Maximus, Human Resources Director
Subject: An Invitation to Physical Fitness

RELATIONSHIP CONNECTION: Invites readers to participate

Leaves the choice to readers

I realize most of you spend lunch hour playing cards, reading, or just enjoying a bit of well-earned relaxation in the middle of a hectic day. But I'd like to invite you to join our lunchtime walking/jogging club.

We're starting this club in hopes that it will be a great way for us all to feel better. Why not give it a try?

This second version evokes a sense of identification, of shared feelings and goals. Instead of being commanded, readers are invited—they are given a real choice. This *relationship connection* establishes goodwill.

Often, the biggest factor in persuasion is a reader's perception of the writer. Readers are more receptive to people they like, trust, and respect. Of course, you would be unethical in appealing to the relationship or in faking the relationship merely to hide the fact that you had no evidence to support your claim (R. Ross 28). Audiences still need to find the claim believable ("Exercise will help me feel better") and relevant ("I personally need this kind of exercise").

Here is a third version of our memo. As you read, think about the ways it makes a persuasive case.

Memo

To: All Employees 5/20/08
From: G. Maximus, Human Resources Director
Subject: Invitation to Join One of Our Jogging or Walking Groups

RATIONAL CONNECTION: Presents authoritative evidence

A recent Health Canada study reports that adults who walk two miles a day could increase their life expectancy by three years. Other research shows that 30 minutes of moderate aerobic exercise at least three times weekly has a significant and long-term effect in reducing stress, lowering blood pressure, and improving job performance.

Offers alternatives

As a first step in our exercise program, our company is offering a variety of daily jogging groups: the One-Milers, Three-Milers, and Five-Milers. All groups will meet at designated times on our brand-new, quarter-mile, rubberized clay track.

Offers a compromise

For beginners or skeptics, we're offering daily two-mile walking groups. For the truly resistant, we offer the option of a Monday-Wednesday-Friday two-mile walk.

Leaves the choice to readers

Coffee and lunch breaks can be rearranged to accommodate whichever group you select.

Offers incentives

Why not take advantage of our hot new track? As small incentives, we will reimburse anyone who signs up as much as $100 for running or walking shoes, and will even throw in an extra 15 minutes for lunch breaks. And with a consistent turnout of 90 percent or better, our company insurer may be able to eliminate everyone's $200 yearly deductible in medical costs.

Here the writer shows willingness to compromise ("If you do this, I'll do that"). This *rational connection* communicates respect for the reader's intelligence *and* for the relationship by presenting good reasons, a variety of alternatives, and attractive incentives—all framed as an invitation. Whenever an audience is willing to listen to reason, the rational connection stands the best chance of succeeding.

ASK FOR A SPECIFIC DECISION

Unless you are giving an order, diplomacy is essential in persuasion. But don't be afraid to ask for the specific decision you want, preferably at the end of the message:

Let people know exactly what you want

> Studies show that the moment of decision is made easier for people when we show them what the desired action is, rather than leaving it up to them. . . . Without this directive, people may misunderstand or lose interest in the entire message. No one likes to make decisions: there is always a risk involved. But if the writer asks for the action, and makes it look easy and urgent, the decision itself looks less risky and the entire persuasive effort has a better chance of succeeding. (Cross 3)

As our discussion of *action structure* (Chapter 17) points out, you should let readers know what you want them to do or think.

NEVER ASK FOR TOO MUCH

No amount of persuasion will move people to accept something they consider unreasonable. And the definition of *reasonable* depends on the individual. In response to an attempt to persuade workers to exercise, employees will differ as to which walking/jogging option they might accept. To the jock writing the memo, a daily eight-kilometre jog might seem perfectly reasonable, but some employees would think it outrageous. The company program therefore has to offer something most of its audience will accept as reasonable (except for, say, couch potatoes and those in poor health). Any request that exceeds its audience's "latitude of acceptance" (Sherif et al. 39–59) is doomed, as Figure 11.2 suggests.

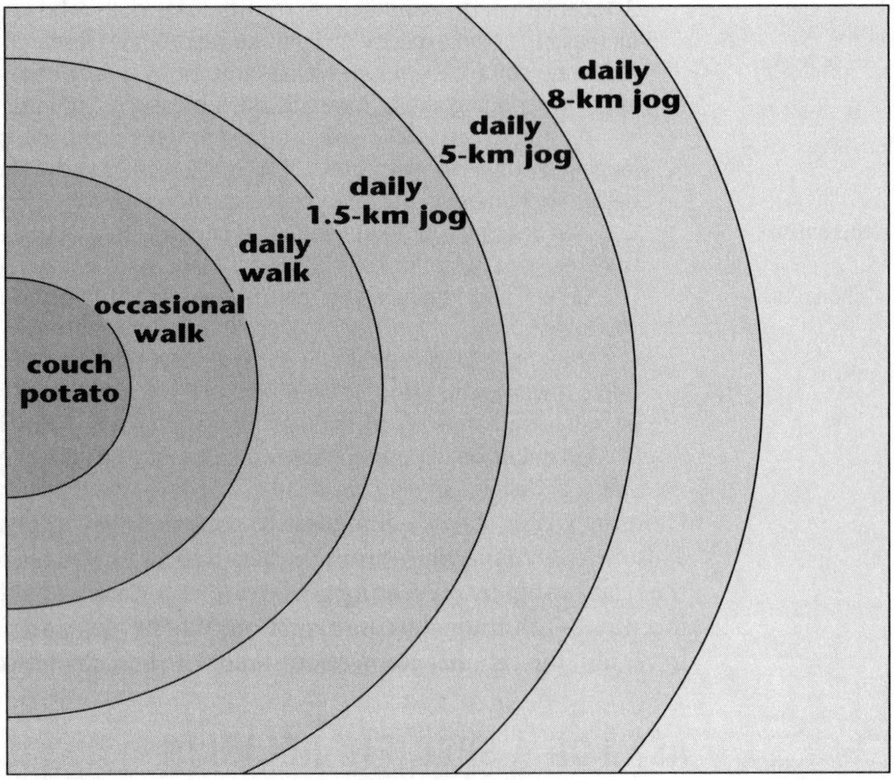

Figure 11.2 Options and Latitude of Acceptance

RECOGNIZE ALL CONSTRAINTS

Persuasive communicators observe certain limits or restrictions imposed by their situation. These *constraints* govern what should or should not be said, who should say it and to whom, when and how it should be said, and through which medium (printed document, online, telephone, face to face, and so on).

Organizational Constraints

Organizations often have their own official constraints such as schedules, deadlines, budget limitations, writing style, the way a document is organized and formatted, and its chain and medium of distribution throughout the organization. But writers also face unofficial constraints:

Decide carefully when to say what to whom

> Most organizations have clear rules for interpreting and acting on (or responding to) statements made by colleagues. Even if the rules are unstated, we know who can initiate interaction, who can be approached, who can propose a delay, what topics can or cannot be discussed, who can interrupt or be interrupted, who can order or be ordered, who can terminate interaction, and how long interaction should last. (Littlejohn and Jabusch 143)

The exact rules vary among organizations, depending on whether communication channels are open and flexible or closed and rigid, on whether employee participation in decision making is encouraged or discouraged. Although the rules of the game mostly are unspoken, anyone who ignores them invites disaster.

Airing even the most legitimate gripe in the wrong way through the wrong medium to the wrong person can be fatal to your work relationships and your career. The following memo, for instance, is likely to be interpreted by the executive officer as petty and whining behaviour, and by the maintenance director as a public attack.

To: P. Susan Singh, Chief Executive Officer

Wrong way to the wrong person

Please ask the Maintenance Director to get his people to do their job for a change. I realize we're all short-staffed, but I've received 50 complaints this week about the filthy restrooms and overflowing wastebaskets in my department. If he wants us to empty our own wastebaskets, why doesn't he let us know?

cc: Robert Stuart, Maintenance Director

Instead, why not address the memo directly to the key person—or better yet, phone the person?

To: Robert Stuart, Maintenance Director

A better way to the right person

I wonder if we could meet to exchange some ideas about how our departments might be able to help one another during these staff shortages.

Legal Constraints

Sometimes what you can say is limited by contract or by laws protecting confidentiality or customers' rights, or by laws affecting product liability. For example, in a collection letter for non-payment, you can threaten legal action but cannot threaten any kind of violence or threaten to publicize the refusal to pay, or pretend to be a lawyer (Varner and Varner 31–40). If someone requests information on one of your employees, you can "respond only to specific requests that have been approved by the employee. Further, your comments should relate only to job performance which is documented" (Harcourt 64). In sales literature or manuals, you and your company are liable for faulty information that leads to injury or damage.

Ethical Constraints

While legal constraints are defined by federal and provincial laws, ethical constraints are defined by good conscience, honesty, and fair play. For example, it may be perfectly legal to promote a new pesticide by emphasizing its effectiveness, while downplaying its carcinogenic effects; whether such action is *ethical,* however, is another issue entirely.

Persuasive skills carry tremendous potential for abuse. There is a difference between honestly presenting your best case and using deception to manipulate the reader. (Chapter 12 is devoted to various ethics problems in communication.)

Time Constraints

Persuasion often depends on good timing. Does your proposal match current needs and priorities? Is your reader preoccupied with other matters at the moment? If so, you should wait until that reader is ready for your message.

Also consider the time required to complete the proposed work. Project proposals are often rejected by decision makers who believe that too much of their time or your time will be required during the project. Perhaps there's apparently not enough time to complete a project by a certain date—say, a research project by the end of a semester, or road repairs before the summer tourist season.

Social and Psychological Constraints

Too often, what we say can be misunderstood or misinterpreted. Here are just a few of the human constraints routinely encountered by communicators.

- *Relationship between communicator and audience:* Are you writing to a superior, a subordinate, or an equal? How well do you and your audience know each other? Can you joke around or should you be serious? Do you have a history of conflict? Do you trust and like one another? What you say and how you say it—and how it is interpreted—will be influenced by the relationship.
- *Audience's personality:* Researchers claim that "some people are easier to persuade than others, regardless of the topic or situation" (Littlejohn 136). A reader's ability to be persuaded might depend on such personality traits as confidence, optimism, self-esteem, willingness to be different, desire to conform, degree of openness, or regard for power (Stonecipher 188–89).
- *Audience's sense of identity and affiliation as a group:* How close-knit is the group? Does it have a strong sense of identity (as in union members, conservationists, or engineering majors)? Will group loyalty or pressure to conform prevent certain appeals from working?
- *Perceived size and urgency of the problem or issue:* In the audience's view, how big is this issue or problem? Has it been understated or overstated? Big problems are more likely to cause exaggerated fears, anxieties, loyalties, and resistance to change—or desperate attempts at quick and easy solutions.

Writers who can assess a situation's constraints avoid serious blunders and can develop their message for greatest effectiveness.

SUPPORT YOUR CLAIMS CONVINCINGLY

The strength of your case depends on the *reasons* you offer to support your claims.

Persuasive claims are backed up by reasons that have meaning for the reader

> *When we seek a project extension, argue for a raise, interview for a job, justify our actions, advise a friend, speak out on issues of the day... we are involved in acts that require good reasons. Good reasons allow our audience and ourselves to find a shared basis for cooperating.... In speaking and writing, you can use marvelous language, tell great stories, provide exciting metaphors, speak in enthralling tones, and even use your reputation to advantage, but what it comes down to is that you must speak to your audience with reasons they understand. (Hauser 71)*

To sell a plan to supervisors and co-workers, you will need good reasons, in the form of *evidence* and *appeals to readers' needs and values* (Rottenberg 104–06).

Offer Convincing Evidence

Evidence is any factual support from an outside source. Evidence is a powerful element in persuasion—as long as it measures up to readers' standards. Discerning readers evaluate evidence by using these criteria (Perloff 157–58):

- *The evidence has quality.* Instead of sheer quantity, readers expect evidence that is strong, specific, new, or different.
- *The sources are credible.* Readers want to know where the evidence comes from, how it was collected, and who collected it.
- *The evidence is considered reasonable.* It falls within a reader's "latitude of acceptance" (Sherif et al. 39–59).

Evidence includes factual statements, statistics, examples, and expert testimony.

Factual Statements. *Facts* can be shown by observation, experience, research, or measurement.

Offer the facts

> Many of our competitors already have installed wireless networks.

When your space and your readers' tolerance are limited—as they usually are—be selective. Decide which facts best support your case.

Statistics. Numbers can be highly convincing. Before considering other details of your argument, many workplace readers are interested in the "bottom line": costs, savings, and profits (Goodall and Waagen 57).

Give the numbers

> The proposed wireless network will cost 20 percent less than a wired network and will provide a 17 percent improvement in upload times

Numbers also can be highly misleading. Any statistics you present have to be accurate, trustworthy, and easy for readers to understand and verify. (See pages 343–47 for ways to avoid faulty statistical reasoning.) Always cite your source.

Examples. By showing specific instances of your point, examples help audiences visualize the idea or the concept. For example, the best way to explain what you mean by "flexibility of the wireless network" is to show a map of the locations where users' laptops would be "connected" to the network.

Good examples have persuasive force; they give readers something solid, a way of understanding even the most surprising or unlikely claim.

Expert Testimony. Expert testimony lends authority and credibility to any claim.

Cite the experts

> Ron Catabia, a consultant who designed Canjet's systems, has studied our needs and strongly recommends we move ahead with a wireless network.

To be credible, however, an expert has to be unbiased and considered reliable by the audience.

Although solid evidence can be persuasive, evidence alone isn't always enough to influence the reader. In many companies, the bottom line might be very persuasive for company executives but could mean little to some managers and employees, who will be asking: *Does this threaten my authority? Will I have to work harder? Will I fall behind? Is my job in danger?* These readers will have to perceive some benefit beyond company profit.

Appeal to Common Goals and Values

Audiences expect a writer to share their goals and values. If you hope to create any kind of consensus, you have to identify at least one goal you and your audience have in common: "What do we all want most?"

Most people want job security, a sense of belonging, control over their jobs and destinies, and a growing and fulfilling career. Any persuasive recommendation will have to take these goals into account. For example:

Appeal to shared goals

> Learning this new software will enhance our skill set and increase career mobility for all of us.

Our goals are shaped by our values (qualities we believe in, ideals we stand for): friendship, loyalty, ambition, honesty, self-discipline, equality, fairness, and achievement, among others (Rokeach 57–58). Beyond appealing to common goals, you can appeal to shared values.

You might appeal to a shared commitment to quality and achievement:

Appeal to shared values

> None of us needs reminding of the fierce competition in the software industry. Improved communication among networking departments will result in better manuals, keeping us on the front line of quality and achievement.

Give your audience reasons that have real meaning for *them* personally. For example, in a recent study of teenage attitudes about the negative consequences of smoking, respondents listed these reasons for not smoking: bad breath, difficulty concentrating, loss of friends, and trouble with adults. None of them listed dying of cancer—presumably because this last reason carries little meaning for young people personally (Baumann et al. 510–30).

CONSIDER THE CULTURAL CONTEXT

Reaction to persuasive appeals can be influenced by a culture's customs and values.[1] Cultures might differ in their willingness to debate, criticize, or express disagreement or emotion. They might differ in their definitions of "convincing support," or they might observe special formalities in communicating. Expressions of feelings and concern for one's family might be valued more than logic, fact, statistics, research findings, or expert testimony. Some cultures consider the *source* of a message as important as its content. Establishing trust and building a relationship might weigh more heavily than proof and might be an essential prelude to getting down to business.

---

[1] Adapted from Beamer 293–95; Gestelend 24; Hulbert, "Overcoming" 42; Jameson 9–11; Kohl et al. 65; Martin and Chaney 271–77; Nydell 61; Thrush 276–77; Victor 159–66.

Cultures might differ in their attitudes toward the environment, big business, technology, or competition. They might value delayed gratification more than immediate reward, stability more than progress, time more than profit, politeness more than candour, age more than youth.

One essential element of reader expectations in all cultures is the primacy of *face saving:*

Some cultures place greater emphasis than others on face saving

> *Face saving [is] the act of preserving one's prestige or outward dignity. People of all cultures, to a greater or lesser degree, are concerned with face saving. Yet… [its] importance… varies significantly from culture to culture.… Indirectness in high face-saving cultures is viewed as consideration for another's sense of dignity; in low face-saving cultures, indirectness is seen as dishonesty. (Victor 159–61)*

To gain a preliminary understanding of how to apply the above questions to a given culture, visit Communicaid's introduction to national cultures, at **www.communicaid.com**. This site provides overviews of 24 countries, including

IN BRIEF QUESTIONS FOR ANALYZING CROSS-CULTURAL AUDIENCES

What Are the Values and Attitudes?

- Attitude toward the environment, big business, technology, competition, risk taking, status, youth versus age, rugged individualism versus group loyalty
- Preference for immediate reward or delayed gratification, progress or stability
- Importance of gender equality, interaction, and differences in the workplace
- Importance of the personal relationship in a business transaction
- Importance of time ("Time is money!" or "Never rush!")
- Importance of feelings versus logic and facts, results versus relationships
- Importance of candour versus saving face and sparing other people's feelings
- Extent of belief in fate, luck, or destiny
- View of our culture (admiration, contempt, envy, fear)

What Is Accepted Behaviour?

- Formalities for making requests, expressing disagreement, criticism, or praise
- Preferred form for greetings or introductions (first or family names, titles)
- Willingness to criticize or request clarification
- Willingness to argue, debate, or express disagreement
- Willingness to be contradicted
- Willingness to express emotion (pleasure, gratitude, anger)
- Importance of trust and relationship building
- Importance of politeness and euphemism and leaving certain things unsaid
- Preference for casual or formal interaction
- Preference for directness and plain talk or for indirectness and ambiguity
- Preference for rapid decision making or for extensive analysis of a topic

How Do the Social and Legal Systems Work?

- Social/political system inflexible or open
- Class distinctions
- Democratic, egalitarian ideals or rank-conscious, authoritarian system
- Relative importance of the law versus interpersonal trust
- Formality of the contract process: a mere handshake or extensive legal documents
- Extent of lawyer involvement
- Extent to which the legal system enforces contractual agreements
- Role of gift giving (viewed as bribery or as a display of respect)

This list was largely adapted from Caswell-Cowardo 265; Weymouth 144; Beamer 293–95; Martin and Chaney 271–77; Victor 159–61.

Canada, along with some description of each country's key cultural concepts, core values, and local business culture. Of course, this information just begins to delve into the intricacies of each national culture. Companies such as Communicaid provide in-depth workshops that help people work or do business in most of the world's major trading nations. Such workshops are very popular because learning a different culture from trial and error while "on the ground" is very inefficient, often costly (in terms of lost goodwill and lost business), and sometimes even dangerous.

Training workshops are not restricted to international cultural studies. In Canada, for example, a variety of universities, colleges, and private trainers conduct training that helps Aboriginal people and other Canadians understand how to live and work with each other.

GUIDELINES for Persuasion

Later chapters offer specific guidelines for various persuasive documents. For all types of documents, remember this principle:

No matter how brilliant, any argument rejected by its audience is a failed argument.

If readers find cause to dislike you or conclude that your argument has no meaning for them personally, they usually reject *anything* you say. Connecting with an audience means being able to see things from their perspective. The following guidelines can help you make that connection.

1. *Assess the political climate.* Can you be outspoken? Who will be affected by your document? How will they react? How will your motives be interpreted? Will the document enhance your reputation or damage it? The better you assess readers' political feelings, the less likely your document will backfire. Do what you can to earn confidence and goodwill:

   - Be diplomatic; try not to make anyone look bad or lose face.
   - Be aware of your status in the organization; don't overstep.
   - Don't expect anyone to be perfect—including yourself.
   - Ask your intended readers to review early drafts.

   When reporting company negligence, dishonesty, stupidity, or incompetence, expect political fallout. Decide beforehand whether you want to keep your job or your dignity (more in Chapter 12).

2. *Learn the unspoken rules.* Know the constraints on what you can say, to whom you can say it, and how and when you can say it.
3. *Be clear about what you want.* Diplomacy is important, but people won't like having to guess about your purpose.
4. *Never make a claim or ask for something you know readers will reject outright.* Be sure readers can live with whatever you're requesting or proposing. Offer a genuine choice.
5. *Anticipate your audience's reaction.* Will they be defensive, surprised, annoyed, angry, or what? Try to address their biggest objections beforehand.

(continued)

GUIDELINES
for Persuasion
(continued)

Express your judgments ("We could do better") without making people defensive ("It's your fault").

6. *Decide on a connection (or combination of connections).* Does the situation call for you to merely declare your position, appeal to the relationship, or appeal to common sense and reason?
7. *Avoid an extreme persona.* Persona is the image or impression of the writer's personality suggested by a document's tone. Resist the urge to "sound off," no matter how strongly you feel, because audiences tune out aggressive people, no matter how sensible the argument. Try to be likeable and reasonable. Admit the imperfections in your case—a little humility never hurts. Don't hesitate to offer praise when it's deserved.
8. *Find points of agreement with your audience.* Focusing on a shared value, goal, or concern can reduce conflict and help win agreement on later points.
9. *Never distort the opponent's position.* A sure way to alienate people is to cast the opponent as more of a villain or simpleton than the facts warrant.
10. *Try to concede something to the opponent.* Surely the opposing case is based on at least one good reason. Acknowledge the merits of that case before arguing for your own. Instead of seeming like a know-it-all, show some empathy and willingness to compromise.
11. *Use only your best material.* Not all your reasons or appeals will have equal strength or significance. Decide which material—from your *audience's* view—best advances your case.
12. *Make no claim or assertion unless you can support it with good reasons.* "Just because" does not constitute adequate support!
13. *Use your skills responsibly.* Persuasive skills are easily abused. People who feel they have been bullied, manipulated, or deceived most likely will become your enemies. Know when to back off.
14. *Seek a second opinion of your document before you release it.* Ask someone you trust and who has no stake in the issue at hand.
15. *Decide on the appropriate medium.* Given the specific issue and audience, should you communicate in person, in print, by phone, email, fax, newsletter, bulletin board, or what? Should all recipients receive your message via the same medium?

An Example

Figure 11.3 on the following page illustrates how our guidelines are employed in an actual persuasive situation. This letter is from a company that distributes and installs a variety of home heating systems. General manager Manson Harding writes a persuasive answer to a potential customer's question: "Why should I invest in a geothermal heat pump system you propose for my home?" As you read the letter, notice the kinds of evidence and appeals that support the opening claim. Notice also how the writer focuses on reasons important to the reader.

Harding Heartland HVAC

Bay 17, 1699 Larose Avenue, St. Boniface, Manitoba
R4C 2Y1
(204) 948-6662

May 12, 2008

Mr. Pascual di Santos
245 Carleton Way
Winnipeg, Manitoba R3T 6L7

Dear Mr. di Santos:

The writer states his claim

Bill Neville has asked me to suggest a heating/cooling system for the new house he has contracted to build for you. I understand you had planned to install a conventional natural gas furnace and standard air conditioner, but I recommend a geothermal heat pump system as the best long-term system for your needs.

Provides background, in case the reader has little previous knowledge

Geothermal heat pumps use electricity to move heat; thus, the same pumps would take heat from the earth in winter and dissipate heat from the house to the earth in summer. Enclosure A describes a horizontal-loop geothermal system that would best suit your house design and your six-acre location.

States major reason and gives supporting figures

A geothermal system would result in major savings for your proposed residence. We've calculated heat loss for your home design and we've projected the costs for both a conventional system and a geothermal system. Over the next 10 years, your 4950-square-foot residence would average $3,500 annually in heating costs and $2,450 in annual air conditioning costs. By contrast, a geothermal system would cost $1,500 annually. All calculations are listed in Enclosure B.

Acknowledges potential reader resistance, and refutes reason for reader concern

A geothermal system would cost $14,250 more to install than a conventional system. However, I understand that you have a contingency fund for "necessary modifications." More to the point, at an annual operating saving of $4,450, the geothermal system's additional cost would be regained in less than four years.

States a second "reason"—appeals to emotion

Offers additional proof

Geothermal systems also offer increased comfort and a healthy environment. My clients comment about the air feeling cleaner and they've observed that the temperature doesn't vary like it does with gas furnaces. Allergy sufferers tell me that they notice fewer symptoms in winter, now that they've switched to a geothermal system. If you wish, I can put you in contact with clients who've reported feeling better about the air they breathe with a geothermal system. Further, geothermal systems contribute to a cleaner external environment, because fossil fuels aren't burned and because geothermal systems use less electricity than conventional air conditioners.

Figure 11.3 Supporting a Claim with Good Reasons *(continued)*

Mr. di Santos May 12, 2008 Page 2

Deals with another potential cause of reader resistance

You'll be pleased to know that geothermal systems require little maintenance. Thus, warranties are impressive—10 years for heat pumps and 50 years for the remainder of the system. A typical closed-loop system has a life expectancy of 100 years.

Appeals to reader's need for security

Gives reasons to trust the writer

To be totally effective and dependable, any HVAC system must be installed by skilled, knowledgeable people. We've been designing and installing heating systems for 14 years; over the past four years we've designed and installed 17 geothermal systems. My file of letters from satisfied customers is available for your perusal. Bomber Drilling, which installs the underground piping for our projects, has had extensive geothermal loop field experience in Manitoba and in northern Minnesota.

Leads to suggested action

For more information about geothermal heating and cooling, and for several Canadian case studies, see www.geothermop.ca. Please call me at 948-6662 to discuss any aspect of the HVAC system for your new home.

Sincerely,

Manson Harding
General Manager

Enclosures:

A: Geothermal system description
B: Operating cost calculations

Figure 11.3 Supporting a Claim with Good Reasons

WEB CONNECT

These sites discuss persuasive techniques applied to a variety of genres and media:

www.webpagecontent.com/arc_archive/42/5/
www.superwriter.com/persuasi.htm
www.bly.com/Pages/documents/TFOPW.html
http://owl.english.purdue.edu/handouts/general/gl_argpers.html

EXERCISES

1. Find an example of an effective persuasive letter. In a memo to your instructor, explain why and how the message succeeds. Base your evaluation on the persuasion guidelines listed on pages 220–21. Attach a copy of the letter to your evaluation memo. Be prepared to discuss your evaluation in class.

   Now, evaluate a poorly written document, explaining how and why it fails.

2. Think about some change you would like to see on your campus. Perhaps you would like to make something happen, such as a campus-wide policy on plagiarism, changes in course offerings or requirements, more access to computers, a policy on sexist language, or a daycare centre. Or perhaps you would like to improve something, such as the grading system, campus lighting, or the system for student evaluation of teachers. Decide whom you want to persuade, and write a memo or email to that audience.

   Anticipate carefully your audience's implied questions, such as:

   - Do we really have a problem or need?
   - If so, should we care enough about it to do anything?
   - Can the problem be solved?
   - What are some possible solutions?
   - What benefits can we anticipate? What liabilities?

   Can you envision additional audience questions? Complete an audience/purpose profile (see page 35).

   Don't think of this memo as the final word, but as a consciousness-raising introduction that gets the reader to acknowledge that the issue deserves attention. At this early stage, highly specific recommendations would be premature and inappropriate.

COLLABORATIVE PROJECT

Assume that you work for an environmental consulting firm that is under contract with various countries for a range of projects, including these:

- a plan for rainforest regeneration in Latin America and sub-Saharan Africa
- a plan for "clean" industries in developing countries
- a plan for organic agricultural development in Africa and India

Each project will require environmental impact statements, feasibility studies, grant proposals, and a legion of other documents. These are often prepared in collaboration with members of the host country, and in some cases prepared by your company for audiences in the host country: from political, social, and industrial leaders to technical experts and so on.

For such projects to succeed, people from different cultures have to communicate effectively and sensitively, creating goodwill and cooperation. Before your company begins work in earnest with a particular country, your co-workers will need to develop cultural awareness. Your assignment is to select a country and to research that culture's behaviours, attitudes, values, and social system in terms of how these variables influence the culture's communication preferences and expectations. What should your colleagues know about this culture in order to communicate effectively and diplomatically? Do the necessary research using the questions from In Brief on page 219 as a guide.

CHAPTER 12

Writing Ethically

LEARNING OBJECTIVES

After reading this chapter, you should be able to

- Recognize the potential for unethical communication in a variety of situations.
- Apply guidelines for ethical communication.
- Understand how to deal with group pressure and other sources of unethical communication.
- Know how and when to report unethical communication.

Effective messages (that achieve their informative and persuasive purposes) are not necessarily *ethical*. For example, an advertisement that says "our potato chips contain no cholesterol" may be technically accurate but misleading, because potato chips contain saturated fats that produce cholesterol. Or a technical report may present accurate facts and conclusions about the causes of a mining accident but may not describe a history of neglect and poor safety practices at the mine.

When people "do the right thing," what causes them to do so? Which of the following bases of ethical behaviour prompt you to act honestly and fairly, in others' as well as your own interests?

What makes me act ethically?"

- *The moral basis:* "Treat others as you would have them treat you" is a basic tenet of many religions' moral teaching.
- *A practical basis:* "What consequences will result from my actions?" "How will my behaviour affect others?"
- *The authoritative stance:* "Follow the listed rules of ethical behaviour, or face penalties!"
- *The institutional stance:* "This is the way we do things here."
- *The peer group pressure stance:* "Our group believes in fair, open, honest behaviour; we expect you to share those beliefs."
- *The familial/environmental approach:* "I was raised to be honest and to respect others; these values are part of who I am."

The above list assumes ethical thinking and behaviour, but can unethical persons learn to behave ethically? Socrates didn't think so, but still spent his life trying to teach virtue. Perhaps a more practical approach is based on the possible consequences of ethical and unethical actions. Critical thinking skills, then, help us recognize unethical behaviour and help us find ways to act ethically in the workplace.

RECOGNIZE UNETHICAL COMMUNICATION

Thousands of people are injured or killed yearly in avoidable accidents, the result of faulty communication that prevented intelligent decision making. The following tragedies were caused ultimately by unethical communication.

The *Columbia* Accident

Unethical communication has consequences

On February 1, 2003, the Space Shuttle *Columbia*, with seven crew members, disintegrated as it re-entered Earth's atmosphere on its way home. A seven-month investigation by the independent Columbia Accident Investigation Board (CAIB) identified the primary physical cause as "a breach in the Thermal Protection System on the leading edge of the left wing, caused by a piece of insulating foam" during the launch on January 16, 2003 (CAIB 9).

The CAIB also concluded that "the organizational causes of this accident are rooted in the Space Shuttle Program's history and culture" (9). The CAIB report describes "compromises. . . . resource constraints. . . . schedule pressures. . . . and organizational barriers that prevented effective communication of critical safety information and stifled differences of opinion" (9).

Similar pressures played a part in a previous shuttle disaster, the 1986 explosion of the Space Shuttle *Challenger*, 43 seconds into its launch. For a chronology of the event, see the website maintained by the Online Ethics Center for Engineering and Science, at **http://temp.onlineethics.org/topics/index.html.** Click on "Moral Exemplars," then "Boisjoly," for Roger Boisjoly's account and analysis of the *Challenger* disaster.

The Westray Coal Mining Accident

On May 9, 1992, 26 men were killed in an explosion at the Westray coal mining operation in Plymouth, Nova Scotia. The mine, employing the latest mining technology, had been operating for about eight months when the explosion occurred. In a subsequent report of the Westray Mine Public Inquiry, Mr. Justice K. Peter Richard said that the Westray disaster was a "complex mosaic of actions, omissions, mistakes, incompetence, apathy, cynicism, stupidity, and neglect."[1] As the evidence emerged during the inquiry, it became clear that many people and entities had not communicated appropriately, had not acted on clear directives, and had not applied or enforced coal mine and occupational health and safety regulations. While criminal negligence and manslaughter charges were withdrawn late in 1998, in 1999 the families of the victims of the disaster commenced a negligence lawsuit against the federal and Nova Scotia governments, former mine officials, and equipment manufacturers.

1. *The Westray Story: A Predictable Path to Disaster*. Executive Summary (www.gov.ns.ca/enla/pubs/westray/execsumm.asp).

These catastrophes make for dramatic headlines, but more routine examples of deliberate miscommunication rarely are publicized. Outcomes like the following succeed because the people communicate unethically by saying whatever works.

- A person lands a great job by exaggerating credentials, experience, or expertise.
- A marketing specialist for a chemical company negotiates a huge bulk sale of the company's powerful new pesticide by downplaying its carcinogenic hazards.
- To meet the production deadline on a new auto model, the test engineer suppresses, in the final report, data indicating that the fuel tank could explode upon impact.
- A manager writes a strong recommendation to get a friend promoted, while overlooking someone more deserving.

Can you recall some instances of deliberate miscommunication from your personal experience or that you learned about in the news? What were some of the effects of this miscommunication? How might the problems have been avoided?

Ethical decisions are not always black and white

To save face, escape blame, or get ahead, anyone might be tempted to say what people want to hear or to suppress bad news or make it seem "rosier." Some of these decisions are not simply black and white. Here is one engineer's description of the grey area in which issues of product safety and quality often are decided:

> The company must be able to produce its products at a cost low enough to be competitive.... To design a product that is of the highest quality and consequently has a high and uncompetitive price may mean that the company will not be able to remain profitable, and be forced out of business. (Burghardt 92)

Do you emphasize to a customer the need for extra-careful maintenance of a highly sensitive computer—and risk losing the sale? Or do you downplay maintenance requirements, focusing instead on the computer's positive features? Do you tell a white lie so as not to hurt a colleague's feelings, or do you "tell it like it is" because you're convinced that lying is wrong in any circumstance? The decisions we make in these situations often are influenced by the pressures we feel.

EXPECT SOCIAL PRESSURE TO PRODUCE UNETHICAL COMMUNICATION

Pressure to get the job done can cause normally honest people to break the rules. At some point in your career you might have to choose between doing what your employer wants ("just follow orders" or "look the other way") and doing what you know is right. Maybe you will be pressured to ignore a safety hazard in order to meet a project deadline:

> Just as your company is about to unveil its hot new pickup truck, your safety engineering team discovers that the reserve gas tanks (installed beneath the truck but outside the frame) can explode on impact in a side collision. The company has spent a small fortune developing this new model and doesn't want to hear about this problem.

Companies often face the contradictory goals of *production* (which means *making* money on the product) and *safety* (which means *spending* money to avoid accidents that may or may not happen). When productivity receives exclusive priority, safety concerns may suffer (Wickens 434–36). Thus it seems no surprise that well over 50 percent of managers studied feel "pressure to compromise personal ethics for company goals" (Golen et al. 75). These pressures come in varied forms (Lewis and Reinsch 31):

Pressure to "look the other way"

- the drive for profit
- the need to beat the competition (other organizations or co-workers)
- the need to succeed at any cost, as when superiors demand more productivity or savings without questioning the methods
- an appeal to loyalty—to the organization and to its way of doing things

Figure 12.1 depicts how such pressures can add up.

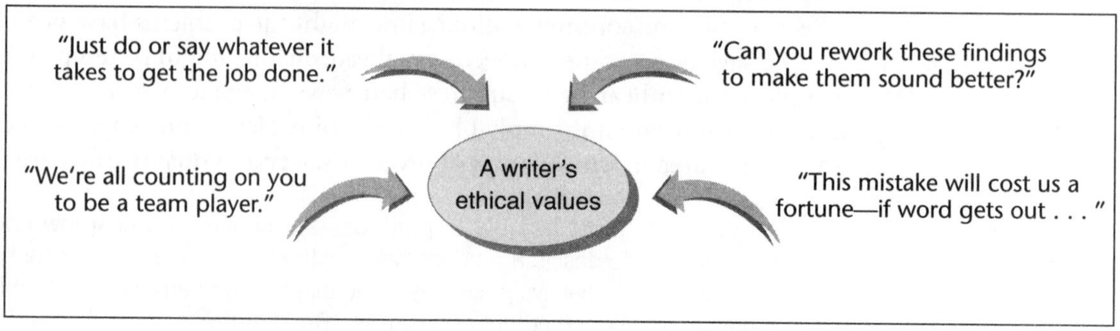

Figure 12.1 How Workplace Pressures Can Influence Ethical Values

Following is a tragic example of how organizational pressure and/or personal agendas can help create a climate where important information is not reported or not heeded by those who receive the reports.

The Walkerton Tragedy

On May 17, 2000, many of the residents of Walkerton, Ontario, began to display symptoms of bacterial poisoning—bloody diarrhea, vomiting, cramps, and fever. Eventually, more than 2300 of the town's fewer than 5000 citizens became seriously ill. Seven died. The tragic results were preventable, if various public officials had fulfilled their obligations.

The outbreak was primarily caused by *Escherichia coli 0157:H7* (*E. coli*) and by *Campylobacter jejuni,* traced to bacteria from cattle manure that was washed into the No. 5 well, which supplied most of Walkerton's water supply during the time that supply became contaminated.

Sadly, many of Walkerton's residents might have escaped the illness if Stan Koebel, Walkerton's water manager, had notified the public, the Ministry of the Environment, or the public health office that tests of water sampled May 15 had revealed *E. coli* contamination. Koebel sat on these results from May 18 to 23. Indeed, when health officials called on May 19 and 20 to inquire about Walkerton's water supply, he lied; he said that the water was safe to drink. So the health officials looked for other possible causes of contamination.

On May 21, in response to more and more cases of *E. coli* poisoning, and with increasing likelihood of a water contamination, medical officer Dr. Murray McQuigge issued a "boil water" advisory. McQuigge's unit took samples on May 21 and on May 23, and learned on May 23 that Walkerton's water was indeed *E. coli* contaminated. When confronted with the health unit findings, Koebel admitted that he had known about the contamination since May 18 and also that another well's chlorination equipment had not been working for several days (Evenson A9).

Mr. Justice Dennis O'Connor was commissioned to head an inquiry into the disaster. His report concluded that "the outbreak would have been prevented by the use of continuous chlorine residual and turbidity monitors at Well 5. The failure to use continuous monitors at Well 5 resulted from shortcomings in the approvals and inspections programs of the Ministry of the Environment" (O'Connor, "Summary" 3). The Walkerton Inquiry, in May and June 2001, uncovered a number of possible contributing factors:

- From 1997 through 1999, a London, Ontario, lab found *E. coli* bacteria in Walkerton water on five separate occasions; the lab also noticed unusually low levels of chlorine disinfectant. Microbiologist Gary Palmateer faxed the results to Walkerton officials and the Ministry of the Environment, but no corrective actions were taken (Canadian Press, "Notifying Government").
- Despite knowing about water safety issues in Walkerton and elsewhere, the Ministry of the Environment did not "release [water safety] reports and test results documenting the severity of the situation" (Canadian Press, "Ontario Ministry").
- Dr. Richard Schabas was Ontario's chief medical officer of health in May 1997 when he tried to warn Premier Mike Harris, among others (at a meeting of the provincial cabinet's policy and priorities committee), that eliminating provincial funding for regional health boards would allow small-town politicians to bully or circumvent local medical health officers. Ignoring such warnings, the government downloaded public health boards to municipalities.
- Also, at Schabas's request, health minister Jim Wilson sent, on August 20, 1997, a letter to Norm Sterling, minister of the environment. In that letter, Wilson urgently recommended that the Ontario Water Resources Act be amended to require local waterworks to inform medical health officers of tests showing water contamination. In the 2001 inquiry, Sterling said he didn't recall receiving the letter; at the time, he was "distracted by other issues" (Mittelstaedt, "Tory Didn't See"). But Sterling said he would accept some blame for the Walkerton tragedy if the inquiry established that his failure to react to the letter contributed to the *E. coli* outbreak.
- Previous to Norm Sterling's tenure at the Ministry of the Environment, Brenda Elliott was the minister responsible for chopping the provincial environmental-protection budget by nearly 50 percent from June 1995 to August 1996. Under Elliott's leadership, the ministry moved to privatize water-testing services in two months, not in the three years recommended in reports submitted by ministry staffers. At the Walkerton Inquiry, Elliott said that she had been "acting as part of a team" and that she should not be held personally responsible for the Walkerton *E. coli* outbreak (Mittelstaedt, "Tory 'Team' Made Cuts").
- For years, Stan Koebel had not reported any test results that would reflect badly on his municipal water operation. And, along with his brother Frank (waterworks maintenance foreman), Koebel for years had "routinely falsified water samples, test results, and chlorination records" (Canadian Press, "Doctor"). Indeed, in his annual reports, Stan Koebel had described a conscientious, competent staff and a safe, secure water system (Blatchford A1).

- At the apex of the pyramid of responsible officials, Premier Mike Harris initially claimed at the Walkerton Inquiry that he didn't know of risks associated with eliminating government water-testing labs. Later at the inquiry, he admitted that he did know of such risks but considered them "manageable" and that therefore the public didn't need to be informed.
- Justice O'Connor's report concluded, however, that "there is no evidence that the specific risks, including the risks arising from the fact that the notification protocol was a guideline rather than a regulation, were properly assessed or addressed" (O'Connor, "Summary" 35). In effect, concluded O'Connor, the government's drive to reduce "red tape" led to the Walkerton tragedy because privatizing lab testing of water samples led directly to the events of May 2000, and reducing the Ministry of the Environment's approvals and inspections indirectly helped cause the outbreak by reducing the chance of reporting negative test results (Full Report 406–08).
- Dr. Murray McQuigge, who blew the whistle on Stan Koebel, faced intense criticism from Koebel's lawyer at the Walkerton Inquiry. Also, inquiry witnesses suggested that McQuigge's office knew about "problems with Walkerton's water system two years earlier but did nothing about it" (Blackwell A3) and therefore McQuigge was not above reproach himself. Such criticism illustrates one of the potential difficulties faced by whistle blowers.

NEVER CONFUSE TEAMWORK WITH GROUPTHINK

Any successful organization relies on teamwork, everyone cooperating to get the job done. But teamwork is not the same as *groupthink* (Janis 9).

Groupthink occurs when group pressure prevents individuals from questioning, criticizing, or "making waves." Group members feel a greater need for acceptance and a sense of belonging than for critically examining the issues. In a conformist climate, critical thinking is impossible. Anyone who has lived through adolescent peer pressure has already experienced a version of groupthink.

Yielding to pressure can be especially tempting in a large company or on a complex project, where individual responsibility is easy to hide in the crowd:

How some corporations evade responsibility for their actions

> Lack of accountability is deeply embedded in the concept of the corporation. Shareholders' liability is limited to the amount of money they invest. Managers' liability is limited to what they choose to know about the operation of the company. The corporation's liability is limited by governments. . .by insurance, and by laws allowing corporations to duck liability by altering their. . .structure. (Mokhiber 16)

RELY ON CRITICAL THINKING FOR ETHICAL DECISIONS

Because of their impact on people and on your career, ethical decisions challenge your critical thinking skills:

Ethical decisions require critical thinking

- How can I know the "right thing" in this situation?
- What are my obligations, and to whom, in this situation?
- What values or ideals do I want to stand for in this situation?
- What is likely to happen if I do X, or Y?

Can you rely on more than intuition or conscience in navigating the grey areas of ethical decisions? How will you make a convincing case against danger or folly to a roomful of people caught up in groupthink? Although ethical issues resist simple formulas, you can avoid two major fallacies that obstruct good judgment: the fallacy of "doing one's thing" (personal preference or *relativism*) and the fallacy of "one rule fits all" (regardless of the circumstances; *absolutism*).

Reasonable Criteria for Ethical Judgment

Somewhere between the extremes of relativism and absolutism are *reasonable criteria* (standards of measurement that most people would consider acceptable). These criteria for ethical judgment take the form of *obligations, ideals,* and *consequences* (Ruggiero 55–56; Christians et al. 17–18).

Obligations are the responsibilities we have to everyone involved:

- *obligation to ourselves,* to act in our own self-interest and according to good conscience
- *obligation to clients and customers,* to stand by the people to whom we are bound by contract—and who pay the bills
- *obligation to our company,* to advance its goals, respect its policies, protect confidential information, and expose misconduct that would harm the organization
- *obligation to co-workers,* to promote their safety and well-being
- *obligation to the community,* to preserve the local economy, welfare, and quality of life
- *obligation to society,* to consider the national and global impact of our actions

When the interests of these parties conflict—as they often do—we have to decide very carefully where our primary obligations lie.

Ideals are "notions of excellence" (Ruggiero 55), the positive values that we believe in or stand for: loyalty, friendship, courage, compassion, dignity, fairness, and whatever qualities make us who we are.

The *consequences* of our actions may be beneficial or harmful, immediate or delayed, intentional or unintentional, obvious or subtle (Ruggiero 56). Some consequences are easy to predict; some are impossible to know ahead of time.

Figure 12.2 depicts the relationship among these three criteria.

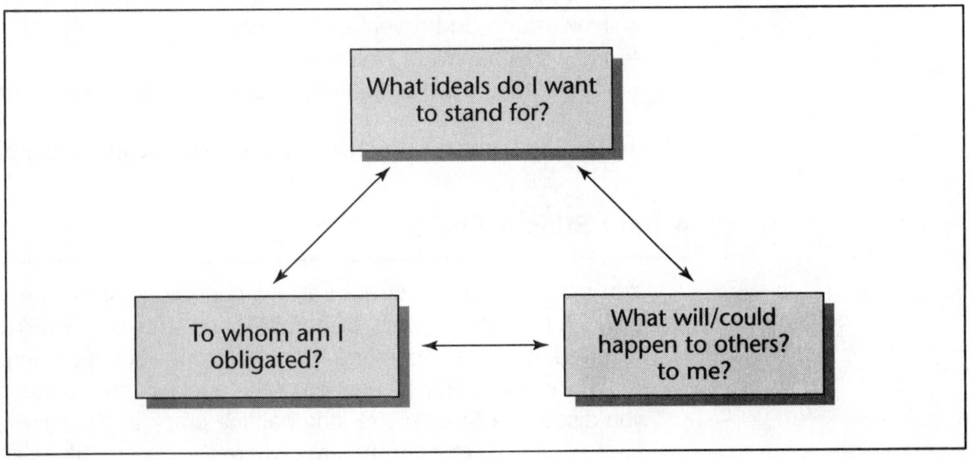

Figure 12.2 Reasonable Criteria for Ethical Judgment

The criteria help us understand why even good intentions can produce bad judgments, as in the following situation:

What seems like the right thing might be the wrong thing

> Someone observes. . .that waste from the local mill is seeping into the water table and polluting the water supply. This serious situation requires a remedy. But before one can be found, extremists condemn the mill for lack of conscience and for exploiting the community. People get upset and clamour for the mill to be shut down and its management tried on criminal charges. The next thing you know, the plant does close, 500 workers are without jobs, and no solution has been found for the pollution problem. (Hauser 96)

Because of their zealous dedication to the *ideal* of a pollution-free environment, the extremist protestors failed to anticipate the *consequences* of their protest or to respect their *obligation* to the community's economic welfare.

Ethical Dilemmas

Ethics decisions are especially frustrating when no single answer seems acceptable:

> [An ethical] dilemma exists whenever the conflicting obligations, ideals, and consequences are so very nearly equal in their importance that we feel we cannot choose among them, even though we must. (Ruggiero 91)

Ethical questions often resist easy answers

In private and in public, such dilemmas are inescapable. For example, politicians speak of drastic plans to eliminate the federal deficit in five years. One could argue that such a dedication to the *consequences* (or results) would violate our *obligations* (to the poor, the sick, etc.) and our *ideals* (of compassion, fairness, etc.). On the basis of our three criteria, how else might the deficit issue be considered?

ANTICIPATE SOME HARD CHOICES

Communicators' ethical choices basically are concerned with honesty in choosing to reveal or conceal information:

- What exactly do I report, and to whom?
- How much do I reveal or conceal?
- How do I say what I have to say?
- Could misplaced obligation to one party be causing me to deceive others?

The following scenario illustrates a hard choice at a workplace.

A Hard Ethical Choice

You may have to choose between the goals of your organization and what you know is right

You are an assistant structural engineer working on the construction of a nuclear power plant. After years of construction and cost overruns, the plant finally has received its limited operating licence from the Atomic Energy Control Board (AECB).

During your final inspection of the nuclear core containment unit on February 15, you discover a three-metre long hairline crack in a section of the reinforced concrete floor, within 6 metres of the area where the cooling pipes enter the containment unit. (The especially cold and snowless winter likely has caused a frost heave under a small part of the foundation.) The crack either has just appeared or was overlooked by AECB inspectors on February 10.

The crack could be perfectly harmless, caused by normal settling of the structure; and this is, after all, a "redundant" containment system (a shell within a shell). But then again, the crack could signal some kind of serious stress on the entire containment unit, which furthermore could damage the entry and exit cooling pipes or other vital structures.

You phone your supervisor, who is just about to leave on a ski vacation, and who tells you, "Forget it—no problem," and hangs up.

You know that if the crack is reported, the whole start-up process scheduled for February 16 will be delayed indefinitely. More money will be lost; excavation, reinforcement, and further testing will be required; and many people with a stake in this project (from company executives to construction officials to shareholders) will be furious—especially if your report turns out to be a false alarm. All segments of plant management are geared up for the final big moment. Media coverage will be widespread. As the bearer of bad news—and bad publicity—you suspect that, even if you turn out to be right, your own career could be hurt by what some people will see as your overreaction, which has made them look bad.

On the other hand, ignoring the crack could compromise the system's safety, with unforeseeable consequences. Of course, no one would ever be able to implicate you. The AECB has already inspected and approved the containment unit, leaving you, your supervisor, and your company in the clear. You have very little time to decide. Start-up is scheduled for tomorrow, at which time the containment system will become intensely radioactive.

Working professionals often face similar choices caused by conflicting goals and expectations and the pressure to meet deadlines and achieve results. What the employee feels is right may be countered by the need to be a loyal employee and team player, and to consider the bottom line. Often, choices have to be made alone or on the spur of the moment, without the luxury of meditation or consultation. It's a good idea, then, to be prepared to make hard choices *before* sticky situations occur.

ON THE JOB...

Ethical Issues

"You want to present your information in the most compelling way without misleading. It's easy to go over the edge in your effort to make your case. That's why our company requires a legal review for most customer communications..."

—Mary Hoffmann, marketing communications manager for a major computer company

NEVER DEPEND ONLY ON LEGAL GUIDELINES

Can the law tell you how to communicate ethically? Sometimes. If you stay within the law, are you being ethical? Not always. Legal standards "sometimes do no more than delineate minimally acceptable behaviour." In contrast, ethical standards "often attempt to describe ideal behaviour, to define the best possible practices for corporations" (Porter 183). Consider this legal paradox:

- It is perfectly legal to advertise a cereal made with oat bran (which allegedly lowers cholesterol) without mentioning that another ingredient in the cereal is coconut oil (which raises cholesterol).

Lying is rarely illegal, except in cases of lying under oath or breaking a contractual promise (Wicclair and Farkas 16). But putting aside these and other illegal lies, such as defamation of character or lying about a product so as to cause injury, we see plenty of room for the kinds of legal lies depicted in Figure 12.3. Later chapters cover other kinds of legal lying, such as page design that distorts the real emphasis or words that are deliberately unclear, misleading, or ambiguous.

What, then, are a communicator's legal guidelines? Workplace writing is regulated by the types of laws described below.

- *Laws against libel* prohibit any false written statement that attacks or ridicules anyone. A statement is considered libellous when it damages someone's reputation, character, career, or livelihood or when it causes humiliation or mental suffering. Material that is damaging but *truthful* would not be considered libellous unless it was used intentionally to cause harm. In the event of a libel suit, a writer's ignorance is no defence; even when the damaging material has been obtained from a source presumed reliable, the writer and publisher are legally accountable.[2]
- *Copyright laws* protect the ownership rights of authors—or of their employers, in cases where the writing was done as part of an individual's employment. You will find the Copyright Act posted at **http://laws.justice.gc.ca/en/C-42**.
- *Laws protecting software* provide penalties for illegally duplicating copyrighted software. (Guidelines for ethical, legal use of software are provided through Access Copyright's website: **www.accesscopyright.ca**.) Also, in Canada and internationally, the Software and Information Industry Association fights software piracy through education and enforcement measures.
- *Laws against deceptive or fraudulent advertising* make it illegal, for example, to falsely claim or imply that a product or treatment will cure cancer, or to represent and sell a used product as new. Fraud can be defined as "lying that causes another person monetary damage" (Harcourt 64).
- *Liability laws* define the responsibilities of authors, editors, and publishers for damages resulting from the use of incomplete, unclear, misleading, or otherwise defective information. The misinformation might be about a product (failure to warn about the toxic fumes from a spray-on oven cleaner) or a

Figure 12.3 Some Legal Lies in the Workplace

2. Thanks to Peter Owens for the material on libel.

procedure (misleading instructions in an owner's manual for using a tire jack). Even if misinformation is given out of ignorance, the writer is liable (Walter and Marsteller 164–65).

- Legal standards that govern product literature vary from country to country. A document must satisfy the legal standards for safety, health, accuracy, language, or other issues for any country in which it will be distributed. For example, instructions for any product requiring assembly or operation have to carry warnings as stipulated by the laws of the country in which the product will be sold. Inadequate documentation, as judged by that country's standards, can result in a lawsuit (Caswell-Coward 264–66; Weymouth 145).

ON THE JOB...

Social and Business Responsibilities

"Although we feel we're ethical and we really do try to be socially responsible in our designs and our construction, we can fall into a trap. Clients make demands because they have their own pressures. Some of these demands may result in reduced quality if we follow the principle that 'the client gets what he wants'! I'm not always comfortable with that attitude, especially if we don't exercise due diligence in our pre-project research and in our project designs...."

—Jan Bath, Civil engineering technologist

UNDERSTAND THE POTENTIAL FOR COMMUNICATION ABUSE

On the job, you write in the service of your employer. Your effectiveness is judged by how well your documents speak for the company and advance its interests and agendas (Ornatowski 100–01). You walk the proverbial line between telling the truth and doing what your employer expects (Dombrowski 79).

Workplace writing influences the thinking, actions, and welfare of different people: customers, investors, co-workers, the public, policy makers—to name a few. These people are victims of communication abuse whenever we give them information that is less than the truth as we know it, as in the sections below.

Suppressing Knowledge the Public Deserves

Except for disasters that make big news (Bhopal, Walkerton, Chernobyl, Westray mine), people hear plenty about the *wonders* of technology: how fluoride eradicates tooth decay, how smart bombs and cruise missiles never miss their targets, how nuclear power will solve our energy problems—but they rarely hear about the failures or the dangers (Staudenmaier 67).

In fact, the pressure to downplay failure sometimes results in censorship. For instance, some prestigious science journals have refused to publish studies linking chlorine and fluoride in drinking water with cancer risk, and fluorescent lights with childhood leukemia. The papers allegedly were rejected as part of widespread suppression of news about dangers of technological products (Begley 63).

Exaggerating Claims about Technology

Organizations that have a stake in a particular technology (say, bioengineered foods) may be especially tempted to exaggerate its benefits, potential, or safety, and to downplay the technology's risks.

Unwarranted claims help technology sell

> An entrepreneur needs financiers. Scientists in a large corporation need advocates high enough in the hierarchy to allocate funds. And government-supported researchers at universities and national labs have an obvious incentive to overstate their progress and understate the problems that lie ahead: the better the chances for success, the more money an agency is willing to shell out. (Brody 40)

Stealing or Divulging Proprietary Information

Proprietary information is any document or idea that can be considered the exclusive property of the company in which it originated. Proprietary documents may include company records, test and experiment results, surveys paid for by clients, market research, minutes of meetings, plans, and specifications (Lavin 5). In theory, such information is legally protected, but it remains vulnerable to sabotage or theft. Rapid developments in technology create fierce competition among rival companies for the very latest intelligence, giving rise to measures like these:

Examples of corporate espionage

> Companies have been known to use business school students to garner information on competitors under the guise of conducting "research." Even more commonplace is interviewing employees for slots that don't exist and wringing them dry about their current employer. (Gilbert 24)

Moreover, employees within a company can leak confidential information to the press or to anyone else who has no legal right to know.

Hiding Conflicts of Interest

Can scientists and other experts who have a financial stake in a particular issue or experiment provide fair and impartial information about the topic?

- In one analysis of 800 scientific papers, Tufts University's Sheldon Krimsky found that 34 percent of authors had "research-related financial ties," but none had been disclosed (King B1).
- *Los Angeles Times* medical writer Terence Monmaney recently investigated 36 drug review pieces in a prestigious medical journal and found "eight articles by researchers with undisclosed financial links to drug companies that market treatments evaluated in the articles" (quoted in Rosman 100).

Falsifying or Fabricating Data

Research data might be manipulated or invented to support specific agendas (say, by a scientist seeking grant money). Sometimes it's a matter of timing: developments in fields such as biotechnology often occur too rapidly to allow for adequate peer review of articles before they are published (Turner, "Misconduct Scandal" 2).

Using Visual Images That Conceal the Truth

Pictures are generally more powerful than words and can easily distort the real meaning of a message. For example, U.S. law requires that TV commercials for prescription medications must identify a drug's side effects, which can sometimes be serious. But typically drug commercials show images of smiling, healthy people at the same time as the side effects are listed. The happy images eclipse the sobering verbal message. (Direct-to-consumer advertising of prescription drugs is prohibited in Canada and in most other industrialized countries.)

Misusing Electronic Information

Much personal information is stored in databases (by schools, governments, banks, mail-order retailers, credit card companies, insurance companies), and, of course, all employers keep data about their employees. So how we combine, use, and share that information raises questions about privacy (Finkelstein 471). Also, a database is easy to alter; one simple command can change or wipe out facts. Private or inaccurate information can be sent from one database to many others, but "correcting information in one database does not guarantee that it will be corrected in others" (Turner, "Online Use" 5).

Here are some examples of the potential for communication abuse connected with web usage:

- plagiarizing or republishing electronic sources without getting permission or giving proper credit—although internet-based information may be free, the source of paraphrased or copied material must still be properly cited (see Chapter 19)
- failing to safeguard the privacy of personal information about a website visitor's health, finances, buying habits, or affiliations
- publishing anonymous attacks or smear campaigns against people, products, or organizations
- offering inaccurate medical advice or information

Withholding Information People Need to Do Their Jobs

Nowhere is the adage that "information is power" more true than among co-workers. One sure way to sabotage a colleague is to withhold vital information about the task at hand.

Beyond these deliberate communication abuses is this reality: *all* information is a matter of personal or social interpretation (Dombrowski 79); therefore, "objective reporting," practically speaking, is impossible. What we say on the job and how we say it are influenced by the expectations of our employer and by our own self-interest.

Exploiting Cultural Differences

Cross-cultural documents carry great potential for communication abuse. Based on its level of business experience, technological development, or financial need, a particular culture might be especially vulnerable to manipulation or deception. Some countries, for instance, are persuaded to purchase, from North American companies, pesticides and other chemicals whose use is banned in North America. Other countries witness depletion of their natural resources or exploitation of their labour force by more developed countries—all in the name of progress. All communication in all cultural contexts should embody universal standards of honesty and fairness.

KNOW YOUR COMMUNICATION GUIDELINES

How do you balance self-interest with the interests of others—the organization, the public, your customers? How can you be practical and responsible at the same time? Here are two practical guidelines for ethical communication (G. Clark 194):

1. *Give the audience everything it needs to know.* To see things as clearly as you do, people need more than just a partial view. Don't bury readers in needless details, but do make sure they get all the facts and get them straight.
2. *Give the audience a clear understanding of what the information means.* Even when all of the facts are known, they can be misinterpreted. Do all you can to ensure that your readers understand the facts as you do.

The Checklist for Communicators on page 240 incorporates additional guidelines from various chapters. Use the checklist for any document you prepare or for which you are responsible. Also, see science ethics resources at **www.chem.vt.edu/chem-ed/ethics**.

DECIDE WHERE AND HOW TO DRAW THE LINE

Suppose your employer asks you to do something unethical, such as alter data to cover up a violation of federal pollution standards. If you decide to resist, your choices seem limited: resign or go public (i.e., blow the whistle).

Walking away from a job isn't easy, however, and whistle blowing can spell career disaster (Rubens, "Reinventing" 330). Many organizations refuse to hire anyone blacklisted as a whistle blower (Wicclair and Farkas 19). Even if you aren't fired, expect your job to become hellish. Here is one communicator's gloomy assessment, based on personal experience:

> Most of the ethical infractions [you] witness will be so small that blowing the whistle will seem fruitless and self-destructive. And leaving one company for another may prove equally fruitless, given the pervasiveness of the problem. (Bryan 86)

Anglo-Canadian law tends to protect employees who blow the whistle and are then dismissed. An employee has the right to bring a wrongful dismissal lawsuit and, in certain circumstances, to include human rights and/or labour relations claims. The outcome of these claims varies.

Even if an employer doesn't act against a whistle-blowing employee, that employee might still feel compelled to leave the company, as in the case of Melvin Crothers, who revealed that his employer, WestJet, had spied electronically on its main competitor, Air Canada. In December 2003, Mr. Crothers accidentally discovered the spying. Unable to contact the WestJet CEO (who was on vacation) and morally shaken, he contacted a former WestJet manager who had moved to Zip Air, an Air Canada subsidiary. On April 6, 2004, Air Canada filed suit against WestJet. Four days later, Mr. Crothers felt that he had to quit working for WestJet, even though he loved working in the airline industry. As of October 2006 he had not found another airline job (Jang and Brethour A1, A12).

ON THE JOB...

Ethics in Environmental Consulting

"We don't struggle with ethical reporting because of the way we do things. We make a point of scrupulously gathering and interpreting data and then carefully writing conclusions. There's no long-term future in being anything other than completely straightforward and honest, from your experimental design through to your data collection and analysis. You achieve success for your client when you're thorough and honest in the data gathering and interpretation, especially in today's regulated business environment. You certainly don't do your clients any favours by hiding or misrepresenting data...."

—Dr. Brian Guy, president and senior geoscientist, Summit Environmental Consultants

Employees covered by a contract or collective agreement can seek advice from their union or from a lawyer. Employees not covered by a contract or collective agreement often seek initial advice from local departments of labour or from their personal lawyer.

Anyone who reports employer violations to an agency such as the Canadian Centre for Occupational Health and Safety (CCOHS) and who is punished can ask the province's labour department to investigate. Employees whose claims are ruled valid can win reinstatement and reimbursement for back pay and legal expenses.

Even with such protections, an employee who takes on a company without the backing of a labour union or other powerful group can expect lengthy court battles, high legal fees (which may or may not be recouped), and disruption of life and career. Exactly where you draw the line (on having your integrity or health instead of your job) will be strictly your own decision.

If you do decide to take a stand, be reasonable and cautious, and follow these suggestions (Unger 127–30):

- *Get your facts straight, and get them on paper.* Don't blow matters out of proportion, but do keep a paper trail in case of legal proceedings.
- *Appeal your case in terms of the company's interests.* Instead of being pious and judgmental ("This is a racist and sexist policy, and you'd better get your act together"), focus on what the company stands to gain or lose ("Promoting too few women and minorities makes us vulnerable to legal action").
- *Aim your appeal toward the right person.* If you have to go to the top, find someone who knows enough to appreciate the problem and who has enough clout to make something happen.
- *Get professional advice.* Contact a lawyer and your professional society for advice about your legal rights.

Before accepting a job offer, discreetly research the company's ethical reputation. (Of course, you can learn only so much about a company before actually working there.) Lynn Brewer, a former Enron executive who blew the whistle on Enron's unethical and illegal practices, describes early warning signals in her book *Confessions of an Enron Executive* and in her talks at university campuses.

Some companies have ombudspersons who help employees lodge complaints. Others offer hotlines for advice on ethics problems or for reporting violations. Also, realizing that good ethics is good business, companies increasingly are developing codes for personal and organizational behaviour. Without such supports, don't expect to last long as an ethical employee in an unethical organization.

Remember that very few employers tolerate any public statement, no matter how truthful, that makes the company look bad.

A final note: sometimes the right choice is obvious, but often it is not so obvious. No one has any sure way of always knowing what to do. This chapter is only an introduction to the inevitable hard choices that, throughout your career, will be yours to make and to live with. For further guidance, see the website maintained by the Online Ethics Center for Engineering and Science, established by the Institute of Electrical and Electronics Engineers (IEEE) at **http://temp.onlineethics.org/codes/index.html**. This website covers a wide range of ethics issues for technical people trying to cope with difficult situations. Particular cases are listed under the pull-down menus "Engineering Practice," "Responsible Research," "Diverse Workplace," and "Computers and Software."

CHECKLIST FOR COMMUNICATORS

Use this checklist[3] to help you write documents that reflect reasonable, ethical judgment.

- Am I reasonably sure this document will harm no innocent persons or damage their reputation?
- Am I respecting all legitimate rights to privacy and confidentiality?
- Do I inform readers of the consequences or risks (as I am able to predict) of what I'm advocating?
- Do I state the case clearly, instead of hiding behind jargon and generalities?
- Do I give candid feedback or criticism, if it is warranted?
- Am I distributing copies of this document to every person who has the right to know about it?
- Do I credit all contributors and sources of ideas and information?
- Do I avoid exaggeration, understatement, sugar-coating, or any distortion or omission that leaves readers at a disadvantage?
- Do I make a clear distinction between "certainty" and "probability"?
- Am I being honest and fair?
- Have I explored all sides of the issue and all possible alternatives?
- Are my information sources valid, reliable, and unbiased?
- Do I actually believe what I'm saying, instead of being a mouthpiece for groupthink or advancing some hidden agenda?
- Would I still advocate this position if I were held publicly accountable for it?
- Do I provide enough information and interpretation for readers to understand the facts as I know them?

WEB CONNECT

This website covers a wide range of ethics issues for technical people trying to cope with difficult situations. In particular, see the "Moral Exemplars" and "Engineering Practice" sections.

http://temp.onlineethics.org/codes/index.html

The following sites present Canadian engineering codes of ethics:

Canadian Council of Professional Engineers
www.ccpe.ca/e/guide_guidelines.cfm

Professional Engineers of Ontario
www.peo.on.ca/publications/code_of_ethics.html

EXERCISES

In your workplace communications, you may end up facing hard choices concerning what to say, how much to say, how to say it, and to whom. Whatever your choice, it will have definite consequences. Discuss the following cases in terms of

- obligations faced by the person at the centre of the case (see page 231)
- appropriate moral values or ideals (see page 231)
- likely consequences of the action(s) you discuss (see page 231)

Case 1. In the scenario described in Chapter 1 on pages 8 and 11, Erika Song faces some difficult decisions. Should she omit or include data that reflects badly on the

3. Adapted from Brownell and Fitzgerald 18; Bryan 87; Johannesen 21–22; Larson 39; Unger 39–46; Yoos 50–55.

firm that employs her? Even though the data do not support conclusions that favour her company's bid for a contract extension and that show that her company's data gathering is not redundant, should she write those conclusions and improve her own chances of continuing employment? Should she "tell the truth," knowing that her boss will likely edit the report to enhance his firm's business potential?

Case 2. Review the scenario entitled "A Hard Ethical Choice"pages 232-33. What would you do? Come to the class prepared to justify your decision on the basis of the obligations, ideals, and consequences involved.

Case 3. You are in the last semester of your college or university program. Your classmate, a hard worker who has earned good grades until recently, has been neglecting her class work for the last month as she spends time with a younger sister who is dying of cancer. She approaches you to complete a report that she has researched and partly organized, but not written. The report, which is a major assignment in a technical writing course, is worth 40 percent of the final grade. It is due in three days. Your classmate did poorly on the last assignment and mid-term exam, and will likely fail the course if she doesn't get at least a C on this report. You have submitted your report, but you had planned to spend the next week studying hard for your final exams. She has offered to pay you $200 to write the report that she will submit under her name. What should you do?

Case 4. You are one of three employees being considered for a yearly production bonus, which will be awarded in six weeks. You've just accepted a better job, which you can start anytime in the next two months. Should you wait until the bonus decision is made before announcing your plans to leave?

Case 5. While travelling on assignment that is being paid for by your employer, you visit an area in which you would really like to live and work, an area in which you have lots of contacts but never can find time to visit on your own. You have five days to complete your assignment, and then you must report on your activities. You complete the assignment in three days. Should you spend the remaining two days checking out other job possibilities, without reporting this activity?

Case 6. You have been authorized to hire a technical assistant, and so you are about to prepare an advertisement. This is a time of threatened cutbacks for your company. People hired as temporary, however, have never seemed to work out well. Should your ad include the warning that this position could be only temporary?

Case 7. You are employed by a biotechnology company working on an AIDS vaccine. At a national conference, a researcher from a competing company secretly offers to sell your company crucial data that could speed discovery of an effective vaccine. Should you accept the offer?

COLLABORATIVE PROJECT

1. In a group of three to five people, discuss the "right thing to do" in any one of the seven cases described above. In a memo to your supervisor, outline what action you would recommend and explain why. Be prepared to defend your group's ethical choice in class on the basis of the obligations, ideals, and consequences involved.
2. At this book's text enrichment site (**www.pearsoned.ca/lannon**) click on "Writing Exercises" and then on "Ethics Case Analysis." There you'll find a group ethics assignment and advice on how to adapt the Harvard Case Study method to help make hard ethical choices.
3. Discuss the ethical implications of taking money to "review" a product or service in a personal blog or discussion forum. Should the blogger disclose that he or she receives payment to discuss a product or service? Before accepting payment from an advertiser, should the blogger insist that the comments must state an honest opinion, not contrived praise for a product that the blogger has never tried or believes to be second-rate? Does "blogvertising" betray loyal readers of that blog? (To get an idea of the commercial aspect of this issue, visit **http://ReviewMe.com** or **http://JohnChow.com.**)

CHAPTER 13

Workplace Correspondence: Letters, Memos, and Email

LEARNING OBJECTIVES

After reading this chapter, you should be able to

- Recognize and use accepted formats for letters and memos.
- Adapt the format of each email to suit the content, purpose, and audience.
- Follow guidelines for appropriate, effective, readable emails.
- Consider the interpersonal aspects affecting correspondence and adapt the action structure to reflect the document's purpose and reader.

Many reports are completed by a team of writers for multiple readers, but letters, memos, and email are usually written by a single writer for one or more definite readers. Also, workplace correspondence is more direct and personal than reports and often has a persuasive purpose, so proper tone is essential. You want your reader to be on your side. Because successful relationships depend on two-way transactions in which both participants meet their needs, you must use a "you" attitude. You must look at the situation from the reader's viewpoint.

ON THE JOB...

Letters vs. Email

"I have clients in South Africa, England, and Germany, so nearly all of my communication with them is via email. Letters would take too long, and phone conversations are difficult because of the eight-hour time difference...."

—Ken Langedyk, consulting civil engineer

This chapter looks at four correspondence media: letters, memos, email, and text messaging. The chapter presents current formats, introduces factors common to all four media, and discusses issues that concern each separate medium.

Letters appeared on the scene first, followed in the mid-20th century by memos. Then, as that century drew to a close, new technologies brought facsimile transmission (faxes), email messaging, and phone-based text messaging.

Developments at the beginning of this century have revealed three certainties:

1. Rapid technological change will bring new varieties of electronic correspondence, **but**
2. We will want relatively permanent records of that correspondence, **and**
3. The basic principles of successful correspondence will work in any correspondence medium, paper-based or electronic.

Although letters and memos are being replaced by email, this chapter describes letter and memo format for three main reasons:

Why letter and memo formats are discussed in this chapter

1. Letters and memos still have uses, particularly for messages that go beyond the 200–300 words that can comfortably fit on an email screen.
2. When writers wish to format their message, and they're unsure whether the receiver's email software will properly "read" bolding or italics or quotation marks, they attach a formatted letter or memo to a brief introductory email.
3. Knowing the history and format of letters and memos helps email writers understand and adapt aspects of letter-style and memo-style email messages.

LETTER FORMAT

North American business correspondence blends ordered, elaborate formatting with streamlined, direct phrasing. (By contrast, European letters often *look* less formal but are phrased more formally and elaborately than Canadian and American letters.)

Letter formats have evolved

As the 21st century begins, two traditional formats are out of fashion and a third may soon lose favour. The *semi-block* and *block formats,* shown in Figures 13.1 and 13.2, were both popular in the 1960s and early 1970s in Canada, but neither format is widely used now.

In the 1970s and early 1980s, IBM and others championed the *full-block format* because its left-justified set-up saved keying time. The full-block format (Figure 13.3) led the way through the 1980s and 1990s, but as the 1990s drew to a close, it started to give way to an even more streamlined layout, which had been introduced as the "simplified letter" by the U.S. National Office Management Association in the early 1960s. Figure 13.4 shows a contemporary version of the *simplified format.*

Today's version of the simplified format responds to a growing discomfort with the formal greeting ("Dear...") and complimentary close ("Yours..."), which seem characteristic of an earlier era. Notice that a subject line replaces the salutation and that the complimentary close is eliminated. In other respects, a simplified letter copies a full-block letter, although the simplified format's overall appearance resembles contemporary memos. In other words, letter and memo formats are becoming similar.

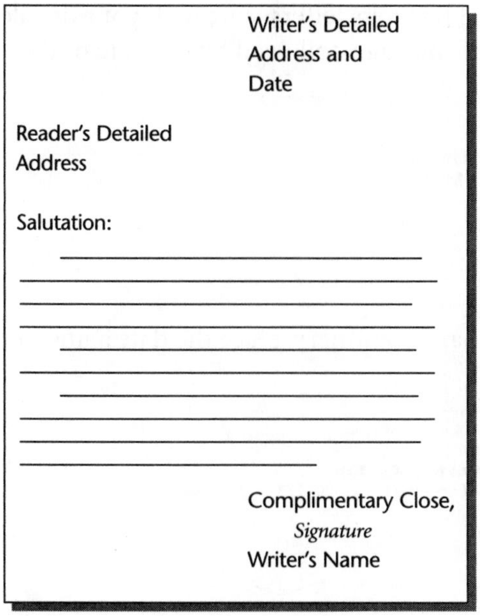

Figure 13.1 A Semi-block Format

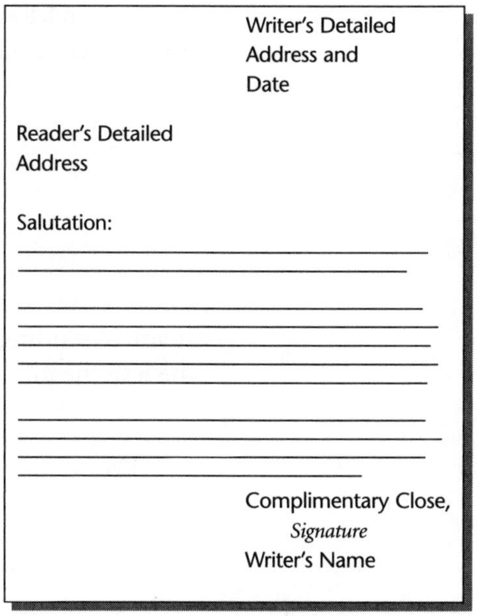

Figure 13.2 A Block Format

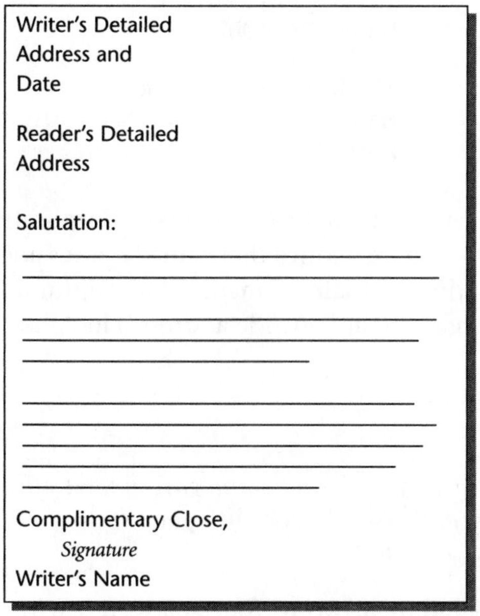

Figure 13.3 A Full-block Format

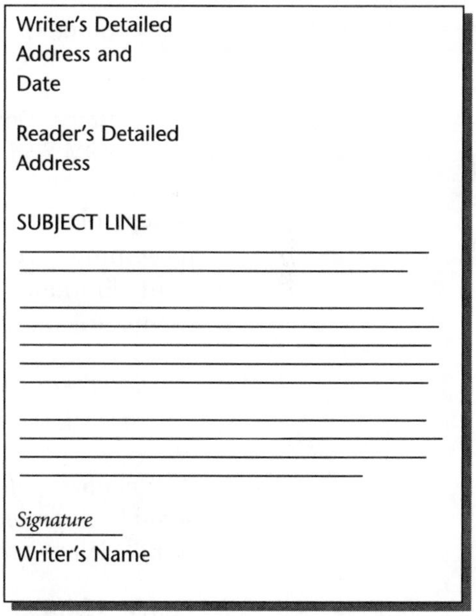

Figure 13.4 A Simplified Format

Basic Elements of Letters

Business letters have traditionally included five elements (in order from top to bottom): heading and date, inside address, salutation, letter text, and closing.

Heading and Date. Your personal business letters start with your detailed address (but not your name) at the top of the page, followed by the date of the letter.

> 127 Marchbank Avenue
> Barrie ON K9M 7H3
>
> June 23, 2008

If you're sending a letter on company stationery, place the date a line or two below the letterhead.

> **ROCKWOOD INDUSTRIES CO. LTD.**
> 1222 Terminal Road Rockwood ON N0B 2K3 (413) 554-7863
>
> June 23, 2008

Canadian usage includes four ways of writing addresses:

1. 127 Marchbank Avenue
   Barrie ON K9M 7H3
2. 127 Marchbank Avenue
   Barrie, ON K9M 7H3
3. 127 Marchbank Avenue
   Barrie, Ontario
   K9M 7H3
4. 127 Marchbank Avenue
   Barrie, Ont.
   K9M 7H3

Acceptable form #1, above, has been instituted by Canada Post Corporation to help its computerized optical scanners operate. Notice that Canada Post's address standard eliminates internal punctuation. Actually, Canada Post's "optimum requirements" for the address on the envelope (the "outside address") look like this:

> 127 MARCHBANK AVENUE
> BARRIE ON K9M 7H3

NOTE *The majority of businesses, with the exception of some government offices, use the second acceptable form of writing addresses. Check with your employer. This book's sample letters use acceptable forms 1, 2, and 3.*

Inside Address. Place the inside address two to four spaces below the date and abutting the left margin. Whenever possible, address your letter to a specifically named reader, and include your reader's job title. Using a form of address such as "Mr." or "Ms." before the name is optional.

Inside address format

> Mr. Saul Kaufman, General Manager
> Bluenose Engineering Co.
> 1774 Robie Street
> Halifax NS B3H 3G7

or

> Bluenose Engineering Co.
> 1774 Robie Street
> Halifax NS B3H 3G7
>
> Attention: Mr. Saul Kaufman
> General Manager

NOTE *Depending on the length of your letter, adjust the vertical placement of the heading and inside address to achieve a page that appears balanced.*

Salutation format

Salutation. The salutation usually appears two line spaces below the inside address. A standard salutation begins with *Dear* and ends with a colon (*Dear Mr. Kaufman:*). If you don't know the person's name, an attention line (*Attention: General Manager*) is preferable to using the position title (*Dear* General Manager:).

No satisfactory guidelines exist for addressing several people within an organization. *Gentlemen* or *Dear Sirs* shows implied bias. *Ladies and Gentlemen* sounds too much like the beginning of a speech. *Dear Sir or Madam* is too old-fashioned. *To Whom It May Concern* is vague and impersonal. Your best bet is to use an attention line (*Attention: Personnel Department*) and eliminate the salutation (use a simplified format).

Letter Text. Begin the text of your letter two line spaces below the salutation or subject line. Workplace letters typically include (1) a brief *introductory* paragraph (two or three sentences) that identifies your purpose and connects with the reader's interest; (2) one or more paragraphs that present the *details* of your message; and (3) a *closing* paragraph that sums up and encourages action. Some letters provide *background* information immediately after the introduction.

Keep your paragraphs short, usually fewer than eight lines. If a paragraph goes beyond eight lines, or if the paragraph contains detailed supporting facts or examples, consider using bulleted or numbered lists to make the paragraph readable. On average, letter paragraphs should not exceed 60 words per paragraph.

Closing. The closing, placed one line space below the last line of text, includes three components in traditional formats: complimentary close, signature, and writer's name and position.

Complimentary close

Yours truly,

Writer's identity

Maris McGovern
Sales Manager

Yours truly and *Sincerely* are the most commonly used complimentary closes. Others, in order of decreasing formality, include:

Respectfully,
Cordially,
Best wishes,
Warmest regards,
Regards,
Best,

Align the three-part closing with the letter's heading.

If you are representing a company or group that bears legal responsibility for the correspondence, key the company's name in full caps two line spaces below your complimentary closing; place your keyed name and title four line spaces below the company name and sign in the triple space between.

Yours truly,
ROCKWOOD INDUSTRIES

Mary Baxter
Research Coordinator

Specialized Parts of Letters

Some letters require one or more of the following specialized parts. Examples appear in sample letters in this chapter.

Other format elements

Attention Line. Use an attention line when you direct a letter to a specific department or position within an organization but don't know the reader's name. (Or use it in the simplified letter format.)

Rockwood Industries Inc.
335 – 11th Avenue S.W.
Calgary AB T2R 1L9

Attention: Director of Research and Development

or

ATTENTION: Director of Research and Development

Subject Line. Because it announces the topic of your letter, the subject line is a good device for attracting a busy person's attention.

Subject: Improvements in Client Service

or

SUBJECT: Improvements in Client Service

Place the subject line below the salutation with one line space before and after it.

Dear Mr. Patrese:

SUBJECT: Improvements in Client Service

If you are using a simplified-style letter, place the subject line below the inside address and attention line, with two line spaces before and after the subject line.

Initials. If someone else keys your letter, your initials (in caps) and his or hers (in lowercase letters) should appear below the writer's keyed name, flush with the left margin. This practice is disappearing because the overwhelming majority of writers key their own letters these days.

J. Mansonneau
Manager

JM/to

Enclosure Notation. When other documents accompany your letter, add an enclosure notation one line space below the initials (or writer's name and position), flush with the left margin. State the number of enclosures, or name them, or both.

Enclosure: Contract 145-X-2309
Enclosures 2
Encl. 3-page résumé

Distribution Notation. If you distribute copies of your letter to other readers, insert the notation *Copy,* or *c,* or *cc,* or *Distribution,* two line spaces below the previous line (such as an enclosure line).

Copy: B. Grammel
c: M. Henderson

Distribution: Hamilton Better Business Bureau
Hamilton Chamber of Commerce
Ontario Ombudsman

Most copies are distributed on an FYI (for your information) basis, but writers sometimes use the distribution notation to maintain a paper trail or to signal that the letter is being shared with others (e.g., superiors or legal authorities).

NOTE *The notation* bc *or* bcc *means "blind copy" or "blind carbon copy." It appears on copies other than the original and indicates that the recipient of the letter is not aware that a copy is being sent to others.*

DESIGN FACTORS

Letter design factors

Design starts with a choice of formats. Currently, the format most favoured by Canadian business writers is the full-block layout, but the simplified format is gaining in popularity. Both these forms look businesslike and eliminate the need to tab and centre.

Additional design factors enable workplace letters to appear inviting, accessible, and professional:

Quality Stationery. Use high-quality 20-pound or 24-pound, 21.5 cm × 28 cm ($8^{1}/_{2}$" × 11") white paper with a minimum fibre content of 25 percent. Hundreds of varieties of coloured, specially textured papers are available, but you should exercise caution in using anything other than white stationery.

Uniform Margins and Spacing. When using stationery without a letterhead, frame your letter with 2.5–3.75 cm (1"–$1^1/_2$") margins, depending on the amount of space required by the letter's text. Strive for a balanced look. Use single spacing within paragraphs and double spacing between paragraphs.

Page Continuation Format. If your letter continues beyond a first page, begin each additional page with a notation identifying the addressee, date, and page number.

Saul Kaufman June 25, 2008 Page 2

If there's sufficient space, you can stack the notation at the left margin.

Saul Kaufman
June 25, 2008
Page 2

Begin the text two line spaces below the page continuation notation. Never use an additional page solely for the closing section. Instead, reformat the letter so that the closing appears on the first page or so that at least two lines of text appear above the closing on the subsequent page.

MEMO USAGE AND FORMAT

Memos have many uses

Memoranda (usually called "memos") are used within organizations for a wide variety of messages. Originally, memos were intended for relatively brief messages, but now they're also used for longer messages, including informative and analytical reports of up to four pages, as Chapter 17 demonstrates. Memos are also used for proposals and other persuasive messages.

A major form of communication in most organizations until recently, memos leave a paper trail of the directives, inquiries, instructions, requests, recommendations, and daily reports needed to run an organization.

Organizations rely heavily on memos to trace decisions and responsibilities, track progress, and recheck data. Therefore, any memo you write can have far-reaching ethical and legal implications. Be sure your memo includes the date and your initials or signature. Also, make sure your information is specific, unambiguous, and accurate. Finally, remember that your memos must provide the information and analysis that the reader needs, but *no more* than the reader needs.

Format

Basically, there are two varieties of memos: intra-office (within an office) and inter-office (between offices of the same firm). Both use the same type of format, with minor variations.

Memohead. Intra-office memos usually feature the designation *Memorandum* (or *Memo*) at the top of the page, sometimes in conjunction with the company's name and logo, sometimes by itself. (See Figure 17.6 and Figure 17.7) Inter-office memos usually name the company at the top of the page, followed by the term "Inter-office Memo." (See Figure 3.4.)

Heading Guides. Four heading guides are mandatory: date line, receiver's name and title, sender's name and title, and subject line.

DATE:	June 25, 2008
TO:	John Tarnowski, Purchasing Coordinator
FROM:	May Krienke, Explorations Chief
RE:	Cost Estimates for the Churchill River Project

Provide the titles held by you and your reader, even if you are both well aware of each other's position. Why? First, it's a formal courtesy used within most organizations. Second, the title designations provide a record that may prove useful in the future.

Additional heading information might include file locators (FILE, or OUR FILE, or YOUR FILE), the sender's phone number or email address, or a distribution line. Distribution lines more often appear at the end of a memo, but if you prefer to include your distribution list in the heading, incorporate that list in the TO section or place a DISTRIBUTION line between the TO and FROM sections. If you want to direct copies of a memorandum to certain personnel, include a COPIES or COPY TO line after the TO section.

Margins and Spacing. Use block format for memos: do not indent paragraphs. Instead, leave an open space between paragraphs. Create 2.5 cm (1") left and right margins. Do not right-justify paragraphs; leave a ragged right edge. Do not worry about balancing memos on the page; start the heading guides one or two line spaces below the memohead and continue until the memo is complete.

Normally, memo writers leave a line space between heading guides. Also, it's common practice to tab the information following the heading guides so that the information is aligned. (See the example of heading guides usage above.)

Signature versus Initials. Many memo writers simply sign their initials beside their name in the FROM section (see Figure 17.11). Others choose the more formal (and, they say, the more businesslike) practice of signing their name or placing their initials at the end of the memo.

J. Mansonneau

This practice has the added advantage of identifying the writer on each page of a two-page memo.

Attachments. An effective way to include detailed background or corroborative data is to attach it to the memo. If such material were included in the body of the memo, it might interfere with the memo's smooth development and easy reading, so it's better placed where the readers can read it if they wish. For example, an internal proposal of an expansion of the firm's advertising program might attach a demographic analysis of the firm's target market and some sample newspaper ads. To indicate the presence of an attachment, place an "Attachment" line at the bottom of the memo, using the same format as a letter enclosure line.

Graphic Highlighting. Memo readers are usually busy people who want easily understood documents. One way to provide readability is to use bulleted or numbered lists of information and ideas. Headings also make documents easier to read. Tables or columns of information can present material concisely and clearly. So remember to use combinations of these techniques, even for relatively short memos.

Page Continuation Format. For memos, use the page continuation format that you would use for letters.

The Demise of the Memo

With each passing year, memos (and to a lesser extent, letters) are being replaced by businesslike emails. Still, studying memo structures and format provides useful background for understanding how to use email correctly and effectively.

ELECTRONIC MAIL

Perhaps the most widely used application on the internet is electronic mail, known simply as email. As early as 1997, the Electronic Messaging Association estimated that internet users sent more than two trillion messages that year. Who knows what that figure might be this year?

Email Format

In effect, email is a new hybrid of written correspondence and one-on-one conversation. Most email messages have been relatively casual in tone and format, reflecting the democratic, "free" nature of the medium. However, as uses for email increase and as software becomes more sophisticated, email messages are starting to look more formal and writers are taking more care with their phrasing, especially in business settings. Until recently, email has been best suited to simple messages. Now, however, new software with enriched formatting and the ability to attach more complex documents means that you can send fully formatted documents via email.

In late 2001, Mykon Communications surveyed the email practices of 45 Canadian organizations (engineering firms; forest products companies; financial firms;

ON THE JOB...

The Ascendancy of Email

"A lot of my communication now is email. Initially, there's a consultant meeting with the engineers, the architect, and the developer. From there, my early communication with the client is through preliminary engineering drawings. But the whole process now is moved forward through a steady stream of emails, most of which go to all the interested parties. This collaborative process helps us catch potential problems, if everyone reads their emails!"

—Tom Guenther, consulting structural engineer

educational institutions; service industries; manufacturers; retailers; high-tech firms; environmental consultants; federal, provincial, and municipal government agencies; biotech firms; and others). The survey revealed a growing trend toward formal emails as email format evolves into three main levels of formality:

- *Personal, brief notes.* Similar to the unstructured, casual messages sent in the early stages of email development, these notes are often carelessly written and contain spelling errors. They're fine for chatting but not for business and professional messages.
- *Memo style.* Internal email messages tend to look like standard, informal memos, with carefully constructed block-format paragraphs. Shorter internal emails tend to look less formal than the ones sent externally, especially if the message is only one or two paragraphs. However, longer internal emails sometimes take on characteristics of formal memos and letters: bulleted or numbered lists, bolding and italic text, spell-checked text, and even bolded headings.

  Some internal emails even use salutations ("Hello," "Good afternoon," "Greetings") and complimentary closes ("Regards," "Best regards," "Cheers," "Sincerely"). Still, 84 percent of respondents to the Mykon survey said that they and their fellow workers tend to send less formal-looking emails for internal messages.
- *Letter style.* Formal business emails sent to clients, service providers, or associates often have the characteristics of formal business letters—bulleted or numbered lists, headings, bolding, and italics help clarify meaning and impart a professional look.

  Respondents to the Mykon survey said they use salutations: 40 percent use formal greetings such as "Dear Mr.," while 60 percent said that they use less formal salutations. Formal address is used most often in making an initial business contact. Letter-style emails also use complimentary closes—70 percent of the respondents regularly use closes like "Regards," "Best regards," and "Sincerely."

  Alternatively, external emails are used to introduce the reader to attached formal documents (in Word, WordPerfect, or PDF formats). PDF is particularly favoured by engineering firms and others who want to prevent readers from altering an attached document's findings and recommendations.

GUIDELINES for Email Format

1. *Use a clear subject line to identify your topic* ("Subject: Request for Beta Test Data for Project #16"). This line helps recipients decide whether to read the message immediately, and helps the recipient file and retrieve the message.
2. *Refer clearly to the message to which you are responding* ("Here are the Project #16 Beta test data you requested on October 10").
3. *Choose the degree of formality that reflects your reader and your purpose;* the more important the message, the more formal the format. Short, abrupt messages such as the following do not require salutations or closings: "The attached file summarizes the tender process you requested. If you'd like to discuss the process, please call."

(continued)

GUIDELINES for Email Format *(continued)*

4. *Use block format.* Don't indent paragraphs. Keep paragraphs and sentences short.
5. *Where appropriate in formal emails, use graphic highlighting* (headings, bullets, numbered lists, bolding, and italics) to improve readability and impart professionalism. However, a little goes a long way.
6. *Avoid wildly varying line lengths on your receiver's screen by limiting line length.* Set Word Wrap to create line lengths of 64 characters or less.
7. *Where appropriate, use formal salutations and closings for letter-style emails* ("Dear Sir," "Sincerely"), but use less formal greetings and closings for most emails ("Hello," "Regards").
8. *Close with a signature section that names you, your company, or department;* your telephone and fax number; and any other information the recipient might consider relevant. If you have the technology, include your electronic signature.
9. *Do not write in FULL CAPS,* unless you want to SCREAM at the recipient!

Figure 13.5 illustrates a note-style email, and Figure 13.6 shows a letter-style email. An email inquiry is illustrated later in this chapters.

Email Benefits

Email facilitates communication and collaboration

Compared with phone, fax, or conventional mail (or even face-to-face conversation, in some cases), email offers benefits:

- *Email is fast, convenient, efficient, and relatively unintrusive.* Unlike conventional mail, which can take days to travel, email travels instantly. Although a fax network can transmit printed copy rapidly, email eliminates paper shuffling, dialling, and a host of other steps. Moreover, email makes for efficiency by eliminating "telephone tag." It intrudes less than the phone, allowing the recipient to choose when to read and respond to a message.

  Thus, it is hardly surprising that in the 2001 Mykon email survey, 78 percent of respondents said that email messages had replaced at least half of their organization's letters and memos. Of those same respondents, 60 percent said that emails had replaced at least 50 percent of their phone calls. Follow-up interviews in 2007 revealed that email has almost entirely replaced memos in many settings.
- *Email is democratic.* With few exceptions, email messages appear as plain print on a screen, with no special typestyles, fancy letterheads, paper design, or paper texture—enabling readers to focus on the message instead of the medium. Email also allows for transmission of messages by anyone at any level in an organization to anyone at any other level. For instance, the mail clerk conceivably could email the company president directly, whereas a conventional memo or phone call would be routed through the chain of management or screened by administrative assistants (Goodman 33–35). In addition, people who are ordinarily shy in face-to-face encounters may be more willing to express their views in an email conversation.

Reply Reply All Forward Follow Up

This message was sent with high priority.

From: Marie Szarbynski
To: Markus Anstenson
Sent: February 11, 2008 11:13 AM
Subject: **Updates for PURE Anti-virus Software**

Please see the forwarded enquiry from customer Bart Nickel. I can't answer his questions until I know which version he's purchased. Will you please check the registration records to see which version he has and when he registered it? If he has Version 4.0, can you tell me why he would have received an updated message?

If possible, I'd like to respond to his enquiry before noon, so your prompt reply would be appreciated.

Marie

Figure 13.5 A Note-style Email

Reply Reply All Forward Follow Up

This message was sent with high priority.

From: Marie Szarbynski [custserv@pure.com]
To: Bart Nickel [bartn@peg.net]
Sent: February 11, 2008 11:48 AM
Subject: **Your Enquiry about PURE Anti-virus Software Updates**

Dear Mr. Nickel,

Thank you for purchasing our PURE anti-virus software. We've checked our records, from which we've learned that you purchased Version 3.0; since its release in March 2001, we've released Version 4.0, on October 1, 2003.
Future Computers should have sold you Version 4.0, which features automatic updates sent through the Internet; we asked all our retailers to discontinue Version 3.0 as of October 1, 2003.

Version 3.0 vs. Version 4.0
I can answer your question, as follows:

- Version 3.0 does not contain automatic Internet updates. It does, however, contain date-specific prompts to maintain coverage against new viruses; to do so, you e-mail PURE (as the prompt directs) and you will be shown how to upgrade your virus protection. Unfortunately, Version 3.0 is no longer capable of handling some of the new types of viruses, and is not compatible with Version 4.0's software platform.
- Version 4.0 automatically updates your computer's anti-virus system through your computer's Web connection, whenever new viruses are detected. That service is free for your first year of use and $10 for each succeeding year.
- Version 4.0, when updated in your computer, detects and eliminates all new viruses (and all previously detected viruses) as they arise.
- Our software engineers have devised master detection software that continuously searches for new viruses on the major networks (Netscape, AOL, etc.).

Your Options
We have advised Future Computers to accept your Version 3.0 for full credit toward Version 4.0, if you would like to do that. The suggested retail price for Version 4.0 is $59.95, plus taxes. We recommend you upgrade to Version 4.0; Version 3.0 can detect all of the viruses that were around before mid-2003. However, Version 3.0 is incapable of handling some especially new nasty viruses that seem to have been designed to bypass the previous standard for anti-virus software platforms. Also, Version 4.0 provides up-to-the-minute protection against new viruses.

In future, if we must change Version 4.0's platform, you'll be able to get full credit for your old version when you choose the new one. Please contact me if you have any other questions.

Sincerely,
Marie Szarbynski

Customer Service Representative
PURE Inc.
1125 B Gordon Road

Figure 13.6 A Letter-style Email

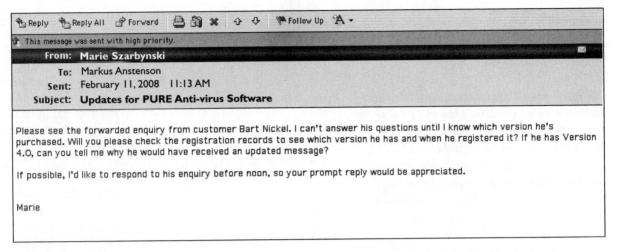

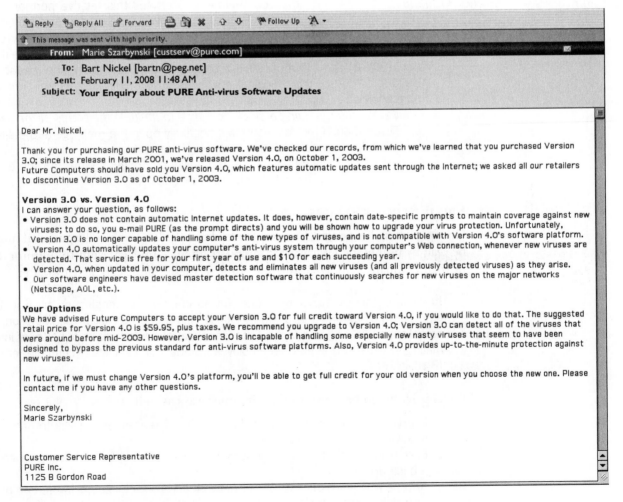

ON THE JOB...

Email Benefits and Drawbacks

"Email is taking over, especially if the client lives in another city. But even our local clients receive frequent emails that detail on-site decisions. Also, I send digital photos. The problem with email is that it happens so quickly. People seem to expect immediate responses to their email, but a thoughtful, quantified response takes time—often, I have to get quotes or other information first. And I get 30 to 40 pertinent emails a day. So, I've had to hire office staff just to manage these communication issues. Then we can respond to our clients with timely information...."

—Ken Dahlen, Keith Construction

- *Email can foster creative thinking.* Email dialogues involve give-and-take, much like a conversation. Writers feel encouraged to express their thoughts spontaneously, thinking as they write, without worrying about page design, paragraph structure, perfect phrasing, or the like. The focus is on conveying your meaning to the recipients, who in turn will respond with thoughts of their own. This relatively free exchange of views can lead to all sorts of new insights or ideas (Bruhn 43).
- *Email is excellent for collaborative work and research.* Collaborative teams keep in touch via email, and researchers contact people who have the answers they need. Especially useful for collaborative work is the email function that enables documents or electronic files of any length to be attached and sent for downloading by the receiver.
- *Email provides a record of agreements.* Among other benefits, this record makes it easier to hold people to their commitments. Perhaps this relative permanence explains why so many emails are printed and stored as paper documents. A 2007 *Backbone* article by Gail Balfour says that "Canadian firms are printing more than ever" (20). It seems that people like paper's tactility, portability, and readability (Balfour 24). Also, technological advances have made printers and printing more affordable.
- *Email is good for sending a single message to multiple recipients at the same time.* Even though the recipients will not likely open the message at the same time, there's a record of when the message was sent.
- *Current email software allows for well-designed "pages,"* either on the email screen itself or as a formal attached document.

Email Privacy Issues

Gossip, personal messages, or complaints about the boss or a colleague—all might be read by unintended receivers. Employers often claim legal right to monitor *any* of their company's information, and some of these claims can be legitimate:

Monitoring of email by an employer may be legal

> In some instances it may be proper for an employer to monitor email, if it [the employer] has evidence of safety violations, illegal activity, racial discrimination, or sexual improprieties, for instance. Companies may also need access to business information, whether it is kept in an employee's drawer, file cabinet, or computer email. (Bjerklie 15)

Email privacy can be compromised in other ways as well:

Email offers no privacy

- Everyone on a group mailing list—intended reader or not—automatically receives a copy of the message.
- Even when deleted from the system, messages often live on for years, saved in a back-up file.
- Anyone who gains access to your network and your private password can read your document, alter it, use parts of it out of context, pretend to be its author,

forward it to whomever, plagiarize your ideas, or even author a document or conduct illegal activity in your name.

Email privacy concerns have led to encryption technology and to "self-destructing" emails that exist for a limited time only. Encrypted messages are scrambled so that they can be opened only by someone with a password or with the answer to a predetermined question. Encryption can also prevent forwarding or altering a message. After they're first opened, self-destructing emails expire within a range of 10 seconds to two weeks, as chosen by the sender. (Or, the sender can choose to not have the message expire.) Meanwhile, the sender keeps a copy of the sent message.

For a fee of less than a dollar, emails can even be sent as "registered mail," with all the features that registered paper mail provides. Users of registered email, such as lawyers and technology professionals, wish to protect themselves from email-related liability—email is increasingly being used as evidence in court cases.

Email Quality Issues

Free exchange via computer screen adds to the quantity of information exchanged, but not always to its quality. As the following examples show, information quality can be compromised by email communication:

Email does not always promote quality in communication

- The ease of sending and exchanging messages can generate overload and junk mail—a party announcement sent to 300 employees on a group mailing list, or the indiscriminate mailing of a political statement to dozens of newsgroups (*spamming*).
- Some electronic messages may be poorly edited and long-winded.
- Off-the-cuff messages or responses might offend certain recipients. Email users often seem less restrained about making rude remarks (*flaming*) than they would be in a face-to-face encounter.
- Recipients might misinterpret the tone. *Emoticons* or *smileys*, punctuation cues that signify pleasure :-), displeasure :-(, sarcasm ;-), anger :-<, and other emotional states, offer some assistance but are not always an adequate or appropriate substitute for the subtle cues in spoken conversation. Also, common email abbreviations (FYI, BTW, HAND—which mean "for your information," "by the way," and "have a nice day") might strike some readers as too informal.

Email Offshoots

Internet forums

Internet email forums allow various groups to discuss topics of common interest. One such forum, Power Globe, brings together persons interested in electrical power engineering at **http://powerglobe.powerquality.com**. Here, subscribers discuss technological trends, announce conferences and new publications, post job openings, and request information.

E-newsletters

Newsletters delivered by email provide news stories, background information, member updates, and human-interest articles to such diverse groups as cross-country ski clubs, Manchester United soccer fans, and fashion design aficionados. In-house electronic newsletters focus on company news, industry developments, employee information, and stories about employees. These company e-newsletters can provide a forum for employee feedback that is missing from printed newsletters.

Converged messaging is rapidly gaining popularity—it had 1 million users worldwide in 2000; by 2005, this number had jumped to 40 million. The technology uses Voice over Internet Protocol (VoIP) and converging software to send phone messages, faxes, and text messages as email attachments to a receiver's email inbox.

Converged messaging offers several advantages:

Advantages of converged messaging

- The technology saves time and effort by directing all messages to one device; therefore, the receiver is more likely to make the effort to look at all incoming phone calls and faxes.
- When the receiver sees who has phoned, he or she can tell at a glance which messages need to be heard and will likely need a quick response. Using traditional voice mail, receivers are less likely to plough through many messages to discover which ones are important enough to warrant an immediate response.
- The technology is compatible with smart phones and PDAs, so receivers can pick up all their messages when they're out of the office.
- Therefore, converged messaging facilitates timely communication, an important consideration in today's business climate.

Complex versions of converged messaging systems for large companies require expensive software, VoIP hardware, and a subscription to a telephone system vendor. The cost of the total package for a company can run "well into five or six figures," according to Info-Tech Research's Carmi Levy (Blackwell B8). However, less expensive alternatives are available for small businesses, and Mr. Levy believes that converged messaging (also known as "unified messaging" or UM) could be particularly useful for small businesses that rely on quick responses to customer demands.

GUIDELINES for Using Email Effectively

Recipients who consider an email message poorly written, irrelevant, offensive, or inappropriate will only end up resenting the sender. These guidelines offer suggestions for effective email use.

1. *Check and answer your email daily.* Like an unreturned phone call, unanswered mail annoys people. If you're really busy, at least acknowledge receipt and respond later.
2. *Don't use email when a more personal medium would be better.* Sometimes an issue is best resolved with a phone call or personal visit.
3. *At work, consider email to be correspondence, not conversation.*
4. *Assume your email correspondence is permanent and could be read by anyone anytime.* **Electronic mail is not a private medium.** Increasingly, employers monitor their email networks—Forrester Research's 2006 survey of 294 large U.S. companies revealed that 38 percent of the companies hire staff to read outbound employee email and 46.9 percent regularly audit outbound email (*Globe and Mail* staff C2).
5. *Don't use email to send confidential information.* Avoid complaining, evaluating, criticizing, or saying anything private. And don't use the company email network for personal correspondence or for anything not work

(continued)

GUIDELINES
for Using Email Effectively
(continued)

related. **Violating company email policy can result in severe penalties.** The Forrester Research survey found that 31.6 percent of companies had fired employees for violations and 52.4 percent had disciplined employees during the previous 12 months.

6. *Check your distribution list before each mailing,* to be sure the message reaches only the intended primary and secondary readers.
7. *Before you forward an incoming message to other recipients, obtain permission from the sender.* Assume that everything you receive is the sender's private property.
8. *Write subject lines that catch the reader's attention and that provide a context for the message.* Good subject lines are like good news headlines. Use action-oriented phrasing in the subject line and the opening paragraph to suggest how the reader can use the information contained in the email.
9. *Limit your message to a single topic.* Remain focused and concise. (Yours may be just one of many messages confronting the recipient.) Don't ramble. *Limit your topic to a single screen, if possible.* Don't force recipients to scroll needlessly.
10. *Don't use email for a detailed discussion.* Send a letter or memo or report instead. In cases where time is of the essence, especially for in-house recipients and others who can easily receive and print your form of word-processed documents, attach your paper document to an introductory email. By doing so, you include the best features of both media.
11. *Carefully check the spelling, grammar, and tone. Especially, spell recipients' names correctly! Even short messages reflect your image.*
12. *Pause before hitting the "send" button.* Catch errors and omissions. Make sure that attachments are attached!
13. *Clean out your mailboxes.* Mail that piles up in employee inboxes and deleted folders can eventually clog up a company's email database.

INTERPERSONAL ELEMENTS OF WORKPLACE CORRESPONDENCE

In addition to presenting the reader with an accessible and inviting design, effective correspondence enhances the relationship between writer and reader. Various interpersonal elements forge a *human* connection, as the following advice explains.

Focus on Your Reader's Interests: The "You" Perspective. In speaking face to face, you unconsciously modify your statements and expression as you read the listener's signals: a smile, a frown, a raised eyebrow, a nod. In a telephone conversation, a voice provides cues that signal approval, dismay, anger, or confusion. Writing a letter, memo, fax, or email, however, carries a major disadvantage; you can easily forget that a flesh-and-blood person will be reacting to what you are saying or seem to be saying.

Correspondence that displays a "you" perspective subordinates the writer's interests to those of the reader. Besides focusing on what is important to the reader, the "you" perspective conveys respect for the reader's feelings and attitudes.

To achieve a "you" perspective, put yourself in the place of the person who will read your correspondence; ask yourself how the reader will react to what you have written. Even a single word, carelessly chosen, can offend. In writing to correct a billing error, for example, you might feel tempted to say this:

A needlessly offensive tone

> Our record keeping is very efficient and so this obviously is your error.

Such an accusatory tone might be appropriate after numerous failed attempts to achieve satisfaction on your part, but in your initial correspondence it will alienate the reader. The following version is more considerate. Instead of indicting the reader, it conveys respect for the reader's viewpoint.

A tone that conveys the "you" perspective

> If my paperwork is wrong, please let me know and I will send you a corrected version immediately.

Use Plain English. Workplace correspondence too often suffers from *letterese*, those tired, stuffy, and overblown phrases some writers think they need to make their communication seem important. Here is a typically overwritten closing sentence:

Letterese

> Humbly thanking you in anticipation of your kind cooperation, I remain
> Faithfully yours,

Although no one *speaks* this way, some writers lean on such heavy prose instead of simply writing this:

Clear phrasing

> I will appreciate your cooperation.

Here are a few of the many old standards that would be better presented in plain English:

Letterese	**Plain English**
As per your request	As you requested
Contingent upon receipt of	As soon as we receive
I am desirous of	I want, I would like
Please be advised that I	I
This writer	I
In the immediate future	Soon
In accordance with your request	As you requested
Due to the fact that	Because
I wish to express my gratitude	Thank you

Be natural. Write as you would speak in a classroom or office.

Anticipate Your Reader's Reaction. Like any effective writing, good correspondence does not just happen. It is the product of a deliberate process. As you plan, write, and revise, answer these questions:

1. *What do I want the reader to do, think, or feel after reading this correspondence?* Do you want him or her to offer you a job, give advice or information, answer an inquiry, follow instructions, grant a favour, enjoy good news, accept bad news?
2. *What facts will my reader need?* Do you need to give measurements, dates, costs, model numbers, enclosures, other details?
3. *To whom am I writing?* Do you know the reader's name? When possible, write to a person, not a title.
4. *What is my relationship to my reader?* Is the reader a potential employer, an employee, a person doing a favour, a person whose products are disappointing, an acquaintance, an associate, a stranger?

Answer those four questions *before* drafting correspondence. After you have a draft, answer the following three questions, which pertain to the *effect* of your correspondence. Will readers be inclined to respond favourably?

5. *How will my reader react to what I've written?* With anger, hostility, pleasure, confusion, fear, guilt, resistance, satisfaction?
6. *What impression of me will my reader get from this correspondence?* That you are intelligent, courteous, friendly, articulate, pretentious, illiterate, confident?
7. *Am I ready to sign my correspondence with confidence?* Think about it.

Send correspondence only when you've answered each question to your satisfaction.

Decide on a Direct or Indirect Plan. The reaction you anticipate from your reader should determine the organizational plan of your correspondence: either *direct* or *indirect.*

- Will the reader feel pleased or neutral about the message?
- Will the message cause resistance, resentment, or disappointment?

Each reaction calls for a different organizational plan. The direct plan puts the main point right in the first paragraph, followed by the explanation. Use the direct plan when you expect the reader to react with approval or when you want the reader to know immediately the point of your letter (e.g., in good-news, inquiry, or application letters—or other routine correspondence).

If you expect the reader to resist or to need persuading, consider an indirect plan. Give the explanation *before* the main point (as in refusing a request, admitting a mistake, or requesting a pay raise). An indirect plan might make readers more tolerant of bad news or more receptive to your argument.

Whenever you consider using an indirect plan, think carefully about its ethical implications. Never try to deceive the reader—and never create an impression that you have something to hide.

STRUCTURES FOR WORKPLACE CORRESPONDENCE

Trial and error, along with perceptive analysis of readers and purposes for letters, memos, and emails, will allow you to find the best ways to organize your workplace correspondence. The best structure for each message will depend on the circumstances. You can start by using the audience/purpose analysis form to choose the content of the message. Then you can adapt the action structure described in Chapter 17 for virtually any letter, memo, or email you write.

Let's review that structure:

1. *Action opening:* Connect with the reader's interest and (where appropriate) summarize the full message in one or two sentences.
2. *Background:* Provide any information the reader needs to understand the main message that follows. Many letters and memos don't need this section; in others, you'll be able to fit a one-sentence background overview into the introductory paragraph.
3. *Details:* Present the main message. (Answer the reader's questions; describe your idea; present your information and analysis; argue your case; explain your point of view.)
4. *Action closing:* Request the desired action from your reader and/or describe the action you intend to take. Provide information that the reader needs to perform the requested action.

Examples of direct and indirect approaches appear in this chapter and in Chapter 17

Now let's see some examples of how that structure can work for workplace messages. The scope of this book does not allow coverage of every kind of letter, memo, or email you might eventually write in your working life, but a careful study of the following examples will help you learn how to adapt the action structure to many other kinds of messages.

Notice that some messages require a *direct approach:* the main point or bottom line is provided in the opening paragraph because you've realized that's what the reader wants, and you've concluded that your own purpose will not be jeopardized by doing so. Other messages require an *indirect plan,* where the opening paragraph previews the document's structure and the main point comes at the end of the document.

The inquiry described in Table 13.1 (and later illustrated by Figure 13.7) employs a direct pattern; the reader will want to immediately know the message's main purpose. Then, seeing the potential for business, the reader will be motivated to read carefully.

Figure 13.7 illustrates the phrasing that might be used for the message that Table 13.1 outlines. The situation outlined in Table 13.2 also uses a direct pattern: stating the requested action and its contribution to the *reader's* goals will get the reader's attention and help hold that attention throughout the memo.

Figure 13.8 illustrates the phrasing that might be used for the message that Table 13.2 outlines. The writer feels comfortable using Rich Text Format for this email, including bolded headings and quotation marks, because both the sender and receiver use Outlook Express as their email software.

Table 13.1 Inquiry (Letter or Email) Structure

Section	Situation: Enquiry about updates for PURE anti-virus software Reader: PURE Inc. Customer Services Department
Action Opening	State purpose for writing/general nature of enquiry (paragraph 1)
Background	Say how long you've had the PURE software installed; say whether you purchased a CD-ROM version or downloaded it from the internet (paragraph 2)
Details	Ask detailed questions about the updates: ◆ range of virus types detected ◆ methods of receiving updates/frequency of updates ◆ company's main strategy for discovering viruses ◆ costs of updates/types of payment accepted by PURE (paragraph 3 uses numbered or bulleted list)
Action Closing	Provide email address and phone number; ask PURE rep to respond; give deadline for response, if that's an issue (paragraph 4)

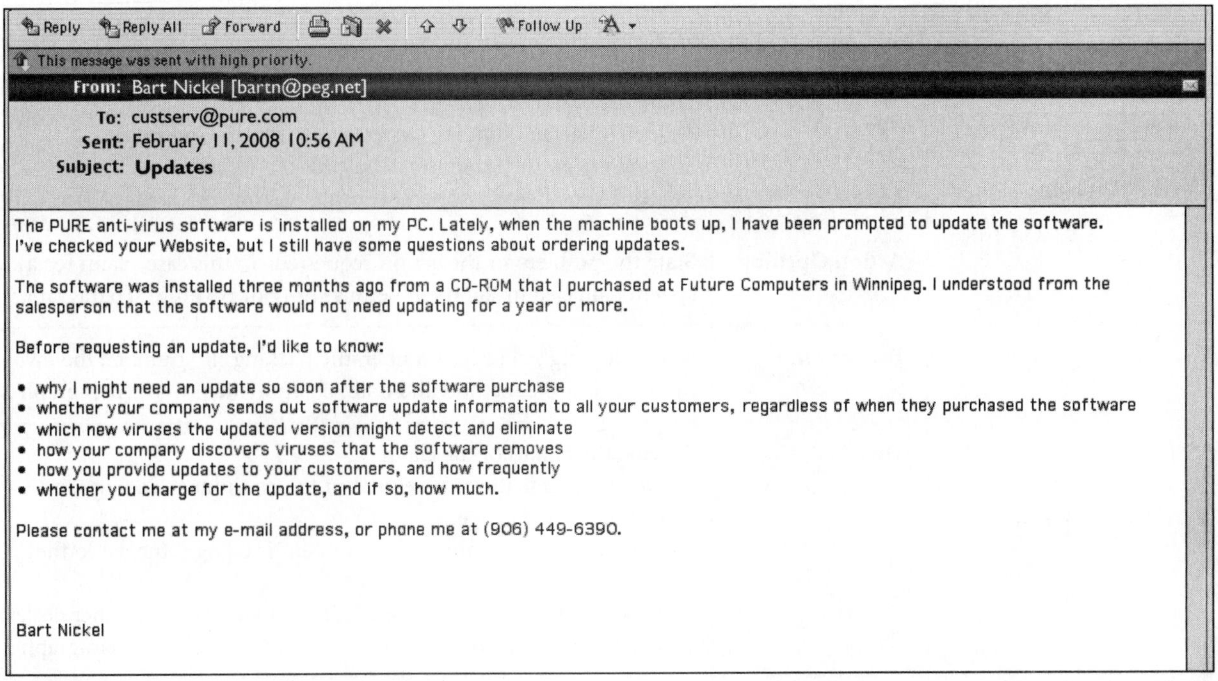

Reply Reply All Forward Follow Up

This message was sent with high priority.

From: Bart Nickel [bartn@peg.net]
To: custserv@pure.com
Sent: February 11, 2008 10:56 AM
Subject: **Updates**

The PURE anti-virus software is installed on my PC. Lately, when the machine boots up, I have been prompted to update the software. I've checked your Website, but I still have some questions about ordering updates.

The software was installed three months ago from a CD-ROM that I purchased at Future Computers in Winnipeg. I understood from the salesperson that the software would not need updating for a year or more.

Before requesting an update, I'd like to know:

- why I might need an update so soon after the software purchase
- whether your company sends out software update information to all your customers, regardless of when they purchased the software
- which new viruses the updated version might detect and eliminate
- how your company discovers viruses that the software removes
- how you provide updates to your customers, and how frequently
- whether you charge for the update, and if so, how much.

Please contact me at my e-mail address, or phone me at (906) 449-6390.

Bart Nickel

Figure 13.7 A Sample Email Inquiry

Table 13.2 Request Memo Structure

Section	Situation: Request for funds to design a company website Reader: General Sales Manager Writer: Sales Representative
Action Opening	State the main action that needs to be taken and the primary reason for that action; connect with reader's interests relative to this action (paragraph 1)
Background	Describe the circumstances leading to this situation or events affecting the situation (paragraph 2)
Details	Provide a detailed description of what is being requested or needs to be done: ◆ staffing required ◆ equipment and software required and whether the company currently has these requirements in inventory ◆ timelines and schedule ◆ costs (one or more paragraphs)
Action Closing	Request the specific desired action or reader's approval for the writer's proposed action (final paragraph)

Next, the structure for a claim letter (also know as an adjustment letter or a complaint letter) in Table 13.3 also uses a direct pattern. The writer immediately gets to the point.

Table 13.3 Claim Letter (or Email) Structure

Section	Situation: Claim for damages Reader: Manager, Shipping Department, Genesis Computer Systems Co. (an Edmonton wholesaler) Writer: Home-based computer consultant, Fort McMurray, Alberta
Action Opening	State the problem or the action requested (in this case, claim for a system damaged in shipment because of poor packing) (paragraph 1)
Background	Name the original order number, the packing slip number, the invoice number, and the method and date of shipment (paragraph 2)
Details	Provide the details of the claim: ◆ Describe the nature and extent of the equipment damage and estimate the damage. ◆ Refer to how the damaged equipment is being returned to the supplier. ◆ Describe the loss of business (the customer went to another dealer). ◆ Refer to enclosed documents. (paragraph 3)
Action Closing	Close politely, but firmly—say what you expect to be done, and confirm that you desire continued business relations with the reader (paragraph 4)

Reply | Reply All | Forward | Follow Up

This message was sent with high priority.

From: Marc Bessier [mbessier@magnum.com]
To: Kordell Dobson [kdobson@magnum.com]
Sent: June 23, 2008 11:48 AM
Re: **Company website**

Hello Kordell,

In Monday's monthly sales meeting, you mentioned the possibility of using ecommerce as a way of building our market base. Recent developments in my sales territory reinforce the need to establish a company website as a first step toward ecommerce.

Background

My territory primarily consists of mining operations in northern Ontario and northern Manitoba. Because many of the mines are quite remote, they use the internet to keep in touch with the world and to shop for equipment and supplies. I've been using the mail, phone calls, and fax messages to send product information and answer their enquiries, but I'm on the road 8 days out of 10, so it's difficult for me to respond promptly.

Several purchasing officers have told me that they'd prefer to go to the internet for product information, prices, and availability. And they'd like to order on the net, too.

Action Required

Our chief competitor, Allan-Price, has set up a homepage. There's not much on it right now, and it's not very well organized, but Allan-Price "has a presence on the web," as Marco Corrazini of Canway's Musquean Mine pointedly told me on the phone yesterday. I think we have to keep up with Allan-Price.

What will establishing a website require? I called a friend at Merced Industrial Machines to learn how his company set up its top-quality site. He told me that some of the Merced head office people had computer experience, so they tried to do the work themselves. In the end, though, they had to call in a consultant, who charged about $5000 to design and build the site. In addition, Merced purchased about $1500 worth of software. And it continues to pay a part-time webmaster $400 per month to update and troubleshoot the site.

I contacted that same consultant, June Paschke, yesterday. She has three years' experience as a webpage designer. She said that building a site for us would take about the same amount of time (10 working days) and cost about the same as the Merced contract. Of course, she would have to meet with us before presenting a detailed proposal of her work plan and fees.

Authorization

May I arrange a meeting next Monday for June Paschke to discuss our needs and her solutions with you, me, and our other three regional sales representatives? We'll all be in town for the AGM. Also, may I meet with you to discuss my possible involvement in the project? I have a special interest in a website project because of its potential for building business. I'll be in Cochrane and Kapuskasing for the next two days, but I'll check frequently for messages on my pager, 689-4352.

Regards,

Marc

Figure 13.8 A Request

As the preceding tables show, the direct, four-part action structure can be adapted for a variety of situations. Some of those situations, such as a refusal of a request, will require an indirect pattern. Table 13.4 presents a suggested structure for refusing a request.

When Kordell Dobson writes to refuse Marc Bessier's request (Figure 13.9), note the phrasing Kordell uses.

Table 13.4 Refusal Message Structure

Section	Situation: Respond to request for funds to design a company website Reader: Sales Representative Writer: General Sales Manager
Action Opening	Express appreciation for the sales rep's initiative; acknowledge that there has recently been discussion of creating a company website (paragraph 1)
Background	Without actually saying "no" just yet, explain the circumstances that preclude creating a website at this time (perhaps the firm is in the process of contracting a web consultant or joining forces with another firm, or perhaps the company is analyzing its entire marketing strategy) (paragraph 2)
Details	Soften the bad news by ◆ placing it in the middle of the paragraph ◆ using the passive voice (not "We cannot grant your request at this time," but "Funds are therefore not available for this project at this time") ◆ focusing on the reasons for the refusal, not on the refusal itself (part of paragraph 2, or perhaps a new paragraph)
Action Closing	Thank the reader for his or her commitment and ideas; encourage the reader to pursue an interest in website design; assure the reader that he or she will be consulted when the project is next discussed (final paragraph)

LENGTH OF WORKPLACE CORRESPONDENCE

All letters and memos should be as short as you can make them. Restrict them to one page, if you can. (Emails should fit on one screen.) Although one-page messages are not always possible—see several samples in Chapter 17, for example—you can restrict some messages to one page by placing the main message in a cover letter and the remaining details in enclosures. For instance, a complex order for supplies might be organized in order sheets enclosed with a cover letter that

- authorizes the purchase, designates the delivery method, and names the source of your information about the supplies
- quickly summarizes the nature of the order and refers to the enclosed order "forms" (which provide details of items, quantities, order numbers, prices, taxes, shipping, and overall costs)
- closes by saying how you will pay and when you expect delivery

Reply | Reply All | Forward | Follow Up

This message was sent with high priority.

From: Bart Nickel [bartn@peg.net]
To: Marc Bessier [mbessier@magnum.com]
Sent: June 23, 2008 2:20 PM
Re: **Your Ideas for a Company Website**

Marc,

Thank you for your initiative in promoting the creation of our own website. Over the past few months there have indeed been some discussions about establishing a presence on the web.

I'm going to be in Montreal until next week, and then next week my preparations for the AGM and my participation in the AGM's follow-up meetings will occupy my time.

We are in negotiations to merge with a Western Canadian firm, in order to give both firms a national presence. (I'm sure you've heard the rumours.) If indeed that merger happens, we will combine our strategies and resources with that firm on many fronts. In the meantime, all new projects are on hold, including the creation of new marketing vehicles and ecommerce. We haven't discussed the possibility of establishing a website with our potential merger partner; too many other issues need to be resolved first.

I appreciate your commitment to the firm's goals. Please continue your interest in webpage design, so that you can contribute to future discussion and actions in this exciting method of communicating with our present and future customers. Perhaps we can grab a few minutes to discuss your ideas, after the CEO's address on Monday.

Kordell

Figure 13.9 A Refusal of a Request

WRITE CORRESPONDENCE EFFICIENTLY

When you write workplace correspondence, write efficiently. Very few one-page messages should take more than 45 minutes to plan, compose, and polish. You will, however, take longer if you have to rewrite major sections of letters or memos. That kind of rewriting can be avoided by clear thinking in the early stages of the process.

So remember:

- Consider your audience's needs, interests, and priorities and the purpose of the document.
- Use your audience/purpose analysis to choose the content and arrange that content.
- Work from an outline that identifies the content and/or purpose of each paragraph.
- Revise the content and structure before writing sentences and paragraphs.

You'll be amazed at how efficiently you'll write.

Also remember that how you use workplace correspondence will affect your credibility within your organization. Your colleagues' and supervisors' perceptions of your worth will be affected by the degree of care and skill you put into your letters, memos, and emails.

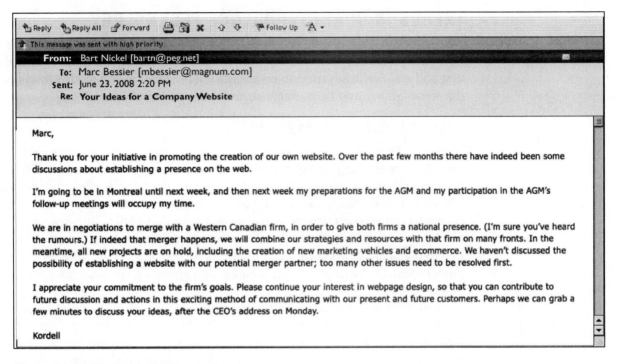

TRENDS IN CORRESPONDENCE TECHNOLOGY

New communications technologies appear with such frequency that only the technologically wise can stay abreast of the trends. By the time this book is published, new and wonderful advances in communications software and hardware will be on the scene. Still, it may be useful to summarize current trends.

Text and Instant Messaging

In the late 1990s, *text messaging* (known primarily outside North America as SMS, for "short messaging services") and *instant messaging* (IM) started to become popular with young people who saw the computer-based and cellular phone–based service as replacements for phone calls and email. Text messages travel via asynchronous cell phone transmission; a sender keys and sends a message, and signs off. A response message will come on a separate transmission. By contrast, instant messaging operates synchronously—writers correspond online together, via computer or text-enabled cell phone. IM also allows people to indicate whether they're online or offline.

Immediacy is the strength of these media, not carefully crafted messages. Screen size and real-time messaging limit the medium to brief bursts of communication (about 160 characters, maximum). So, these media are fine for "I've sent the package today. Should get there soon," but totally inadequate for explaining why the package wasn't sent earlier.

Still, electronic messaging is growing, especially in Asia, the Pacific region, and Europe. Worldwide, text messages sent to and from portable phones are expected to reach 2.3 trillion annually by 2010, according to a survey reported by Reuters News Agency in December 2006 (TextIt). As of August 2007, according to an estimate by the Canadian Wireless Telecommunications Association, Canadians send 26.5 million text messages per day ("Canada's Wireless Industry").

Although text and instant messaging are used primarily for social networking, they do offer advantages in work settings:

- Receivers are more likely to respond to the "ping" of an IM or text message than to an email.
- Text and IM are better than phone calls when privacy is an issue, or when silent conversation is required, or when excessive background noise makes phone usage difficult.
- IM allows for real-time, inexpensive collaboration among two or more workers when specific details are being discussed.
- Special subscription services such as iPiPi.com offer text messaging between computers and cell phones anywhere in the world, which can dramatically reduce the costs of long distance communicating.
- Smart phones and PDAs allow users to direct their correspondents to stored images, websites, email messages, and even to audio and video.
- Large companies can subscribe to "message-brokering" software that prioritizes thousands of text messages coming from sources anywhere in the world. Then the software can place the messages in queues of decreasing relevance and send the messages to appropriate employees within the company. For example, an engineer working on a project in Africa might have a specialized

question that a senior engineer at the company's North American head office could answer.

Weblogs

Technorati, which monitors developments on the World Wide Web, tracks and provides links to over 60 million *weblogs*, a form of online journals. Known commonly as "blogs," these journals provide more than information, ideas, and visuals. They allow visitors to engage in online forums. Topics include the full range of human interests, experience, and knowledge. Basic blogs, most of which are hosted for free, provide text, photo placement, and limited graphics. Premium-level blogs allow for advanced formatting, links, and even video.

Most blogs are created by individual "bloggers," attracted by the opportunity to express themselves and to engage in conversation with people who share their interests. Blogs are particularly good at serving discourse communities, ranging from people interested in technical writing to hang-gliding enthusiasts.

Also, all sorts of businesses use blogs to provide general information and product updates, to interact with their clients, and to market their products and services. Good examples include Google and Microsoft. Companies also host staff blogs that invite posts from employees and that are aimed at employees, not the public—*Fast Company* magazine hosts such a blog at **http://blog.fastcompany.com/**. One can also find hybrid corporate blogs such as "News from the Lab," from F-Secure Security Labs, a multinational company headquartered in Finland. Its blog entries, which are aimed at consumers, seem to be written on a volunteer basis by F-Secure staffers. (The blog appears at **www.f-secure.com/weblog/**.)

Technology has spawned several blog varieties: *vlogs* (composed of videos with complementary text), *linklogs* (focusing on links to other blogs and websites), *sketchlogs* (portfolios of sketches and other art work), and *photoblogs*. A *moblog* is written on a mobile phone or PDA. Blogs that feature streaming audio are called *podcasts*, an amalgam of "iPod" and "broadcast" that was coined by *The Guardian*'s Ben Hammersley in 2005. Several internet sites offer menus of free podcasts—iTunes.com, ipodder.org, and podcast.net are among the better sites.

Podcasting was initially meant for people to distribute their own "radio shows," but it is now used in many other ways: lectures and recorded discussions, museum audio tours, motivational talks, safety messages, foreign language study, and podcasted versions of public radio shows. Subscription services such as iTunes will even send podcasts automatically to subscribers' PCs so that subscribers can listen to the

ON THE JOB...

Podcasting and Receiver Control

"In the digital age, receivers expect that they should be able to access information on their time, their way. People want to be able to place material on their iPod or other MP3 device and listen to it in the car, on the bus, or wherever they want. . . ."

—Marc Arellano, communications professor and podcaster

podcasts at their leisure. The majority of podcasts are produced by individuals, but companies also podcast. Three of the earliest companies to jump on the podcasting bandwagon were TV Guide, Purina Pet Care, and BMC Software.

As with email, bloggers should be careful about what they post. Recent media reports have cited cases where employees have been fired for indiscreet blog posts. Also, tech-savvy employers are searching through the blog universe for blogs, vlogs, and podcasts involving prospective employees. An applicant's star may rise because of what the employer finds, or the applicant's chances of employment may be erased completely.

ON THE JOB...

Benefits of Podcasting

"Podcasting has great potential for training applications. Also, it allows employees to tell their 'stories' and to contribute to the shared wealth of information about how their industry or company works and about how things could be done better. It's very satisfying for employees to have their opinions and experiences recorded and distributed to a wider audience. At the same time, employers can talk about the things they like about their company and its products or services. So, within an organization, podcasts and vlogs help build a sense of community and permit a space for sharing best practices, and externally these genuine employee expressions help build the company's brand and make it easier to recruit new employees. People are influenced by this 'credible buzz'...."

—Marc Arellano, communications professor and a former communications professional in the bicycle industry

WEB CONNECT

Letters and Memos
www.ecf.utoronto.ca/~writing/handbook-memo.html

Email Usage
www.nrcan-rncan.gc.ca/em-ce/emgd-e.htm
www.pimall.com/nais/n.pgp.faq.html
www.webfoot.com
www.iab.net/iab_products_and_industry_services/1421/1443/1458
www.privacy.gov.au/internet/email/
http://larve.net/people/hugo/2000/03/email
www.pao.gov.ab.ca/directives/relations/use-of-information.htm

EXERCISES

1. Collect samples of workplace writing—letters, memos, and email messages. In those samples, look for instances of letterese, clichés, and wordy and unclear phrasing. Improve the phrasing where necessary.
2. Check the tone of emails, memos, and letters that you examine. Do you see phrasing that might antagonize the reader? Do you see phrasing that places the writer's needs and interests ahead of the reader's? If so, rephrase.
3. Examine workplace emails, letters, and memos to see if they use a variation of the four-part action structure. (See Chapter 17.) If the action structure has not been used for a given message, would the message be more effective if it were restructured?
4. Monitor your next composition of a one-page letter, memo, or email. Record how long you take to complete each stage of the writing process. (See Chapter 3.)
5. Examine a corporate blog maintained by a company such as General Motors (at **www.gmblogs.com**), Dell (at **http://direct2dell.com**), or F-Secure Security Labs. (See page 269). Assess the style of writing (formal, informal, technical, lively, serious, etc.). Evaluate the apparent objectivity and degree of "sales hype" in the blog posts—do you trust that the comments in the articles are honestly expressed or do you suspect that the company's marketing department has manipulated the blog posts' content?

COLLABORATIVE PROJECT

In conjunction with other members of your class, survey correspondence practices of businesses in your part of Canada. Ask your survey respondents about the following topics:

- which types of correspondence (letter, memo, email, fax, text message) get used most often
- what standards the business requires for formatting letters and letter-style emails sent to external receivers
- what guidelines or restrictions the company has for email and text messaging

Also ask for a sample letter, a sample internal memo, and a sample formal email.

Members of your group could conduct the survey in person. If so, send a copy of the survey questions with an accompanying letter or email first, and then telephone for an appointment. Emphasize that information found in the sample letters and memos will be held confidential. Also offer to make a copy of the survey's statistical results available to each participating business.

Or, the entire survey could be conducted by mail or by email.

NOTE *All correspondence sent during the survey should be approved by a class-appointed editing team.*

CHAPTER 14

Proposals

LEARNING OBJECTIVES

After reading this chapter, you should be able to

- Distinguish among sales proposals, research proposals, and improvement proposals.
- Understand the process of generating solicited proposals.
- Follow guidelines in planning, phrasing, and designing informal and formal proposals.
- Adapt the structure for a "standard" proposal to a particular situation.

A proposal offers to do something or recommends that something be done. A proposal's general purpose is to improve conditions, authorize work on a project, present a product or service (for payment), or otherwise support a plan for solving a problem or doing a job.

Your proposal may be a letter to your university's dean of engineering to suggest an interdisciplinary program of studies linked with the computer science and arts programs; it may be a memo to your firm's general manager to request funding for computer training; or it may be a 100-page document to the provincial highways ministry to bid for a contract to design a series of highway overpasses. You may write the proposal alone or as part of a team. It may take hours or months.

TYPES OF PROPOSALS

Proposals are as varied as the situations that generate them, but we can identify three main types:

1. *sales proposals*, which promote business
2. *research proposals*, which are used in academic institutions and in business
3. *improvement proposals* (or *planning proposals*), which suggest how to improve situations or ways of doing things, or which present solutions to problems

Some proposals are sent internally; others are sent to external readers. Either way, the proposal writer has reasons for sending the proposal. But, internal or external, the success or failure of the proposal depends almost entirely on the writer's ability to look at the situation from the *reader's* point of view. Table 14.1 shows a variety of proposals whose writers have tried to use supporting arguments that appeal to their readers.

> **ON THE JOB...**
>
> **The Proposal Process**
>
> *"Many of our contracted programs are opened every three years to a competitive public bid process. The continuation of these programs is extremely important to the capacity of our organization, because they provide the activities and salaries for over half of our staff. Consequently, it is imperative that our proposals meet and exceed the expectations of the funding agencies...."*
>
> **—Norm Metcalf, manager of a not-for-profit agency**

Some of the proposals in Table 14.1 have been solicited by their readers. These proposals may have to be presented differently from unsolicited proposals that have likely not been anticipated by their receivers.

A *solicited proposal* is received by a client who is not surprised or annoyed to receive that proposal. However, the client usually states definite requirements and expects to see those requirements met. Also, frequently, the client indicates the conditions and/or the format for the proposal. In these cases, the proposal writer has to pay strict attention to the reader's expectations.

The writer of an *unsolicited proposal* has a different challenge: often, the reader initially feels reluctant to accept the proposal. Perhaps the reader doesn't see a problem or is happy with the current way of doing things. Perhaps the reader is not aware of the product you have to sell, or has other priorities. However, if you can convince the reader of the need for your proposed solution, you have a chance of persuading the reader. If you can't establish that need in the reader's mind, there's no point in proposing how to meet the need!

THE PROPOSAL PROCESS

The basic proposal process for a solicited proposal can be summarized simply: someone offers a plan for something that needs to be done. In business and government, this process has five stages:

1. Client X recognizes a need for a service or product.
2. Client X draws up detailed requirements and advertises its need in a Request for Proposal (RFP).
3. Firms A, B, and C research Client X and its needs. (Likely they will request a more detailed version of the RFP.)
4. Firms A, B, and C propose a plan for meeting the need.
5. Client X awards the job to the firm offering the best proposal.

Table 14.1 Types of Proposals

Type	Internal	External
Sales	The design unit in a company that designs and manufactures auto parts solicits proposals for testing new magnesium-alloy brake parts. In keeping with the company's budgetary policies, the company's design unit can choose the company's own research lab's proposals or an external lab's proposal. Either way, the design unit will be billed for the testing. If the company lab wins the testing contract, it gains credits for salaries and new equipment.	An engineering firm that specializes in environmental studies proposes the assessment methods, timeline, staffing, and budget for assessing the potential environmental impact of a proposed golf course. The proposal responds to a Request for Proposal (RFP) issued by the provincial Ministry of the Environment. The RFP lists several pages of requirements that a successful proposal must meet.
Research	A truck manufacturing company's engine design team proposes a project to determine methods of reducing engine vibration. In arguing its case, the design team points to negative customer and dealer feedback about excessive engine vibration and noise. The design team also cites examples of how engine vibration has created warranty problems for the manufacturer.	A university physicist proposes a four-year computer modelling study of the properties of surface molecules. The physicist knows that his readers at the Natural Sciences and Engineering Research Council will understand his highly technical proposal, but for possible public consumption he attaches an executive summary that explains the potential applications of his research on the upper ozone layer.
Improvement	A research chemist in a petroleum firm's product development branch proposes a new way of blending methanol with gasoline. This new blending method would reduce production costs. In response to a supervisor's request, a fisheries biologist proposes a software package that tracks costs of extended research studies.	A software development firm, after reading newspaper reports about sailing delays and operating cost overruns for an East Coast ferry fleet, proposes a software program that fully coordinates the ferries' sailing schedules, maintenance schedules, staff training, supply loading, and fuelling. Before submitting the proposal, the software firm's partners learn all they can about who screens proposals at the ferry corporation.

The complexity of each phase will, of course, depend on the situation. In practice, the process could look like the following.

The situation

Tony Mutu, a civil engineering technologist with seven years of experience, works for EnviroMax Engineering Consultants in Penticton, in British Columbia's Okanagan Valley. On February 2, 2008, Tony's supervisor, Ken Guenther, assigns Tony to plan and write a proposal responding to an RFP that appears in a local newspaper and on the District of Beachland's website.

District of Beachland

Request for Proposal
17PW – 2008d

The Request for Proposal

The District of Beachland requires restoration of the beach and protection of the beach, shore, and foreshore at 2056 Beach Avenue, Town of Beachland. The proposal must describe a method of repairing the current damage. The firm that wins the contract will design the improvements and supervise the Beachland Public Works crew, who will carry out the restorative measures.

Requirements that must be met

Submitted proposals must

- describe a long-term solution to the erosion problem
- provide a large, protected swimming area and a protected sandy beach
- show how the work will be completed by June 20, 2008, in time for the summer tourist season
- be submitted to the District of Beachland by February 21, 2008
- use Beachland Public Works equipment and workers as much as possible, to control costs

Detailed information and a guided site inspection may be requested from

Contact person

John Warren, Public Works Manager
District of Beachland Public Works
Box 732
Beachland, British Columbia V9H 1X0
Phone: (250) 792-2343 pubworks@beachland.ca

After consulting reports about Lake Okanagan water levels, stream inlets, prevailing winds, and erosion control measures, Tony arranges to meet John Warren. From his site visit and a 2007 report about restoration measures at 2054 Beach Avenue, Tony learns the following:

Critical factors to be considered

1. The report indicates that the shoreline at 2054 Beach Avenue receded 2 metres from 1995 to 2006, an average of 19.3 centimetres per year. However, measurements taken by the owners of 2054 and 2056 show that the shoreline has eroded an average of 33 centimetres per year for the past four years.
2. Beachland businesses noticed a marked decline in business in 2006 and 2007.
3. In September 2004, the District of Beachland placed 21 metric tons of fine sand on the beach at 2054 Beach Avenue. By 2007, few traces of that sand remained.

Next, Tony consults Ken Guenther and other EnviroMax staff to learn who will be available to lend their expertise to the project. Also, Tony gleans information from

Many proposals require exhaustive research

- a visit to the Beachland Public Works (BPW), to examine BPW heavy equipment and BPW's stockpile of blast rock, gravel, and sand
- a visit with the District's financial controller, Donna Potter
- consultations with Bettina Chiu, biologist, and Tom Orman, hydrologist, of the B.C. Ministry of the Environment
- response to Tony's email inquiries about heavy equipment rental, underwater video camera rental, and marine construction insurance
- Ministry of the Environment records—Okanagan water levels, 1943 to 2005
- an EnviroMax report about the building of a breakwater for Holiday Houseboats' marina on Shuswap Lake
- a preliminary study, by Tony and civil technologist Theresa Mucci, regarding current water depths and soil depths offshore in front of 2056 Beach Avenue

Again, Tony consults Ken Guenther. EnviroMax's Doug Nygren joins in. Together, they reject two short-term solutions and choose a long-term solution described by Tony, even though it's considerably more expensive than the other two. Ken endorses Tony's proposed fee structure and the involvement of several EnviroMax personnel. Tony is nearly ready to write the proposal.

Other firms would also bid for a project such as the one described above. The client would award it to the firm submitting the best proposal, based on the criteria listed in the RFP, and the following criteria, which are generally used to assess proposals:

Typical assessment criteria

- understanding of the client's needs
- soundness of the firm's technical approach
- quality of the proposed project's organization and management
- ability to complete the job by the deadline
- ability to control costs
- specialized experience of the firm in this type of work
- qualifications of staff assigned to the project
- the firm's record for similar projects

Variation: assessment criteria may be weighted

NOTE *Sometimes an RFP will list the client's specific criteria in a point scale, as in the table on the following page, an excerpt from an RFP for harvesting timber on Crown land.*

Variation: pre-proposal conference

Some clients hold a pre-proposal conference for the competing firms. During this briefing, the firms are informed of the client's needs, expectations, specific start-up and completion dates, criteria for evaluation, and other details to guide proposal development. Such a conference does not suit John Warren's casual style of doing business.

Variation: restricted list of selected firms

Nor does the District of Beachland office do what some municipal and government agencies do: restrict a given project to a list of pre-selected firms. Usually, this is done on a rotation basis—if, for example, a city department has 15 firms on its contractor list, it might send invitations to bid to the first five firms on the list, and then to the next five firms for the next project, and so on. Or an agency might require firms to present their qualifications for a certain kind of project before actually soliciting proposals for it. Only those firms that clear the qualifications hurdle will be allowed to submit a proposal.

Criteria	Weighting
Employment	30
Proximity	10
Existing plant	10
New capital investment	10
Labour value-added	10
Change in value-added	20
Revenue	10
Total Weighting	100

All applicants must submit a proposal that contains a business case for lumber manufacturing or specialty wood products manufacturing and addresses the development objectives of the Crown.

Source: Adapted from a format used by the Ministry of Forests, Province of British Columbia.

In the Beachland case, Tony Mutu knows that the merits of his firm's proposed plan will be evaluated solely on the basis of what he puts on paper. Still, it helps to know who will make the final decision about the competing proposals. John Warren is a no-nonsense person who dislikes high-pressure sales tactics. With that in mind, Tony writes a formal proposal that looks very professional and that lays out EnviroMax's full case, but that is as brief as possible. Tony uses businesslike prose that is free from unnecessary jargon.

His proposal appears in this chapter, starting on page 294.

PROPOSAL GUIDELINES

Readers will evaluate your proposal according to how clearly, informatively, and realistically you answer these questions:

- What are you proposing?
- What problem will you solve?
- Why is your plan worthwhile?
- What is unique about your plan?
- What are your (or your firm's) credentials?
- How will the plan be implemented?
- How long will the project take to complete?
- How much will it cost?
- How will we benefit if we accept your plan?

ON THE JOB...

Evaluating Proposals

"Many proposals are evaluated by a 'scoring grid' that assigns specific values to each section of the document. The judging criteria are provided in advance, allowing the writer a reference guide to ensure each aspect of the proposal is properly addressed. Several committees will read and score the competing proposals so it is vital to provide all the pertinent technical and written information in a clear and concise format. Readability is critical.... The reader must be able to easily understand the content the first time through because the proposal may not get a second chance...."

—Norm Metcalf, manager of a not-for-profit agency

In addition to answering the questions above, successful proposal writers adhere to the following guidelines. This chapter's three sample proposals illustrate the guidelines.

GUIDELINES for Writing Persuasive Proposals

1. *Signal your intent with a clear title.* Decision makers are busy people who have no time for guessing games. The title should clearly signal the proposal's purpose and content. Don't write "Recommended Improvements" when you mean "Recommended Wastewater Treatment." A specific, comprehensive title signals the proposal's intent.
2. *Design an accessible and appealing format.* Format includes such features as
   - the layout of words and graphics, including white space
   - font and font size
   - margins, spacing, headers, and footers
   - headings and illustration labels
   - highlights and lists

   A poorly designed proposal suggests a careless attitude toward the project. Well-designed proposals help readers quickly find what they need.
3. *Focus on audience needs.* Readers want specific suggestions for filling specific needs. Their biggest question is "What's in this for me?" Show them that you understand their problem and offer a plan for improving their products, sales, or services.
4. *Explain the benefits of implementing your plan.* A persuasive proposal shows readers how they (or their organization) will benefit by adopting your plan. Relate those benefits to the factors that are critical to their business success. Also, *analyze your readers' major concerns* and anticipate their likely questions and objections. Such concerns might include personal concerns ("This proposal means a lot of extra work for me!") as well as role concerns ("I like this proposal, but I can't see how we can fit it into this year's budget").
5. *Provide concrete, specific information.* Vagueness is a fatal flaw in a proposal. Be sure to spell things out. *Show* as well as *tell.* Instead of writing, "We will install state-of-the-art equipment," write, "To meet your automation requirements, we will install 12 Dell PC computers with 100-GB hard drives. The system will be networked for rapid file transfer between offices. We will interconnect four HP laser printers, and one HP DeskJet colour printer." To avoid any misunderstanding and to reflect your ethical commitment, a proposal must elicit *one* interpretation only.
6. *Treat contingencies and limitations realistically.* Do not underestimate the project's complexity. Identify contingencies (occurrences subject to chance) that readers might not anticipate, and propose realistic methods for dealing with the unexpected. If the best available solutions have limitations, let readers know. Otherwise, you and your firm could be liable in the case of project failure. Avoid overstatement. If you can't guarantee "eliminate," then write "diminish" or "help avoid."

(continued)

GUIDELINES

for Writing Persuasive Proposals

(continued)

7. *Propose realistic timetables and budgets.* Complex projects need to be carefully planned and accurately represented, perhaps in a Gantt chart (Chapter 20). Also, provide a realistic, accurate budget, with a detailed cost breakdown of all costs that can be anticipated. Indicate variables that will affect final costs, and the predicted range affected by those variables.
8. *Write readable prose.* Avoid language that is overblown or too technical for your audience. Keep paragraphs short, or use lists.
9. *Use convincing language.* Your proposal should move people to action. Review Chapter 11 for persuasion guidelines. Keep your tone confident and encouraging, not bossy and critical. For more on tone, see Chapter 4.
10. *Emphasize key points with effective visuals.* Tables, flow charts, photographs, drawings, and other visuals are sometimes essential to convince the reader. Table 14.4, provides useful advice.
11. *Tailor supplements for a diverse audience.* A single proposal often addresses a diverse audience: executives, managers, technical experts, lawyers, politicians, and so on. Various reviewers are interested in various parts of your proposal. Experts look for the technical details. Others might be interested in the recommendations, costs, timetable, and expected results, but will need some explanation of technical aspects. Both short and long proposals may include supporting materials (maps, blueprints, specifications, calculations, and so forth). Place supporting material in an appendix to avoid interrupting the discussion.

    If the primary audience is expert or informed, keep the proposal text technical and provide a summary, a glossary, and specialized information in appendices for uninformed secondary audiences. If you're unsure as to which supplements to include in an internal proposal, ask the intended reader or study other proposals. For a solicited proposal (one written for an outside agency) follow the agency's instructions *exactly*.
12. *Cite sources and contributors.* To benefit your proposal, source and contributor citations help provide authority and a sense that you've been thorough. Also, of course, you have an ethical obligation to acknowledge sources of information and ideas. Proposal experts Friedland and Folt offer these suggestions:
    - *Review the literature on the subject.* Limit your focus to "the few most important or influential" background studies (135).
    - *Don't cite sources of "common knowledge" about this topic* (136). Information available in multiple sources usually qualifies as common knowledge.
    - *Provide adequate support.* "In general, cite all papers that are essential to establish credibility" (135).
    - *Provide up-to-date principal references.*
    - *Give credit to all contributors.* Recognize everyone who has worked on or contributed to the proposal (22). This requirement is more important for academic proposals than for business proposals.

A GENERAL STRUCTURE FOR PROPOSALS

To be successful, a proposal must clearly explain the proposed actions and it must present supporting arguments that recognize the reader's needs and priorities. In practice, a proposal also needs to open with an overview of its purpose, method, and benefits. Finally, it needs to close with a request for action—either the reader's authorization or a meeting to discuss the proposal in more detail.

Typical Sections of Proposals

Although a proposal's complexity determines exactly which sections will be included, the sections listed in Table 14.2 are usually present.

Table 14.2 Typical Sections of Proposals

Section	What to Include
Introduction	◆ Connect with your reader by referring to the reader's request or to a problem that has led to this proposal. ◆ Briefly summarize the proposed plan, service, or product. Perhaps highlight your (or your team's) qualifications. ◆ "Hook" the reader by previewing the main benefit. ◆ Describe the scope of the project and list the topics covered in the proposal. ◆ Match the length of the introduction to the length of the proposal. For example, use a single paragraph for a short letter proposal or one or more pages for a report-length document. Or put the introduction in the accompanying transmittal letter.
Background	◆ Discuss the problem or need that has led to the proposal. This discussion will be more extensive in an unsolicited proposal. In a solicited proposal, show that you understand the problem completely. ◆ Discuss the general situation that has led to the current problem (when appropriate) and discuss the significance of solving that problem. ◆ Talk about the requirements for a solution.
Project Description	◆ Describe your solution to the problem: – What will be done – When and where – By which methods ◆ Include headings such as: – Plan of the work – Schedule – Task breakdown – Projected results ◆ Incorporate the project components specified in the client's detailed guidelines when responding to an RFP.

(continued)

Table 14.2 Typical Sections of Proposals *(continued)*

Section	What to Include
Supporting Material: **Facilities/equipment** **Personnel** **Past experience**	◆ Provide evidence of ability to complete all aspects of the project: – Show that you have access to required facilities, equipment, and other resources. – Show that the project leaders have the required qualifications and experience to complete the project. ◆ Provide examples of similar work performed by your team. ◆ Include résumés (where appropriate).
Supporting Arguments	◆ Show that the proposed plan is feasible (for example, that it can indeed be completed in the projected time frame, or that a similar solution has been successfully implemented in a similar situation). ◆ Discuss the benefits of the proposed action and, if necessary, address potential reader concerns.
Budget	◆ Complete this section carefully, to avoid problems due to potential increases in your costs—you're legally bound during the time period you specify. Some proposals need detailed cost breakdowns; others need only a bottom-line figure.
Authorization	◆ Use this closing action statement to request your reader to authorize your proposed plan, or request a meeting to present your proposal. ◆ Include the authorization request in the closing paragraph of informal proposals (along with a reminder of the proposal's main benefits). For formal proposals, place the authorization request in the transmittal letter.

Additional Sections in Formal Proposals

In addition to the standard seven sections found in informal proposals, include the following sections in longer, formal proposals (Table 14.3).

Table14.3 Additional Sections of Proposals

Section	What to Include
Transmittal Document	◆ Use this persuasive letter to address the person who receives the proposal or is responsible for the final decision. This is your only chance to directly address the gatekeeper or decision maker who will decide the fate of the proposal, so word this letter very carefully. ◆ Refer to the RFP. ◆ Describe (briefly) the main points and benefits of the proposal. ◆ Indicate the time limit of your bid. ◆ Ask for the action you desire.
Copy of RFP	◆ Include a copy of the RFP when you know or suspect that the receiving organization has recently issued more than one RFP.
Summary	◆ Summarize the proposal's highlights in one page or less. ◆ Use the headings "Summary" or "Abstract" for technical readers. ◆ Use the heading "Executive Summary" for less technical summaries designed for managers and others. ◆ Include both types of summaries if more than one type of reader may read the proposal.
Title Page	◆ Include, in order: – The title of the proposal – The name of the client organization – The RFP number or other identifier – The author's name (if appropriate) and that of the organization – The date of submission
Table of Contents	◆ Include all section headings and the pages where they appear. ◆ Do not list the RFP, transmittal letter, and title page. ◆ List the names of appendices.
Supporting Documents	◆ Include such appendices as: – Testimonials from satisfied clients – Résumés – Technical evidence – Relevant news or magazine articles, brochures, or photos of previous projects

SAMPLE PROPOSALS

Now, let's see how the identified sections are implemented in three different proposals:

1. An informal improvement proposal
2. An informal research proposal
3. A formal sales proposal

An Informal Improvement Proposal

Here's a planning proposal titled "A Proposal to Prevent Damage to the Office Network."

The situation

The writer, Justine Amarjan, is an engineer in the Moncton office of New Brunswick's Larouche Construction, a multifaceted company that provides engineering services as well as road and bridge construction throughout the Maritimes. She sends an unsolicited proposal to her office manager, Yannick Larose, trying to persuade him to approve the purchase and installation of an anti-virus software package on each of the eight networked computers in the office. In the past, these computers have not needed anti-virus protection because the office intranet has been only recently connected to the internet.

This proposal will not be easy to sell

Amarjan has to meet the following challenges to persuade her reader:

1. This proposal has not been solicited, so Amarjan must convince her reader (Larose) that there's a problem (or potential problem) that's serious enough to justify the proposed expense.
2. With two months left in the fiscal year, the Moncton office's discretionary budget is nearly exhausted, as Larose has pointedly informed his staff.
3. The reader uses computers because he must do so, in order to do his job. However, he doesn't really like computers and he doesn't learn any more about them than he absolutely has to. He has essentially delegated computer decisions to Amarjan and another young staff engineer, but his role requires him to approve all spending decisions, including computer equipment purchases.
4. The reader knows very little computer jargon.

So Amarjan faces a formidable task. Still, she does have two points in her favour:

The reader can be persuaded if approached in the right way

- Yannick Larose is a logical, reasonable person who bases decisions on what is best for his work team and for the Moncton office's operation.
- This reader makes a point of trusting his staff's decisions, provided that the staff present reasonable evidence to support those decisions. In particular, he has told Amarjan that he values her expertise with computers and computer software.

Let's see in Figure 14.1 how well Amarjan follows the guidelines listed on pages 279-80.

An Informal Research Proposal

An informal student research proposal is illustrated in Figure 14.2. This proposal memo describes a computer student's idea for a research project required by the English 116 class that she's taking. That project will culminate in an analytical report for a "real-world" reader.

K Larouche Construction **MEMO**

To: Yannick Larose, Manager

From: Justine Amarjan, Planning Engineer

Date: December 17, 2007

Re: **A Proposal to Prevent Damage to the Office Network**

Connects with reader

You've asked me to keep you informed about how our new computer network is working. It's working well; everyone is pleased, and productivity seems to have improved. However, we have an urgent security issue that I think should be addressed.

The nature of the problem

At last week's company planning meetings in Fredericton, I was reminded of a potential problem that has worried us since we updated our office intranet and connected to the internet two months ago. Colleagues in Fredericton and Dartmouth reported that their offices have been hit by viruses in the past few weeks. The Dartmouth office lost most of its archived files in addition to current project files.

An urgent note

We can't afford the same kind of disaster—we have too many ongoing projects, some of which have files dating back to 2002. With thousands of hours invested in engineering plans and project management details, we can't afford to have our files corrupted or erased. It could easily happen: now that we're connected to the internet, computer viruses and worms could enter our network via email or internet downloads at any time. Even if we could retrieve our files, it might take days to do so.

Solutions

Three main kinds of approaches can provide protection:

1. hardware solutions such as Cisco PIX 520
2. server-based software solutions such as Microsoft's ISA Server software
3. any one of several anti-virus software packages designed for individual PCs

Shows her appreciation of the reader's cost concerns

I haven't considered the hardware solution because it's very expensive; when we looked at adding Cisco's firewall to our system in October, we were quoted $17,000 Cdn plus tax. Likewise, I have discounted the Microsoft server software because it would cost at least $3,500 for the kind of "low end configuration" we would need.

Provides useful background for an uninformed reader

So I've considered five readily available anti-virus products that could be loaded on each of our machines. We would pay to load the software on each machine and then would pay an annual subscription fee for each machine, starting one year from the time of initial installation. The five packages include McAfee VirusScan, Norton AntiVirus, AVG Anti-Virus Pro, Kaspersky 6.0, and BitDefender Standard Edition version 10.

Figure 14.1 An Informal Improvement Proposal *(continued)*

Yannick Larose December 17, 2007 Page 2

Evaluation Criteria

Basically, the software can be assessed by four groups of criteria:

Establishes a consistent set of evaluation criteria

1. How well does the software work?
   - Does it identify all viruses and worms, whether they come via email, IM apps, or web browsing?
   - Does it effectively clean or isolate infected files?
   - Does it report the result of its scans and what it did with infected files?
   - What kind of scanning engine does it use?
2. Is the software easy to install and use?
3. Is the software compatible with our Windows XP operating system and Windows 2005 Advanced server?
4. Is it affordable? (Cost includes purchase price, annual subscription, and the cost of technical support.)

Documentation to support opinion

In order to consistently and fairly compare the five software programs, I read a number of software reviews. I found the most useful of these reviews at <www.anti-virus-software-review.com>. This site's review summary is attached to this memo.

The Best Anti-virus Package

Ethical: the writer admits that another product is also very good

I propose installing Softwin's BitDefender Standard Edition v10, although it was a close call: BitDefender and Kaspersky are both ranked very highly in terms of performance and ease of use, both are compatible with Windows XP and our Windows server, and both are among the least expensive packages. (See the attached detailed comparison.)

The key reason

Although Kaspersky joined BitDefender in passing all the tests run by PC World, PCMag.com, and TopTenReviews, BitDefender's user-friendly features and cost make it the best product under review.

Benefits and Features

As identified by the independent TopTenReview's Anti-virus Software Review, BitDefender has several features to recommend it:

The benefits are phrased in language that the reader can understand

- The product is well designed and very easy to use, so our staff will require very little training in its use.
- BitDefender has a full set of protection and virus removal features, including automatic or manual virus checks, frequent automatic updates of the viruses and worms detected by the software, and quick check times.
- The package is very easy to install, so I will be able to install all the machines on a weekend morning.
- This software was awarded the VB 100% certification going to anti-virus software that detects all viruses thrown at it, while generating no false positives.
- Full-time technical support is available by phone or email.

Figure 14.1 An Informal Improvement Proposal *(continued)*

Yannick Larose December 17, 2007 Page 3

This schedule is relatively simple

Most plan schedules require more explanation

Installation and Training Plan

As I mentioned, the software will be easy to install, so I propose to install it next weekend on each of the seven PCs and the server. The packages can be ordered over the internet and delivered within two working days from Montreal. Then, the following Monday morning, following our staff meeting, I propose to take half an hour to train all staff on how to use BitDefender. It's as simple as that!

Personnel

Unlike most of our projects, this proposal involves a one-person band! With your approval, I propose to order the software, install it on the first available weekend morning, and train the staff in its use. Also, I will monitor BitDefender's operation and consult Softwin's technical help desk if necessary.

Why am I volunteering my time to implement the proposed plan? I have two motivations, really:

While discussing her motivations, the writer establishes her credentials

1. I'm very concerned about the possibility of a virus or worm taking down our entire system, so I'm willing to help reduce costs in order to make the proposed solution feasible. (We'll save about $250 in installation and training costs if I perform those tasks instead of an outside technician.)
2. As you know, I studied network engineering technology for two years before switching to civil engineering, and I retain a strong interest in all aspects of computer networking. Also, I continue to read networking articles, so my knowledge is current. This project, although relatively straightforward, helps develop my knowledge in the area.

This section is very important to the reader

Costs

The total costs are low, compared to the benefits of installing first-rate anti-virus software on our network:

BitDefender purchase	8 X $24.95 =	$199.60 (U.S. dollars)
Installation		$0.00
Training		$0.00
		Total U.S. $199.60 (CDN $232.00)
Annual updates subscription	8 X $24.50 =	U.S. $196.00 (CDN $228.00)

An attempt to "close the sale"

Authorization

May I have your authorization to order the software, install the packages, and train the staff? I believe that our office network remains at great risk without anti-virus protection. Most of the staff are very careful about opening suspicious emails and about researching on the internet, but without protection we could download a devastating virus by simply turning on a computer!

Justine

Justine Amarjan

Attachment: Anti-virus Software Review's detailed rating chart from <www.anti-virus-software-review.com/index.html>).

Figure 14.1 An Informal Improvement Proposal *(continued)*

The student, Amy Suen, chooses to examine firewall systems that might provide network security for the networked systems at 2020 Design, an electronics design and manufacturing company. Amy does some preliminary research to confirm that she can find information on firewalls. Also, through a contact at 2020 Design she learns that her report would interest Mark Reuters, 2020's computer networking specialist. Mark has been too busy designing and installing his company's new array of computers to pay much attention to the external security issue. Still, 2020 is committed to marketing its products on the internet and therefore risks incursions into its internal communications, including its proprietary designs.

Amy knows that 2020 Design will not make decisions based on a first-year computer student's report, but Mark Reuters assures her that her report could provide a springboard for his own investigation of firewall software. For that reason, he is willing to help Amy with her preliminary research.

In preparing her proposal for her instructor, Devon Koenig, Amy starts by analyzing her reader and her purpose for writing the proposal, as follows:

Audience: Devon Koenig, project supervisor. He will use my proposal to decide whether to approve my proposed approach. If my proposal is rejected, I'll have to prepare another.

<u>His knowledge:</u> severely limited (so I'll have to provide background)
<u>His questions:</u> (in the assignment memo dated January 17)

1. What's your topic? Who's the reader for your proposed report?
2. What main question does your reader want answered? (Identify the report's specific analytical purpose.)
3. How will the proposed report achieve that purpose? (Here, an attached detailed outline would help establish that you do indeed have a plan.)
4. Do you have the time, resources, and commitment to complete the project? (You should include a time budget and a resources budget.)
5. Will you find sufficient information to answer the report's overall question? (Attach a tentative bibliography.)

Purpose: Convince Prof. Koenig that the topic has merit and that the project is feasible. (Show that I can research, that I can manage the project, that I can afford it, that I can think, that I can write well enough to handle a report of this complexity.)

Audience attitude and temperament: Has high standards and expectations. Therefore, I'll have to answer all his questions thoroughly. He said he'll be skeptical, so I'll have to support all my statements. This won't be an easy sell! I don't think he cares much about how much the project will cost me, as long as I can prove I can afford it. He's a tough marker, so I'll need to phrase the memo carefully and get it proofread.

Audience expectations: He doesn't want more than three pages, not including attachments. His comments in class emphasized our need to provide proof of all positive statements. That's the only way I'll get his support. I'll need to use a direct, businesslike tone—he doesn't like extra words or pompous language. (I'd better stay away from words like "utilize.") And I'd better stick pretty close to the proposal structure he recommended: connect with reader/provide "hook" in the proposal pre-summary/give background/show need for report/describe planned approach/propose schedule/prove that it's feasible—sources/my qualifications/budget/request authorization.

The memo that Amy Suen presents (Figure 14.2) to her project supervisor begins on page 289.

Communication 116 Memorandum

Date: February 4, 2008
To: Professor Devon Koenig, English Department
From: Amy Suen, Computer Systems 1st year
Re: **Proposed Research Project for English 116**

In response to the proposal assignment that you announced in our January 25 class, this memo outlines my proposal to research firewall products. The research will lead to a recommendation of which product will best suit the needs of 2020 Design, a local electronics company. Its networking specialist, Mark Reuters, has indicated his interest in my findings.

Background

Mark Reuters has recently revamped 2020 Design's total network of computers. He is now in the process of installing new networking software, and will continue fine tuning the network and training 2020 Design personnel for the next three months. At that time he will turn his attention to the challenges of partially linking 2020's internal network to the internet.

One of the major problems to solve will be the issue of internal network security. 2020 Designs stays competitive by developing new electronic designs, so it doesn't want outsiders tapping into its research and development work. Still, the company wants to market its products on the internet and engage in ecommerce.

Recently, "firewall" has come to mean software products for blocking unwanted access to protected information, but its original meaning included all aspects of network security strategy—software, hardware, and personnel. Mark Reuters has asked me to focus on software products.

Developing appropriate software is very expensive, so most companies purchase rather than develop. Firewall software ranges from a few thousand dollars to about $100,000, depending on performance and user requirements. Each product has advantages and disadvantages that depend on network configurations and the method of implementing the software. Therefore, it's not easy to choose an appropriate firewall product.

Proposed Plan

My initial research into the topic indicates that the following process would be best.

1. **Determine the client's needs.** Subject to your approval of my proposal, Mark Reuters will provide me with details of the network he administers. Those details will include the special features and challenges built into that network (which apparently is unique). With Mark Reuters's help, I'll be able to choose the criteria that I can use to evaluate and compare firewall software products.
2. **Research available software.** As the attached tentative bibliography shows, there seems to be plenty of information available. In addition, I have arranged to possibly interview Marsha Campbell, one of my computer instructors, and Guy Larivière, the network administrator for our college. I'll proceed with those interviews if I receive your authorization for this project.
3. **Evaluate information gathered about firewall products.** Please see the attached outline, which describes the general approach I plan to take. So far, I have identified three products (AltaVista, Check Point, and CyberGuard), but I'll continue to look for others. I expect to discuss three to five products in the final report; that means that I may have to do a preliminary assessment to weed out inappropriate firewall products.
4. **Rigorously apply the assessment criteria and choose the best product for 2020 Designs.** Part of this assessment can come from the specifications and product information provided by the manufacturers on their websites. The full assessment will come from actually testing the software.

Figure 14.2 A Student Research Proposal *(continued)*

Prof. Koenig
February 4, 2008
Page 2

Feasibility of Project

I've looked at this project quite carefully and I think it's feasible because

- Information is available and I have access to expert opinion here at the college.
- My strong interest in this subject has already prompted me to read all the sources listed in the attached bibliography and I've made notes on three of the articles.
- Professor Campbell has agreed to help me assess software on the network in computer lab 218, and she is accepting this project for credit in her Networking class.
- I can get access to firewall products through Mark Reuters, who will request demo software from manufacturers.

Schedule

According to your January comments about task requirements, I have overestimated the time required for the following tasks, but my semester time budget can still accommodate the following:

Activity	Time Required	Dates	Document Produced
Research re: firewalls (types and leading products) and 2020 system configuration	10–15 hrs	Feb. 2–14	Refine planning outline
Interview Campbell and Larivière	2–2 1/2 hrs	Feb. 15 Feb. 16	Refine planning outline
Evaluate data	5–8 hrs	Feb. 22	Adjusted research plan (?)
Analyze/organize data	6–10 hrs	Feb. 27–28	Working outline (due Mar. 8)
Plan/write progress report	4 hrs	Mar. 5–6	Progress report (due Mar. 8)
Write report from outline	6–10 hrs	Mar. 14–16	Analytical report—draft
Edit report and polish format	5–8 hrs	Mar. 24–27	Analytical report—due Mar. 31

Budget

Because I won't have to buy firewall products, and because I use my home internet connection for many purposes, my budget for this project is minimal:

Photocopy articles	$20
Bus travel for interviews	$15
Report printing and binding	$14
	Total: $49

Authorization

I hope that you agree that my proposal topic and approach is appropriate for the English 116 project, because I'm committed to doing an excellent job. For one thing, I'm also doing the project for my Networking class, and I can afford to put more effort into a project that fulfills two sets of requirements. Also, I think I may be able to get a student co-op job at 2020 Design this May if I do well on this project.

May I have your authorization to proceed? If you wish to contact me outside of class, please email me at amysuen@silk.net.

AS

Attachments: Tentative Bibliography
Planning Outline

Figure 14.2 A Student Research Proposal *(continued)*

PLANNING OUTLINE: REPORT PROJECT
Communication 116

Topic: Firewalls

Reader (needs/reason for reading/knowledge level):

Mark Reuters, 2020 Design; he's interested in firewall products for his firm's network; he's very knowledgeable, but not about current products

Purpose: Assess firewall products suitable for 2020 Design (maybe recommend best one)

Tentative Structure/Topics:

Reason for report
Background re: current firewall technology

- list of products (CyberGuard, AltaVista, Check Point, and others)
- manufacturers
- concepts behind the products

2020 Design's network structure
Client's general and special requirements
Product evaluations:

- supporting operating system and services
- performance
- price
- installation and training
- does it meet client's particular requirements?

Conclusion re: which products satisfy the criteria/which *best* satisfies the criteria

Tentative Sources:

Interviews: Prof. Campbell, Guy Larivière, and Mark Reuters

Check Point Technologies Ltd. (Updated 2008, February 1). *Firewall-1 products and solution.* Retrieved February 2, 2008, from www.checkpoint.com

Computer Security Institute. (n.d.). *CSI firewall matrix.* Retrieved January 31, 2008, from www.gocsi.com

Digital Equipment Corp. (copyright 2004). *AltaVista firewall 04.* Retrieved January 29, 2008, from www.altavista.software.digital.com

Firewall guide. (2007). Retrieved January 27, 2008, from www.firewallguide.com

Hallogram reviews. (copyright 2001–2007). Retrieved January 22, 2008, from http://hallogram.com/avfirewall/

Markus, H.S. (Last updated 2007, February 3). *Home PC firewall guide.* Retrieved February 4, 2008, from www.firewallguide.com

Novell Corp. (n.d.). *Border manager enterprise edition.* Retrieved February 2, 2008, through the *Firewall product overview* at www.thegild.com/firewall

Rubin, A., Geer, D., & Ranum, M.J. (2004). *Web security source book* (3rd ed.). New York: Wiley Computer Publishing.

Stein, L.S. (2006). *Web security, a step-by-step reference guide.* Reading: Addison-Wesley.

Figure 14.2 A Student Research Proposal *(continued)*

A Formal Sales Proposal

The formal proposal (Figure 14.3) that begins on page 293 presents a commercial sales pitch. Its writer, Tony Mutu, uses a formal report format to impress his reader with a professional-looking document, even though the main body proposal is only six pages (or perhaps *because* the main part of the proposal is only six pages). Note, though, that another 12 pages of supplements are included as appendices.

One of those appendices includes a copy of the RFP and accompanying documents that the writer retrieved from the client. To some extent, this inclusion is overkill: as far as the writer knows, the client has just this one RFP outstanding at the moment.

This proposal does not include a separate summary—after all, the proposal report is just six pages and its main points are already summarized in the transmittal letter. Also, the concluding authorization request ("closing the sale") is included in the transmittal letter, so it is not repeated on page 8 of the proposal report.

Notice that this proposal uses imperial measurements, a system often still used in construction projects. The writer has been told that his reader, John Warren, is "old school," and not eager to use the metric system.

Other aspects of the writer's audience and purpose analysis have been discussed in the "Proposal Process" section of this chapter, starting on page 274.

ON THE JOB...

Successful Commercial Proposals

"Over the years, I've ghost-written dozens of proposals for clients, and I write my own proposals to bid for editing and writing contracts. Typically, these proposals range from 15 to 40 pages, but I have produced proposals that exceed 100 pages. The secret of writing successful proposals is to clearly show how the reader will benefit from the proposed product or service. I'm now well established in Ottawa, and on the standing offer lists of several government departments, but I must write clear, comprehensive proposals to win contracts. One of my successful techniques is a 'compliance matrix' that matches client requirements with components of my proposal—this matrix could present several pages that show details of how my proven skills and knowledge will allow me to fulfill each requirement listed in the client's full RFP. . . ."

—Judith Whitehead, writer and editor, Vankellers Editorial and Writing Services

AN INTERPERSONAL PERSPECTIVE

Some of the examples on the preceding pages show external proposals, most of which attempt to win business contracts. Often, however, as employees we feel the need to improve workplace conditions or ways of doing things. If we try to ignore our feelings, we can end up feeling bitter and helpless. But if we have methods of convincing others to make necessary changes, we can feel better about ourselves and the place where we work.

⁝⁝ ***EnviroMax Engineering Consultants*** ⁝⁝

103-1025 Ellis Street Penticton, British Columbia V5T 2W9
Ph: (250)493-2380 Fax: (250)493-2395 email: emax@shaw.ca

11 February 2008

Mr. John Warren, Public Works Manager
District of Beachland Public Works
Box 732
Beachland, British Columbia
V0H 1X0

Dear Mr. Warren:

Re: RFP 17PW – 2008d

Thank you for the opportunity to bid on the engineering design and supervision of the project to improve the beach and swimming areas fronting 2056 Beach Avenue, Beachland. As your RFP describes, the situation at 2056 Beach Avenue has serious implications for Beachland businesses and requires a long-term solution. EnviroMax believes that the problems outlined in RFP 17PW-2008d can be solved by the right engineering work.

Our enclosed proposal meets the RFP's requirements by building an offshore breakwater and by repairing previous erosion damage.

As our proposal indicates, we have considered all the available information concerning the problems at 2056 Beach Avenue. In addition, we have conducted a preliminary study of the current lake water levels and the underwater soil depths fronting the property. Further, we have consulted with faculty members in the Water Quality and Environmental Sciences programs at Okanagan University College to learn more about the potential environmental impact of our proposed construction. Those faculty have volunteered their expertise in return for the chance of project work for their senior students.

EnviroMax trusts you agree that our proposal is the best long-term (and most cost-effective) solution to the erosion problem and recreation needs at 2056 Beach Avenue. May we have your authorization to proceed? To discuss the proposal, please call me at 493-2380 or email me at tmutu@emax.ca.

Sincerely,

Tony Mutu

Tony Mutu, C.E.T.

Figure 14.3 A Formal Sales Proposal

(continued)

PROPOSAL FOR
BEACH RESTORATION
AND EROSION PROTECTION
RFP 17PW – 2008d

Prepared for

John Warren
Public Works Manager

District of Beachland
Beachland, British Columbia

Prepared by
Tony Mutu, C.E.T.
Project Manager
EnviroMax Engineering Consultants
Penticton, British Columbia

February 11, 2008

Figure 14.3 A Formal Sales Proposal *(continued)*

TABLE OF CONTENTS

- ii -

Figure 14.3 A Formal Sales Proposal *(continued)*

⁞⁞ *EnviroMax Engineering Consultants* ⁞⁞

INTRODUCTION

EnviroMax is well qualified to supply the network design and implementation outlined in RFP 17PW–2008d. We are an established business in the Okanagan Valley with a reputation for providing outstanding quality and customer service. We have extensive experience in construction design, in environmental solutions, and in environmental project management. This proposal details our plan to create a long-term, cost-effective solution to the erosion problems at 2056 Beach Avenue. EnviroMax is excited about the possibility of contributing to the beauty and economic viability of Beachland's lakefront.

Statement of Need

Before designing the proposed solution to the problems at 2056 Beach Avenue, EnviroMax considered the following key factors:

- Research conducted from 1995 to 2006 shows the shoreline receding at an average rate of 7.6 inches per year, but measurements taken by the owners of 2054 and 2056 Beach Avenue show that the shoreline has eroded an average of 13 inches per year for the past four years. *In other words, the erosion seems to be worsening.* As a result, the beach sand in front of the 125 feet of shoreline at 2056 Beach Avenue has been eroded away, leaving a pebble and rock beach. This erosion has made the campground at 2056 less desirable for tourist campers, and Beachland businesses have noticed a marked decline in business the last few years.
- Simply replacing the beach sand does not seem to work, as has been shown by the eroded sand that was placed at 2054 Beach Avenue in 2004.
- In addition to restoring the beach, the restorative work should create a large, safe swimming area.
- Beachland Public Works equipment, materials, and employees are available to complete much of the required work, which could result in substantial cost savings to the municipality.
- In winter, the prevailing winds come from the east and northeast, while in the other three seasons the prevailing winds come from the south or southeast.
- Current Okanagan water levels are slightly lower than normal for this time of year.

Potential Solutions

EnviroMax's experience, supplemented by research into erosion scenarios in British Columbia, Alberta, Manitoba, and Washington State, suggested three main types of solutions:

- a compacted bed of river rock covered by sand
- a foreshore retaining wall, with an inner area filled with rock and covered with sand, to reclaim the 11 feet of eroded shoreline and create a larger beach
- an offshore breakwater, supplemented by beach restoration

The first two options were examined, and then rejected because they do not meet stated requirements:

- 1 -

Figure 14.3 A Formal Sales Proposal *(continued)*

⁝ *EnviroMax Engineering Consultants* ⁝

1. **A compaction method** would place a bed of rock about 60 feet out into the lake, to a water depth of 6.5 feet. The first layer would consist of 3-inch to 6-inch rocks at the 6.5-foot depth, to anchor the entire rock bed. Then, progressively smaller rocks would be placed as the water depth decreases, closer and closer to shore. Close to the lakeshore, the underwater rocks would be only about 1.5 inches. On the lakeshore, gravel and sand would be used to reconstruct the surface layer of the beach. Finally, the entire new surface would have to be compacted, right out to the 6.5-foot water level.

   The compaction is usually time consuming and difficult because of the water depth in which the compaction equipment must operate. Also, an extensive environmental study must be completed before the work can proceed. This method repairs existing damage, but will not prevent subsequent erosion at 2056 Beach Avenue, especially from the waves driven by northeast and southeast winter winds. Also, it would not provide a safe swimming area.

2. **A foreshore retaining wall** would be built parallel to the existing shoreline, about 11 feet out (in order to reclaim the shore lost to erosion). Five steps are required: ① conducting an environmental study; ② preparing the site for the retaining wall; ③ building the wall so that it extends about 6.5 feet above the September low water mark; ④ filling in the area on the land side of the wall; ⑤ compacting the fill and surfacing the compacted fill with sand, gravel, or grass.

   The retaining wall would cost $72 000 to build—costs include fuel, Public Works employees' wages, Public Works equipment repairs, equipment rentals, and the services of a professional stonemason. The filling and surfacing and cleanup would cost $8500. The environmental study and EnviroMax's engineering fees would cost $31 250.

   This method repairs existing damage and will prevent subsequent erosion. However, it does not provide for a protected swimming area, a major consideration for families who vacation at this beach. Therefore, we propose an offshore breakwater and a restored beach.

Information Sources

EnviroMax has researched several sources in preparing the proposal:

- examination of the 2007 report based on the study Beachland commissioned in 2004
- consultations with Mario Zumbo, an experienced stonemason
- investigation of the operational and maintenance costs of using Beachland Public Works employees and heavy equipment
- enquiries regarding rental costs for specialized trenching and excavating equipment
- probes of the lake bottom where we propose to build the breakwater—this survey has revealed the current water depth (6.5'), soil thickness (18" to 6'), and the lake bed profile (relatively flat)
- Ministry of the Environment records of Lake Okanagan water levels, recorded since 1943

Figure 14.3 A Formal Sales Proposal *(continued)*

⁞⁞ *EnviroMax Engineering Consultants* ⁞⁞

THE PROPOSED PLAN

Restorative and Protective Measures

Building a breakwater and repairing existing damage would require a six-stage process, shown in the following table.

Stage	Performed By	Comments
1. Conduct *environmental study* re: impact on aquatic life and impact on water quality (Figure 1)	Instructors and students from OUC's Water Quality and Environmental programs, supervised by EnviroMax engineers	Required by the Ministry of the Environment, this study may result in modifications to the original project design
2. Lay a *delivery causeway* from the centre of the beach to the centre of the proposed wall. (Figure 2)	Beachland Public Works (BPW) employees and equipment, supervised by EnviroMax	Requires trucks to haul dirt and blast rock from the Public Works materials yard
3. *Prepare the site* for the breakwater wall. An 8-ft.-wide, 150-ft.-long trench must be dug to remove lake bed soil and thus provide a solid base for the wall. (Figure 2)	BPW employees and equipment, supervised by EnviroMax	The soil thickness varies from 1.5 ft. to 6 ft., so the excavator arm will operate in water as deep as 14 ft. Thus, a special excavator must be rented at a cost of $1200 per day.
4. *Build the wall,* in 3 steps		
• use the excavated soil and hauled material to form a causeway parallel to the trench, on the beach side	BPW employees and equipment, supervised by EnviroMax	For this first stage, BPW's Caterpillar 920C excavator could be used, but the rental machine would have more capacity.
• place large blast rock in the trench, to a point 2 ft. above the waterline	BPW employees and equipment, supervised by EnviroMax and Mario Zumbo, stonemason	Here, the rented excavator and rented underwater video monitors would be needed.
• build the upper wall, with jagged blast rock on the wave side and mortared flat rock on the beach side (Figure 3)	BPW would deliver the blast rock from its stockpile; Mario Zumbo and his assistant would construct the wall	The rental equipment would not be needed for this step. Special marine mortar would be used.
5. *Remove the causeway*	BPW employees and equipment, supervised by EnviroMax	The rental excavator would be needed for depths greater than 4 ft.
6. *Clean up and restore the beach*	BPW employees and equipment, supervised by EnviroMax	After the beach area is graded and cleaned, about 60 tons of of fine sand (from the BPW yards) will be placed on the beach and on the lake bed, 12 ft. out from the shoreline

Figure 14.3 A Formal Sales Proposal *(continued)*

⁞⁞ *EnviroMax Engineering Consultants* ⁞⁞

Proposed Location of Work
The following figures show the location of the proposed work.

Figure 1. Approximate Location of the Breakwater (shown in red)

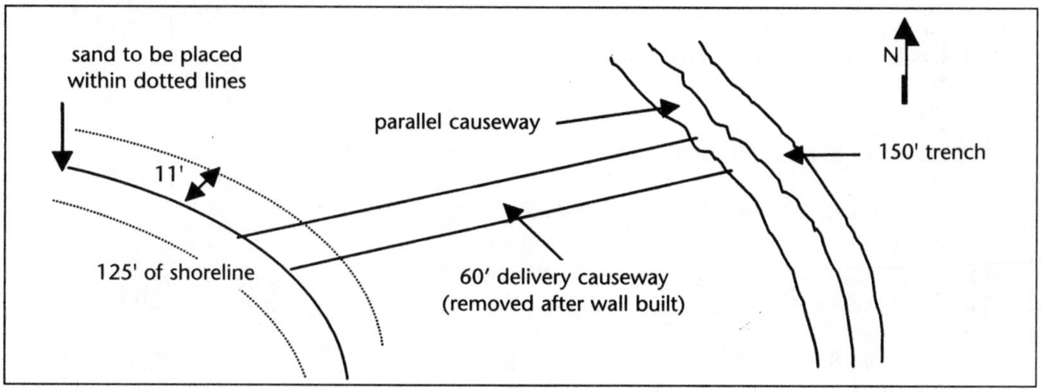

Figure 2. Top View: Location of Causeway and Trench (not drawn to scale)

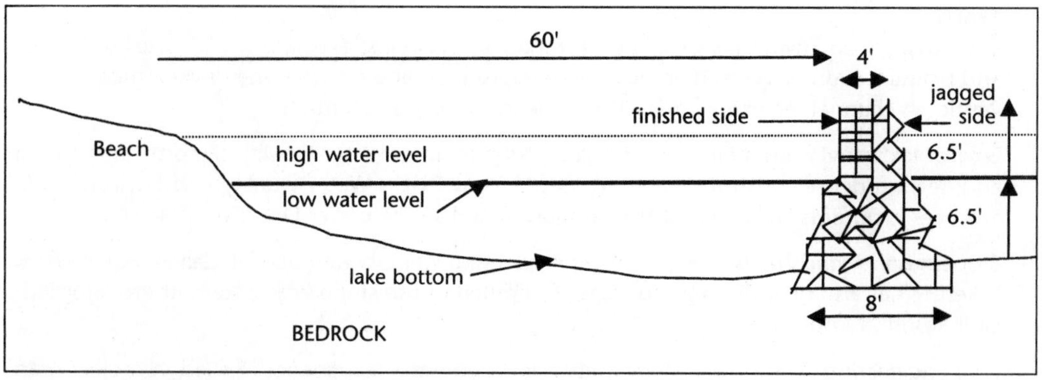

Figure 3. Side View: The Finished Wall (not drawn to scale)

- 4 -

Figure 14.3 A Formal Sales Proposal *(continued)*

⁞⁞ *EnviroMax Engineering Consultants* ⁞⁞

Proposed Schedule

The following schedule allows for unforeseen delays due to bad weather, equipment breakdown, or environmental factors. If begun by March 1, work will be completed before the June 15 deadline.

Task	Time Required	Completion Date
environmental study	10 to 15 days	March 19
building a delivery causeway	5 to 8 days	March 30
preparing the site for the wall	10 to 12 days	April 18
building the parallel causeway	5 to 6 days	April 26
building the wall	15 to 18 days	May 14
removing the causeway	5 to 6 days	June 7
cleaning the site; placing sand on the existing beach and in the water	4 days	June 11

Budget

The construction costs represent maximum estimates; the work will likely cost less.

Construction costs: fuel, BPW employee salaries;
equipment rental; marine construction insurance;
stonemason contract; marine mortar and other materials $148 000
Place sand/clean site $5 500
EnviroMax Fees
conduct environmental study $13 750
design wall and supervise construction $17 500
Total: $184 750

Staffing

Gary Stewart, an EnviroMax Civil Engineer, has several years' experience with local recreation and beautification projects. (For example, he designed and oversaw the development of the Penticton channel recreation area.) He will lead the design team.

EnviroMax's environmental specialist *Doug Nygren* has a Water Quality diploma and a Civil Engineering degree. Instructors and students from OUC's Water Quality and Environmental Sciences programs will conduct the environmental study, under Doug's supervision.

Stonemason *Mario Zumbo* has recently completed a stone breakwater at Gallant Bay, Shuswap Lake. He has also built the stone bridges and much of the stone wall system at Predator Ridge Golf Resort, Vernon.

Civil Engineering Technologist *Tony Mutu* has seven years' experience. Skilled in project management, he specializes in slope stability and erosion issues.

- 5 -

Figure 14.3 A Formal Sales Proposal *(continued)*

⁝ *EnviroMax Engineering Consultants* ⁝

CONCLUDING COMMENTS

Scope of Services

The prices in this proposal are valid until February 28, 2008. The scope of the services offered is only for the provision of a "large, protected swimming area and a protected beach" as specified in RFP 17PW–2008d.

Benefits

The proposed work offers a long-term solution to the erosion problem. The dual-sided breakwater will be functional and attractive:

a. the points of the jagged rocks on the wave side will dissipate wave energy and reduce the impact on the wall (stonemason Mario Zumbo estimates a minimum wall life of 50+ years)
b. the mortared smooth beach-facing wall will feature a classic Italian look, with a flat finished top. Similar breakwaters built on Shuswap Lake and on Washington State's Lake Chelan have added attractive components to the local landscape.

The wall will require no maintenance.

The proposed work repairs existing damage and fully restores the sandy beach. Between the beach and the breakwater, campers will have a large, protected swimming area.

The plan is the most expensive of the three plans considered, but it provides excellent value because BPW workers, materials, and equipment are used. Possibly, the wage costs, fuel costs, and some of the rental costs can be folded into the existing 2008 BPW budget. Also, the environmental study costs are considerably reduced by involving OUC students.

Supporting Documents

- 6 -

Figure 14.3 A Formal Sales Proposal

NOTE: To save space in this textbook, the appendices have not been included.

The following action gradient (Figure 14.4), which becomes more positive as it moves to the right, illustrates the value of suggesting improvements.

negative	**neutral**	**positive**
Emotional response	*Complaint re: specific incident*	*Rational analysis*
Childish reaction		Adult reaction
Emphasis on momentary relief	Emphasis on specific compensation	Emphasis on improving the overall situation
Employee feels powerless and bitter	Employee feels good if specific problem is handled	Employee feels empowered

Figure 14.4 The Action Gradient

Here's an example of the action gradient at work.

> Let's assume that you work as an engineering technologist for a civil engineering firm that specializes in developing city subdivisions. Because you're frequently placed in charge of projects, you essentially act as an assistant manager. Your office manager is technically competent and works hard, but she uses negative feedback as her primary motivational tool; the only time she comments on a person's work is when that person has made a mistake. Usually, she presents her criticisms in a hostile, aggressive manner. Employee morale and productivity are starting to suffer.
>
> By contrast, your co-workers prefer your positive motivational techniques. You give credit for work well done. When you have to comment on incomplete or shoddy work, you take care to focus on the work itself, not on the worker. Lately, though, the manager's attitude and behaviour have been particularly hard to stomach because everyone has been working extra hard to meet a contract deadline.

Avoiding Action

If you operate at the left side of the action gradient, you don't confront the problem directly; instead, you use passive aggression by talking behind your manager's back. This approach allows you and the other employees to take care of your resentment and frustration for a moment, but you don't feel good about yourself, and meanwhile, the interpersonal climate steadily worsens.

Taking Limited Action

If you operate in the middle ground, you may comment about a specific incident and ask for an apology. However, even if you receive that apology, the basic situation hasn't changed because you haven't confronted the underlying problem.

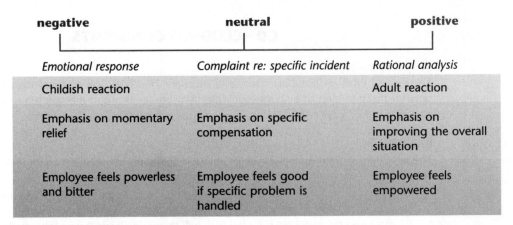

Taking Positive Action

The advantage of operating on the right side of the gradient is that you try to improve the overall situation. This response pattern requires a rational analysis of the problem and the formulation of a workable solution. Once you believe you have a valid solution, you have a choice of presenting it as a proposal or as recommendations. In the proposal, you single-mindedly argue in favour of a definite course of action, while the recommendations report assesses two or more possible solutions and then chooses one of those solutions.

Whether you chose the proposal route or the (apparently) more objective recommendations report, you have set in motion a series of productive possibilities. For example, your proposal of an incentive plan for managers and staff may get adopted. But even if it doesn't gain approval, you will feel good about yourself for positively confronting the situation. Moreover, you could be perceived as a positive influence within the organization, which will not hurt your subsequent chances for promotion. And, in the long run, positive actions improve the working climate, which was your goal in the first place.

GRAPHICS IN PROPOSALS

Proposals tend to feature text, not graphics. Still, as Table 18.4 suggests, visuals can help make proposals more persuasive.

Table 14.4 Graphics in Proposals

The Message	The Graphic
We offer high performance at low costs	◆ Line, bar, and pie charts ◆ Tables
Our plan is logical	◆ Flow chart
Our system or equipment does the job	◆ Schematic diagram ◆ Hybrid graphic (such as drawings, photos, and tabular data pasted onto a flow diagram)
The parts are easy to assemble	◆ Exploded view drawing
We can meet the schedule	◆ Timeline with milestones ◆ Critical path diagram
We have the resources and experience	◆ Data charts ◆ Résumés with experience timelines ◆ Photos (people, facilities, and equipment)

Source: Adapted from G. Edward Quimby, "Make Text and Graphics Work Together," *Intercom* [Newsletter of the Society for Technical Communication] January 1996: 34.

CHECKLIST FOR REVISING AND EDITING PROPOSALS

Use this checklist as a guide to revising and refining your proposals.

Format

- Have you chosen the best format (letter, memo, report) for your purpose and audience?
- Does the long proposal include appropriate appendices?
- Does the title forecast the proposal's subject and purpose?

Content

- Is the problem clearly identified?
- Is the objective clearly identified?
- Does everything in the proposal support its objective?
- Does the proposal *show* as well as *tell*?
- Does the proposed plan, service, or product benefit the reader's personal or organizational needs?
- Are the proposed methods practical and realistic?
- Are all foreseeable limitations and contingencies identified?
- Is the proposal free of overstatement?
- Is the proposal's length appropriate to the subject?

Arrangement

- Does the proposal include all *relevant* sections of the recommended structure?
- Does the introduction provide sufficient orientation to the problem and the plan?
- Does the plan explain *how*, *where*, and *how much*?
- Are there clear transitions between related ideas?

Style

- Is the writing style clear, concise, and fluent?
- Is the level of technicality appropriate for the primary reader?
- Do supplements follow the appropriate style guidelines?
- Does the tone connect with the readers?
- Is the language convincing and precise?
- Is the proposal grammatical?
- Is the proposal ethically acceptable?

WEB CONNECT

First, you'll find a Canadian government site that provides RFPs for suppliers and contractors. Check out the University of Toronto's advice. Also, the University of Wisconsin's focus on grant proposals, Deborah Kluge's proposal checklist, and the Ontario Healthy Communities Coalition's handbook may be useful.

http://contractscanada.gc.ca
www.ecf.utoronto.ca/~writing/handbook.html
http://grants.library.wisc.edu/organizations/proposalwebsites.html
www.proposalwriter.com/checklist.html
www.healthycommunities.on.ca/publications/misc/fundproposal.pdf

EXERCISES

1. After identifying your primary and secondary audience, compose a short planning proposal for improving an unsatisfactory situation in the classroom, on the job, in your dorm, or in your apartment (e.g., poor lighting, drab atmosphere, health hazards, poor seating arrangements). Choose a problem or situation whose resolution is more a matter of common sense and lucid observation than of intensive research. Be sure to (a) identify the problem clearly, give brief background, and stimulate the readers' interest; (b) state clearly the methods proposed to solve the problem; and (c) conclude with a statement designed to gain readers' support for your proposal.
2. Write a research proposal to your instructor (or an interested third party) requesting approval for the final term project (an analytical report or formal proposal). Identify the subject, background, purpose, and benefits of your planned inquiry, as well as the intended audience, scope of inquiry, data sources, methods of inquiry, and a task timetable. Be certain that adequate primary and secondary sources are available. Convince your reader of the soundness and usefulness of the project.
3. As an alternative term project to the formal analytical report (Chapter 18), develop a long proposal for solving a problem, improving a situation, or satisfying a need in your college, community, or job. Choose a subject sufficiently complex to justify a formal proposal, a topic requiring research (mostly primary). Identify an audience (other than your instructor) who will use your proposal for a specific purpose. Compose an audience/purpose profile, using the sample on page 404 as a model. Here are possible subjects for your proposal:
   - improving living conditions in your dorm or fraternity/sorority
   - creating a daycare centre on campus
   - creating a new business or expanding a business

- saving labour, materials, or money on the job
- improving working conditions
- improving campus facilities for the disabled
- supplying a product or service to clients or customers
- eliminating traffic hazards in your neighbourhood
- reducing energy expenditures on the job
- improving in-house training or job-orientation programs
- improving tutoring in the learning centre
- making the course content in your major more relevant to student needs
- changing the grading system at your school
- establishing more equitable computer use

COLLABORATIVE PROJECT

Exercise 1, 2, or 3 may be used for a collaborative project.

CHAPTER 15

Gathering Information

LEARNING OBJECTIVES

After reading this chapter, you should be able to

- Adapt the standard stages of the research process to suit a particular project.
- Identify, select, and explore primary and secondary information sources.
- Plan and conduct surveys, interviews, and questionnaires.

Major workplace decisions typically are based on careful research, with the findings recorded in a report. The report's readers expect current information that helps answer their questions.

Research is classified as *primary* or *secondary.* Primary research involves an original, first-hand study of your topic or problem: observations, interviews, questionnaires, inquiry letters, personal experiments, analysis of samples, fieldwork, or company records. Secondary research includes materials published by other researchers: journal articles, books, handbooks, reports, online articles, electronic databases, government documents, internet sites, and material held by public agencies and special interest groups.

ON THE JOB...

Trends in Research

"The sheer amount of quality information in structured databases is increasing and readily available in electronic formats. It used to be mostly articles, but now reports are available, such as the Conference Board of Canada's e-library, which made its whole library available online and provided access to current information on industries, companies, and business trends in Canada. Statistics are becoming more and more available from a variety of government and private sources. So, the types of sources, the range of sources, and the sheer volume of sources are forcing students and other researchers to be very particular in the early stages of their research..."

—Ross Tyner, research librarian

ON THE JOB...

Advice for an In-depth Library Search

"Step back, before typing words into a database or search engine or library catalogue. Think carefully about (a) the questions to be answered, (b) the types of sources that will have answers, and (c) where you can find those sources. Then plan a search strategy and write a list of key words. Approach the process methodically and systematically. The 'natural mistake' is to accept the first source that pops up...."

—Ross Tyner, research librarian

Research strategies and resources differ widely among disciplines. This chapter focuses on research for preparing a formal technical report.

THINKING CRITICALLY ABOUT THE RESEARCH PROCESS

Research is a deliberate form of inquiry, a process of problem solving, in which certain procedures follow a recognizable sequence, as shown in Figure 15.1.

But research does not simply follow a numbered set of procedures ("First, do this; then, do that"). The procedural stages depend on the many decisions that accompany any legitimate inquiry (see Figure 15.2).

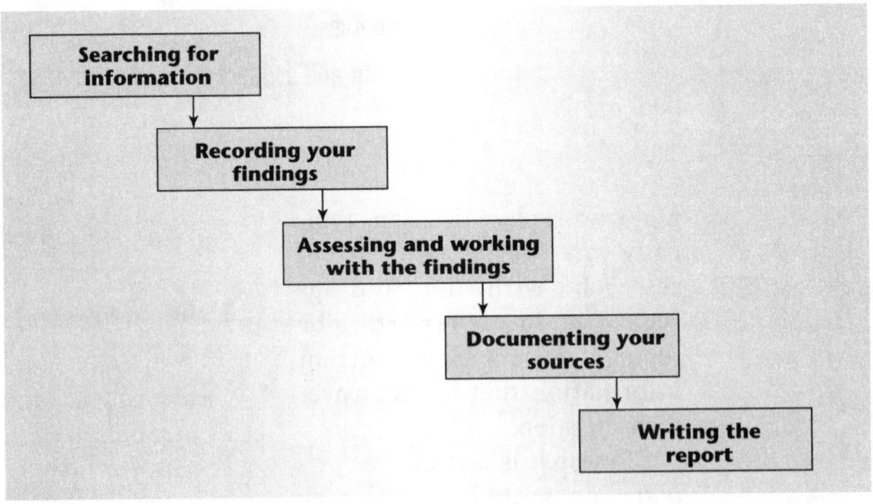

Figure 15.1 Procedural Stages of the Research Process

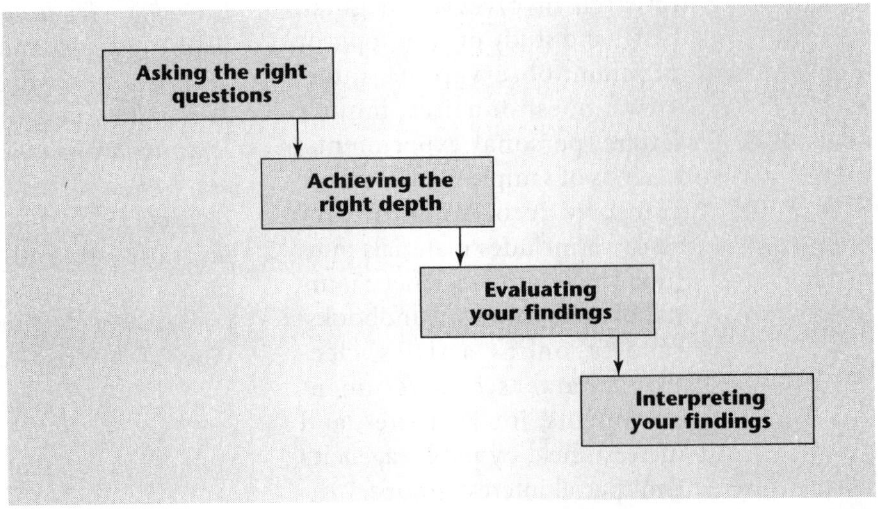

Figure 15.2 Inquiry Stages of the Research Process

ASKING THE RIGHT QUESTIONS

The answers you uncover will depend on the questions you ask. Assume, for instance, that you are faced with the following scenario.

Defining and Refining a Research Question

You are the public health manager for a small New Brunswick town in which high-tension power lines run within 30 metres of the elementary school. Parents are concerned about the danger from electromagnetic radiation (EMR) emitted by these power lines in energy waves known as electromagnetic fields (EMFs). Town officials ask you to research the issue and prepare a report.

First, you need to identify the exact question(s) you want answered. Initially, the major query might be: *Do the power lines pose any real danger to our children?* Discussions with townspeople reveal their three major concerns about electromagnetic fields: *What are they? Do they endanger our children? If so, what can be done?*

To answer these questions, you need to consider a range of subordinate questions, like those in the Figure 15.3 tree chart. As research progresses, this chart will grow. For instance, you learn that electromagnetic fields radiate not only from power lines but also from all electrical equipment, and even from the earth itself. So you face an additional question: *Do power lines present the greatest hazard as a source of EMFs?* You now wonder whether the greater hazard comes from power lines or from other sources of EMF exposure. Critical thinking has enabled you to define and refine the essential questions.

> **ON THE JOB...**
>
> **The Importance of Written Communication**
>
> *"Research is far more convenient now. Most of our students do their research from home, or from wireless-enabled locations on campus. However, the electronic environment has made the process much more complex. In the old days, you could get, for example, Canadian population statistics from numbered publications on a bookshelf. But now that same data is buried in an online table somewhere, and it may even be a 'dynamic table' that requires the searcher to combine some variables. In such situations, research librarians can help students and faculty locate highly specific sorts of data...."*
>
> **—Ross Tyner, research librarian**

Achieving Adequate Depth in Your Search

Balanced research examines a broad *range* of evidence; *thorough research*, however, examines that evidence at an appropriate *depth*. As depicted in Figure 15.4, different types of secondary information about any topic occupy different levels of detail and dependability.

1. At the surface level are items from the popular media (newspapers, radio, TV, general magazines). Designed for general consumption, this layer of information

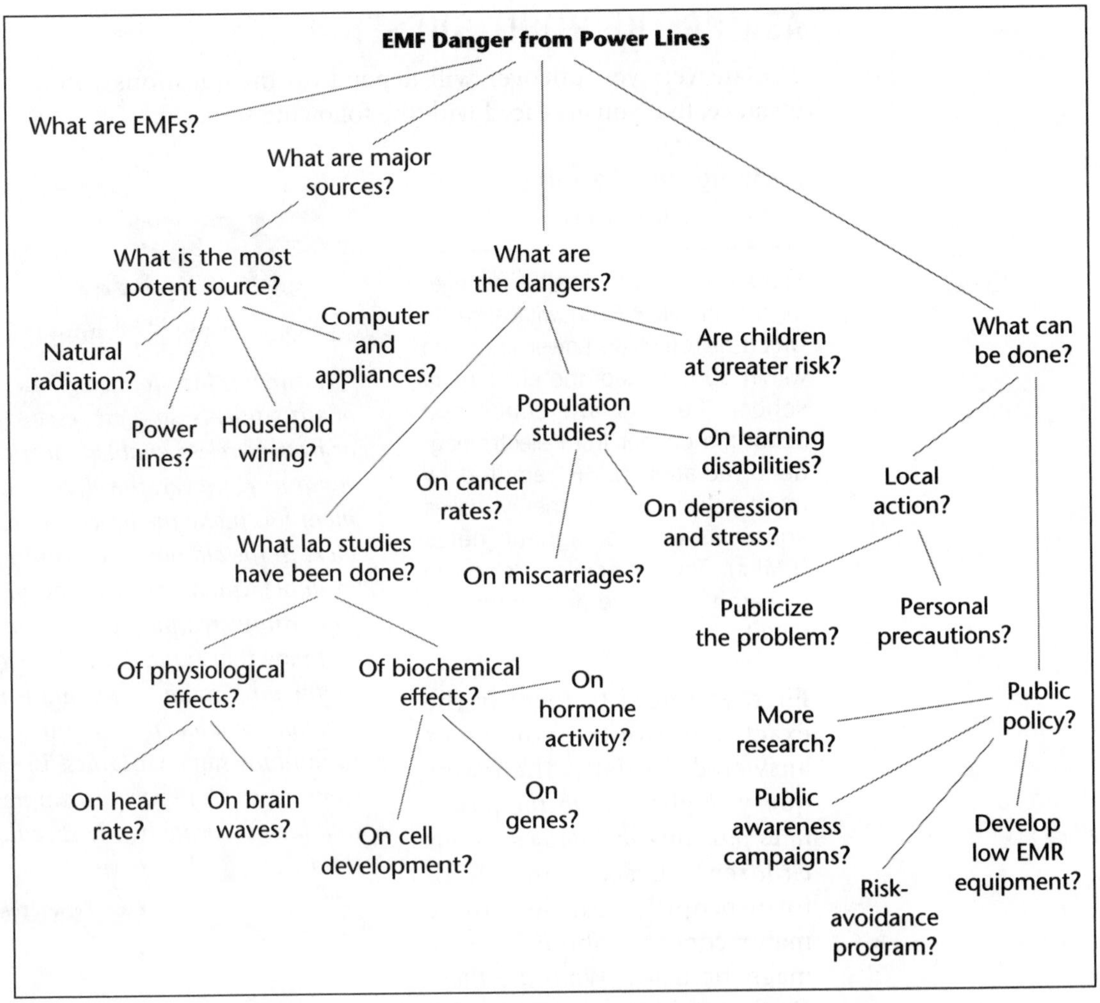

Figure 15.3 How the Right Questions Help Define a Research Problem

ON THE JOB...

The Role of Research

"If I have to do research, I look everywhere—books, online, databases, newsgroups, library, periodicals, etc. And I have to say—if you ever get stuck for information, do check out a newsgroup or mailing list about the subject. Everyone interested in the subject will be there and someone will be able to get you started..."

—Lorraine Patsco, director of prepress source and multimedia production

often contains more journalistic interpretation than factual detail.

2. At the next level are trade and business publications, such as *Construction Safety* magazine, published by the Construction Safety Association of Ontario, and *Dreams Alive*, an online home and garden design magazine. Designed for readers who range from moderately informed to highly specialized, this level focuses more on practice than on theory, on items newsworthy to group members, on issues affecting the field, on public relations, on viewpoints that tend to reflect the particular biases of that field.
3. At a deeper level is specialized literature (journals from professional associations: medical, legal,

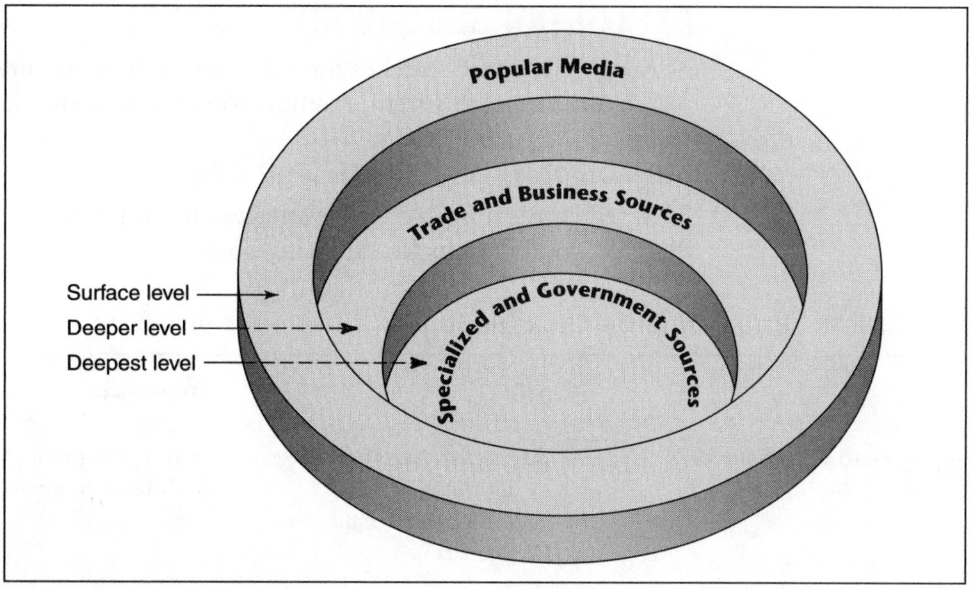

Figure 15.4 Effective Research Achieves Adequate Depth

engineering, etc.). Designed for practising professionals, this level of information focuses on theory as well as practice, on descriptions of the latest studies—written by the researchers themselves and scrutinized by others for accuracy and objectivity—on debates among scholars and researchers, and on reviews, critiques, and refutations of prior studies and publications.

Also at this deeper level are government sources and corporate documents. Designed for anyone willing to investigate its complex resources, this layer of information offers hard facts and highly detailed and (in many instances) *relatively* impartial views of virtually any issue or topic in any field.

Webpages, of course, offer links to increasingly specific levels of detail. But the actual "depth" and quality of a website's information depends on the sponsorship and reliability of that site. How deep is deep enough? It depends on your purpose, your audience, and your topic. But the real story and the hard facts more likely reside at the deeper levels of information.

Evaluating Your Findings

As your research progresses, you should start to consider whether your gathered data are legitimate:

- Does the research answer the question you've posed on behalf of your reader?
- Are the data consistent? Reliable? Verifiable?
- Do you need more information?

Also, as you conduct your research, you should start to interpret the data to determine if findings conflict and whether you should reconsider your approach. For more advice on evaluating and interpreting data, see Chapter 16.

EXPLORING SECONDARY SOURCES

Although electronic searches for information have become the norm, a *thorough* search often requires careful examination of hard copy sources as well.

Hard Copy versus Electronic Sources

Each search medium has its advantages and drawbacks (as Table 15.1 shows), so there are good reasons for exploring both types.

Table 15.1 Hard Copy versus Electronic Sources: Benefits and Drawbacks

	Benefits	Drawbacks
Hard Copy Sources	◆ discovered and organized by librarians ◆ easier to preserve and keep secure	◆ time-consuming and inefficient to search ◆ difficult to update
Electronic Sources	◆ more current, efficient, and accessible ◆ searches can be narrowed or broadened ◆ can offer material that has no hard copy equivalent	◆ access to recent material only ◆ not always reliable: sources may be very biased ◆ user might get lost ◆ material may disappear

Types of Hard Copy Sources

Many hard copy sources are now published electronically

Where you begin your hard copy search depends on whether you are searching for background and basic facts or the latest information. If you are an expert in the field, you might simply do a computerized database search or browse through specialized journals and listservs.

If you have limited knowledge or you need to focus your topic, you probably will want to begin with general reference sources, such as reference works (dictionaries, handbooks, almanacs, directories, indexes, abstracts, and bibliographies) Increasingly, however, such reference books are being published only in online versions, to which you will have access via your college or university library's subscription—ask the library's reference librarians for assistance in identifying the appropriate publications for your search.

The Card Catalogue

Access points for an electronic card catalogue

All books, reference works, journal articles, and other materials held by a library are usually listed in its card catalogue under author, title, and subject.

Nearly all libraries have automated their card catalogues, and many allow their users electronic access from outside locations, even from home. These electronic catalogues offer additional access points (beyond *author, title,* and *subject*):

- *Descriptor:* for retrieving works on the basis of a keyword or phrase (for example, *electromagnetic* or *power lines and health*) in the subject heading, in the work's title, or in the full text of its bibliographic record (its catalogue entry or abstract)

- *Document type:* for retrieving works in a specific format (video, audio, compact disk, film)
- *Organizations and conferences:* for retrieving works produced under the name of an institution or professional association (for example, Brookings Institution or Canadian Heart and Stroke Foundation)
- *Publisher:* for retrieving works produced by a particular publisher (for example, Pearson Education Canada.)
- *Combination:* for retrieving works by combining any available access points (a book about a particular subject by a particular author or institution)

Many newspaper, magazine, and professional journal articles are stored as "full-text" electronic articles accessible through databases to which your university or college library subscribes. Figure 15.5 on the following page displays the result of an automated search of Okanagan College's electronic library. From a home computer, the user gained access to the "Voyager" system. He then entered the descriptor "impact of electromagnetic fields on health" and chose a "keyword relevance search" that produced 10 000 entries, of which only the first 11 seemed truly relevant. The first five appear in Figure 15.5. Clicking on entry no. 5 produced more information about the book and its current availability. The user was then able to reserve the book and have it sent to the campus where he studies.

ON THE JOB...

The Role of the Library Catalogue

"The library catalogue was once the first and most important tool for locating credible research sources, but now it is just one of many in the range of available tools. People are focusing more on material available in various online formats. The catalogue was designed as an access system for the book warehouse and the journal warehouse found in each library, and it is still important for research that requires book material."

—Ross Tyner, research librarian

Interlibrary loan

If your library does not hold the article you need, you can search an online database to identify a holding library, and then request the article through interlibrary loan. It may be sent as a photocopy, as a PDF attachment, or as an electronic full-text journal article.

Access Tools for Government Publications

The Canadian and U.S. federal governments publish maps, periodicals, books, pamphlets, manuals, monographs, annual reports, research reports, and a bewildering array of other information. The Canadian Research Index lists a wide range of Canadian federal and provincial government publications.

Types of Canadian information available to the public include ministerial and government proclamations, government bills and reports, judiciary rulings, and publications from all other government agencies. Much of this information can be searched online as well as in printed volumes. Your best bet for tapping this valuable but complex resource is to request assistance from the librarian in charge of government documents.

Figure 15.5 Searching an Electronic Card Catalogue

Source: Courtesy of Okanagan College.

Here are some basic access tools for documents issued or published at government expense, as well as some privately issued documents. Fees are charged for most of these tools, but you can use many of them free at your university or college library.

- Micromedia ProQuest's Canadian news and periodical reference services provide access to the Canadian Business and Current Affairs Index (CBCA), Canadian Newsstand, Canadian Education Index, and the Canadian Research Index and its microlog collection.
- *Canadian Research Index.* This comprehensive research guide includes all depository publications of research value issued by federal and provincial government agencies and departments. It also indexes scientific and technical reports issued by research institutes and government laboratories. It even lists policy, social, economic, and political reports, and theses and dissertations from Canadian universities.

A growing body of government information is posted to the internet. One starting point is the Government of Canada's federal departments and agencies homepage: **http://canada.gc.ca**; then choose "Departments and Agencies" from the side menu.

Examples of government agency postings include the following:

1. The Canadian Food Inspection Agency (**www.inspection.gc.ca**) provides links to information on a wide variety of topics, from avian influenza to plant imports. The agency also highlights current information on its homepage, such as food recalls and safety tips to avoid *E. coli.*
2. The U.S. Food and Drug Administration's electronic bulletin board lists information on experimental drugs to fight AIDS, drug and device approvals, recalls and litigations involving drugs or devices, health fraud, and a host of related items.

Internet Sources

Today's internet connects computer users by the billions. Over 100 million websites and addresses (uniform resource locators, or URLs) increase by thousands daily across the globe.

Internet service providers (ISPs), including *Sympatico*, *CompuServe*, and *Microsoft Network*, provide internet access via "gateways," along with aids for navigating their many resources (see Figure 15.6 on the following page).

Web Usage. Each website has its own homepage that serves as an introduction to the site and is linked to additional "pages" that individual users can explore according to their information needs.

Through the internet, you can search files, databases, and homepages. You can participate in various newsgroups, subscribe to discussion lists, send email inquiries, and gain access to publications that exist only in electronic form. Using a browser, you can explore sites on the web, locate experts in all types of specialties, read the latest articles in journals, such as *Nature* or *Science*, or review the

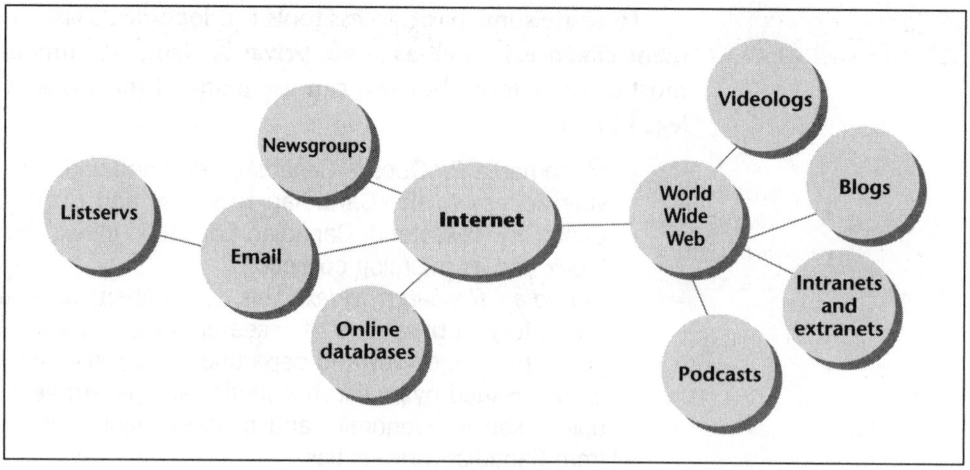

Figure 15.6 Various Parts of the Internet

latest listings of jobs in your specialty. For online databases in your field, ask your librarian.

CAUTION *Assume that any material obtained from the internet is protected by copyright. Before using such material any place other than in a college paper (properly documented), obtain written permission from its owner.*

IN BRIEF GUIDELINES FOR INTERNET RESEARCH

1. *Try to focus your search beforehand.* The more precisely you identify the information you seek, the lower your chance of wandering aimlessly through cyberspace.
2. *Select keywords or search phrases that are varied and technical, rather than general.* Some search terms generate better hits than others. In addition to "electromagnetic radiation," for example, try "electromagnetic fields," "power lines and health," or "electrical fields." Specialized terms (for example, *vertigo* versus *dizziness*) offer the best access to sites that are reliable, professional, and specific. Always check your spelling.
3. *Look for websites that are specific.* Compile a *hot list* of sites that are most relevant to your needs and interests. (Specialized newsletters and trade publications are good sources for site listings.)
4. *Set a time limit for searching.* It's no secret that internet searching ("surfing") can be addictive. Recent surveys indicate that employees spend sizable amounts of time surfing for personal instead of business-related information. As you begin a search, set a 10- to 15-minute time limit, and avoid tangents that are irrelevant to your search, no matter how engaging they are.
5. *Expect limited results from any search.* Each search engine (*Google, AltaVista, Excite, HotBot, GO.com, WebCrawler, Yahoo,* etc.) has its own strengths and weaknesses. Some are faster and more thorough while others yield more targeted and updated hits. Some search titles only—instead of the full text—for keywords. In addition, studies show that "Web content is increasing so rapidly that no single search engine indexes more than about one-third of it"

Adapted from Baker 57; Branscrum 78; Busiel and Maeglin 39–40, 76; Fugate 40–41; Kawasaki, "Get Your Facts" 156; Matson 249–52.

(continued)

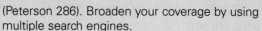

(Peterson 286). Broaden your coverage by using multiple search engines.

6. *Use bookmarks and hot lists for quick access to favourite websites.* Mark a useful site with a bookmark, which you then add to your hot list.
7. *Expect material on the internet to have a brief life span.* Site addresses can change overnight; material is rapidly updated or discarded. If you find something of special value, save or print it before it changes or disappears.
8. *Be selective about what you download.* Download only what you need. Unless they are crucial to your research, omit graphics, sound, and video files because these consume time and disk space. Focus on text files only.
9. *Never download copyrighted material without written authorization from the copyright holder.* According to the Copyright Policy Branch of the Department of Canadian Heritage, "the same copyright rules which apply to conventional media also apply to new media such as the Internet. The fact that certain works may be accessible on the Internet does not imply that the copyright owner of these works authorizes reproduction or any other use." Only material in the public domain (page 118) is exempted. Such crimes are punishable by heavy fines and/or prison sentences.

Before downloading *anything* from the internet, ask yourself: "Am I violating someone's privacy (as in forwarding an email or a newsgroup entry)?" or "Am I decreasing, in any way, the value of this material for the person who owns it?" Obtain permission beforehand and cite the source.

In addition to the above advice, see the following websites that provide tips and tutorials for successful, efficient internet searches: **www.internettutorials.net/checklist.html** (or **www.internettutorials.net/**), **www.mta.ca/library/search_strategy.html**, and **www. mta.ca/library/gov_info.html**. (Also, your college or university library likely has online help for internet research.)

EXPLORING PRIMARY SOURCES

Work-related research is often based on primary research, an original, first-hand study of the topic, involving sources like those in Figure 15.7.

The Informative Interview

An excellent primary source of information unavailable in any publication is the personal interview. Much of what an expert knows may never be published (Pugliano 6). Also, a respondent might refer you to other experts or sources of information.

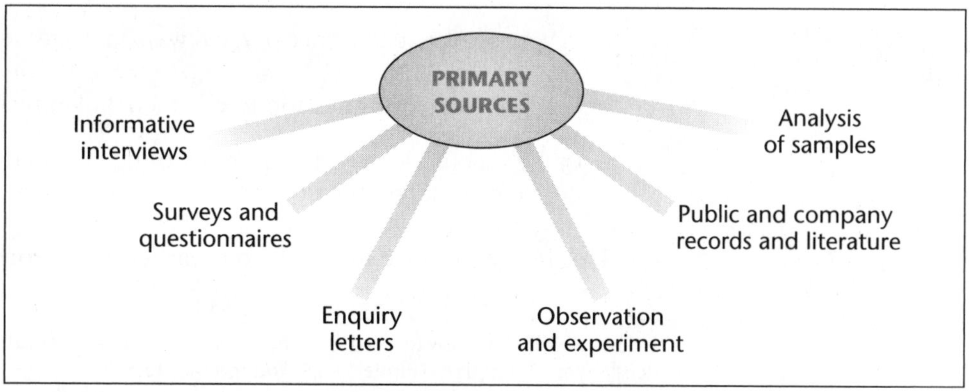

Figure 15.7 Sources for Primary Research

GUIDELINES for Informative Interviews[2]

Planning the Interview

1. *Focus on your purpose.* Determine exactly what you hope to learn from this interview. Write out your purpose.

Purpose statement

> I will interview Anne Hector, chief engineer at Northport Electric, to ask her about the company's approaches to EMF risk avoidance—within the company as well as in the community.

2. *Do your homework.* Learn all you can about the topic beforehand. The more you know, the better your chance of getting the facts straight. If the respondent has published anything relevant, read it before the interview. Be sure the information this person might provide is unavailable in print.
3. *Contact the intended respondent.* Do this by telephone, letter, or email, and be sure to introduce yourself and your purpose.
4. *Request the interview at your respondent's convenience.* Give the respondent ample notice and time to prepare, and ask whether she or he objects to being quoted or taped. If you use a tape recorder, insert fresh batteries and a new tape, and set the recording volume loud enough.

Preparing the Questions

5. *Make each question clear and specific.* Vague, unspecific questions elicit vague, unspecific answers.

A vague question

> How is this utility company dealing with the problem of electromagnetic fields?

Which problem—public relations, potential liability, danger to electrical workers, to the community, or what?

Clear and specific question

> What safety procedures have you developed for risk avoidance among electrical work crews?

6. *Avoid questions that can be answered with a mere "yes" or "no."*

An unproductive question

> In your opinion, can technology find ways to decrease EMF hazards?

Instead, phrase your question to elicit a detailed response:

A productive question

> Of the various technological solutions being proposed or considered, which do you consider most promising?

This is one instance in which your earlier homework pays off.

2. Several guidelines are adapted from Blum 88; Dowd 13–14; Kotulak 147; McDonald 190; Rensberger 15; Hopkins-Tanne 23, 29; Young 114, 115.

(continued)

GUIDELINES
for Informative Interviews
(continued)

7. *Avoid loaded questions.* A loaded question invites a particular bias:

A loaded question

> Wouldn't you agree that EMF hazards have been overstated?

An impartial question does not lead the interviewee to respond in a certain way.

An impartial question

> In your opinion, have EMF hazards been accurately stated, overstated, or understated?

8. *Save the most difficult, complex, or sensitive questions for last.* Leading off with your toughest question might annoy respondents, making them uncooperative.

Conducting the Interview

1. *Make a good start.* Dress appropriately and arrive on time. Thank your respondent; restate your purpose; explain why you believe she or he can be helpful; explain exactly how you will use the information.
2. *Be sensitive to cultural differences.* If the respondent belongs to a culture different from your own, then consider the level of formality, politeness, directness, relationship building, and other behaviours considered appropriate in that culture.
3. *Let the respondent do the most talking.* Keep opinions to yourself.
4. *Be a good listener.* Don't doodle or let your eyes wander. People reveal more when the listener seems genuinely interested.
5. *Stick to your interview plan.* If the respondent wanders, politely nudge the conversation back on track (unless the added information is useful).
6. *Ask for clarification or explanation whenever necessary.* If you don't understand an answer, say so. Request an example, an analogy, or a simplified version—and keep asking until you understand.

Clarifying questions

- Would you go over that again please?
- Is there a simpler explanation?

Science writer Ronald Kotulak argues that "No question is dumb if the answer is necessary to help you understand something.... Don't pretend to know more than you do" (144).

7. *Keep checking on your understanding.* Repeat major points in your own words and ask if the technical details are accurate and if your interpretation is correct.
8. *Be ready with follow-up questions.* Some answers may lead to additional questions.

Follow-up questions

- Why is it like that?
- Could you say something more about that?
- What more needs to be done?
- What happened next?

(continued)

GUIDELINES
for Informative Interviews
(continued)

9. *Keep note-taking to a minimum.* Record statistics, dates, names, and other precise data, but not every word. Jot key terms or phrases that later can refresh your memory.

Concluding the Interview

1. *Ask for closing comments.* Perhaps the respondent can lead you to additional information.

Concluding questions

- Have I missed anything?
- Would you care to add anything?
- Is there anything I've neglected to ask?
- Is there anyone else I should talk to?
- Is there anyone who has a different point of view?

2. *Invite the respondent to review your version.* If the interview will be published, ask the respondent to check your final draft (for misspelled names, inaccurate details, misquotations, and so on) and to approve it. Offer to provide copies of any document in which this information appears.
3. *Thank your respondent and leave promptly.*
4. *As soon as you leave the interview, write a complete summary (or record one verbally).* Do this while responses are fresh in your memory.

Of course, an expert opinion can be just as mistaken or biased as anyone else's. Like patients who seek second opinions about serious medical conditions, researchers seek a balanced range of expert opinions about a complex problem or controversial issue—not only from a company engineer and environmentalist, for example, but also from an independent and presumably more objective third party, such as a professor or journalist who has studied the issue.

Selecting an Interview Medium. Once you decide whom to interview about what, select your medium carefully:

- *In-person interviews* are most productive because they allow human contact (Hopkins-Tanne 24).
- *Phone interviews* can be convenient and productive, but they lack the human contact of in-person interviews—especially when the interviewer and respondent have not met.
- *Email interviews* are convenient and inexpensive, and they allow plenty of time for respondents to consider their answers.

Whatever your medium, obtain a respondent's approval *beforehand*—instead of waylaying this person with an unwanted surprise.

Surveys and Questionnaires

Surveys help us develop profiles and estimates about the concerns, preferences, attitudes, beliefs, or perceptions of a large, identifiable group (a *target population*) by studying representatives of that group (a *sample group*).

Surveys help us make assessments like these:

- Do consumers prefer brand A or brand B?
- What percentage of students feel safe on our campus?
- Is public confidence in technology increasing or decreasing?

The questionnaire is the tool for conducting surveys. While interviews allow for greater clarity and depth, questionnaires offer an inexpensive way to survey a large group. Respondents can answer privately and anonymously—and often in more detail than in an interview.

However, questionnaires carry certain limitations:

Limitations of survey research

- *A low rate of response (often less than 30 percent).* People refuse to respond to a questionnaire that seems too long, complicated, or in some way threatening. They might be embarrassed by the topic or afraid of how their answers could be used.
- *Responses that might be non-representative.* A survey will get responses from the people who want to respond, but you will know nothing about the people who didn't respond. Those who responded might have extreme views, a particular stake in the outcome, or some other motive that represents inaccurately the population being surveyed (Plumb and Spyridakis 625–26).
- *Lack of follow-up.* Survey questions do not allow for the kind of follow-up and clarification possible with interview questions.

Even surveys by professionals carry potential for error. As consumers of survey research, we need to understand how surveys are designed, administered, and interpreted, and what can go wrong in the process.

Defining the Survey's Purpose. Why is this survey being done? What, exactly, is it measuring? How much background research is needed? How will the survey findings be used?

Defining the Target Population. Who is the exact population being studied ("the chronically unemployed," "part-time students," "computer users")?

Identifying the Sample Group. How will intended respondents be selected? How many respondents will there be? Generally, the larger the sample surveyed, the more dependable the results (assuming a well-chosen and representative sample). Will the sample be randomly chosen? In the statistical sense, *random* does not mean "chosen haphazardly": a random sample means that any member of the target population stands an equal chance of being included in the sample group.

Even a sample that is highly representative of the target population carries a measure of *sampling error.*

A type of survey error

> The particular sample used in a survey is only one of a large number of possible samples of the same size that could have been selected using the same sampling procedures. Estimates derived from the different samples would, in general, differ from each other. (U.S. Department of Commerce 949)

The larger the sampling error (usually expressed as the *margin of error*), the less dependable the survey findings.

Defining the Survey Method. What type of data (opinions, ideas, facts, figures) will be collected? Is timing important? How will the survey be administered—in person, by mail, by telephone? How will the data be collected, recorded, analyzed, and reported (Lavin 277)?

Telephone, email, and in-person surveys yield fast results, but respondents consider telephone surveys annoying and, without anonymity, people tend to be less candid. They generate high response rates, but mail surveys are less expensive and more confidential. Computerized surveys create the sense of a video game: the program analyzes each response and automatically designs the next question. Respondents who dislike being quizzed by a human researcher seem more comfortable with this automated format (Perelman 89–90).

Guidelines for Developing a Questionnaire.

1. *Choose the types of questions.* (Adams and Schvaneveldt 202–12; Velotta 390). Questions can be *open-ended* or *closed-ended.* Open-ended questions allow respondents to express exactly what they're thinking or feeling in a word, phrase, sentence, or short essay:

   Open-ended questions

   How much do you know about electromagnetic radiation at our school?
   What do you think should be done about electromagnetic fields (EMFs) at our school?

   Since one never knows what people will say, open-ended questions are a good way to uncover attitudes and obtain unexpected information. But essay-type questions are difficult to answer and tabulate.

   When you want to measure where people stand on an issue, choose closed-ended questions:

   Closed-ended questions

   Are you interested in joining a group of concerned parents?
   YES ______ NO ______

   Rate your degree of concern about EMFs at our school.
   HIGH ______ MODERATE ______ LOW ______ NO CONCERN ______

   Circle the number that indicates your view about the town's proposal to spend $20 000 to hire its own EMF consultant.

   1..........2..........3..........4..........5..........6..........7

   Strongly Approve — No Opinion — Strongly Disapprove

Respondents may be asked to *rate* one item on a scale (from high to low, best to worst), to *rank* two or more items (by importance, desirability), or to select items from a list. Other questions measure percentages or frequency.

How often do you...?

ALWAYS _____ OFTEN _____ SOMETIMES _____ RARELY _____ NEVER _____

Although closed-ended questions are easy to answer, tabulate, measure, and analyze, they might elicit biased responses. Some people, for instance, automatically prefer items near the top of a list or the left side of a rating scale (Plumb and Spyridakis 633). Also, people are prone to agree rather than disagree with assertions in a questionnaire (Sherblom, Sullivan, and Sherblom 61).

2. Design an engaging introduction and opening questions. Persuade respondents that the survey relates to their concerns, that their answers matter, and that their anonymity is assured. Explain how respondents will benefit from your findings, or offer an incentive (say, a copy of your final report).

A survey introduction

Your answers will enable our school board to speak accurately for your views at our next town meeting. Results will appear in our campus newspaper. Thank you.

Researchers often include a cover letter with the questionnaire.

Begin with the easiest questions. Once respondents commit to these, they are likely to complete more difficult questions later.

3. *Make each question unambiguous.* All respondents should be able to interpret identical questions identically. An ambiguous question leaves room for misinterpretation.

An ambiguous question

Do you favour weapons for campus police? YES _________ NO _________

Weapons might mean tear gas, clubs, handguns, all three, or two out of three. Consequently, responses to the above question would produce a misleading statistic, such as "Over 95 percent of students favour handguns for campus police," when the accurate conclusion might be "Over 95 percent of students favour some form of weapon." Moreover, the limited choice ("yes/no") reduces an array of possible opinions to an either/or choice.

Do you favour (check all that apply):

A clear, incisive question

_______ Having campus police carry mace and a club?

_______ Having campus police carry non-lethal stun guns?

_______ Having campus police store handguns in their cruisers?

_______ Having campus police carry small-calibre handguns?

_______ Having campus police carry large-calibre handguns?

_______ Having campus police carry no weapons?

_______ Don't know

To ensure a full range of possible responses, include options such as "Other________," "Don't know," "Not applicable," or an "Additional comments" section.

4. *Make each question unbiased.* Avoid *loaded questions* that invite or advocate a particular viewpoint or bias:

A loaded question

Should our campus tolerate the needless endangerment of innocent students by lethal weapons?

YES ________ NO ________

Emotionally loaded and judgmental words (*endangerment, innocent, tolerate, needless, lethal*) in a survey are unethical because their built-in judgments manipulate people's responses (Hayakawa 40).

5. *Make it brief, simple, and inviting.* Try to limit questions and response space to two sides of a single page. Include a stamped, return-addressed envelope, and give a specific return date. Address each respondent by name, sign your letter or your introduction, and give your title.

A Sample Questionnaire

The student-written questionnaire in Figure 15.8, sent to presidents of local companies, is designed to elicit responses that can be tabulated easily. Written reports of survey findings usually include an appendix that contains a copy of the questionnaire as well as the tabulated responses.

Inquiries

Letters, phone calls, or email inquiries to experts listed in webpages are handy for obtaining specific information from government agencies, legislators, private companies, university researchers, trade associations, and research foundations.

Office Files

Organization records (reports, memos, computer printouts, etc.) are good primary sources. Most organizations also publish pamphlets, brochures, annual reports, or prospectuses for consumers, employees, investors, or voters. But be alert for bias in company literature. If you were evaluating the safety measures at a local nuclear power plant, you would want the complete picture. Along with the company's literature, you would also want studies and reports from government agencies and publications from environmental groups.

Personal Observation and Experiments

If possible, amplify and verify your findings with a first-hand look. Observation should be your final step because you now know what to look for. Have a plan. Know how, where, and when to look, and jot down observations immediately. You might even take photos or make drawings.

Informed observations can pinpoint real problems. Here is an excerpt from a report investigating low morale at an electronics firm. This researcher's observations and interpretation are crucial in defining the problem:

Communication Questionnaire

1. Describe your type of company (e.g., manufacturing, high tech) ______________________________
____

2. Number of employees? (Please check one.)

______ 0–4	______ 26–50	______ 101–150	______ 301–450
______ 5–25	______ 51–100	______ 151–300	______ 450+

3. What types of written communication occur in your company? (Label by frequency: never, rarely, sometimes, often.)

______ memos	______ letters	______ advertising
______ manuals	______ reports	______ newsletters
______ procedures	______ proposals	______ other (specify)
______ email	______ catalogues	______________________

4. Who does most of the writing? (Please give titles.) ______________________________
____

5. Please characterize your employees' writing effectiveness.

______ good ______ fair ______ poor

6. Does your company have formal guidelines for writing?

______ no ______ yes (Please describe briefly.) ______________________________
____

7. Do you offer in-house communication training?

______ no ______ yes (Please describe briefly.) ______________________________
____

8. Please rank the usefulness of the following areas in communication training (from 1 to 10, 1 being the most important).

______ organization information	______ audience awareness
______ summarizing information	______ persuasive writing
______ editing for style	______ grammar
______ document design	______ researching
______ email etiquette	______ webpage design
______ other (Please specify.) ______________________	

9. Please rank these skills in order of importance (from 1 to 6, 1 being the most important).

______ reading	______ listening	______ speaking to groups
______ writing	______ collaborating	______ speaking face to face

10. Do you provide tuition reimbursement for employees?

______ no ______ yes

11. Would you consider having UMD communication interns work for you part time?

______ no ______ yes

12. Should UMD offer Saturday seminars in communication?

______ no ______ yes

Additional comments/suggestions: ______________________________
____

Figure 15.8 A Sample Survey

Direct observation is often essential

> Our on-site communication audit revealed that employees were unaware of any major barriers to communication. Over 75 percent of employees claimed they felt free to talk to their managers, but the managers, in turn, estimated that fewer than 50 percent of employees felt free to talk to them.
>
> The problem involves misinterpretation. Because managers don't ask for complaints, employees are afraid to make them, and because employees never ask for an evaluation, they never get one. Each side has inaccurate perceptions of what the other side expects, and because of ineffective communication, each side fails to realize that its perceptions are wrong.

An experiment is a controlled form of observation designed to verify an assumption (e.g., the role of fish oil in preventing heart disease) or to test something untried (the relationship between background music and worker productivity). Each specialty has its own guidelines for experiment design.

Even direct observation is not foolproof; for instance, you might be biased about what you see (focusing on the wrong events or ignoring something important), or instead of behaving normally, people being observed might behave in ways they think are expected of them (Adams and Schvaneveldt 244).

Analysis of Samples

Workplace research can involve collecting and analyzing samples: water, soil, or air, for contamination and pollution; foods, for nutritional value; ore, for mineral value; or plants, for medicinal value. Investigators analyze material samples to find the cause of an airline accident. Engineers analyze samples of steel, concrete, or other building materials to determine their load-bearing capacity. Medical specialists analyze tissue samples for disease.

WEB CONNECT

The first of the following sites offers a comprehensive guide to web search engines. The Okanagan College and Mount Royal College sites advise how to use a variety of traditional and electronic research tools.

www.monash.com/spidap.html
www.okanagan.bc.ca/Page9409.aspx
http://library.mtroyal.ca/

EXERCISES

1. Begin researching for the analytical report (Chapter 18) due at semester's end. Complete these steps. (Your instructor might establish a timetable.)

   Phase One: Preliminary Steps

   a. Choose a topic of *immediate practical importance,* something that affects you or your community directly.
   b. Identify a specific audience and its intended use of your information. Complete an audience/purpose profile (page 35).
   c. Narrow your topic, and check with your instructor for approval.
   d. Make a working bibliography to ensure sufficient primary and secondary resources. Don't delay this step!
   e. List things you already know about your topic.
   f. Write a clear statement of purpose and submit it in a proposal memo (pages 285–89) to your instructor.
   g. Develop a tree chart of possible questions (as on page 310).
   h. Make a working outline.

   Phase Two: Collecting Data (Read Chapter 16 in preparation for this phase.)

   a. In your research, move from general to specific; begin with general reference works for an overview.
   b. Skim your material, looking for high points.
   c. Take selective notes. Don't write everything down! Use notecards.
   d. Plan and administer questionnaires, interviews, and inquiry letters.

e. Whenever possible, conclude your research with direct observation.
f. Evaluate and interpret your findings.
g. Use the checklist on page 348 to reassess your research methods and reasoning.

Phase Three: Organizing Your Data and Writing Your Report

a. Revise and adjust your working outline, as needed.
b. Compose an audience/purpose analysis, like the sample on page 35.
c. Fully document all sources of information.
d. Proofread carefully and add all needed supplements (title page, letter of transmittal, abstract, summary, appendix, glossary).

Due Dates: To Be Assigned by Your Instructor
List of possible topics due:
Final topic due:
Proposal memo due:
Working bibliography and working outline due:
Notecards due:
Copies of questionnaires, interview questions, and inquiry letters due:
Revised outline due:
First draft of report due:
Final draft with supplements and documentation due:

2. Using the printed or electronic card catalogue, locate and record the full bibliographic data for five books in your field or on your semester report topic, all published within the past year.
3. List the title of each of these specialized reference works in your field or on your topic: a bibliography, an encyclopedia, a dictionary, a handbook, an almanac (if available), and a directory.
4. Identify the major periodical index in your field or on your topic. Locate a recent article on a specific topic (e.g., use of artificial intelligence in medical diagnosis). Photocopy the article (get Access Copyright clearance) and write an informative abstract.
5. Revise these questions to make them appropriate for inclusion in a questionnaire:
   a. Would a female prime minister do the job as well as a male?
   b. Don't you think that euthanasia is a crime?
   c. Do you oppose increased government spending?
   d. Do you think welfare recipients are too lazy to support themselves?
   e. Are teachers responsible for the decline in literacy among students?
   f. Aren't humanities studies a waste of time?
   g. Do you prefer Rocket Cola to other leading brands?
   h. In meetings, do you think men interrupt more than women?
6. Arrange an interview with someone in your field. Decide on general areas for questioning: job opportunities, chances for promotion, salary range, requirements, outlook for the next decade, working conditions, job satisfaction, and so on. Compose specific interview questions; conduct the interview, and summarize your findings in a memo to your instructor.

COLLABORATIVE PROJECT

Divide into small groups, and decide on a campus or community issue or some other topic worthy of research. Elect a group manager to assign and coordinate tasks. At project's end, the manager will provide a performance appraisal by summarizing, in writing, the contribution of each team member. Assigned tasks will include planning, information gathering from primary and secondary sources, document preparation (including visuals) and revision, and classroom presentation. (See page 54–55 for collaboration guidelines.) Conduct the research, write the report, and present your findings to the class. (In conjunction with this project, your instructor may assign Chapter 18.)

CHAPTER 16

Recording and Reviewing Research Findings

LEARNING OBJECTIVES

After reading this chapter, you should be able to

- Use a consistent, recoverable method of recording research findings.
- Carefully record all information sources.
- Evaluate the quality and value of the researched data by answering pertinent questions about information sources and about the evidence that supports findings.
- Be particularly careful in evaluating internet-based material.
- Interpret the data using effective inductive and deductive reasoning, and avoid fallacies.

As you discover material during research, you confront questions like these: How much is worth keeping? How should I record it? Can I trust this information? What, exactly, does it mean? How will I credit the source? These latter stages of the research process require the same quality of critical thinking as the earlier stages discussed in Chapter 15.

RECORDING THE FINDINGS

Findings should be recorded in ways that enable you to easily locate, organize, and control the material as you work with it. Record primary research findings by using a laptop computer, photographs, drawings, tape recorder, videotape, or whichever medium suits your purpose. Record secondary research findings as notes.

Taking Notes

Notecards are convenient because they are easy to organize and reorganize. In place of notecards, many researchers take notes on a laptop computer, using information or database management software that allows notes to be filed, rearranged, and retrieved by author, title, topic, date, and so forth.

Follow these suggestions when making notes:

1. Make a separate bibliography card (Figure 16.1) or computer file for each work you plan to consult. Record the complete entry, using the identical citation format that will appear in your document. (Chapter 19 has sample entries.) When searching an online catalogue, you can print or electronically save the full bibliographic record for each work, thereby ensuring accurate citation.
2. Skim the entire work to locate relevant material.
3. Decide what to record. Use a separate card or electronic file for each item.
4. Decide how to record the item: as a quotation or a paraphrase. When quoting others directly, be sure to record words and punctuation accurately. When restating or adapting material in your own words, be sure to preserve the original meaning and emphasis. **Record the sources of all internet-based material.**

Quoting the Work of Others

When you borrow exact wording, whether the words were written or spoken (as in an interview or presentation) or whether they appeared in electronic form, you must place quotation marks around all borrowed material. Even a single borrowed sentence or phrase, or a single word used in a special way, needs quotation marks, with the exact source properly cited.

If your notes fail to identify quoted material accurately, you may forget to credit the source in your report. Even when this omission is unintentional, writers face the charge of *plagiarism* (misrepresenting as one's own the words or ideas of someone else). Possible consequences of plagiarism include expulsion from school, the loss of your job, or a lawsuit.

In recording a direct quotation, copy the selection word for word (Figure 16.2 on the following page) and include the page numbers. If your quotation omits parts of a sentence, use an *ellipsis* (three periods:...) to indicate each part that you have omitted from the original. If your quotation omits the end of a sentence, the beginning of the subsequent sentence, or whole sentences or paragraphs, show the ellipsis with four periods (....).

Ellipsis within and between sentences

If your quotation omits parts...use an ellipsis....And if your quotation omits the end....

Record each bibliographic citation exactly as it will appear in your final report

Pinsky, Mark A. *The EMF Book: What You Should Know about Electromagnetic Fields, Electromagnetic Radiation, and Your Health*. New York: Warner, 1995.

Figure 16.1 Bibliography Card

Place quotation marks around all directly quoted material

Pinsky, Mark A. pp. 29–30.

"Neither electromagnetic fields nor electromagnetic radiation cause cancer per se, most researchers agree. What they may do is promote cancer. Cancer is a multistage process that requires an 'initiator' that makes a cell or group of cells abnormal. Everyone has cancerous cells in his or her body. Cancer—the disease as we think of it—occurs when these cancerous cells grow uncontrollably."

Figure 16.2 Notecard for a Quotation

Be sure that your elliptical expression is grammatical and that the omitted material in no way distorts the original meaning.

If you insert your own words within the quotation, place them inside brackets to distinguish them from those of your source:

Brackets setting off personal comments within quoted material

> "This profession [aircraft ground controller] requires exhaustive attention."

Sentences and paragraphs that include quotations must be clear and understandable. Read your sentences aloud to be sure they make sense and they read smoothly and grammatically. Generally, integrated quotations are introduced by phrases such as "Wong argues that" or "Dupuis suggests that," so that readers know who said what. More importantly, readers must see the relationship between the quoted idea and the sentence that precedes it. Use a transitional phrase that emphasizes this relationship by looking back as well as ahead:

An introduction that unifies a quotation with the discussion

> After you decide to develop a program, "the first step in the programming process. . ."

Besides showing how each quotation helps advance the main idea you are developing, your integrated sentences should also be grammatical:

Quoted material integrated grammatically with the writer's words

> "The agricultural crisis," Marx acknowledges, "resulted primarily from unchecked land speculation."
>
> "She has rejuvenated the industrial economy of our region," Smith writes of Berry's term as regional planner.

Use a direct quotation only when precision, clarity, or emphasis requires the exact words from the original. Avoid excessively long quoted passages. Research writing is more a process of independent thinking, in which you work with the ideas of others in order to reach your own conclusions; you should, therefore, paraphrase, instead of quoting, much of your borrowed material.

Paraphrasing the Work of Others

We paraphrase not only to preserve the original idea but also to express it in a clear, simple, direct, or emphatic way—without distorting the idea. *Paraphrasing* means more than changing or shuffling a few words; it means restating the original idea in your own words and giving full credit to the source.

To borrow or adapt someone else's ideas or reasoning without properly documenting the source is plagiarism. To offer as a paraphrase an original passage only slightly altered—even when you document the source—also is plagiarism. It is equally unethical to offer a paraphrase, although documented, that distorts the original meaning.

Effective paraphrases display all or most of these elements (Weinstein 3):

Elements of an effective paraphrase

- reference to the author early in the paraphrase, to indicate the beginning of the borrowed passage
- keywords retained from the original, to preserve the meaning
- original sentences restructured and combined, for emphasis and fluency
- needless words from the original deleted, for conciseness
- your own words and phrases that help explain the author's ideas, for clarity
- a citation (in parentheses) of the exact source, to mark the end of the borrowed passage and to give full credit
- preservation of the author's original intent

Figure 16.3 shows an entry paraphrased from the passage in Figure 16.2. Paraphrased material does not have quotation marks, but you must acknowledge your debt to the source. Failing to acknowledge ideas, findings, judgments, lines of reasoning, opinions, facts, or insights not considered *common knowledge* is plagiarism—even when these are expressed in your own words.

Signal the beginning of the paraphrase by citing the author, and the end by citing the source

Pinsky, Mark A.

Pinsky explains that electromagnetic waves probably do not directly cause cancer. However, they might contribute to the uncontrollable growth of those cancer cells normally present—but controlled—in the human body (29–30).

Figure 16.3 Notecard for a Paraphrase

EVALUATING AND INTERPRETING INFORMATION

Not all information is equal. Not all interpretations are equal. Whether you work with your own findings or the findings of other researchers, you need to decide if the information is valid and reliable. Then you need to decide what your information means. Figure 16.4 on the following page outlines this challenge.

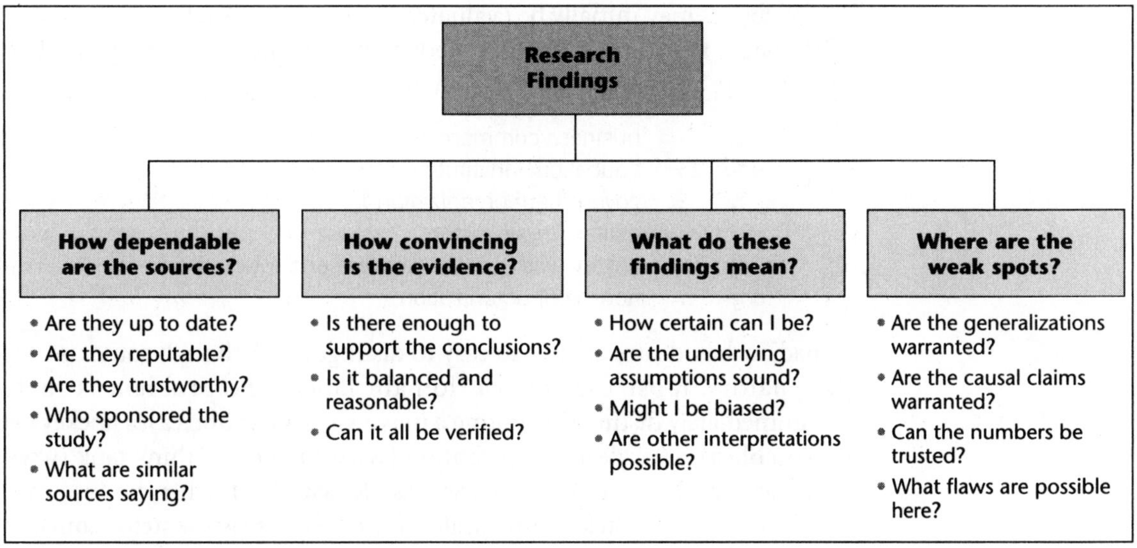

Figure 16.4 Decisions in Reviewing Research Findings

Evaluating the Sources

Not all data sources are equally dependable. A source might offer information that is out of date, inaccurate, incomplete, mistaken, or biased.

How current is the information?

Is the Source Up to Date? Newly published books contain information that can be more than one year old, and journal articles often undergo a lengthy process of peer review.

Certain types of information become outdated more quickly than others. Topics that focus on *technology* (superconductivity, internet censorship, alternative cancer treatments) may be outdated. Except for historical or background research, sources in those areas generally should offer the most recent information available. Information on topics that focus on *people* (business ethics, management practices, workplace gender equality, employee motivation) might offer valuable perspective on present situations even if the information is several decades old.

What is the source's reputation?

Is the Source Reputable? Some sources enjoy better reputations than others. For research on alternative cancer treatments, you could depend more on reports in the *Canadian Medical Association Journal* or *Scientific American* than on those in scandal sheets or movie magazines. Even researchers with expert credentials, however, can disagree or be mistaken.

One way to assess a publication's reputation is to check its copyright page. Is the work published by a university, professional society, museum, or respected news organization? Is the publication *refereed* (all submissions reviewed by experts prior to acceptance)?

One way to assess an author's reputation is to check citation indexes to see what others have said about this research. Many periodicals also provide brief biographies or descriptions of authors' earlier publications and other achievements.

Websites may initially be evaluated by their domain type and sponsor. A typical URL places the domain type immediately after the first part of the URL (usually *www*). Here are some common domain types:

.com	=	business/commercial organization
.edu	=	educational institution
.gov	=	government organization
.mil	=	military organization
.net	=	anyone with simple software and internet access
.org	=	non-profit organization

Canadian-based sites are not so easy to distinguish. Although some use *.org* and *.com* designators, most use the *.ca* domain label. The problem is that one cannot immediately distinguish among a university (**www.ubc.ca**), a hockey organization (**www.chl.ca**), a car dealer organization (**www.tada.ca**), a think tank (**www.fraserinstitute.ca**), and a manufacturer (**www.stelco.ca**). To further confuse matters, some companies, such as Stelco, run parallel *.com* websites (**www.stelco.com**).

However, Canadian government ministries and agencies usually insert *gc*, *gov*, or *gouv* into their URLs:

- **www.inspection.gc.ca/english/toce.shtml** (homepage for the Canadian Food Inspection Agency)
- **www.msss.gouv.qc.ca** (Quebec's Ministère de Santé et Services sociaux)
- **www.health.gov.on.ca** (Ontario Ministry of Health and Long-Term Care)
- **www.gov.bc.ca/health** (British Columbia Ministry of Health)

Can the source be trusted?

Is the Source Trustworthy? The internet offers information that may never appear in other sources: for example, from listservs and newsgroups. But much of this information may reflect the bias of the special interest groups that provide it. Moreover, anyone can publish almost anything on the internet—including a great deal of misinformation—without having it verified, edited, or reviewed for accuracy (Snyder 89–90).

Even in a commercial database, decisions about what to include and what to leave out depend on the biases, priorities, or interests of those who assemble that database. In general, try not to rely on any single information source.

Who sponsored the study?

Is the Information Biased? Much of today's research is paid for by private companies or special interest groups that have their own social, political, or economic agendas (Crossen 14, 19). Medical research may be sponsored by drug or tobacco companies; nutritional research, by food manufacturers; and environmental research, by oil or chemical companies. Public policy research (on gun control, seat-belt laws, endangered species) may be sponsored by opposing groups (environmentalists versus the logging industry), producing opposing results. Instead of a neutral and balanced inquiry, this kind of "strategic research" is designed to support one special interest group or another. Those who pay for strategic research are not likely to publicize findings that contradict their original claims, opinions, or beliefs (profits lower than expected, losses or risks greater than expected). As consumers of research, we should try to determine exactly what the sponsors of a particular study stand to gain or lose from the results.

IN BRIEF COPYRIGHT PROTECTION AND FAIR USE OF PRINTED INFORMATION

Copyright Law

A copyright is the exclusive legal right to reproduce, publish, and sell a literary, dramatic, musical, or artistic work. The law grants the copyright owner the exclusive rights to do and to authorize any of the following:

1. To reproduce the copyrighted work.
2. To prepare derivative works.
3. To distribute copies of the copyrighted work to the public by sale, rental, lease, or lending.
4. In certain cases, such as for literary and musical works, to perform the copyrighted work publicly.
5. In certain cases, such as for graphics, images, or other audiovisuals, to display the copyrighted work publicly.

You must obtain written permission to use all copyrighted material. Works are copyrighted for the author's life plus 50 years. If the author is unknown, the copyright lasts for 50 years from the document's publication date.

Public Domain

Public domain refers to material on which copyright has expired or material that is not protected by copyright. Commonplace pieces of information such as height and weight charts are in the public domain. These works occasionally contain copyrighted material used with permission and properly acknowledged. **However, a new translation or version of a work in the public domain can be protected by copyright;** if you are not sure whether something is in the public domain, obtain permission. In Canada, government publications are *not* in the public domain.

Fair Dealing

Fair dealing allows quotes from, or reproduction of, minor excerpts of a copyrighted work, if the quotation or reproduction is for bona fide private study, research, criticism, or newspaper summary. But there's a problem: it's difficult to tell the difference between fair dealing and copyright infringement. The limits of fair dealing copying have not yet been defined in the Canadian Copyright Act or by case law.

Copyright law provides the following criteria to be considered in the determination of fair dealing:

1. The purpose and character of the use, including whether such use is of a commercial nature or is for non-profit educational purposes.
2. The nature of the copyrighted work.
3. The amount and substantiality of the portion used in relation to the whole.
4. The effect of the use upon the potential market for or value of the copyrighted work.

When the quoted material forms the core, distinguishable creative effort of the work being cited, use of the material without permission isn't considered fair.

Fair dealing ordinarily does not apply to use of poetry, musical lyrics, dialogue of a play, entries in a diary, case studies, charts and graphs, author's notes, private letters, testing materials, or quotations for use as epigraphs.

Copying Under the Access Copyright Licence

Many Canadian college, university, high school, and public libraries have signed licence agreements with Access Copyright, a non-profit organization representing Canadian and foreign authors and publishers. Under such licences, library users can copy certain portions of certain kinds of documents without permission. **However, each licence imposes clear legal restrictions**, so ask your librarian for details.

Based on *HarperCollins Author's Guide*. Copyright ©1995, and on Canada's Copyright Act, as amended by Bill C-32.

The following hints may further help you evaluate internet sites:

How to evaluate the validity of internet sites

1. *Identify the purpose of the page or message.* Decide whether the message is intended to merely relay information, to sell something, or to promote a particular ideology or agenda.
2. *Don't be satisfied with generalities.* Look for specific facts, examples, or statistics. Then, check to see which of these "facts" can be verified by other sources.

IN BRIEF COPYRIGHT PROTECTION AND FAIR DEALING OF ELECTRONIC INFORMATION

The Problem

Copyright and fair dealing law is quite specific for printed works or works in other tangible form (paintings, photographs, music). But how do we define "fair dealing" (see page xxx) of intellectual property in electronic form? How does copyright protection apply (Dyson 137)? How do fair dealing restrictions apply to material used in multimedia presentations or to text or images that have been altered or reshaped to suit the user's specific needs (Steinberg 30)?

Information obtained via email or discussion groups presents additional problems: sources often do not wish to be quoted or named or to have early drafts made public. How do we protect source confidentiality? How do we avoid infringing on works in progress that have not yet been published? How do we quote and cite this material without violating ownership and privacy rights (Howard 40–41)?

Present Status of Electronic Copyright Law

Subscribers to commercial online databases pay fees, and copyholders in turn receive royalties (Communication Concepts, Inc. 13). But as of this writing, few specific legal protections exist for noncommercial types of electronic information. Since April 1989, however, most works are considered copyrighted as soon as they are produced—even if they carry no copyright notice. Fair dealing of electronic information generally is limited to brief excerpts that serve as a basis for response—for example, in a discussion group. Except for certain government documents, no internet posting is in the public domain unless it is expressly designated as such by its author (Templeton).

Until specific laws are enacted, the following examples can be considered violations of copyright (Communication Concepts, Inc. 13; Templeton):

- downloading a work from the internet and forwarding copies to other readers
- editing, altering, or incorporating an original work as part of your own document or multimedia presentation
- putting someone else's printed work online without the author's written permission
- copying and forwarding an email message without the sender's authorization.

Penalties for Copyright Infringement

Individuals, businesses, or organizations that hold copyright may sue those who infringe copyright. Canadian legislation stipulates minimum penalties for copyright infringements. Violations of copyright on printed or electronic works may exceed the boundaries of civil law and may be prosecuted as summary convictions under criminal law. When in doubt, assume the work is copyrighted and obtain written permission for its use.

3. *Compare the site with other sources.* Check related sites, publications, and other sources to compare the quality of information and to discover what others might have said about this site or author. Comparing many similar sites helps you create a *benchmark*, a standard for evaluating any particular site (based on the criteria in these guidelines). Ask a librarian for help.
4. *Look at your own attitudes and beliefs* to see if you're predisposed to automatically accept certain things that you read.
5. *Exercise extreme caution* in using anything picked up from online discussion groups.
6. *When considering material provided in an academic discussion group, look at the author's credentials.* Does the author have a solid track record of publications or other contributions to the field discussed by that group?
7. *Decide whether the assertions/claims make sense.* How well is each assertion supported? Never accept any claim that seems extreme without verifying it through other sources, such as a professor, a librarian, or a specialist in the field.

Evaluating the Evidence

Evidence is any finding used to support or refute a particular conclusion. While evidence can serve the truth, it also can create distortion, misinformation, and deception. For example, how much money, material, or energy does recycling really save? How good for your heart is oat bran? How well are public schools educating our children? Which investments or automobiles are safest? Conclusions about such matters are based on evidence that often can be manipulated in support of one view or another. As consumers of research, we have to assess for ourselves the quality of the evidence presented.

We assess the quality of evidence by examining it critically to understand its limitations, to see if findings conflict; to discover connections, similarities, trends, or relationships; to determine the need for further inquiry; and to raise new questions.

Is there enough evidence?

Is the Evidence Sufficient? Evidence is sufficient when it enables us to reach an accurate judgment or conclusion. A study of the stress-reducing benefits of low-impact aerobics, for example, would require a broad survey sample: people who have practised aerobics for a long time; people of different genders, different ages, different occupations, and different lifestyles before they began aerobics; and so forth. Even responses from hundreds of practitioners might constitute insufficient evidence unless those responses were supported by laboratory measurements of metabolism, heart rates, and blood pressure.

Personal experience usually offers insufficient evidence from which to generalize. You cannot tell whether your experience is representative, no matter how long you might have practised aerobics. Although anecdotal evidence ("This worked well for me!") might offer a good starting point for an investigation, personal experience should be evaluated within the broader context of *all* available evidence.

Is the evidence hard or soft?

Can the Evidence Be Verified? *Hard evidence* consists of factual statements, expert opinion, or statistics that can be verified (shown to be true). *Soft evidence* consists of uninformed opinion or speculation, data obtained or analyzed unscientifically, and findings that have not been replicated or reviewed by experts. Reputable news organizations employ fact-checkers to verify information before it appears in print.

Evidence that seems scientific can turn out to be soft. For example, information obtained from polling often is reported in fancy charts, graphs, and impressive statistics—but it is based on public opinion, which is almost always changing (Crossen 104).

Base your conclusions on hard evidence. For example, suppose an article makes positive claims about low-impact aerobics but provides no data on measurements of pulse, blood pressure, or metabolic rates. Although these claims might coincide with your own experience, your evidence so far consists of only two opinions: yours and the author's—without scientific support. Any conclusion at this point would rest on soft evidence. Only after carefully assessing dependable sources can you decide which conclusions are supported by the bulk of the evidence.

Interpreting the Evidence

Interpreting means trying to reach the truth of the matter: an overall judgment about what the evidence means and what conclusion or action it suggests.

Unfortunately, research does not always yield answers that are conclusive or about which we can be certain. Instead of settling for the most *convenient* answer, we should pursue the most *reasonable* answer by examining critically a full range of possible meanings.

What Level of Certainty Is Warranted? As possible outcomes of research, we can identify three distinct and very different levels of certainty:

A practical definition of "truth"

1. The definitive truth—the *conclusive answer:*

   Truth is…the reality of the matter, as distinguished from what people wish were so, believe to be so, or assert to be so. From another perspective, in the words of Harvard philosopher Israel Scheffler, truth is the view "which is fated to be ultimately agreed to by all who investigate." The word ultimately *is important. Investigation may produce a wrong answer for years, even for centuries.… Does the truth ever change? No.… One easy way to spare yourself any further confusion about truth is to reserve the word* truth *for the final answer to an issue. Get in the habit of using the words,* belief, theory, *and* present understanding *more often. (Ruggiero 21–22)*

ON THE JOB…

Certainty in Environmental Reports

"There's always some uncertainty. Everything we do is constrained by budget and the time frame. With more money and time, we could always generate more data that would bring us closer to certainty. So, the key is to be clear about your level of confidence in the data and inferences, and very clear about the level of uncertainty in your conclusions. There's no definite benchmark for the required level of certainty—it depends on the identified scope of the project. For example, an early Phase 1 contamination assessment project would use a broad approach of enquiries and general observations that may suggest potential areas of ground contamination that should be tested. The wording of the conclusions reflects the inherent degree of uncertainty at that level of analysis. A Phase 2 approach would cost 5 to 10 times more because expensive data gathering and lab analysis would be involved; the resulting report would be able to say with more certainty whether the ground and water are contaminated. A subsequent phase might involve more extensive assessment and remediation, which would cost many times more than a Phase 1 study, but would be able to say with considerably more certainty that the area is free of contaminants and fit for, say, a housing development.…"

—Dr. Brian Guy, president and senior geoscientist, Summit Environmental Consultants

We often are mistaken in our certainty about the *truth.* For example, in the second century A.D., Ptolemy's view of the universe concluded that the earth was its centre. Though untrue, this judgment was based on the best information available at that time. Ptolemy's view survived for 13 centuries, even after new information had discredited this belief. When Copernicus and Galileo proposed more truthful views in the 15th century, they were labelled heretics.

Conclusive answers are the research outcome we seek, but often we have to settle for answers that are less than certain.

2. The *probable answer:* the answer that stands the best chance of being true or accurate—given the most we can know at this particular time. Probable answers are subject to revision in the light of new information.
3. The *inconclusive answer:* the realization that the truth of the matter is far more elusive, ambiguous, or complex than we expected.

Exactly how certain are we?

To ensure an accurate outcome, we must decide what level of certainty the findings warrant. For example, we are *highly certain* about the perils of smoking or sunburn, *reasonably certain* about the benefits of fruits and vegetables and moderate exercise, but *far less certain* about the perils of coffee drinking, or electromagnetic waves, or the benefits of vitamin supplements.

Are the Underlying Assumptions Sound? *Assumptions* are notions we take for granted, things we accept without proof. The research process rests on assumptions like these: that a sample group accurately represents a larger target group, that survey respondents remember certain facts accurately, and that mice and humans share enough biological similarities for meaningful research. For a particular study to be valid, the underlying assumptions must be accurate.

Consider this example: You are an education consultant evaluating the accuracy of IQ testing as a predictor of academic performance. Reviewing the evidence, you perceive an association between low IQ scores and low achievers. You then check your statistics by examining a cross-section of reliable sources. Can you then conclude that IQ tests do predict performance accurately? This conclusion might be invalid unless you could verify the following assumptions:

1. That neither parents, teachers, nor children had seen individual test scores, which could produce biased expectations.
2. That, regardless of score, each child had completed an identical curriculum at an identical pace, instead of being "tracked" on the basis of his or her score.

Do I Have a Personal Bias? To support a particular version of the truth, our own bias might cause us to overestimate (or deny) the certainty of our findings.

Personal bias is a fact of life

> *Expect yourself to be biased, and expect your bias to affect your efforts to construct arguments. Unless you are perfectly neutral about the issue, an unlikely circumstance, at the very outset... you will believe one side of the issue to be right, and that belief will incline you to... present more and better arguments for the side of the issue you prefer. (Ruggiero 134)*

Because personal bias is hard to transcend, *rationalizing* often becomes a substitute for *reasoning*:

Reasoning versus rationalizing

> *You are reasoning if your belief follows the evidence—that is, if you examine the evidence first and then make up your mind. You are rationalizing if the evidence follows your belief—if you first decide what you believe and then select and interpret evidence to justify it. (Ruggiero 44)*

Personal bias often is unconscious until we examine our own value systems, attitudes long held but never analyzed, notions we've inherited from our own backgrounds, and so on. Recognizing our own biases is a crucial first step in managing them.

What else could this mean?

Are Other Interpretations Possible? Perhaps other researchers would disagree with the meaning of these findings. Some controversial issues (the need for defence spending or causes of inflation) will never be resolved. Although we can get verifiable data and can reason persuasively on some subjects, no close reasoning by any expert and no supporting statistical analysis will prove anything about a controversial subject to everyone's satisfaction. For instance, one could only *argue* (more or less effectively) that federal funds will or will not alleviate poverty or unemployment.

Using Effective Reasoning

Interpreting the evidence involves inductive and/or deductive reasoning, which can later be used to persuasively present interpreted data.

Induction draws conclusions from related data

Inductive Reasoning argues from specific cases to general principles. In other words, induction develops and tests hypotheses that explain available data. The more data, and the more similarities observed among the data, the better chance of formulating an accurate hypothesis.

Here's an example of induction. Forty students in a technical writing class wrote two case study exams. The first exam occurred two weeks before an intensive series of instruction in language basics—grammar, spelling, punctuation, and sentence structure. The students wrote the second exam shortly after the language series. Their results were dramatically different:

1. On average, the second exam grades were 8.3 percent higher than the first exam grades.
2. Of the 40 students, 31 improved their grade, four earned the same grade, and five received a lower grade. The range was from –10 percent to +21 percent.

Cause–effect analysis could lead to the conclusion that the language instruction led to the improved grades, although the results might be partly due to increased familiarity with case study exams.

Inductive reasoning depends on adequate data

The sample size and group composition (group members came from similar backgrounds) might be too limited to allow the conclusion that intensive language instruction will help all technical writing students improve their grades. A larger study with more students and more diversity of backgrounds would help establish a wider application for the hypothesis that improved language skills acquired through intensive instruction lead to improved grades.

The above example includes two of four common forms of inductive reasoning:

Several forms of induction

1. *The IMRAD pattern:* This reporting format includes introduction of a problem initiating the research, materials and methods used to explore the topic, quantitative results, and a discussion that uses analogies, examples, and causal analysis to prove a hypothesis that explains the gathered data.
2. *Analogy:* What happens in one environment will work in another, if it's clear that the conditions in both environments are sufficiently similar (analogous). For example, new drugs are tested on laboratory animals and then on small groups of humans, with the understanding that a larger human population will experience the same results as the small groups.

3. *Cause–effect analysis:* What cause will effect a certain outcome. Does exposure to electromagnetic fields created by power lines cause cancer in humans? In a given geographical area, does loss of fish habitat constitute the major cause of declining fish populations? Does the design of SUVs explain their much greater chance of being involved in rollover accidents?
4. *Examples:* After presenting the pertinent data and arriving at a hypothesis, the writer can provide an actual example that further demonstrates the asserted hypothesis.

Deduction is based on widely accepted principles

Deductive Reasoning moves in the opposite direction from inductive reasoning, as it applies a general principle to specific cases. That general, widely accepted principle is called the **major premise**. The second statement, called a **minor premise**, represents a particular instance of the class identified in the major premise. The following example was reported on CBC Radio One: "Insurance carriers in Ontario automatically pay compensation claims made by veteran firefighters who have contracted leukemia (after 15 years' service) or brain tumours (after 20 years' service)."

Major premise: (Based on *inductive* reasoning: several studies have shown that firefighters have a much higher risk of getting certain kinds of cancers than the general population.) Exposure to a variety of chemicals encountered in fighting fires over an extended period of time can lead to brain tumours (after 20 years of firefighting) or to leukemia (after 15 years of fighting fires).
Minor premise: Firefighter A has leukemia.
Minor premise (or observation): Firefighter A has worked fighting fires for 15 years or more.
Conclusion: Firefighter A's leukemia is likely due to his or her occupation. The disease is classed as a workplace disease, and firefighter A is entitled to full compensation.

Premises must be accurate

Deductions work if, and only if, premises are accurate. Consider this example: "Don't expect Bill to write well—he's an engineer."

Major premise: (implied) Engineers don't write well.
Minor premise: Bill is an engineer.
Conclusion: Bill doesn't write very well.

Avoiding Errors in Reasoning

Finding the truth, especially in a complex issue or problem, often is a process of elimination, of ruling out or avoiding errors in reasoning. As we interpret, we make *inferences:* we derive conclusions about what we don't know by reasoning from what we do know (Hayakawa 37). For example, we might infer that a drug that boosts immunity in laboratory mice will boost immunity in humans, or that a rise in campus crime statistics is caused by the fact that young people have become more violent. Whether a particular inference is on target or dead wrong depends largely on our answers to one or more of these questions:

- To what extent can these findings be generalized?
- Is Y really caused by X?
- How much can the numbers be trusted, and what do they mean?

Following are four major reasoning errors that can distort our interpretations.

How much can we generalize?

Faulty Generalizations. When we accept research findings uncritically and jump to conclusions about their meaning, we commit the error of *hasty generalization*. For example, "We didn't see any of the expected endangered vegetation species during our April 2 field survey, so we conclude that this area doesn't contain such species and thus there's no threat from the proposed development." (This report conclusion doesn't consider that most of the plant species are annuals that don't usually appear until late April.)

When we overestimate the extent to which the findings reveal some larger truth, we commit the error of *overstated generalization*: for example, "At three points of observation along the three kilometres of creek there's no apparent erosion, so we conclude that last fall's erosion control methods have been successful." (This conclusion has not considered that the following spring runoff levels were lower than usual, nor has the writer admitted that three observation points over three kilometres are not adequate to draw such a definitive conclusion.)

Are we limiting our perspective?

Limited Thinking. Our biases and limited experience may restrict our ability to make accurate inferences. *Either/or thinking* may limit the possible hypotheses for a set of phenomena. (For example, "If you're not at your desk, you're not working." "Either the East Coast cod stocks will revitalize in 10 years or the fish will disappear entirely.")

One-valued thinking: When our thinking is based on only one set of values, we fail to realize how people from different cultures or different value systems might form a different conclusion from a body of information. (For example, it is likely that real estate developers and Native groups will have conflicting responses to the discovery of ancient Native artifacts in an excavated basement in a new city subdivision.)

Faulty Causal Reasoning. Causal reasoning tries to explain *why* something happened or *what* will happen: often very complex questions. Faulty causal reasoning oversimplifies or distorts the cause–effect relationship through errors like these:

Ignoring other causes	Investment builds wealth. (Ignores the role of knowledge, wisdom, timing, and luck in successful investing.)
Ignoring other effects	Running improves health. (Ignores the fact that many runners get injured, and that some even drop dead while running.)
Inventing a cause	Right after buying a rabbit's foot, Felix won the 6/49 lottery. (Posits an unwarranted causal relationship merely because one event follows another.)
Confusing correlation with causation	Poverty causes disease. (Ignores the fact that disease, while highly associated with poverty, has many causes unrelated to poverty.)
Rationalizing	My grades were poor because my exams were unfair. (Denies the possible causes of one's failures.)

Because of bias or impatience, we can be tempted to settle for a hasty cause or to confuse possible, probable, and definite causes.

Did X possibly, probably, or definitely cause Y?

Sometimes a definite cause is apparent (e.g., "The engine's overheating is caused by a faulty radiator cap"), but usually much analysis is needed to isolate a specific cause. Suppose you want to answer this question: why does our local university not have daycare facilities? Brainstorming yields these possible causes:

- lack of need among students
- lack of interest among students, faculty, and staff
- high cost of liability insurance
- lack of space and facilities on campus
- lack of trained personnel
- prohibition by law
- lack of government funding for such a project

Say you proceed with interviews, questionnaires, and research into provincial laws, insurance rates, and availability of personnel. You begin to rule out some items, and others appear as probable causes. Specifically, you find a need among students, high campus interest, an abundance of qualified people for staffing, and no provincial laws prohibiting such a project. Three probable causes remain: lack of funding, high insurance rates, and lack of space. Further inquiry shows that lack of funding and high insurance rates *are* issues. These obstacles, however, could be eliminated through new sources of revenue: charging a fee for each child, soliciting donations, or diverting funds from other campus organizations.

Finally, after examining available campus space and speaking with school officials, you arrive at one definite cause: lack of space and facilities. One could argue that lack of space and facilities is somehow related to funding, and the university's being unable to find funds or space may be related to student need, which is not sufficiently acute, or student interest, which is not sufficiently high to exert real pressure. Lack of space and facilities, however, appears to be the *immediate* cause.

When you report on your research, be sure readers can draw conclusions identical to your own on the basis of the evidence. The process might be diagrammed like this:

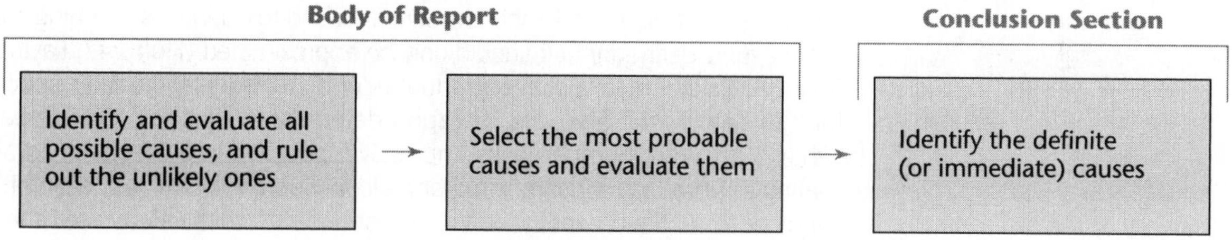
Body of Report
Conclusion Section
Identify and evaluate all possible causes, and rule out the unlikely ones
Select the most probable causes and evaluate them
Identify the definite (or immediate) causes

Initially you might have based your conclusions hastily on soft evidence (an opinion—buttressed by a newspaper editorial—that the campus was apathetic). Now you base your conclusions on solid, factual evidence. You have moved from a wide range of possible causes to a narrow range of probable causes, and finally to one definite cause.

Sometimes, finding a single cause is impossible, but this reasoning process can be tailored to most problem-solving analyses. Anything but the simplest effect is likely to have more than one cause. By narrowing the field, you can focus on the real issues.

Faulty Statistical Reasoning. The purpose of statistical analysis is to determine the meaning of a collected set of numbers. In primary research, our surveys and questionnaires often lead to some kind of numerical interpretation ("What percentage of respondents prefer X?" "How often does Y happen?"). In secondary research, we rely on numbers collected by primary researchers. Numbers seem more precise, more objective, more scientific, and less ambiguous than words. They are easier to summarize, measure, compare, and analyze. But numbers can be misleading. For example, radio or television phone-in surveys produce grossly distorted data: although 90 percent of callers might express support for a particular viewpoint, callers tend to be those with the greatest anger or the strongest feelings about the issue—representing only a fraction of overall attitudes (Fineman 24). Mail-in surveys can produce similar distortion because only people with certain attitudes might choose to respond.

Before relying on any set of numbers, we need to know exactly where they came from, how they were collected, and how they were analyzed (Lavin 275–76). Can the numbers be trusted, and if so, what do they mean?

Faulty statistical reasoning produces conclusions that are unwarranted, inaccurate, or downright deceptive. The following are some common statistical fallacies:

"Exactly how well are we doing?"

- *The sanitized statistic*: Numbers are manipulated (or "cleaned up") to obscure the facts. For instance, a recently revised formula enables the government to exclude from its unemployment figures an estimated 5 million people who remain unemployed after one year—thus creating a far rosier economic picture than the facts warrant. Similar formulas allow for all sorts of sugarcoating in reports of wages, economic growth, inflation, and other statistics that affect the political climate (Morgenson 54). In the United States, the College Board's recentring of SAT scores has raised the average math score from 478 to 500 and the average verbal score from 424 to 500 (a boost of almost 5 and 18 percent, respectively) although actual student performance remains unchanged (Samuelson 44).

"How many rats was that?"

- *The meaningless statistic:* Exact numbers are used to quantify something so inexact or vaguely defined that it should only be approximated (Huff 247; Lavin 278): "Only 38.2 percent of college graduates end up working in their specialty." "Toronto has 3 247 561 rats." "Zappo detergent makes laundry 10 percent brighter." An exact number looks impressive, but certain subjects (child abuse, cheating in university, virginity, drug and alcohol abuse on the job, eating habits) cannot be quantified exactly because respondents don't always tell the truth (because of denial, embarrassment, or merely guessing). Or they respond in ways they think the researcher expects.
- *The undefined average:* The mean, median, and mode are confused in determining an average (Huff 244; Lavin 279). The *mean* is the result of adding up the value of each item in a set of numbers, then dividing by the number of items. The *median* is the result of ranking all the values from high to low, then choosing the middle value (or the 50th percentile, as in calculating SAT scores). The *mode* is the value that occurs most often in a set of numbers.

Each of these three measurements represents some kind of average, but unless we know which average is being presented, we cannot interpret the figures accurately. Assume that we are computing the average salary among female vice presidents at XYZ Corporation:

Vice President	*Salary*
A	$90 000
B	90 000
C	80 000
D	65 000
E	60 000
F	55 000
G	50 000

"Why is everybody griping?"

In the above example, the mean salary (total salaries divided by people) equals $70 000; the median salary (middle value) equals $65 000; the mode (most frequent value) equals $90 000. Each is legitimately an average, and each could be used to support or refute a particular assertion (for example, "Women vice presidents are paid too little" or "Women vice presidents are paid too much").

Research expert Michael Lavin sums up the potential for bias in reporting averages:

Depending on the circumstances, any one of these measurements [mean, median, or mode] may describe a group of numbers better than the other two.... [But] people typically choose the value which best presents their case, whether or not it is the most appropriate to use. (279)

Although the mean is the most commonly computed average, this measurement can be misleading when values on either end of the scale are extremely high or low. Suppose, for instance, that vice president A received a $200 000 salary. Because this figure deviates so far from the normal range of salary figures for B through G, it distorts the average for the whole group—increasing the mean salary by more than 20 percent (Plumb and Spyridakis 636).

- *The distorted percentage figure:* Percentages are reported without explanation of the original numbers used in the calculation (Adams and Schvaneveldt 359; Lavin 280): "Seventy-five percent of respondents prefer our brand over the competing brand"—without mention that only four people were surveyed. Or "Sixty-six percent of employees we hired this year are women and minorities, compared to the national average of 40 percent"—without mention that only three people have been hired this year, by a company that employs 300 (mostly white males).

"Is 51 percent really a majority?"

Another fallacy in reporting percentages occurs when the *margin of error* is ignored. This is the margin within which the true figure lies, based on estimated sampling errors in a survey. For example, a claim that most people surveyed prefer brand X might be based on the fact that 51 percent of respondents expressed this preference; but if the survey carried a 2 percent margin of error, the true figure could be as low as 49 percent or as high as 53 percent. In a survey with a high margin of error, the true figure may be so uncertain that no definite conclusion can be drawn.

"Which car should we buy?"

- *The bogus ranking:* Items are compared on the basis of ill-defined criteria (Adams and Schvaneveldt 212; Lavin 284): "Last year, the Carmobile was the number-one selling car in Canada"—without mention that some competing car makers actually sold *more* cars to private individuals, and that the Carmobile figures were inflated by hefty sales to rental-car companies and corporate fleets. Unless we know how the ranked items were chosen and how they were compared (the criteria), a ranking can produce a scientific-seeming number based on a completely unscientific method.

"Garbage in, garbage out."

- *The fallible computer model:* Computer models process complex assumptions to produce impressive but often inaccurate statistical estimates about costs, benefits, risks, or probable outcomes.

  Computer models to predict global warming levels, for instance, are based on differing assumptions about wind and weather patterns, cloud formations, ozone levels, carbon dioxide concentrations, sea levels, or airborne sediment from volcanic eruptions. Despite their seemingly scientific precision, different global warming models generate 50-year predictions of sea-level rises that range from a few inches to several feet (Barbour 121). Other models suggest that warming effects could be offset by evaporation of ocean water and by clouds reflecting sunlight back to outer space (Monastersky, "Do Clouds" 69). Still other models suggest that the 0.56°C (1°F) warming over the last 100 years may not be the result of the greenhouse effect at all, but of "random fluctuations in global temperatures" (Stone 38). The estimates produced by any model depend on the assumptions (and data) programmed in.

  Choice of assumptions might be influenced by researcher bias or the sponsor's agenda. For example, a prediction of human fatalities from a nuclear plant meltdown might rest on assumptions about availability of safe shelter, evacuation routes, time of day, season, wind direction, and structural integrity of the containment unit. But the assumptions could be manipulated to produce an overstated or understated estimate of risk (Barbour 228). For computer-modelled estimates of accident risk (oil spill, plane crash) or of the costs and benefits of a proposed project or policy (a space station, welfare reform), consumers rarely know the assumptions behind the numbers. We wonder, for example, about the assumptions underlying NASA's pre-*Challenger* risk assessment, in which a 1985 computer model reportedly showed an accident risk of less than 1 in 100 000 shuttle flights (Crossen 54).

"Does a beer a day keep the doctor away?"

- *Confusion of correlation with causation: Correlation* is the measure of association between two variables (between smoking and increased lung cancer risk, or between education and income). *Causation* is the demonstrable production of a specific effect (smoking causes lung cancer). Correlations between smoking and lung cancer or education and income signal a causal relationship that has been proven by studies of all kinds. But not every correlation implies causation. For instance, a recently discovered correlation between moderate alcohol consumption and decreased heart disease risk offers insufficient proof that moderate drinking causes less heart disease.

  Many highly publicized correlations are the product of "data dredging." In this process, computers randomly compare one set of variables (various eating habits) with another set (a range of diseases). From these countless comparisons, certain relationships are revealed (say, between coffee drinking and pancreatic cancer risk). As dramatic as such isolated correlations may be, they constitute no proof of causation and often lead to hasty conclusions (P.E. Ross 135).

"Is this good news or bad news?"

- *Misleading terminology:* The terms used to interpret statistics sometimes hide their real meaning. For instance, the widely publicized figure that people treated for cancer have a "50 percent survival rate" is misleading in three ways: (1) *survival* to laypersons means "staying alive," but to medical experts, staying alive for only five years after diagnosis qualifies as survival; (2) the

"50 percent" survival figure covers *all* cancers, including certain skin or thyroid cancers that have extremely high cure rates, as well as other cancers (such as lung or ovarian) that rarely are curable and have extremely low survival rates; (3) more than 55 percent of all cancers are skin cancers with a nearly 100 percent survival rate, thereby greatly inflating survival statistics for other types of cancer ("Are We" 5; *Facts and Figures* 2).

Even the most valid and reliable statistics require that we interpret the reality behind the numbers. For instance, the overall cancer rate today is higher than it was in 1910. This may mean that people are living longer and thus are more likely to die of cancer and that cancer today rarely is misdiagnosed—or mislabelled because of stigma ("Are We" 4). The finding that rates for certain cancers double after prolonged exposure to electromagnetic waves may really mean that cancer risk actually increases from 1 in 10 000 to 2 in 10 000.

These are only a few examples of statistics and interpretations that seem highly persuasive but that in fact cannot always be trusted. Any interpretation of statistical data carries the possibility that other, more accurate, interpretations have been overlooked or deliberately excluded (Barnett 45).

IN BRIEF HOW STANDARDS OF PROOF VARY FOR DIFFERENT AUDIENCES AND CULTURAL SETTINGS

How much evidence is enough to "prove" a particular claim? The answer often depends on whether the inquiry occurs in the science lab, the courtroom, or the boardroom—as well as on the specific cultural setting:

- The scientist demands evidence that indicates at least 95 percent certainty. A scientific finding must be evaluated and replicated by other experts. Good science looks at the entire picture. Findings are reviewed before they are reported. Inquiries and answers in science are never "final," but open-ended and ongoing: what seems probable today may be shown improbable by tomorrow's research.
- The juror demands evidence that indicates only 51 percent certainty (a "preponderance of the evidence").
- Jurors are not scientists. Instead of the entire picture, jurors get only the information made available by lawyers and witnesses. A jury bases its opinion on evidence that exceeds "reasonable doubt" (Monastersky, "Courting" 249; Powell 32+). Courts have to make decisions that are final.
- The corporate executive demands immediate (even if insufficient) evidence. In a global business climate of overnight developments (in world markets, political strife, military conflicts, natural disasters), important business decisions often are made on the spur of the moment, often on the basis of incomplete or unverified information—or even hunches—in order to react to crises and capitalize on opportunities (Seglin 54).
- Specific cultures may have their own standards for authentic, reliable, and persuasive evidence. "For example, African cultures rely on story telling for authenticity. Arabic persuasion is dependent on universally accepted truths. And Chinese value ancient authorities over recent empiricism" (Byrd and Reid 109).

REASSESSING THE ENTIRE RESEARCH PROCESS

Chapters 15 and 16 show that the research process is a minefield of potential errors, in what we do and how we reason: we might ask the wrong questions; we might rely on the wrong sources; we might collect or record data incorrectly; we might analyze or document data incorrectly. We therefore need to critically examine our methods and our reasoning before reporting findings and conclusions. The following research checklist helps guide our assessment.

ON THE JOB...

Research and Critical Thinking

"Much of the real research involves critical thinking, as the researcher sorts through the gathered material to see where it leads. Each new 'discovery' not only produces potentially useful data, but also leads to other avenues that could be explored. In other words, much research happens after the bulk of the raw data has been collected. It's the thought, the digesting, the analysis, the synthesis of facts and ideas. It's not something you do for 15 minutes between classes. However, sometimes in the 'real world' the busy college student who needs facts in a hurry doesn't necessarily have time to reflect and to thoroughly explore a topic. Here's where a librarian can help find the most useful sources and avoid time-consuming detective work in the internet jungle...."

—Ross Tyner, research librarian

CHECKLIST FOR THE RESEARCH PROCESS

Use this checklist to assess your research process.

Reasoning

- Am I reasonably certain about the meaning of these findings?
- Does my final answer seem definitive, only probable, or inconclusive?
- Am I reasoning instead of rationalizing?
- Is this the most reasonable conclusion (or merely the most convenient)?
- Can I rule out other possible interpretations or conclusions?
- Have I accounted for all sources of bias, including my own?
- Are my generalizations warranted by the evidence?
- Am I confident that my causal reasoning is correct?
- Can all of the numbers and statistics and interpretations be trusted?
- Have I resolved (or at least acknowledged) any conflicts among my findings?
- Should the evidence be reconsidered?

Method

- Did I ask the right questions?
- Are the sources appropriately up to date?
- Is each source reputable, trustworthy, and relatively unbiased?
- Does the evidence clearly support all of the conclusions?
- Can all of the evidence be verified?
- Is a fair balance of viewpoints presented?
- Has the research achieved adequate depth?
- Has the entire research process been valid and reliable?
- Is all quoted material clearly marked throughout the text?
- Are direct quotations used sparingly and appropriately?
- Are all quotations accurate and integrated grammatically?
- Are all paraphrases accurate and clear?
- Have I documented all sources not considered common knowledge?
- Is the documentation consistent, complete, and correct?

WEB CONNECT

These sites provide wide-ranging advice on how to critically evaluate web-based material.

http://library.usm.maine.edu/guides/webeval.html
www.library.cornell.edu/olinuris/ref/research/webeval.html
www.lib.berkeley.edu/TeachingLib/Guides/Internet/Evaluate.html

EXERCISES OR COLLABORATIVE PROJECTS

1. Assume you are an assistant communication manager for a new organization that prepares research reports for decision makers worldwide. (A sample topic: "What is the expected long-term impact of the North American Free Trade Agreement on the Canadian computer industry?") These clients expect answers based on the best available evidence and reasoning.

   Although your recently hired co-workers are technical specialists, few have experience in the kind of wide-ranging research required by your clients. Training programs in the research process are being developed by your communication division but will not be ready for several weeks.

   Meanwhile, your manager directs you to prepare a one- to two-page memo that introduces employees to major procedural and reasoning errors that affect validity and reliability in the research process. Your manager wants this memo to be comprehensive but not vague.

2. Assume the scenario from Exercise 1. In a memo to colleagues, offer guidelines for avoiding unintentional plagiarism in quoting, paraphrasing, and citing the work of others. Explain what to document and how, using MLA style (see Chapter 19) for a parenthetical reference and a works-cited entry. (Illustrate with examples, but not those from the book!)

3. From print or broadcast media or from personal experience, identify an example of each of the following sources of distortion or of interpretive error:

   - a study with questionable sponsorship or motives
   - reliance on soft evidence
   - overestimating the level of certainty
   - biased interpretation
   - rationalizing
   - faulty causal reasoning
   - hasty generalization
   - overstated generalization
   - sanitized statistic
   - meaningless statistic
   - undefined average
   - distorted percentage figure
   - bogus ranking
   - fallible computer model
   - misinterpreted statistic

Submit your examples to your instructor, along with a memo explaining each error, or be prepared to discuss your material in class.

CHAPTER 17

Short Reports

LEARNING OBJECTIVES

After reading this chapter, you should be able to

- Appreciate the importance of "short" reports in business and industry.
- Compare the structural and page design elements of semi-formal and formal reports.
- Adapt an action structure to a wide range of one- to six-page job-related reports.
- Choose the format that best suits a given report's content, length, and required degree of formality (letter, memo, email, semi-formal, programmed form).

Short reports form the bulk of the writing done by technologists, technicians, research scientists, engineers, and other technical and business writers. Such reports provide information and analysis that readers use to stay informed and to make practical decisions.

Some reports emphasize *information*:	Other reports focus on *analysis*:
progress reports	feasibility reports
field trip reports	causal analyses
field observations	assessment reports
project completion reports	yardstick (comparison) reports
periodic activity reports	justification reports
meeting minutes	recommendations reports

FORMATS

When a document is quite short (one to three pages), or when its subject matter suits a direct, informal address to the reader, use a *correspondence format*, such as a letter, memo, or email.

How to choose formal or semi-formal report format

When a document is somewhat longer (4 to 10 pages), and when its subject matter is serious enough to warrant a more formal approach, use a *semi-formal report format*. However, use the *formal report format* illustrated in Chapter 18 when you want to influence policy within your organization: the more formal the document, the better chance of its being heeded. So consider "dressing up" even 6- to 10-page reports in formal report clothing if you really want to impress the reader. Table 17.1 summarizes the differences between semi-formal and formal reports.

Table 17.1 Semi-formal and Formal Report Formats

Item	Semi-formal	Formal
Length	4–10 pages	6 pages +
Required Sections		
Transmittal document	optional	yes
Cover	no	optional
Title page	optional—title could be placed on first page of report body	yes
Summary	no	yes
Table of contents	optional	yes
List of illustrations	optional	yes
Glossary	incorporate into text	optional
Introduction	yes	yes
Background	optional	optional
Central analysis	one or more sections	one or more sections
Conclusion	yes	yes
Recommendations	optional	optional
Sources section	optional	yes (if sources were cited)
Sources consulted	optional	optional
Format and Appearance	**Semi-formal**	**Formal**
Headings system	more relaxed; seldom more than two levels of headings; main headings placed where they come on the page	formal; usually three or four levels; each main heading placed at the top of a page
Page numbering	all page numbers placed at same location on page	different for first page of a section than for subsequent pages in that section
Margins	all pages use same margins layout	top and bottom margins for first page of a section are larger than for subsequent pages
Indentation	paragraphs not indented (double space between paragraphs); bulleted and numbered lists may be indented	paragraphs not indented; (double space between paragraphs); bulleted and numbered lists may be indented
Headers	seldom used in most professional	optional, but headers reports

A STRUCTURE FOR ALL PURPOSES

The action structure gives readers what they want

Readers of business reports are generally busy people. They want reports to be as brief as possible. They usually want a report's main point in the first or second paragraph and they want clear, logical idea patterns. The *action structure* illustrated in Figure 17.1 satisfies those readers' desires.

Action Opening

Using the action structure, you immediately "connect" with your reader by

- referring to an issue that concerns the reader (and you); or
- referring to comments made in a recent meeting; or
- responding to the reader's previous communication (memo, email, letter, telephone call) on the subject.

By making such a connection, you gain the reader's attention. Then, in the same paragraph you summarize the report's main point *or* you preview the approach taken in the report.

Background

Next, you provide any background needed by your reader to understand the report's detailed information and analysis. You may have to

- review the circumstances leading to the issue discussed in the report
- define terms or provide technical background
- review a problem or a proposed solution

Not all reports require background information. Your audience/purpose analysis will help you determine whether your reader needs to be briefed. You may be

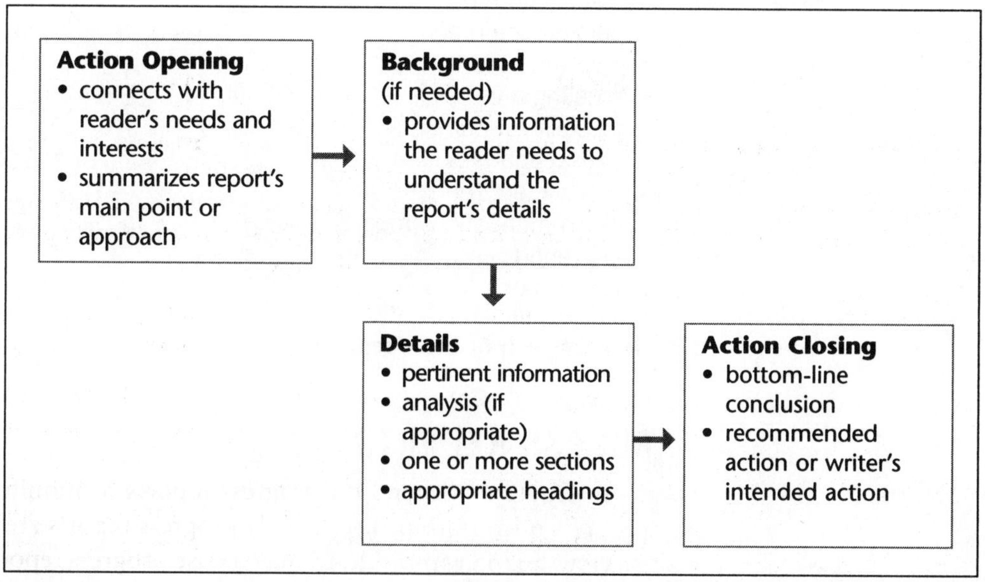

Figure 17.1 An Action Structure for Informal and Semi-formal Reports

able to go straight from the opening paragraph to the details section of the report.

Most readers appreciate subject headings for both the background and the details sections, even for a one-page report. Clearly, the number of headings you use depends on the depth and complexity of the report's topic. See this chapter's sample reports for examples of heading usage. As you read the reports, distinguish between standard topical headings ("Project Costs") and talking headings, which speak directly to the reader ("How Much We've Spent").

Details

Essentially, a report's details section answers most, if not all, of the questions posed by any good reporter: *What? Where? When? Who? How? How much? Why?* The order in which you answer such questions depends on the subject matter and your reader's priorities.

Action Closing

Finally, the report provides bottom-line conclusions. Most reports also discuss what should be done next. Some reports recommend action to be taken by the reader or the reader's organization; others state what action the writer intends or proposes. Still other reports simply list possible actions without indicating who might take responsibility.

The action structure can be adapted to develop any type of correspondence or short report. The remainder of this chapter demonstrates the action structure's valuable adaptability to various reports:

The action structure is adaptable

- progress reports
- periodic activity reports
- project completion reports
- incident reports
- inspection reports
- compliance reports
- field trip reports
- meeting minutes
- feasibility reports
- causal analyses
- assessment reports
- recommendations reports
- lab reports
- form reports

Let's look at each of these reports.

PROGRESS REPORTS

Progress reports serve many purposes

Large organizations depend on progress reports to monitor activities, problems, and progress on various projects. Daily progress reports are vital in a business that assigns crews to many projects. Managers use progress reports to evaluate a project and its supervisor, and to decide how to allocate funds. Managers also need to know about delays that could dramatically affect outcomes and project costs.

Also, managers need information to coordinate the efforts of the work groups. For example, a hydro manager responsible for restoring power transmission lines after a severe ice storm will have to coordinate clean-up crews, construction crews, and line crews. A large project such as a major power line restoration would require several written *periodic progress reports.*

When work is performed for an external client, the reports explain to the client how time and money have been spent and how difficulties have been overcome. The reports can therefore be used to assure the clients that the work will be completed on schedule and on budget. Many contracts stipulate when progress will be reported. Failure to report on time may invoke contractual penalties.

To inform managers and clients, progress reports should answer these questions:

1. How much has been accomplished since the last report?
2. Is the project on schedule?
3. If not, what went wrong? How was the problem corrected? How long will it take to get back on schedule?
4. What else needs to be done? What is the next step?
5. Have you encountered any unexpected developments?
6. When do you anticipate completion? Or (on a long project) when do you anticipate completion of the next phase?

Table 17.2 shows how to adapt the action structure to organize the information in progress reports.

The following general structures adapt the action structure to periodic progress reporting. Exactly how you structure the report will depend on the nature of the project and on the aspect you want to stress. You could organize the report by

- the different tasks or subcontracts
- the amount of work completed versus the amount remaining
- phases or time frames identified by the company contact or project manager

Figures 17.2 to 17.4 illustrate outlines for the three possible structures. These outlines are for the third in a series of reports for a six-month highway reconstruction project. Which structure would you use?

"Problems" and "setbacks" should be discussed in an appropriate location

Where needed, any of the three variations could incorporate a special category for a description and possible solutions of "Problems and Setbacks," as shown in Figure 17.2. Or this topic could be discussed in another section, if the difficulties do not require special treatment. In Figure 17.3, for example, problems and setbacks are discussed under "Work Completed."

Notice that in each of the three sample structures only two main sections are included for reporting actual progress ("road base preparation" and "paving"), but three or more sections could be required, depending on the nature of the work.

Table 17.2 Progress Reports

Section	Content Instructions	Comments
Action opening	Identify the project and, in some cases, the project's special requirements. Refer to previous reports, if any. In a sentence or two, summarize progress to date.	The reader connection might be placed in a transmittal letter or memo if a report format is used. A letter or memo report will not need a heading for the opening paragraph or two.
Background	Remind the reader about key background information. Summarize progress that has been previously reported and, where appropriate, summarize previously discussed problems and whether they've been solved. Use appropriate subheadings.	The content depends on ◆ whether progress has been previously reported ◆ whether thorny issues have been previously discussed This section should not exceed two paragraphs. Extra detail can be placed as attachments.
Details of progress	Describe the progress achieved in the most recent reporting period. (If no progress has previously been reported, then start at the beginning of the project.) Use suitable subheadings; organize by ◆ tasks or subcontracts ◆ completed work vs. remaining work ◆ contract time frames or project phases Include, where appropriate, ◆ problems, how they've been handled, and how well ◆ a cost analysis of the work just completed, and the project so far	Detailed test data and other tabulated material should appear in an attachment or appendix. The format (letter, memo, semi-formal report, formal report) will depend on the length of the document and on the writer's assessment of the document's importance. Discussing problems gives the writer an opportunity to justify requests.
Action closing	Provide bottom-line conclusions: Is the project on time and on budget? Is the work up to standards? Predict whether the project will be completed on time and on budget. Where appropriate, recommend changes; ask for approval of these recommendations.	All conclusions must be solidly based on material presented in the body of the report. Subheadings might be appropriate. Where appropriate, the writer should ask for action from the reader.

VARIATION 1: Organized by Task

- Intro: connect with reader/refer to project
- Project description or summary

ROAD BASE PREPARATION

Progress to date
- in previous reporting period(s)
- work done in period just closing

Work to be completed
- work planned for next work period
- work planned for periods thereafter

PAVING

Progress to date
- in previous reporting period(s)
- work done in period just closing

Work to be completed
- work planned for next work period
- work planned for periods thereafter

PROBLEMS AND SETBACKS
- description
- methods used to overcome the setbacks
- degree of success

COST ANALYSIS
- costs to date
- costs in period just closing

CONCLUSION
- overall appraisal of work to date
- cost appraisal
- conclusions and recommendations re: work

Figure 17.2 A Progress Report Organized by Task

VARIATION 2: Organized by Work Completed

- Intro: connect with reader/refer to project
- Project description or summary

WORK COMPLETED

Road base preparation
- in previous reporting period(s)
- work done in period just closing
- problems and setbacks
- measures taken to recover from the setbacks

Paving
- work planned for next work period
- work planned for periods thereafter

WORK REMAINING

Road base preparation
- work planned for next work period
- work planned for periods thereafter

Paving
- work planned for next work period
- work planned for periods thereafter

COST ANALYSIS
- costs to date
- costs in period just closing

CONCLUSION
- overall appraisal of work to date
- cost appraisal
- conclusions and recommendations re: work

Figure 17.3 A Progress Report Organized by Degree of Project Completed

VARIATION 3: Organized by Time Frame

- Intro: connect with reader/refer to project
- Project description/set up chronology

PHASE 1 (specific dates go here)

Road base preparation
- work completed
- work to be done or changed

Paving
- work completed
- work to be done or changed

PHASE 2 (specific dates go here)

Road base preparation
- work completed
- work to be done or changed

Paving
- work completed
- work to be done or changed

COST ANALYSIS
- costs to date
- costs in period just closing

CONCLUSION
- overall appraisal of work to date
- cost appraisal
- conclusions and recommendations re: work

Figure 17.4 A Progress Report Organized by Project Time Frame

Two Sample Progress Reports

A workplace progress report

Figure 17.5 shows a periodic progress report that organizes its information by distinguishing between "work completed" and "work in progress."

Art Basran, the writer of the report shown in Figure 17.5, manages the Kelowna, British Columbia, office of MMT Consulting. Art's report is the fourth in a series of oral and written progress reports for his regional manager, Brenda Backstrom, regarding a project that is very important to MMT Consulting. (Chapter 3 features the proposal he wrote to Backstrom to get her approval for the project.)

This progress report continues to "sell" the innovative engineering/accounting method (Equivalent Uniform Annual Costs, or EUAC) that was the crux of the proposal memo in Figure 3.4. Art also uses the "Recommendations" at the end of the report to argue for one of his preferences—the use of professionally produced graphics in his firm's reports.

For this progress report, Art has chosen a semi-formal report format instead of a memo because of the six-page length and because he is trying to persuade his supervisor to support a new method of analyzing combined engineering and accounting data.

PROGRESS REGARDING MMT'S COST ANALYSIS OF FOUR ALTERNATIVES FOR HAULING COAL FROM JACKSON MINING'S PROPOSED OTHELLO MINE

For Brenda Backstrom, Regional Manager
MMT Consulting, Calgary Regional Office

Prepared by Art Basran
Kelowna Branch Office Manager
MMT Consulting

Submitted:
March 5, 2009

Figure 17.5 Semi-formal Progress Report Organized by Degree of Completion ***(continued)***

INTRODUCTION

The Jackson Mining Company has discovered a high-grade coal deposit in the mountains about 90 kilometres due north of Grand Forks, British Columbia. The company expects the market for this grade of coal to increase dramatically in the near future, and thus anticipates developing the deposit if development and transportation costs are acceptable. Jackson Mining has tentatively named its proposed mine site the Othello mine. MMT Consulting has been authorized to determine the most cost-effective method(s) of transporting the coal from that mine site to the mainline railroad, a distance of approximately 80 kilometres.

Four transport alternatives are being considered:

1. Diesel trucks
2. Diesel trains
3. Electric trains
4. Electric fleets

The criterion used to evaluate each alternative is the Equivalent Uniform Annual Cost (EUAC). The EUAC discussed in this report is in dollars per ton for the haul to the railhead. The four alternatives will be studied over periods ranging from one to twenty years, and at interest rates varying from 6% to 10%.

The EUAC formula provides clear comparisons of the transportation alternatives. Using this method, and capitalizing on hard work by our staff and good surveying weather, the project seems certain to be completed under budget and ahead of schedule. Details are provided in the following sections.

BACKGROUND

The Othello mine under study has anticipated coal sales of 5 million tons annually. Each of the following transportation alternatives would have to handle this volume. Also, the ability to expand in the future would be an asset.

1. **Diesel trucks**
   The CAT 777B truck was chosen for this study because of its load capacity of 95 tons and its output of 920 horsepower. These trucks would be running 24 hours a day.
2. **Diesel trains**
   Each train would be running with six diesel engines and 98 coal cars. It would take 11.2 hours to complete a round trip, and 17.2 hours to produce the amount of coal the train would haul. Thus, the train would haul a complete load and then idle for about six hours until the next load was ready.
3. **Electric trains**
   Each train would run four electric engines and 98 coal cars, with the same haul times as for the diesel train.
4. **Electric fleets**
   Each fleet would consist of three of the above electric trains. The first train would be loaded and then depart. While it is en route, the second train would be loaded, and this load-and-go process would be repeated for the third train. The departures would be timed so that the second train would leave just as the first train crested the highest point of the rail line pass. In this way, the electricity generated by the downgrade trains would be conserved and used to assist in powering the upgrade trains.

1.

Figure 17.5 Semi-formal Progress Report Organized by Degree of Completion *(continued)*

MMT'S INVOLVEMENT

After the initial negotiations between the respective head offices of Jackson Mining and MMT, our Kelowna office prepared a detailed proposal that Jackson Mining approved on January 6. Since then, two engineers and three technologists from our Kelowna office have researched this project with advice from Brendan Winters, a Penticton chartered accountant who has special expertise in mining projects.

Work Completed
Since January 6, our team has completed the following tasks:

- completed a preliminary survey of the proposed rail line and haul road; the elevations and other data collected from this survey are being used to help calculate tractive and grade resistances for the diesel trucks and for the two types of trains
- researched construction costs for both a rail line and a haul road, and for associated construction costs (such as maintenance buildings)
- researched maintenance costs for both a rail line and a haul road
- researched labour costs for operating the trucks and the trains
- researched the costs of purchasing trucks, diesel trains, and electric trains
- designed and researched the full costs of a complete communication system, which is required to control the proposed mine's transportation system

Work in Progress
We now have all the data required to complete our calculations and analyses. This work will progress in three stages:

1. Using the data collected from our surveys, we will calculate tractive and grade resistances for the diesel trucks and for the two types of trains. A sample of those calculations is provided below in Table 1. Next, to supplement the information regarding resistances, we will calculate the speed, power, and fuel consumption of each transportation type. A sample of those calculations appears in Table 2 on page 3.

Table 1: Tractive and Grade Resistances for Diesel Trucks

Section	Grade (%)	Truck Wt (ton)	Load Wt	Total Wt	Rt (lb)	Rg	Tr
G	2.0	66.3	95.0	161.3	16 125.0	6450.0	22 575.0
F	1.8	66.3	95.0	161.3	16 125.0	5805.0	21 930.0
E	2.0	66.3	95.0	161.3	16 125.0	6450.0	22 575.0
D	2.1	66.3	95.0	161.3	16 125.0	6772.5	22 897.5

The first column in Table 1 lists the sections into which the road has been divided for analytical purposes. These sections of road have varying grades. Grade resistance (Rg) and tractive resistance (Rt) are found for each section.

2.

Figure 17.5 Semi-formal Progress Report Organized by Degree of Completion *(continued)*

Table 2: Speed, Power, and Fuel Consumption for Diesel Trucks

Section	Grade (%)	Tr (lb)	Power (hp)	Speed (mph)	Dist (mi)	Time (hr)	BTU (x1000)	Fuel (gal)	Total Fuel
G	2.0	22 575.0	920.0	12.55	8.4	0.67	1572.5	11.34	42.62
F	1.8	21 930.0	920.0	12.92	7.2	0.56	1309.3	9.44	35.49
E	2.0	22 575.0	920.0	12.55	5.4	0.43	1010.9	7.29	27.40
D	2.1	22 897.5	920.0	12.38	4.8	0.39	911.4	6.57	24.70

The final calculations for resistances and fuel consumption will be added to labour and maintenance costs to determine annual operating costs for each of the alternatives under study. Thus, we will be able to complete the Cost Comparison table, a draft of which is shown in Draft Table 3 below.

Draft Table 3: Cost Comparisons

Option	Capital Costs	Annual Operating Costs
Diesel Trucks	$115 539 000	$
Diesel Trains	$149 083 000	$
Electric Trains	$161 783 000	$
Electric Fleets	$201 463 000	$

2. Once the capital and annual costs are found, they can be combined with varying interest rates and study periods to calculate tables of Equivalent Uniform Annual Costs (EUAC). The purpose of converting all costs into an EUAC is to provide a common means of comparing all the alternatives. The capital costs are spread over the length of the study period and added to the annual costs. Thus, a comparison of EUACs will yield a qualitative assessment of the alternatives to go with the quantitative assessment suggested by Draft Table 3.

   To provide an idea of how these EUAC tables (and corresponding graphs) will look in the final analysis, we have estimated figures for the four transportation alternatives and placed them in Draft Table 4 and Draft Figure 1 (Appendix).

   The final phase of our work for this project will be to produce a comprehensive report of our findings. This report has been outlined, and some of the preliminary material has been drafted. We expect the final version of this report to total about 40 pages, with the bulk of those pages presenting our detailed calculations. We're using the format that we learned from Mykon Communications last March and that proved successful in our final report to the City of Kelowna regarding the proposed multipurpose arena.

3.

Figure 17.5 Semi-formal Progress Report Organized by Degree of Completion *(continued)*

CONCLUSION

Appraisal of Work to Date

We're satisfied with both the quantity and the quality of the data gathered for the required analysis. Part of this is due to the hard work performed by our Kelowna project team, part is due to our connection to the internet, and part of the credit should go to Brendan Winters, whose experience in gathering and analyzing financial data has been invaluable.

Also, we had some good fortune with the weather during the survey work. Unseasonably warm weather and light snowfalls allowed the surveys to finish one week ahead of our anticipated February 2 completion date, and under budget by 15%. (We would have been even more under budget, but we had to rent a helicopter for three days more than anticipated because of very difficult terrain in the Kelso Pass area.)

Overall, it seems that we will be about $14 000 under budget for the project, partly because of the savings in the surveys and partly because Brendan Winters's research expertise has cut our estimated research time. Full figures will be provided in our final progress report.

Anticipated Completion Date

We expect to have all calculations completed by March 7. After that, it should take two of our staff (one engineer and one technologist) two working days to produce a final draft of the report for examination at Regional Office. Allowing for examination time and for final editing at the Kelowna office, we should be able to have the finished copy of our report produced by March 14, which is 14 days ahead of the date we had scheduled for delivering our analysis to Jackson Mining.

Recommendations

We have forged a positive working relationship with Jessica Proctor, director of mining development at Jackson Mining. Jessica has indicated that her company would like us to bid on the construction engineering contract for the anticipated road/rail line construction project, which may begin as early as this July. In connection with this possible contract, we recommend two courses of action:

1. Have the Jackson Mining report produced professionally by a graphics firm. We have money to spend because we're under budget for this project. Also, a graphics firm such as Apex Graphics (which does annual reports and similar documents for major businesses in the Okanagan) could produce a high-quality colour report in one day if we provide a disk prepared in Microsoft Office, the software we use. My main reason for suggesting this extra expenditure of under $1000 is that Jackson Mining's directors place a high value on professional work. I think it would help project a positive image that will benefit any future proposals we make to this company.
2. Do some preliminary investigation of the parameters and requirements of road construction and rail line construction for Othello Mine's proposed transportation routes. If Jackson Mining presents a Request for Proposal on this construction project in the near future, MMT Consulting will be prepared.

4.

Figure 17.5 Semi-formal Progress Report Organized by Degree of Completion *(continued)*

APPENDIX

Draft Table 4: EUAC for Alternatives at 6% (Based on preliminary estimates)

Study Period	Diesel Trains	Electric Trains	Electric Fleets	Trucks
1	$32.52	$34.91	$43.26	$32.10
2	17.18	18.26	22.53	20.21
3	12.07	12.72	15.63	16.25
4	9.52	9.95	12.18	14.27
5	7.99	8.29	10.12	13.09
6	6.98	7.19	8.75	12.30
7	6.26	6.41	7.77	11.74
8	5.72	5.82	7.04	11.33
9	5.30	5.37	6.48	11.00
10	4.97	5.01	6.03	10.75
11	4.70	4.71	5.66	10.54
12	4.47	4.47	5.36	10.36
13	4.28	4.27	5.10	10.22
14	4.12	4.09	4.89	10.09
15	3.98	3.94	4.70	9.98
16	3.87	3.81	4.54	9.89
17	3.76	3.70	4.40	9.81
18	3.67	3.60	4.27	9.74
19	3.59	3.51	4.16	9.68
20	3.51	3.43	4.07	9.62

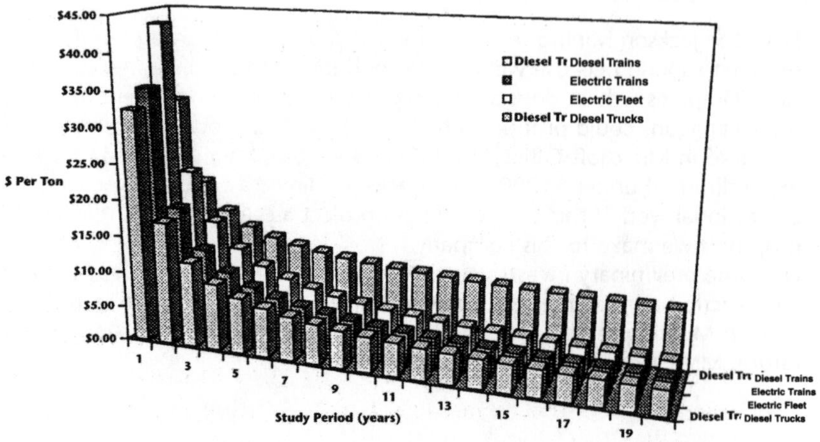

Draft Figure 1: EUAC for Four Alternatives at 6% (based on preliminary estimates)

Figure 17.5 Semi-formal Progress Report Organized by Degree of Completion

A student progress report

The second sample progress report, shown in Figure 17.6, comes from Vince Cummings, who is reporting progress on a research project to his project supervisor.

> Vince is part of the group that produced the recommendations report reproduced in Figure 18.6. He has taken a leading role in the project; his enthusiasm for that project is reflected in the degree of detail and the tone of phrasing in this progress report. Vince and his collaborators have turned hard work and clear thinking into a successful project, but they have been challenged by the need to create a cost-effective design. Therefore, this progress report includes a section on "Problems and Solutions," especially because the project supervisor has previously commented on the cost issue.
>
> The heart of this report is the "Project Progress" section, which contains three subsections: "Work completed," "Work in progress," and "To be completed." Those components are followed by a project schedule, which the writer knows is a concern for his reader.
>
> Vince attaches his team's working outline (which is reproduced in Figure 18.5, starting on Chapter 18.)

Occasional progress reports are written for short-term projects that do not have scheduled reporting dates. Either the writer responds to a supervisor's request (or to a client's request), or the writer reports progress in order to elicit reader support.

PERIODIC ACTIVITY REPORTS

The periodic activity report is similar to a progress report in that it summarizes activities over a specified period. But unlike a progress report, which describes activity on a given *project*, a periodic report summarizes the general activities during a given *period*. Manufacturers requiring periodic reports often have prepared forms, because most of the tasks are quantifiable, such as units produced. Still, not all jobs lend themselves to prepared-form reports, and you will have to develop your own format. If so, the action structure can be readily adapted to your purpose.

PROJECT COMPLETION REPORTS

A project completion report is presented as the concluding progress report for a lengthy project, or the only report arising from a short project. Either way, the action structure can form the report's backbone. (Note, though, that in Table 17.3 the details section is expanded into Project Highlights and Exceptions.)

A project completion report by consulting engineer Ken Langedyk can be found at the text enrichment website that accompanies this book. Go to **www.pearsoned.ca/lannon**. Click "Writing Examples," and then click "Project Completion Report."

OUC Okanagan University College

Memorandum

To: Don Klepp, Professional Communication Department **Date:** March 8, 2008

From: Vince Cummings, MET student

Re: **Progress Report—PCOM 142 Research Project**

On February 2, our group proposed an engineering analysis and engineering redesign of a transmission jack adapter for commercial transport settings. Following your approval of our approach, we continued with our research and development. We have encountered relatively few problems, so our team is confident that we'll meet the April 2 deadline for completing the final report. This memo presents details of our progress to date, and the direction our group has taken as we near project completion.

Background

As you may recall, our goal is to determine exactly what would be necessary to transform an existing jack adapter into a versatile shop tool capable of meeting current industry needs. As we outlined in our proposal, floor- or column-type transmission jacks are usually used to remove heavy components from the under-carriage of commercial transport vehicles. Each of those jacks has its strengths and limitations; we'd like to blend their individual strengths into one unit.

Our project has evolved substantially since its inception, growing from a simple jack adapter to a modular engineered stand capable of many different configurations. Although our analysis and redesign will still focus on its use as a transmission jack adapter, our research has indicated that end users want the device to adapt to several different working environments.

The following section provides details of the project's progress to date.

Project Progress

Work completed

Our group has worked together to complete all work described in this section.

1. *Preliminary research.* The majority of our research has come from a series of interviews with industry professionals. After talking with Dave Cochrane, our client, we asked all interviewees questions about what their working environments demand of engineered stands (such as the jack adapter) and where the CT83 design falls short. The distilled answers to these questions will be found in sections 2.1.1, 2.1.2, and 2.1.3 of our report. (See the attached outline for details.) We also found internet information about various jack components and about competing products; such products are described in section 2.2.
2. *Analysis of gathered data.* In a series of meetings, our team compiled and reviewed the gathered data, as a basis for design changes.
3. *Early concept for a redesign of the adapter.* We viewed the redesign task as one large problem to be solved, rather than several small problems. As a team, we methodically attacked all key design faults. Building on each other's ideas and knowledge, we were able to efficiently suggest improvements that I believe were more successful than if we had worked separately on the design issues.
4. *Final research.* We presented our potential prototype design to the industry professionals whom we had previously interviewed, to get their responses. This second series of meetings indicated a few more design issues to be addressed.

Figure 17.6 A Student Research Progress Report *(continued)*

Don Klepp March 8, 2008 Page 2

5. *Final concept for the redesign.* After once again reviewing the industry feedback, we collectively fine-tuned the prototype design.
6. *Working outline for final analytical report.* By preparing a working outline for our final PCOM 142 report, we have consolidated our thoughts about the project and its results. You'll notice that the attached outline essentially uses a problem-solution pattern, culminating in a cost analysis. Creating the outline has also allowed us to identify and organize our remaining tasks.

Work in progress

Now that we have completed most of the design work and have the report structure in place, we can assign the remaining tasks to individual group members.

1. *Mathematical analysis.* An analysis of the design features of the new jack adapter prototype will provide the information we need to determine material specifications, safety factors, and the adapter's final dimensions. Although these calculations can be time consuming, the proposed design is relatively simple, and will be functioning in static loading conditions. Greysen is leading the team in completing these calculations.
2. *Cost analysis.* Tying in closely with the mathematical analysis is the structure's cost analysis. We will prepare a comprehensive breakdown of the manufacturing costs of the redesigned adapter, based on several production schemes, from small runs to large-scale production. Joe and Brandon are leading this portion of the work.
3. *Engineering drawings and solid computer models.* A full set of detailed engineering drawings and production plans are in the works. Our team started this work very early in the project, and we're well on our way. The mathematical analysis will yield the final dimensions of the adapter, and I will be able to complete the drawings and solid models.

Work to be completed

Our team works well together when collaborating for solid blocks of time. We will complete the majority of the following tasks together, during evenings and weekends.

1. *Draft report.* To gain experience in composing a report of this type, and to edit as we go, we will use the working outline to compose the first draft, which we hope will be close to the final draft.
2. *Oral report preparation.* Once the draft of our written report nears completion, we will be able to work on the oral report.
3. *Completion and submission of the final written report.* As the attached outline shows, the report concludes with a recommendation to build a prototype as the first step in the manufacturing process. I have formatted the report, with all headings, pagination, headers and footers, and spacing ready to go. As you can see in the following project completion schedule, we have left sufficient time to edit, proofread, and polish the document.

Project Completion Schedule

An updated version of the time frame for completing the report follows. We had flexibility early in the project, but now our timelines are rather rigid because of the looming deadline.

Activity	Time Allotted	Dates	Document Produced
Mathematical analysis & engineering drawings	20 hours	Feb 28 – Mar 15	In progress
Write draft of report	20 hours	Mar 6 – Mar 22	In progress
Prepare for oral report (due Mar 29)	6 hours	Mar 20	PowerPoint show
Revise/edit/refine report	8 hours		Final report due Apr 2

Figure 17.6 A Student Research Progress Report *(continued)*

Budget to Complete Report
Building a prototype is not part of our project, so our only expenses are travel between Vernon and Kelowna (for interviews and team meetings), photocopying costs, and report printing costs, as follows:

• Transportation costs (total for all members)	$80.00
• Photocopying costs	$10.50
• Printing (colour printing and paper)	$50.00
Total:	**$140.50**

Project Problems and Their Solutions
One thing you impressed upon us, following both the written and oral proposals, was our omission of cost guidelines for the stand. At the time of our proposals, we didn't have a clear idea of costs, so we didn't address the issue. However, we should have clarified that costs are tied closely to design considerations.

Since your feedback regarding this omission, we have kept cost factors in mind through the research and development process. First, we had to learn what industry wants from a tool such as the jack adapter, so that we could modify the design of the original CT83 pit jack adapter. Factors such as material selection, material size, jack dimensions, and fabrication cost will play a large role in the final price of the adapter. Availability of materials and components will affect the manufacturer's cost as will the production scale. We couldn't consider these factors until our R & D was complete.

I'd like to see the stand sell for about $600, because I'm not sure that industry will pay much more than that. I don't know if such a goal is attainable, even if we produce it on a large scale (500 units or more). The "work in progress" section on the previous page indicates that we're working on the calculations now. When Joe and Brandon have finished that work, we'll be able to plug the results into section 4.0 of the report.

Conclusion
Our team has no doubts about finishing this project by the April 2 deadline. I hope you agree that the times listed in our completion schedule are realistic.

The size and scope of the project has definitely challenged our abilities and current knowledge base, but I must say that I've learned a lot about engineering in this "communication" project. The project is too much for one student taking a full load of classes, so I'm glad that I'm part of a group whose members share the load. The project's challenge level has kept us motivated, and now we're keen to properly complete what we've started. Another major motivating factor is that we think that our client, Dave Cochrane, may very well make some money with this new design! That's a good thing to take with us to our next job interview.

Thank you for your valuable advice on this project. We will take advantage of your offer to bring our document production questions to you as we swing into the final stages of the project. May we please schedule 15 minutes with you in each of our last three writing labs?

Vince Cummings

Vince Cummings

Attachments: Working outline (3 pages)
Sample drawings and solid computer models (4 pages)

Figure 17.6 A Student Research Progress Report

Table 17.3 Project Completion Report Structure

Section	Contents
Action Opening	The reader connection depends on the type of reader: ◆ client? ◆ writer's supervisor? (What are the reader's main concerns?) State that the project is complete; briefly describe the outcome.
Background	Review the job's features: purpose, schedule, budget, location, people involved.
Project Highlights	Describe the project's main accomplishments (work completed, targets met, results obtained). Discuss problems encountered, the impact of these problems on the project, and how the problems were handled.
Exceptions	Describe the deviations from the contract or project plan (if any)—the work not completed or done differently than planned. Give the reason for each deviation and explain its effect on the final project result.
Action Closing	Analyze the reader's main concerns. What type of follow-up is needed?

INCIDENT REPORTS

An incident report resembles news accounts of events. Most of the description is provided as past tense narrative. Note, however, that some incident reports also use present tense to refer to the current situation and future tense to discuss what needs to be done.

INSPECTION REPORTS

Building inspectors, park wardens, gas inspectors, quality-control technicians, and others sometimes use forms to report the results of their inspections. However, often a form is not available or does not suit a particular inspection. In these cases, the adaptation of the action structure shown in Table 17.4 works very well.

The inspection report in Figure 17.7 deals with a troubling incident: a family, against its will, had been evacuated from its home because of dangerous carbon monoxide levels in the home. The writer, who is relatively new in her position, phrases her observations and opinions very cautiously. In particular, notice that she records details very clearly and that she uses passive voice wherever possible to emphasize the *results* of the inspection, *not her part in the inspection and subsequent actions.*

Table 17.4 Inspection Report Structure

Section	Reader Questions to Answer
Action Opening	◆ Why should I read this report? ◆ What is the main result of the inspection?
Background	◆ Why was this inspection conducted? ◆ What was inspected? ◆ Who did the inspection? ◆ When and where did the inspection occur?
Details	What did the inspection reveal? 1. Conditions found: What did the inspectors observe re: the quality of work performed or items provided at the site? In what condition were equipment, facilities, or materials? 2. Deficiencies: What conditions, if any, need to be corrected? Does any work need to be done or redone?
Action Closing	◆ Overall, what is the state of the site (facilities, equipment, etc.)? ◆ Does the writer suggest specific actions?

COMPLIANCE REPORTS

At every level of government, regulatory agencies require organizations to report the degree to which the organizations have complied with the agencies' regulations. Also, industrial and professional associations require their members to report how the members have complied with codes of business conduct. Some compliance reports can be completed on forms provided by the watchdog agency, but more often the reporting organization has to create its own format and structure for the report. In such cases, the structure outlined in Table 17.5 could form the basis for any particular compliance report.

FIELD TRIP REPORTS

Usually, a field assignment is complete only after you have reported on what you observed and what you did. The field trip may have involved a four-hour hike along an abandoned forestry road, or required two weeks of testing pollution levels in salmon spawning rivers. Regardless of the trip's duration and complexity, you need to perform two main tasks in advance of the inevitable report:

1. Make careful, detailed observations and record them in a notebook or on a voice recorder.
2. Organize those notes to answer your reader's questions in the order your reader would prefer.

Prairie POWER Corporation

INSPECTION MEMORANDUM

DATE: January 7, 2008

TO: Randall Johnson, Gas & Electrical Inspections Coordinator

FROM: Miranda Ocala, Gas Inspector

RE: **Clogged Masonry Chimney – 322 Montcalm Crescent, Saskatoon, SK**

On the evening of January 3, an elderly member of the Smith family, resident at 322 Montcalm Crescent, was rushed to the U of S Hospital Emergency Department. An alert resident suspected CO poisoning and alerted SaskEnergy. Later that day, Melvin Trask of SaskEnergy advised the occupants of the two-storey, single-family residence to vacate because

- the chimney was blocked with ice, and
- CO concentrations of .02% were present, apparently due to spillage of gas combustion products.

On January 4, Keith McLeod and I inspected the gas equipment and found

- the masonry chimney was blocked with ice. (We noted a white, lime-like substance on the exterior portion of the chimney that is exposed in the garage.)
- the furnace and the water heater were spilling.
- the home had evidence of excessive moisture – the windows were frozen shut. A serviceperson from Prairie Heating was present; she opened a small passageway at the top of the chimney's interior. Soon after a draft was established (in 30 minutes), the ice began to melt.
- the gas equipment was in good condition. That equipment consists of
  1. a 137,000 BTU standard Lennox furnace with a 6" vent draft hood
  2. a 36,000 John Wood water heater with draft hood (3" vent).

The furnace and the heater operated satisfactorily as soon as the chimney passage was reasonably clear.

- The 1", two-outlet supply pipe was in good condition.
- The masonry chimney, constructed of bricks and concrete and lined with tile throughout, seemed in good condition, although our initial inspection was unable to confirm the chimney's interior condition because of the ice buildup.

On January 6, after the ice had thawed, our subsequent inspection revealed damaged tile liner around the vent connector's entry point. This defect, coupled with the exposure of all four sides of the chimney and the recent cold weather, seems to have led to the icing condition. There is evidence that severe icing has occurred before: there is a white substance on the chimney exterior in the garage.

Because the tile liner measures 6 1/4" by 6 1/4", and a flexible liner measures 6 3/8" OD, I have approved the use of a traditional (shop made) sectional 6" aluminum liner. This is the most economical method of any acceptable corrections.

Still, the owner, Rod Smith, is annoyed that corrections are necessary to a house built just 14 years ago. He is also very angry that an owner's defect has been issued, precluding occupancy until satisfactory corrections have been made. He has threatened to sue for the costs of housing his family in a hotel until the residence is cleared for occupancy. I suggest that our customer service people speak with Mr. Smith to explain all the ramifications of allowing a family to occupy a home with potential for CO-induced deaths.

Miranda Ocala

Figure 17.7 A Sample Inspection Report

Table 17.5 Compliance Report Structure

Section	Content	Comments
Action Opening	Name the report's purpose. Refer to the act or to the body of the regulations prompting the report. State the degree to which the requirements have been met; list the time frame covered by the report.	The reader connection might be placed in a transmittal letter or memo if a semi-formal format is used. In a letter or memo report, use a subject line that names the specific act and its sections. Often, a compliance report has legal implications, so do not connect with the reader in an informal, friendly manner.
Background	Supply necessary details about regulations for a reader who is not familiar with them. For a report to the regulatory agency, possibly review your organization's compliance record.	Background about the regulations will not be necessary in a report to the regulatory agency.
Details of Compliance	Describe specific actions taken to comply with specific regulations, in the order the regulations appear. The report could follow a time pattern—the order in which you've met the reader's expectations. Or organize in the order of importance. Or use an actions-results pattern.	Use bolded headings, bullets, numbered lists, italics, white space, and indents to help make the document easy to read.
Action Closing	Summarize key aspects of the reported activities. State the bottom line, including results, where appropriate. List future methods of complying with regulations or expectations.	In some cases, the report might describe costs of problems of compliance; the conclusion might argue for a relaxed interpretation of the regulations.
Attachments (optional)		Photos, affidavits, test data, shift reports, or other detailed back-up data might be appropriate.

IN BRIEF A COMPLIANCE REPORTING CASE STUDY

Most companies that file compliance reports do not necessarily depend on them to stay in business. However, each radio and television broadcasting licence lasts only seven years, when it may (or may not) be renewed by the Canadian Radio-television and Telecommunications Commission (CRTC). That's why Charlotte Bell's position of Vice-President Regulatory Affairs is so vital to her company, CanWest Global Communications. She is responsible for communicating its compliance with CRTC regulations.

Bell came to CanWest Global after working for the CRTC, so she knows how to report her company's compliance with broadcasting regulations. Still, she takes nothing for granted: "Usually, before the first report concerning a licence renewal or asset transaction, I consult with CRTC staff about what they want to see. I find out what they need to do their job, so that they can easily understand our actions. I don't want to force them to come to us for more details."

Bell really believes in careful audience analysis for all types of communication: "I tell my staff, whether they're writing email, short memos, or long reports, to know their audience and write differently for each audience." She cites the monthly reports that go to CanWest Global's senior managers. Essentially executive summaries, these reports give just enough information for the president and other senior managers to "clearly understand each issue, whether it was resolved, and whether we need follow-up."

Many of CanWest Global's compliance reports have a primary audience (the CRTC staff and commissioners) and a secondary audience (on the public record). Therefore, the content and tone have to be carefully edited to satisfy both audiences. Sometimes, the CRTC full version contains confidential business information that does not appear in the public version. In such cases, the two versions use the same basic structure, with edited variations within that structure. Bell likes the action structure (see Table 17.5) because it keeps reports focused.

Focus is a central concern: "I insist that we stick to the point in our reports. Section after section, we clearly outline what was required, how we fulfilled the requirements, and what is our rationale for any shortfalls." Here's Charlotte Bell's checklist for effective compliance reports:

- carefully analyze your audience before choosing the report's content and tone
- keep all reports as brief as possible
- make all aspects clear by using a logical overall structure and avoiding unnecessary, confusing detail
- itemize all regulations and how you've complied with them
- don't get yourself into trouble by raising issues that really aren't necessary to raise
- design the report to look user-friendly and professional
- accompany the report with a businesslike, one-page transmittal document

Table 17.6 on the next page illustrates a structure that could be used for most field trip reports.

MEETING MINUTES

Many team or project meetings require someone to record the proceedings. Minutes are the records of such meetings. Copies of minutes are distributed to all members and interested parties, to track the proceedings and to remind members of their designated responsibilities. The appointed secretary records the minutes. When you record minutes, answer these questions:

- What group held the meeting? When, where, and why?
- Who chaired the meeting? Who else was present?

Table 17.6 Field Trip Report Structure

Section	Reader Questions to Answer
Action Opening	◆ Why are you reporting this? (optional) ◆ In brief, what have you been doing? What did you accomplish?
Background	◆ Who went where? When? Why? ◆ On whose authority? (optional) ◆ How did the writer travel? (optional) ◆ What was the project? (optional)
Details of Work Accomplished	◆ What did you do? What routine work? Which work specifications were followed? ◆ What work did you perform beyond the routine requirements? ◆ What did you observe? ◆ What meetings, if any, did you have? With whom? What were the results?
Problems Encountered	◆ What were the specific problems, if any? Did you identify the causes of these problems? ◆ What specific actions did you take to solve the problems? ◆ Were you successful? If not, why not?
Action Closing	◆ What remains to be done? What resources are necessary? Who should perform the work? Have you assigned the work? ◆ Are you requesting support or authorization from me, your reader?

- Were the minutes of the last meeting approved (or not approved)?
- Who said what? Was anything resolved?
- Who made which motions and what was the vote? What discussion preceded the vote?
- Who was given responsibility for which actions?

See Figure 17.8 for a sample set of minutes.

The reports discussed so far in this chapter focus on factual information. Now the focus shifts to short analytical reports, all of which logically arrive at a conclusion. Readers of analytical reports want more than the facts; they want to know what the facts mean.

The four major varieties of formal analytical reports (feasibility reports, causal analyses, assessment reports, and recommendations reports) have all been discussed in Chapter 18. Therefore, this chapter discusses only how to modify them for letter, memo, and semi-formal report versions. Like short informational reports, short analytical reports can profitably use the four-part action structure.

MEETING OF THE CAMPUS RECYCLING COMMITTEE
Room 125, Student Services Building, March 28, 2008, 4:00 p.m.

Chair: T. Maguire, Jordan College Student Association President

Present: R.W. Siggia, V.P., Administration
J. Klym, Campus Services
M. O'Connor, Print Services
T. Singh, 3rd year Arts
J. Cormier-Bauer, 2nd year Engineering
H. Calvin, 4th year Business
P. Masinkowski, 4th year Phys. Ed.

Guest: John Maravich, Canadian Waste Disposal, Ltd.

1. Approval of Agenda
T. Maguire asked to add a presentation by John Maravich and suggested that discussion of bottle recycling as a student association fundraiser be tabled to the next meeting, in order to accommodate the address. T. Maguire called for approval of the amended agenda.
Passed Unanimously.

2. Other Business
John Maravich proposed a business arrangement wherein Canadian Waste Disposal would have exclusive rights to recycle paper products at Jordan College in return for an annual $5000 scholarship to a Jordan College Business student and a commitment to hire Jordan College students on a part-time basis. The projected total volume of business was discussed, along with other details provided in Canadian's written proposal (see attached). The committee agreed to hold a special meeting in two weeks to discuss the proposal.

Action by: T. Singh and J. Cormier-Bauer will press class presidents to poll students re: their on-campus paper usage.

M. O'Connor and R.W. Siggia will review administrative and academic paper usage.

J. Klym will determine recycling potential for calendars, phone books, and all other campus service publications.

3. Approval of Previous Meeting
After revision of the numbers relating to recycling of library culls, the previous meeting minutes were accepted.
MOVED: R.W. Siggia SECONDED: J. Klym **Passed Unanimously.**

4. Recycling Ink Products
H. Calvin and J. Klym presented a report on the types and volume of ink used by on-campus photocopiers and computer printers. Their main findings were that in the last fiscal year:
1. $212 700 was spent on ink cartridges for laser printers, inkjet printers, and photocopiers.
2. Of that amount, $192 654 was used to purchase new cartridges and the remainder was spent on recycled cartridges. On average, recycled cartridges cost 62% as much as new ones.
3. The latest editions of <u>Consumer Journal</u> and <u>Computer Equipment Monthly</u> report 93% reliability with recycled cartridges.

MOVED: J. Klym SECONDED: H. Calvin

That Jordan College adopt a one-year trial period of using recycled cartridges. Discussion centred on the issue of whether this committee has a legitimate right to take this action. R.W. Siggia contended it is Administration's prerogative, but agreed to approach President Monroe with the committee's decision.
Passed Unanimously.

Call for adjournment at 5:05 p.m. **Carried.**

Figure 17.8 A Sample Set of Meeting Minutes

As you examine the structures suggested for short analytical reports, notice a key difference between formal and informal analytical reports. A formal report usually places its main point, its "bottom line," at the end of the report and satisfies a reader's immediate "need to know" by placing a summary in the front matter. An informal report, on the other hand, places the report's main finding in the first or second paragraph, to satisfy the reader's curiosity. While this "front-loading" technique suits most informal reports, it doesn't suit every situation, as you'll see in the discussion of indirect recommendations reports, later in this chapter.

FEASIBILITY REPORTS

Your reader for a feasibility analysis will likely want your answer at the beginning, so the structure in Table 17.7 should work well. See Figure 17.9 on the next page for a sample report.

Table 17.7 Short Feasibility Report Structure

Section	Content	Comments
Action Opening	Refer to reader's request or the situation requiring analysis. State whether the examined project or equipment is feasible.	The reader connection might be placed in a transmittal document if a semi-formal format is used. A letter or memo does not need a heading for the opening paragraph.
Background	Describe the situation leading to this feasibility study. Explain exactly what kind of feasibility is studied and list the assessment criteria.	The amount of background depends on the reader's familiarity with the subject. The criteria may have to be justified.
Details of Assessment	Apply each assessment criterion, step by step, to the data. Choose suitable criteria—a proposed equipment purchase, for example, could look at cost, warranty, equipment reliability, performance, and compatibility with current equipment.	The title of this section will depend on the kind of feasibility being discussed, and on the reader's priorities.
Action Closing	Summarize the results of applying all criteria and state the bottom-line conclusion. If appropriate, recommend approval.	A summary table could be effective Brochures, test data, financial projections, or other detailed supporting data could be attached.

Ministry of Transportation **Internal Memo**

DATE: January 10, 2008
TO: Richard Janvier, Engineering Information Systems Coordinator
FROM: Sheri Prasso, Science and Technical Officer
RE: **Sand and Glavine Proposal for Office Networking (RFP 20021209-EIS)**

As you requested, this report assesses the proposal submitted by Sand and Glavine Systems for an office network for our Vernon Engineering Services office. The proposal has merit, but requires changes before the Ministry of Transportation can accept it.

The RFP placed its focus on making better use of the computer information systems by creating a local area network (LAN). Therefore, I used the following criteria to assess the Sand and Glavine computer network proposal:

1. Technical considerations
2. Cost
3. Training and support
4. Efficiency gains

Information for the assessment was collected from current books on the subject, staff at the Vernon Engineering office, and local businesses.

Technical Considerations and Cost
The proposed network will meet Engineering Information Systems' requirements, with minor changes. In particular, the Wang 486 needs to be retained as part of the network (see the attached technical analysis for more detail). These changes put the cost of the network slightly over budget. However, anticipated reductions in cable requirements and installation time should lower the cost. The overall cost of the modified network will be close to the proposal's quoted price of $4000.

Training and Support
Technically, the Sand and Glavine Systems proposed network is simple. Because of this simplicity, and the competence of the staff at the Vernon Engineering Office, the proposed training will be sufficient. Unlike training, support was not included in the proposal's quoted price. It was offered at additional cost through monthly service contracts. The Ministry of Transportation has qualified computer support personnel on staff. Purchasing support from Sand and Glavine Systems would duplicate service and add to the direct cost of this network.

Efficiency Gains
Sand and Glavine's proposed computer network will meet Engineering Information Systems' objective of increasing the efficiency of the Vernon office. The network will save time and allow staff to focus their efforts on engineering rather than on file management. Also, Sand and Glavine will install the system on a weekend, saving two days of down time.

Recommendation
If Sand and Glavine Systems re-submits the proposal with the requested changes, it should be adopted.

Sheri Prasso

Attachments: Technical analysis (cable, topology, hardware, and software)
Cost analysis
Task time comparisons

Figure 17.9 A Sample Feasibility Report

CAUSAL ANALYSES

Your reader's immediate interest in what caused a problem, a failure, or an incident should direct you to state the report's main point in the lead paragraph, as in Table 17.8. Incidentally, not all causal analyses deal with problems, breakdowns, or failures. You might be asked to identify the causes of an unexpected rise in factory productivity, a steady increase in fish breeding stock, or an improvement in the employee turnover rate.

The causal analysis illustrated in Figure 17.10 was commissioned by a homeowner who suspected that a gaping hole under her driveway resulted from her neighbour's faulty driveway design. TerraTech, the consulting firm engaged by the homeowner, presents its findings in detached, carefully measured language. The report writer uses the classic causal analysis technique of identifying and eliminating possible causes until the most likely, primary cause has been found and proved.

A letter format is used for this report because of its relatively short length and straightforward content.

Table 17.8 Informal or Semi-formal Causal Analysis Structure

Section	Content	Comments
Action Opening	Refer to the reader's request or to the writer's role in analyzing the identified situation. State whether the cause(s) can be identified and, if so, name the main cause.	The reader connection might be placed in a transmittal letter or memo if a semi-formal format is used. A letter or memo report does not need a heading for the opening paragraph or two.
Background	Describe the situation (or environment) in which the event occurred or in which the problem developed. Provide background about similar problems or situations.	This section should not exceed two paragraphs. If more detail is necessary, it can be placed as attachments.
Details of Analysis	Describe the step-by-step analytical process and give the results of that process.	Causal analysis usually names possible causes identified from previous experience and based on the relation between an event and prior conditions. For correlation and causation, see page xxs.
Action Closing	Summarize the report's main findings. State the bottom line. If appropriate, recommend remedial or preventative action.	A summary table could be effective. Attached brochures, performance tests, financial projections, or other detailed supporting data could be appropriate.

TerraTech ENGINEERING

1714 Kalamalka Lake Road, Vernon, British Columbia V1G 2N6 Ph. (250) 545-0919
Fax (250) 545-2020 terra@junction.net

June 21, 2008

Ms. L. P. Garcia
306 Melville Court
Vernon, BC V1B 2W9

Dear Ms. Garcia:

Re: Causes of the Undercut Driveway at 306 Melville Court

At your request, we have examined the extent of the undercutting of your 17-month-old driveway and have identified the primary cause of that problem to be water directed from a neighbouring driveway.

Background
In similar situations that we have analyzed, we've determined that open space can develop under a concrete pad if the base soil has not been properly packed, or if flowing water has eroded soil away, or if water has pooled under the pad and thus caused the soil to settle.

Much depends on the soil's composition. In the case of your driveway, the base soil primarily consists of glacial till, a combination of sand, gravel, larger rocks, and small amounts of organic material. Typically, when glacial till gets saturated with water, it turns into a slurry that either flows downhill or collapses into itself, as all loose spaces among the particles are filled.

Investigation and Results
We conducted the investigation in four stages:

1. We determined the nature and extent of damage by examining the concrete deck and by probing the empty space beneath it. Our visual inspection of the concrete revealed no cracks or sagging of the deck; the driveway has stood up very well. We then interviewed your builder, Mark Lambton, who showed us his construction notes. The notes say that the concrete subcontractor used twice the normal amount of reinforcing bar within the concrete slab.

   The driveway has not pulled away from the rebar fitted into the garage footings, despite 23 centimetres of open space under the concrete along the intersection of driveway and footings. The drawing on page 2 shows the extent of open space under the driveway, and other features of the existing situation. (Numbers show the depth of settling or erosion at various points.) The undercutting is quite extensive, as the drawing shows.

2. We ruled out inadequate packing as a cause of the settling. Mark Lambton's notes reveal that the driveway base was packed uniformly, that it was watered between packings, and that it was packed five times over a four-day period. This exceeds normal practice.

Figure 17.10 A Causal Analysis

(continued)

Ms. L. P. Garcia
June 21, 2008
Page 2

3. We ruled out erosion as a major causative factor. There may have been some minor initial erosion along the north edge of the driveway but erosion could not have caused the irregular pattern of open space beneath the slab. That irregular pattern suggests that pooled water has led to irregular soil settling.
4. We determined the source of the amounts of water required to cause the degree of observed settling. We do not believe that the water has come from your driveway, say in last fall's heavy rains. Your driveway has been designed to channel water down toward a collection drain located two metres from the centre of the garage door. To test our belief, we ran water onto your driveway from two hoses simultaneously. All the water was easily channelled down to the drain.

Then, we investigated water flow from the north-neighbouring driveway that slopes away from the garage, toward the street. That driveway is higher than yours at every point of its length, and the entire driveway slopes down toward the rock-covered depression between the two drives. Moreover, a one-metre-wide diagonal depression in the neighbouring driveway channels water toward the catchment area immediately adjacent to the spot where your driveway begins to be undercut (see the diagram).

With your neighbour's permission, we ran water onto his driveway for 45 minutes. All of the released

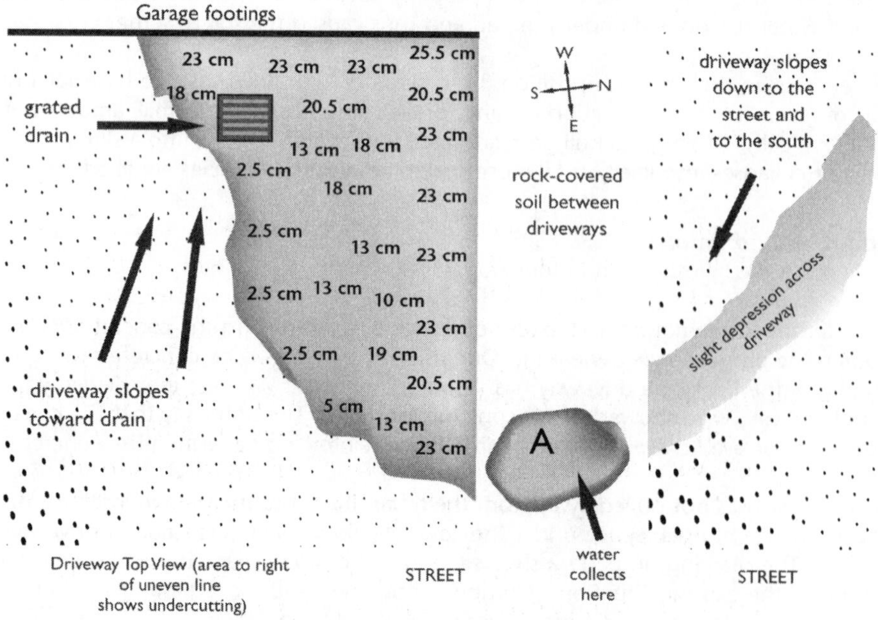

water ran down to the catchment area A, from which the water seeped under your driveway and formed pools of settling water. When we re-inspected in three hours, all that water had soaked in.

Conclusion

We're confident that the driveway undercutting has resulted from water-induced settling and that

Figure 17.10 A Causal Analysis *(continued)*

Ms. L. P. Garcia
June 21, 2008
Page 3

Corrective action will require shoring up the space under the driveway with an impermeable base and diverting water away from possible entry points along the north edge of your driveway. We can recommend Majestic Mudjacking for the former task—this company will pump a rapidly hardening slurry of cement, sand, water, clay, and loam under the exposed slab. If you wish, we'll undertake the water diversion.

We believe that you have grounds for requiring your neighbour to pay the costs of all repair work; local bylaws require each homeowner to control the passage of water off their property, so that the water doesn't flow onto a neighbour's property. Please let us know if we can be of further service. Our invoice is enclosed.

Sincerely,
TerraTech Engineering

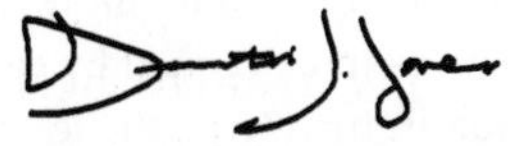

Dimitri J. Jones, C.E.T.

Figure 17.10 A Causal Analysis

ASSESSMENT REPORTS

Assessment reports essentially use the same approach as feasibility reports, except that assessments (also known as *evaluation reports* or *investigation reports*) are conducted *after* a project has been conducted, or *after* changes have been made.

Effective assessments begin by clearly describing the issue or the completed process, project, installation, or equipment purchase that is being studied. A short assessment report provides its main conclusion within the first two paragraphs. Next, it identifies (and in some cases, *justifies*) the criteria used in the evaluation. Applying those criteria, one by one, forms the bulk of the "Details" section that follows. Finally, the "action closing" discusses a more detailed version of the bottom-line statement given at the beginning and, where appropriate, recommends action.

One common variation type of the "assessment" report is actually closer to a feasibility report because it examines solutions that have not yet been implemented. A *yardstick* or *benchmark* report assesses and compares two or more alternative solutions or equipment proposals. In this type of analysis, appropriate criteria act as yardsticks by which the competing alternatives can be compared. Thus, the analysis is handled consistently and fairly. See Table 17.9 for the structure of these types of reports.

Table 17.9 Yardstick Assessment Report Structure

Section	Content	Comments
Action Opening	Define the situation requiring assessment—the problem or challenge. Report the main conclusion.	Only one or two paragraphs are necessary for a letter or memo. Use the heading "Introduction" for a semi-formal report.
Background	Briefly explain possible alternative solutions. Name the assessment criteria and explain how these were developed and selected.	The section could be called "Background" or "Assessment Method." Extensive technical data should be attached to the end of the report, not report, not placed in the background section.
Details of Assessment	Evaluate each alternative, according to the assessment criteria. The assessment could be organized by criteria such as cost, durability, product support. Or the alternatives could be examined, one by one: all the criteria would be applied to the first alternative before moving on to the next alternative.	Use a title like "Data and Assessment." Organize by criteria to allow the alternatives to be ranked by each criterion in turn (e.g., the least to the most expensive). Focus on each alternative in turn.
Action Closing	Conclude which alternative, or combination of alternatives, best meets the assessment criteria.	An implementation plan could be included, but it shouldn't be the focus of an assessment report.

RECOMMENDATIONS REPORTS

Many recommendations reports respond to reader requests for a solution to a problem; others originate with the writer, who has recognized a problem and developed a solution. This latter type is often called a *justification report.*

The purpose of a justification report is, at heart, similar to that of a proposal—both try to "sell" a solution or influence a decision to be made by the reader. However, these two kinds of documents differ in their approach. A proposal openly attempts to persuade the reader, while the justification report uses an apparently more objective approach: it shows how the facts inexorably lead to the recommended solution.

Whether solicited or unsolicited, recommendations reports could use either a direct pattern or an indirect pattern, depending on the reader's needs and attitudes. The *direct pattern* works best when you can anticipate reader support. Perhaps the reader has accepted similar recommendations in the past. Perhaps your recommended choice is so obvious and clear-cut that there is no other course of action. (See Figure 17.11, for such a situation.) Perhaps your recommended action matches company policy and practice. Perhaps the recommendation reflects the reader's own preferred approach or administrative bias.

Table 17.10 shows the direct pattern for the kind of recommendations that would be received favourably.

The direct recommendations report in Figure 17.11 responds to the following identified need.

> At a coal-fuelled electrical power plant, steel outflow pipes carry ash from the coal furnaces to storage lagoons (known as "ash pits" or "lagoons"). Some of these pipes (known as "ash lines") have been eroded and are in danger of failing. The writer knows, as does the reader, that the plant must replace the lines when they are in danger of failing; no other alternative action is available. Still, the recommended action needs to be justified. Also, the report needs to include some background information for the reader, who has recently transferred from a hydroelectric plant.

An *indirect approach* works better in situations where your reader may be unreceptive to your recommendations, or where the recommendations deal with a sensitive

Table 17.10 Direct Recommendations Report Structure

Section	Content	Comments
Action Opening	Refer to the need or problem in a way that your reader will recognize and accept. Use active verbs to recommend action.	Use a heading like "Recommendation" or "Problem and Solution."
Background	Name the alternative solutions you considered and explain the criteria used to assess the alternatives. Briefly explain why you discarded alternatives other than the one you selected.	In some cases, it may not be wise to quickly dismiss potential solutions; your approach may seem arbitrary. In such cases, apply the assessment criteria fully to all alternatives.
Details of Assessment	Discuss the benefits, comparative advantages, and drawbacks of your recommended solution. Detail the required resources and costs of your recommended solution.	Use a title like "Features of the Solution," or "Advantages and Requirements," or "How Our Firm Will Benefit."
Action Closing	Summarize the main reason for choosing the recommended solution and provide a plan for implementing it. Request authorization for your actions or specify the actions you're asking of the reader.	You could attach detailed supporting information such as performance tests, brochures, quotes, and financial projections.

Direct POWER Corporation **MEMORANDUM**

DATE: April 17, 2008

TO: Martin Scherre, Head Engineer, Correl Park Power Station

FROM: Judy Shohat, Plant Engineer, Correl Park Power Station *JS*

RE: Ash Line Replacement

As I mentioned in our plant meeting two weeks ago, some of the ash lines will need replacing. Shimon Barak and I have since examined Production Units 1 through 6 and found potential line failures for the lines leading from Unit 5 and Unit 6.

Recommendation

Correl Park should purchase 915 m of 300 mm (319 mm OD, 9.5 mm WT) commercial-grade black steel pipe for replacement ash line, at an estimated cost of $60 000.

Background

Approximately 2/3 of all ash line failures are detected and repaired with only some welding time required. However, if an ash line fails in the early evening and is not detected until morning, the line downstream of the failure will plug due to reduced flow velocity. When this has happened, we have had to contract a high-pressure washing truck to clean the line at a cost of from $5000 to $10 000. In order to maximize line life, we rotate the lines 1/3 turn every three or four years, to distribute the wear around the inner circumference of the pipe.

Findings

Correl Park Unit 6 has three ash lines—6A and 6B each have one rotation to go, so they will be fine for at least three more years. However, 6C ash line received its third and final turn in May 2004. Last week this line was examined and rotated in whatever direction exposed the thickest remaining wall to the area of highest wear. A random sampling of thickness readings along this pipe showed an average thickness of 4.47 mm, which is less than the original thickness of 9.5 mm. Experience has shown that an average thickness of equal to or less than one-half the original significantly increases the failure frequency. About 765 metres need replacing.

Currently, No. 5 ash pit is being cleaned out, with the ash being used for road construction. Once the cleaning is complete, it will be necessary to install about 150 metres of ash line to make this pit functional again. (We could then restore Unit 5 to service.) We considered installing the required line with used pipe that we have in stock, but that used pipe is no better than the 6C line that needs to be replaced.

Authorization

I request authorization for the recommended replacement so that bidding for the pipe supply contract can proceed. A Purchase Recommendation and a Technical Specification for the required pipe are attached.

Att.

Figure 17.11 A Direct Recommendations Report

issue, such as workplace harassment or strained employer–employee relations. Table 17.11 suggests the sequence for an indirect recommendations report.

To illustrate the indirect pattern at work, consider the challenge faced by Kim Briere and her colleagues in an Engineering Technology Diploma Program.

> Like those of many of her colleagues, Kim's writing skills are not adequate for the Applied English 140 course offered in the first semester of her five-semester program. After lengthy consultations with her colleagues, with a college academic counsellor, and with the chairperson of the Engineering Technology Program, Kim sends the recommendation illustrated in Figure 17.12 to Jake Stroud, the Applied English 140 instructor.
>
> As a result of her audience/purpose analysis, Kim realizes that her needs and those of her colleagues are different from those of Professor Stroud. She's also aware that he is opposed to teaching what he calls "remedial English." He has said that the English 140 class "applies university-level writing skills to real-world situations; there's no time to develop basic skills that university students should bring with them." Kim suspects that Professor Stroud will philosophically oppose her recommendations and that he'll resist her recommended action because it means more work for him. Therefore, she places her recommendations at the end of the report, after leading her reader through an analysis that shows that the majority of the Applied English 140 students really do require some writing instruction.

Table 17.11 Indirect Recommendations Report Structure

Section	Content	Comments
Action Opening	Refer to the situation in such a way that your reader realizes there's a problem or a need to be addressed. Briefly describe the approach used in this report.	A semi-formal report could have an "Introduction"; a letter or memo would not need a heading for this section. In a letter or memo, "connect" with the reader in the first sentence.
Background	Show the extent of the need or problem by presenting quotes, examples, or supporting statistics. List alternative solutions and explain the criteria used to assess the alternatives.	Either semi-formal or informal reports could use a heading such as "Background" or "Problem and Solutions."
Details of Assessment	Evaluate the alternatives with the identified criteria, starting with the least applicable solution. Present the best alternative last; apply the criteria vigorously.	Use titles like "Assessment of Alternative Solutions" or "Possible Solutions."
Action Closing	Summarize your recommedation. Show how it can be implemented. Ask for authorization or specify the actions you're asking your reader to take.	You might attach detailed supporting information such as performance tests, brochures, quotes, and financial projections.

MEMORANDUM

TO: Professor Stroud, English Department **DATE:** October 16, 2008

FROM: Kim Briere, Applied English 140

RE: **Improving Performance in English 140**

As you have stated in class, we have a severe problem in English 140: the overwhelming majority of the 38 students have failed at least two of the first three assignments so far. Students like me, who are committed to success, are very concerned. So we've consulted a College Counsellor and the Engineering Dean and we've identified the solution that is presented in this memo.

Thirty-one of us have met three times to discuss the issue. We need to solve the problem of low grades and we need to pass this class to move on to English 150 next semester. Many of us have also discussed the issue with our Department Chair, who warns us that we need a solid grounding in English to do well in our engineering program.

We see a problem for you, too. It must be difficult to have to correct so many things in our memos, letters, and reports. Also, we ask so many questions about grammar and sentence basics in class that you don't have time to present your full lecture.

The cause of the problem seems to be our "inadequate grasp of the English language" (your comment in the October 12 class). We agree with your assessment. In our meeting yesterday, 29 of us found that we lost an average 21 marks for mechanical errors and poor paragraphing on the last assignment!

So what can we do? We must satisfy three criteria. We need to

1. improve our English grades to succeed in our program of study
2. build our writing skills for future careers
3. find a practical, immediate solution

Following the advice of an Academic Counsellor, who showed us the Harvard Case Study model, we've applied the above criteria to four options:

1. work harder and spend more time on our assignments
2. lobby the college to reinstate the drop-in Writing Centre, which disappeared after last year's budget cuts
3. drop the English 140 course now
4. arrange for special tutorial sessions

The table on page 2 summarizes our thoughts about the four options.

Figure 17.12 An Indirect Recommendations Report *(continued)*

Professor Stroud **October 16, 2008** **Page 2**

Options	Improve Grades	Build for Future?	Practical and Immediate?
Work harder and longer	Not likely—we still need basic skills	No—we're held back by lack of basic skills	No—we carry seven classes each and spend too much time on English now!
Lobby for writing centre	Yes—individual examples and instruction could help us develop basics	Yes—could build the base we need	No—the college is still in a deficit situation and the bureaucracy moves too slowly
Drop the course	Perhaps if we take the course later, we'll succeed	We don't know how to build writing skills on our own	No—we need a solution this semester
Arrange for tutor(s)	Yes—we can develop the skills, individually and collectively	Yes—we need to build skills to get to the next level	This is the only practical possibility of the four options, **if** we can get the needed assistance

As you can see, we have only one viable option. In order to make that option work, two things have to happen:

1. We need times and a place to meet. Dean Cartwright has arranged a classroom for 4–7 p.m. on Mondays, Wednesdays, and Fridays. She has also found $1000 to pay a tutor or tutors.

2. We need your help to direct a tutor (or tutors); you have the best idea of our needs. Also, can you help us find one or two tutors? Perhaps you know capable retired professors or graduate students.

Please support our recommended action. We'd like to start no later than next Monday, so may we have your response in Thursday's class?

Kim Briere

Figure 17.12 An Indirect Recommendations Report

A variation of the indirect recommendations report is known as the Harvard Case Study model, which many business schools use as their primary learning and teaching tool. Listed below are the basics of that logical method of solving problems and viewing issues:

1. *Identify the critical success factors* in a given situation. These factors are used later in the process to evaluate proposed solutions. (In the scenario in Figure 17.12, the critical factors of passing English 140 and succeeding in future careers depend on English writing skills.)
2. *Define the problem* (e.g., "the overwhelming majority of... students have failed at least two of the first three assignments").
3. *Identify the causes* (e.g., "inadequate grasp of the English language").
4. *Develop possible solutions* that address the root causes of the problem (e.g., "work harder"; "lobby for writing centre"; "drop the course"; "arrange for tutors").
5. *Choose evaluation criteria* that emanate from the critical success factors (e.g., "improve grades"; "build for future"; "practical and immediate"). Apply these criteria equally to the potential solutions. (See the evaluation grid in Figure 17.12.)
6. *Choose the solution* that comes closest to satisfying the combined evaluation criteria (hire tutors); rarely does a solution completely meet all criteria, so pick the best of the lot.
7. *Recommend a detailed plan of implementation*—who should do what, when, how? (See the closing eight lines in Figure 17.12.)

This method is useful in all sorts of situations: deciding among competing bids, solving technical problems, making career choices, choosing courses of study, dealing with difficult people, and so on.

LAB REPORTS

The academic lab reports you write during your studies are different from the reports you'll write in industry. First, the names are different; at university or college, you submit *lab reports*; at work, you'll produce *laboratory reports* or *test reports*. The purpose also differs: your university or college lab reports help you learn material or prove a theory, while "real-world" laboratory tests have practical applications, such as the following:

- Water samples are tested to determine if a water treatment plant is working properly.
- Car seat child-restraint systems are tested to see if they are safe and effective.
- Soil core samples are tested to determine if a PCB-contaminated site has been decontaminated.

Various formats and requirements exist for academic and industrial settings. You will have to adapt to the specific requirements at your workplace. However, all laboratory and test reports use the general pattern shown in Table 17.12.

Table 17.12 Lab Report Structure

Section	Content	Comments
Introduction	Name and define the subject; review the subject's significance. Or indicate how this test fits into a project or routine procedure.	Could also include the scope of the research. Might discuss the rationale for the research or the objective of the research. Sometimes this is expressed as a question to be answered, sometimes as a hypothesis to be proved or disproved.
Equipment and Procedure	Where appropriate, describe the design of the investigation. List materials, instruments, and equipment.	Might also be called "Materials and Methods."
	Describe, step by step, how the test, experiment, or study was was done.	Use passive voice, third-person narrative, in the past tense.
	Describe methods for observing, recording, and interpreting results.	Use passive voice, third-person narrative, in the past tense.
Results	List recorded observations. Provide detailed relevant calculations.	Relate these results to the methods used to achieve them.
Conclusion	Analyze the percentage of error and the possible causes of error. Answer: ◆ Do the results answer the questions? ◆ Was the research objective met? ◆ Do you have doubts about the results? Why?	Often called "Discussion." Might also answer: ◆ Was the hypothesis proved? ◆ Are these results consistent with other research? ◆ Are there implications for further research?

FORM REPORTS

Many reporting situations can be handled with pre-printed forms (or electronic templates). Daily and weekly progress reports, for example, often use forms to keep clients and supervisors informed about a project. In many jobs, the best time to learn how to use job-specific forms is during the orientation period—the first two to three weeks on the job. Ask questions about the purpose of each form and the expected standard of completion. Also ask to see completed sample forms. (Some supervisors will prefer to show you how to use a given form only when that form is needed, and not before.)

Employers have passed on the following hints for successfully completing form reports:

- Read headings or questions on the form carefully. If necessary, ask directions, or look for models (precedents). Do not assume you've guessed correctly.
- Before writing or keying the form, read the entire form and make some quick notes of what to include.
- Choose *exact* words and phrases, not approximate descriptive language.
- Use jargon only if necessary; perhaps a non-technical person will read your report.
- Analyze the reader and the purpose for the report, and provide *all* necessary detail.
- Write or print neatly. On multiple-copy forms, press firmly!
- Check for errors in facts and figures, spelling, or logic.
- Know deadlines and stick to them. Remember that form reports are not designed for the writer's convenience; they're used to help you provide information quickly, while the information is still useful to the reader.

CHECKLIST FOR REVISING AND EDITING SHORT REPORTS

Use this checklist as a guide to revising and refining your short reports.

- Have you chosen the best report format for your purpose and audience?
- Does the letter or memo use proper format?
- Does the subject line forecast the contents of the letter or memo?
- Does the semi-formal report format contain the appropriate elements?
- Are readers given enough information for an informed decision?
- Are the conclusions and recommendations clear?
- Did you make the right choice between the direct and indirect patterns of presenting the report's bottom line?
- Are paragraphs single spaced within and double spaced between?
- Do headings, charts, or tables appear whenever needed?
- If more than one reader is receiving copies, does the letter or memo include a distribution notation to identify other readers?
- Does the semi-formal report's title page name other readers?
- Is the writing style clear, concise, exact, fluent, appropriate, and direct?
- Does the document's appearance create a favourable impression?
- Have you included useful details such as supplementary attachments, enclosures, or appendices?

WEB CONNECT

The listed sites discuss, and in some cases illustrate, a variety of job-related reports.

www.io.com/~hcexres/textbook/
www.ecf.utoronto.ca/~writing/handbook-shrtrept.html
http://jerz.setonhill.edu/writing/technical/reports/reports1.htm
http://oas.samhsa.gov/facts.cfm
http://writing.colostate.edu/guides/index.cfm?guides_active=engineer&category1=41

EXERCISES

1. Identify a dangerous or inconvenient area or situation on campus or in your community (endless cafeteria lines, a poorly lit intersection, slippery stairs, a poorly adjusted traffic light). Observe the problem for several hours during a peak-use period. Write a justification report to a *specifically identified* decision maker, describing the problem, listing your observations, making recommendations, and encouraging reader support or action.

2. Assume you have received a $10 000 scholarship, $2500 yearly. The only stipulation for receiving installments is that you send the scholarship committee a yearly progress report on your education, including courses, grades, school activities, and cumulative average. Write the report.
3. In a memo to your instructor, outline your progress on your term project. Describe your accomplishments, plans for further work, and any problems or setbacks. Conclude your memo with a specific completion date.
4. Keep accurate minutes for one class session (preferably one with debate or discussion). Submit the minutes in memo form to your instructor.
5. Write a recommendations report (choose one):
   a. You are a consulting engineer to an island community of 200 families suffering a severe shortage of fresh water. Some islanders have raised the possibility of producing drinking water from salt water (desalination). Write a report for the Island Trust, summarizing the process and describing instances in which desalination has been used successfully or unsuccessfully. Would desalination be economically feasible for a community of this size? Recommend a course of action.
   b. You are a health officer in a town less than one kilometre from a massive radar installation. Citizens are disturbed about the effects of microwave radiation. Do they need to worry? Should any precautions be taken? Find the facts and write your report.
   c. You are an investment broker for a major firm. A long-time client calls to ask your opinion. She is thinking of investing in a company that is fast becoming a leader in fibre optics communication links. "Should I invest in this technology?" your client wants to know. Find out, and give her your recommendations in a short report.
   d. The "coffee generation" wants to know about the properties of caffeine and the chemicals used on coffee beans. What are the effects of these substances on the body? Write your report, making specific recommendations about precautions that coffee drinkers can take.
   e. As a consulting dietitian to the school cafeteria in Blandville, you've been asked by the school board to report on the most dangerous chemical additives in foods. Parents want to be sure that foods containing these additives are eliminated from school menus, insofar as possible. Write your report, making general recommendations about modifying school menus.
   f. Dream up a scenario of your own in which information and recommendations would make a real difference. (Perhaps the question could be one you've always wanted answered.)

COLLABORATIVE PROJECT

Organize into groups of four or five and choose a topic upon which all group members can take the same position. Here are some possibilities:

- Should your college or university abolish core requirements?
- Should every student in your school pass a writing proficiency exam before graduating?
- Should courses outside one's major be graded pass/fail at the student's request?
- Should your school drop or institute student evaluation of teachers?
- Should all students be required to be computer literate before graduating?
- Should campus police carry guns?
- Should dorm security be improved?
- Should students with meal tickets be charged according to the type and amount of food they eat, instead of paying a flat fee?

As a group, decide your position on the issue. Brainstorm collectively to justify your recommendation to a stipulated primary audience in addition to your colleagues and instructor. Complete an audience/purpose profile (page 35), and compose a justification report. Appoint one member to present the report in class.

CHAPTER 18

Formal Analytical Reports

LEARNING OBJECTIVES

After reading this chapter, you should be able to

- Differentiate among four main types of analytical reports: evaluation/assessment, feasibility, causal analysis, and recommendations.
- Incorporate the structural and format elements of formal analytical reports.
- Use a planning outline and detailed working outline to efficiently produce a formal report.

Formal analytical reports are used for lengthy discussions (usually 10 pages or more) or when the topic is important enough to warrant formal presentation (title page, table of contents, formal heading system, formal documentation, and so on).

Less formal reports can use a memo, letter, or semi-formal format, as shown in Chapter 17.

Analytical reports answer these questions:

1. What data, observations, ideas, and background information can we gather about the topic discussed in this report? (*What do we know?*)
2. What inferences can we draw about the individual data? (*What does it mean?*)
3. What bottom-line conclusions can we draw? (*What does it all mean?*)
4. What recommendations stem from our conclusions? (*What should we do?*)

ON THE JOB...

The Report as "Product"

"Providing consulting services is our business. Our reports are our products, along with maps and other forms of documentation. All our reports provide detailed information, but most present analysis as well. After establishing its scope and objectives, the report describes the methodology and resulting data, interprets the data, draws conclusions, and (usually) recommends actions. A long-term project may require a series of informational and analytical documents...."

—Dr. Brian Guy, Summit Environmental Consultants

All readers of analytical reports want the first three questions answered. Many readers want the fourth question answered as well.

"Real-world" analytical reports answer questions for decision makers. Often, such reports provide the main basis for a reader's practical business decision. By contrast, "academic" analytical reports usually employ a more theoretical model although, increasingly, academic researchers are being approached by business firms for answers to difficult "real-world" questions.

FOUR MAIN TYPES OF ANALYSIS

As an employee you may be asked to *evaluate* a new assembly technique on the production line, or to locate and purchase (*recommend*) the best equipment at the best price. You might have to *identify the cause* of a monthly drop in sales, the reasons for low morale among employees, the causes of an accident, or the reasons for equipment failure. You might need to *assess the feasibility* of a proposal for a company's expansion or investment. There are many varieties of these four main types of analysis, but the procedure remains the same: (1) ask the right questions, (2) search for information, (3) evaluate and interpret your findings, and (4) draw conclusions and possibly recommend actions.

In general, then, your prime responsibility is to answer your reader's questions. In providing those answers, you will need to fulfill several attendant responsibilities:

- make the report's purpose clear
- use an appropriate structure for that purpose
- examine the topic at an appropriate level, and use appropriate language
- ensure that the report is readable, by evaluating it objectively
- write ethically: admit data limitations, and do not suppress contrary evidence
- forcefully make points
- make the report professional and error-free so that it gets the attention it deserves

Now, let's examine the nature of productive analysis, which allows readers to make informed decisions.

TYPICAL ANALYTICAL PROBLEMS

Far more than an encyclopedic presentation of information, the analytical report shows how you arrived at your conclusions and recommendations. Here are some typical analytical problems.

Will X Work for a Specific Purpose? Analysis can answer practical questions. For example, imagine that your employer is concerned about the effects of stress on employees. She asks you to investigate the claim that low-impact aerobics has therapeutic benefits—with an eye toward such a program for employees. You design your analysis to answer this question: *Do low-impact aerobics programs significantly reduce stress?* The analysis follows a *questions-answers-conclusions* sequence. Because the report could lead to action, you include recommendations based on your conclusions.

The questions posed in such a *feasibility report* are also termed *assessment criteria.* In order to answer the main question of whether low-impact aerobics reduce stress, supporting questions have to be asked (assessment criteria have to be applied):

- What causes stress?
- How is stress revealed physiologically?
- Can the physical manifestations of stress be measured?
- What kinds of activities reduce stress? How strenuous do they have to be?
- How long do these activities have to be followed before measurable effects are detected?
- Do the stress-reducing activities work equally well for all subjects?

Has X Worked as Well as Expected? *Evaluation (assessment) reports*, like feasibility studies, use a series of evaluation criteria to assess the performance or value of equipment, facilities, or programs. Unlike feasibility reports, however, assessment reports apply those criteria after a decision has been made.

Let's imagine, for example, that your engineering firm decided last year to network all of the firm's computers. Now, in assessing that network's performance, your report might use the following criteria to determine if the predicted gains have actually happened:

- performance gains, if any (the amount and quality of design work)
- communication within the firm (savings in meeting time)
- compatibility with the firm's design and communication software
- network reliability and down time
- the firm's ability to accept more complex projects

Is X or Y Better for a Specific Purpose? Analysis is essential in comparing machines, processes, business locations, computer systems, or the like. Assume that you manage a ski lodge and need to answer this question: *Which of the two most popular ski bindings is best for our rental skis?* In a comparative analysis of the Rossignol FTX and the Tyrolia Cyber D8SX bindings, you would assess the strengths and weaknesses of each binding on the basis of specific criteria (safety, cost, ease of repair, ease of adjustment, dependability, and so on), which you would rank in order of importance.

The comparative analysis follows a *questions-answers-conclusions* sequence and is designed to help the reader make a choice. Examples appear in magazines such as *Consumer Reports* and *Consumers Digest.*

Why Does X Happen? The causal analysis is designed to answer questions like this: *Why do small businesses have a high failure rate?* This kind of analysis follows a variation of the *questions-answers-conclusions* structure: namely, *problem-causes-solution.* Such an analysis follows this sequence:

1. Identify the problem.
2. Examine possible and probable causes, and isolate definite ones.
3. Recommend solutions.

An analysis of low morale among employees would investigate causal relationships.

How Can X Be Improved or Avoided? Another form of problem solving focuses on desired results and recommends methods of achieving these results. This type of analysis answers questions like these: *How can we operate our division more efficiently? How can we improve campus security?*

Usually, a *recommendations report* first identifies causes of a problem or components of a desired result. Then, the report presents possible solutions and uses a consistent set of criteria to evaluate each solution in turn. Finally, the report recommends which solution or combination of solutions to implement.

Many readers of solicited recommendations prefer to see the final recommendations first, *before* the full analysis that leads to those recommendations. Chapter 17 describes when a direct recommendations pattern would be more suitable than an indirect pattern.

What Are the Effects of X? An analysis of the consequences of an event or action would answer questions like these: *How has air quality been affected by the local power plant's change from burning oil to coal? Does electromagnetic radiation pose a significant health risk?*

Another kind of problem-solving analysis is done to predict an effect: *What are the consequences of my changing majors?* Here, the sequence is *proposed action–probable effects–conclusions and recommendations.*

Is X Practical in This Situation? The feasibility analysis assesses the practicality of an idea or plan: *Will the consumer interests of Hicksville support a computer store?* In a variation of the questions-answers-conclusions structure, a feasibility analysis presents *reasons for–reasons against*, with both sides supported by evidence. Business owners often use this type of analysis.

Combining Types of Analysis. Types of analytical problems overlap considerably. Any one study may in fact require answers to two or more of the previous questions. The sample report on page 405–12 is both a feasibility analysis and a comparative analysis. It is designed to answer these questions: *Is technical marketing the right career for me? If so, how do I enter the field?*

ELEMENTS OF ANALYSIS

Successful analytical reports feature the following elements.

Clearly Identified Problem or Question

Know what you're looking for. If your car's engine fails to turn over when you switch on the ignition, you would wisely check battery and electrical connections.

On page 394, a hypothetical employer posed this question: *Will a low-impact aerobics program significantly reduce stress among my employees?* The aerobics question obviously requires answers to three other questions: *What are the therapeutic claims for aerobics? Are they valid? Will aerobics work in this situation?* How aerobic exercise got established, how widespread it is, who practises it, and other such questions are not relevant to this problem (although some questions about background might be useful in the report's introduction). Always begin by defining the main questions and thinking through any subordinate questions they may imply. Only then can you determine the data or evidence you need.

With the main questions identified, the writer of the aerobics report can formulate his or her statement of purpose:

Define

> This report examines and evaluates claims about the therapeutic benefits of low-impact aerobic exercise.

The writer might have mistakenly begun instead with this statement:

Vague

> This report discusses low-impact aerobic exercise.

Words such as *examine* and *evaluate* (or *compare, identify, determine, measure, describe,* and so on) enable readers to understand the specific analytical activity that is the subject of the report.

Notice how the first version sharpens the focus by expressing the precise subject of the analysis: not aerobics (a huge topic), but the alleged *therapeutic benefits* of aerobics.

Define your purpose by condensing your approach to a basic question: *Does low-impact aerobic exercise have therapeutic benefits?* or *Why have our sales dropped steadily for three months?* Then restate the question as a declarative sentence in your statement of purpose.

Subordination of Personal Bias

Interpret evidence impartially. Throughout your analysis, stick to your evidence. Do not force viewpoints on your material that are not substantiated by dependable evidence.

Accurate and Adequate Data

Do not distort the original data by excluding vital points. Say you are asked to recommend the best chainsaw for a logging company. Reviewing test reports, you come across this information.

> Of all six brands tested, the Bomarc chainsaw proved easiest to operate. It also had the fewest safety features, however.

If you cite these data, present *both* findings, not simply the first—even though you may prefer the Bomarc brand. *Then* argue for the feature you think should receive priority.

As space permits, include the full text of interviews or questionnaires in appendices.

Fully Interpreted Data

Explain the significance of your data. Interpretation is the heart of the analytical report. You might interpret the chainsaw data in this way:

> Our cutting crews often work suspended by harness, high above the ground. Also, much work is in remote areas. Safety features therefore should be our first requirement in a chainsaw. Despite its ease of operation, the Bomarc saw does not meet our safety needs.

By saying "therefore" you engage in analysis—not mere information sharing. *Merely listing your findings is not enough.* Tell readers what your findings mean.

Clear and Careful Reasoning

Each stage of your analysis requires decisions about what to record, what to exclude, and where to go next. As you evaluate your data *(Is this reliable and important?)*, interpret your evidence *(What does it mean?)*, and make recommendations based on your conclusions *(What action is needed?)*, you might have to alter your original plan. Remain flexible enough to revise your thinking if contradictory new evidence appears.

Appropriate Visuals

Use visuals generously (Chapter 20). Graphs are especially useful in an analysis of trends (rising or falling sales, radiation levels). Tables, charts, photographs, and diagrams work well in comparative analyses.

Valid Conclusions and Recommendations

Along with the informative abstract, conclusions and recommendations are the sections of a long report that receive most attention from readers. The goal of analysis is to reach a valid *conclusion*—an overall judgment about what all the material means (that *X* is better than *Y*, that *B* failed because of *C*, that *A* is a good plan of action). Here is the conclusion of a report on the feasibility of installing an active solar heating system in a large building:

Offer a final judgment

1. Active solar space heating for our new research building is technically feasible because the site orientation will allow for a sloping roof facing due south, with plenty of unshaded space.
2. It is legally feasible because we are able to obtain an access easement on the adjoining property, to ensure that no buildings or trees will be permitted to shade the solar collectors once they are installed.
3. It is economically feasible because our sunny, cold climate means high fuel savings and faster payback (15 years maximum) with solar heating. The long-term fuel savings justify our short-term installation costs (already minimal because the solar system can be incorporated during the building's construction—without renovations).

Conclusions are valid when they are logically derived from accurate interpretation.

Having explained *what it all means,* you then recommend *what should be done.* Taking into account all possible alternatives, your recommendations urge specific action (to invest in *A* instead of *B*, to replace *C* immediately, to follow plan *A*, or the like). Here are the recommendations based on the previous interpretations:

Tell what should be done

1. I recommend we install an active solar heating system in our new research building.
2. We should arrange an immediate meeting with our architect, building contractor, and solar heating contractor. In this way, we can make all necessary design changes before construction begins in two weeks.
3. We should instruct our legal department to obtain the appropriate permits and easements immediately.

Recommendations are valid when they propose an appropriate response to the problem or question.

Because they culminate your research and analysis, recommendations challenge your imagination, your creativity, and—above all—your critical-thinking skills. Having reached a valid conclusion about *what is,* you now must decide *what ought to be done.* But what strikes one person as a brilliant idea might be seen by others as idiotic or offensive. Depending on whether recommendations are carefully thought out or off the wall, writers earn an audience's respect or its scorn. Figure 18.1 depicts the types of decisions writers encounter in formulating, evaluating, and refining their recommendations.

Consider All the Details

- What exactly should be done?
- How exactly should it be done?
- When should it begin and be completed?
- Who will do it, and how willing are they?
- Any equipment, material, or resources needed?
- Any special conditions required?
- What will this cost, and where will the money come from?
- What consequences are possible?
- Whom do I have to persuade?
- How should I order my list (priority, urgency, etc.)?

Locate the Weak Spots

- Is anything unclear or difficult to follow?
- Is it unrealistic?
- Is it risky or dangerous?
- Is it too complicated or confusing?
- Is anything about it illegal or unethical?
- Will it cost too much?
- Will it take too long?
- Could anything go wrong?
- Who might object or be offended?
- What objections might be raised?

Make Improvements

- Can I rephrase anything?
- Can I change anything?
- Should I consider alternatives?
- Should I reorder my list?
- Can I overcome objections?
- Should I get advice or feedback before I submit this?

Figure 18.1 How to Think Critically about Your Recommendations

Source: Questions adapted from Vincent R., Ruggiero. *The Art of Thinking,* 3rd ed. New York: Harper, 1991, 162–65.

Present the report's recommendations directly and clearly

When you do achieve definite conclusions and recommendations, express them with assurance and authority. Unless you have reason to be unsure, avoid noncommittal statements ("It would seem that" or "It looks as if"). Be direct and assertive ("The earthquake danger at the reactor site is acute," or "I recommend an immediate investment"). Let readers know where you stand.

If, however, your analysis yields nothing definite, do not force a simplistic conclusion on your material. Instead, explain your position ("The contradictory responses to our consumer survey prevent a definite conclusion. Before we make any decision about this product, we should conduct a full-scale market analysis"). The wrong recommendation is far worse than no recommendation at all.

A GENERAL MODEL FOR ANALYTICAL REPORTS

Every analytical report identifies an issue to be examined or an overall question to be answered for the intended audience. That issue or question is eventually settled in the report's conclusion section. In between, the report employs a series of supporting questions (analytical criteria) to lead to the bottom-line answer. Figure 18.2 illustrates the line of reasoning that might be used for a feasibility report about a

Question ⟶ **Answer**

INTRODUCTION	BACKGROUND	ASSESSMENT	CONCLUSION
Report's purpose: *Assess feasibility of proposed arena location* To be evaluated on basis of: ① *Cost of land* ② *Impact on traffic* ③ *City services infrastructure (water, sewer, gas)* ④ *Parking* ⑤ *Impact on business*	Explain process by which this site was identified Explain why other sites will be assessed later: *priority given to downtown development* Explain information sources	***Cost of Land*** • *City property—reserved for public* • *Equivalent value* ***Impact on Traffic*** • *Concerts and conventions* • *Hockey games* ***Availability of Parking*** • *Concerts and conventions* • *Hockey games* ***City Infrastructure*** • *Water* • *Sewer* • *Gas* ***Parking*** • *Requirements for various events* • *On-site parking* • *Parking within 4-block radius* ***Impact on Business*** • *Restaurants* • *Shopping*	*Land cost makes location desirable* *Feasible in terms of traffic flow, parking, existing infrastructure* *Little positive impact on local business* **Recommendation:** *Retain this site as feasible option, but look at other sites also*

Figure 18.2 A Question-to-Answer Development Pattern for Analytical Reports

proposed downtown location for a multipurpose arena. The city council likes the idea of a downtown location but wants to be certain that the location is practical, so it instructs the consultant to question traffic flow in the area, potential parking problems, and the ability of existing city services to handle increased demands. The city also asks the consultant to predict the impact on surrounding businesses.

Figure 18.2 shows the relationships among the introduction, the central sections, and the conclusion in one particular type of analytical report. Though other reports will use the same basic *introduction-analysis-conclusion* pattern, no general model can cover all formal analytical reports. Some reports will have one central section; others will have several. Much depends on the scope of the report and on the complexity of the analysis.

PARTS OF A FORMAL REPORT

Table 18.1 presents the sections that usually appear in formal reports, in the order they most often follow. (The numbers in parentheses refer to the suggested order for preparing the sections; following that order of preparation will help you write the report efficiently.) Your supervisor will tell you which sections are required for the specific report you're writing.

Strictly speaking, the transmittal document (letter or memo) does not belong in the front matter (i.e., between the title page and introduction). Transmittal documents *accompany* reports. For information and advice about transmittal documents and other parts of the front matter and back matter, see Chapter 21.

Introduction

The most important function of an analytical report's introduction is to identify the report's analytical purpose and preview how that purpose will be achieved. Usually that preview includes a list of supporting questions that will be used to answer the report's major question. In other words, the introduction lists the criteria used in the report's assessment or outlines the process used to determine

Table 18.1 Parts of a Formal Report

Front Matter	Body	Back Matter
Transmittal Document (13) Cover (14) Title Page (8)	Introduction (3)	Sources Cited (6)
Summary (4)	Central Section(s) (1)	Recommendation (2) Consulted (7)
Table of Contents (12)	Conclusion (2)	
List of Illustrations (11)	Recommendation (2)	
Glossary (9) List of Symbols (9) Acknowledgments (10)		Appendices (5)

causes, or previews the logical path to be used in arriving at a recommended action. In some cases, you will need to justify your choice of criteria or explain your analytical method.

An introduction may also require some or all of the following elements:

1. the context, situation, or problem prompting this report (background)
2. type of data on which the report is based and the type of source
3. other pertinent theoretical or background information
4. useful illustrations

An introduction also indirectly sets the tone of the report. The phrasing reflects whether the report takes an aggressive stance or uses a more cautious or conciliatory approach. For example, a causal report's direct, no-nonsense approach is signalled as follows:

> The Forest Ministry assembled an investigation team to determine if
>
> 1. forestry activities in the area contributed to the large destructive debris flow that killed three people, and if
> 2. additional investigation is required to assess the future risk of mass mudslides in the area.

Body Sections

Some reports need just one central section. For example, a 10-page causal analysis report might use a central section called "Contributory Causes," with a subsection for each of the factors that may have helped cause the problem or situation.

Other reports may need several central sections. For example, a 35-page assessment of three submitted proposals for a truck-leasing contract might have four central sections, one for each proposal and one entitled "Comparison of Alternatives." Each of four central sections would use the same set of assessment criteria to organize the analysis within each section. The report's conclusion section would identify the best of the three proposals and recommend whether to accept that proposal in its entirety, or to negotiate a modified version.

As you read the body sections of the two sample reports in this chapter, notice how the analytical criteria (supporting or exploratory questions) are presented in the introduction and then used to form logical structures in the report's main body. Notice also that the sample reports use clear, informative headings that identify exactly where you are at any point in the discussion.

Conclusion

The conclusion of an analytical report will interest readers because it answers the questions that sparked the analysis in the first place. Some workplace reports, therefore, place the conclusion *before* the introduction and body sections.

In the conclusion you summarize, interpret, and (perhaps) recommend. Although you have interpreted

ON THE JOB...

Investigation Reports

"We do investigations, which culminate in formal reports that present our technical findings, our explanations, and our recommendations. The reports examine what happened and why. These reports could go to insurance adjustors, lawyers, engineers, or clients, so it would be wise to phrase the summary and recommendations differently for each type of reader...."

—**Tom Guenther, consulting structural engineer**

evidence at each step in the analysis, your conclusion pulls the strands together in a broader interpretation. This final section must be consistent in three ways:

1. The summary must reflect accurately the body of the report, and the bottom-line conclusions must be firmly based on information, ideas, and analysis already presented in the report. Do not introduce new material in the conclusion section.
2. Your overall interpretation must be consistent with the findings in your summary and must present an honest and objective appraisal of the material.
3. If you include recommendations, they must be consistent with the purpose of the report, the evidence presented, and the interpretations given.

Some reports require a separate Recommendations section

Often recommendations form the last part of the conclusion section, especially if the report's primary purpose is to assess or to identify causes, but if the report's main purpose is to advise the reader what action to take, create a separate recommendations section. Remember also that not all reports require a set of recommended actions.

A SAMPLE SITUATION

The report in Figure 18.3 combines a feasibility analysis with a comparative analysis.

Richard Larkin, author of the following report, has a work-study job 15 hours weekly in his school's placement office. His supervisor, Mimi Lim (placement director), likes to keep abreast of trends in various fields. Larkin, an engineering major, has become interested in technical marketing and sales. In need of a report topic for his writing course, Larkin offers to analyze the feasibility of a technical marketing and sales career, both for himself and for technical and science graduates in general. Lim accepts Larkin's offer, looking forward to having the final report in her reference file for use by students choosing careers. Larkin wants his report to be useful in three ways: to satisfy a course requirement, to help him in choosing his own career, and to help other students with their career choices.

ON THE JOB...

Components of a Successful Analytical Report

"It must precisely address the scope of the project, nothing omitted, nothing added. It has to be clear and concise. The report must meet all the study's objectives: each objective must get the appropriate amount of coverage. The objectives must be clearly stated, and then it must be clear that they've all been met. The intended audience must find the report readable. For example, we write direct, no-nonsense environmental management plans for construction managers and contractors, but we also present complex environmental assessments for the government review agencies that issue permits. Different readers require different levels of content and readability...."

—**Dr. Brian Guy, president and senior geoscientist, Summit Environmental Consultants**

With his topic approved, Larkin begins gathering his primary data, using interviews, letters of inquiry, telephone inquiries, and lecture notes. He supplements these primary sources with articles in recent publications. He will document his findings in APA (author-date) style.

As a guide for designing his final report, Larkin completes the following audience/purpose profile.

Audience/Purpose Profile for a Formal Report

AUDIENCE IDENTITY AND NEEDS

My primary audience consists of Mimi Lim, placement director, and the students who will be referring to my report as they choose careers. The secondary audience is my writing instructor. The data I've uncovered will help me make my own career choice.

Lim is highly interested in this project, and she has promised to study my document carefully and to make copies available to interested students. Because she already knows something about the technical marketing field, Lim will need very little background to understand my report. Many student readers, however, may know little or nothing about technical marketing, and so will need background, definitions, and detailed explanations. Here are the questions I can anticipate from my collective audience:

- What, exactly, is technical marketing and sales?
- What are the requirements for this career?
- What are the pros and cons of this career?
- Could this be the right career for me?
- How do I enter the field?
- Is there more than one option for entering the field? If so, which option would be best for me?

ATTITUDE AND PERSONALITY

Readers likely to be most affected by my document are students who will be making career choices. I would expect my readers' attitudes to vary widely.

To connect with this array of readers, I will need to persuade them that my conclusions are based on dependable data and careful reasoning.

EXPECTATIONS ABOUT THE DOCUMENT

I know that my readers are busy and impatient, so I'll want to make this report concise enough to be read in no more than 15 or 20 minutes.

Essential information will include an expanded definition of technical marketing and sales, the skills and attitudes needed for success, the career's advantages and drawbacks, and a description of various paths for entering the career. Throughout, I'll relate my material to many technical and science majors, not just engineers.

The body of this report combines a feasibility analysis with a comparative analysis. Therefore, I'll use a reasons-for and reasons-against structure in the feasibility section. In the comparison section, I'll use a block structure followed by a table that presents a point-by-point comparison of the four entry paths. Because I want this report to lead to informed decisions, I will include concrete recommendations that are based solidly on my conclusions.

To address various readers who may not want to read the entire report, I will include an informative abstract.

My tone throughout should be conversational. Because I am writing for a mixed audience (placement director, students, and writing instructor), I will use a third-person point of view.

This report's front matter (title page and so on) appears in Chapter 21.

INTRODUCTION

Although technical occupations in the petroleum industry will continue to experience strong job prospects for the near future, other technical fields can expect only fair to limited opportunities in the five-year period ending in 2007 (*Job Futures,* 2003).

Therefore, recent and impending graduates might consider alternative careers where they could apply their technical training. One especially attractive field that combines science and engineering expertise with "people" skills is that of sales engineer, a specially trained professional who markets and sells highly technical products and services.

What specific type of work do technical marketers and sales specialists perform? The Ontario Job Futures website offers this job description:

> **[They] sell a range of technical goods and services, such as scientific and industrial products, electricity, telecommunications services and computer services. . . . They usually specialize in a particular line of goods or services. . . . Sales require constant interaction with clients. . . . There is also a growing inter-dependence between product development and sales. This link expands the specialist's role in providing vital information to product developers about customers' needs. (*Job Futures,* 2003, paras. 1, 3, 6)**

(For a more detailed job description, refer to "The Technical Marketing Process," on page 2.)

Undergraduates interested in a technical marketing career need answers to these basic questions:

- **Is this the right career for me?**
- **If so, how do I enter the field?**

To help answer these questions, this report analyzes information gathered from professionals as well as from the literature.

After defining technical marketing, the following analysis examines the field's employment outlook, required skills and personal qualities, career benefits and drawbacks, and various entry options.

Figure 18.3 An Analytical Report *(continued)*

COLLECTED DATA

Key Factors in a Technical Marketing Career

Anyone considering technical marketing needs to assess whether this career fits his or her interests, abilities, and aspirations.

The technical marketing process. Although the terms *marketing* and *sales* are often used interchangeably, technical marketing traditionally has involved far more than sales work. The process itself (identifying, reaching, and selling to customers) entails six major activities (Cornelius & Lewis, 1983, p. 44):

1. *Market research:* gathering information about the size and character of the target market for a product or service.
2. *Product development and management:* producing the goods to fill a specific market need.
3. *Cost determination and pricing:* measuring every expense in the production, distribution, advertising, and sales of the product, to determine its price.
4. *Advertising and promotion:* developing and implementing all strategies for reaching customers.
5. *Product distribution:* coordinating all elements of a technical product or service, from its conception through its final delivery to the customer.
6. *Sales and technical support:* creating and maintaining customer accounts, and servicing and upgrading products.

Fully engaged in all these activities, the technical marketing professional gains a detailed understanding of the industry, the product, and the customer's needs (Figure 1).

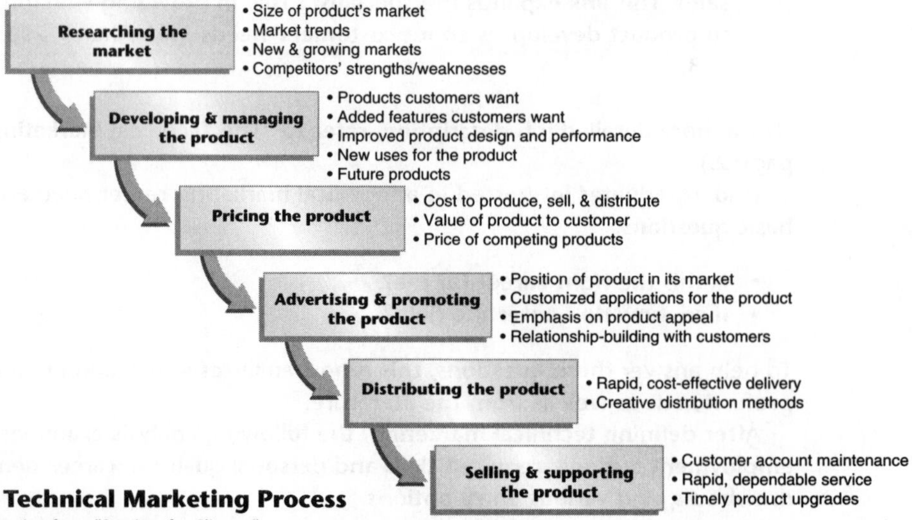

FIGURE 1 The Technical Marketing Process

Source: Selected information from "Services for Clients." Technology Marketing Group, Inc. (1998).

Figure 18.3 An Analytical Report *(continued)*

Employment outlook. The employment outlook for technical marketing appears excellent for graduates with the right combination of technical and personal qualifications. In 2003, Human Resources Development Canada predicted strong growth through 2007: "there will be many opportunities for workers with advanced computer skills, knowledge of import and export regulations, and the ability to speak a second language" (HRDC, 2003, para. 5).

That prediction appears to have been accurate:

- From April 16 to May 26, 2004, Monster.ca posted over 500 Canadian sales and marketing positions in its job listings (2004).
- For the Toronto area alone, on May 26, 2004, AllStarJobs.ca listed 13 technical sales and marketing positions, while on the same day Yahoo Canada's HotJobs site listed 27 such positions in Toronto (2004).
- Ontario Job Futures predicts "employment for this occupation is expected to grow more rapidly than the average for all occupations through the year 2007. As well, replacement needs will create many more additional jobs yearly because of the large size of this occupational group (HRDC, 2002, para. 5).

One especially promising area is environmental technical sales and marketing. Consulting firms, manufacturers of environmental products, recycling programs and equipment providers, purveyors of water purifying equipment and others all require knowledgeable sales specialists, especially in the wake of the Kyoto Accord (CCHREI, n.d., para. 2,3).

Technical skills required. Computer networks, interactive media, and multimedia will increasingly influence the way products are advertised and sold. Also, marketing representatives increasingly work from a "virtual" office. Using laptop computers, fax networks, and personal digital assistants, representatives in the field have real-time access to electronic catalogues of product lines, multimedia presentations, pricing for customized products, inventory data, product distribution, and customized sales contacts (Tolland, 1999).

With their rich background in computer, technical, and problem-solving skills, engineering graduates are ideally suited for (a) working in automated environments, and (b) implementing and troubleshooting these complex and often sensitive electronic systems.

Other skills and qualities required. In marketing and sales, not even the most sophisticated information can substitute for the "human factor": the ability to connect with customers on a person-to-person level (Young, 1995, p. 95). One senior sales engineer

Figure 18.3 An Analytical Report *(continued)*

Feasibility Analysis 4

praises the efficiency of her automated sales system, but thinks that automation will "get in the way" of direct customer contact. Other technical marketing professionals express similar views about the continued importance of human interaction (94).

Besides a strong technical background, marketing requires a generous blend of those traits summarized in Figure 2.

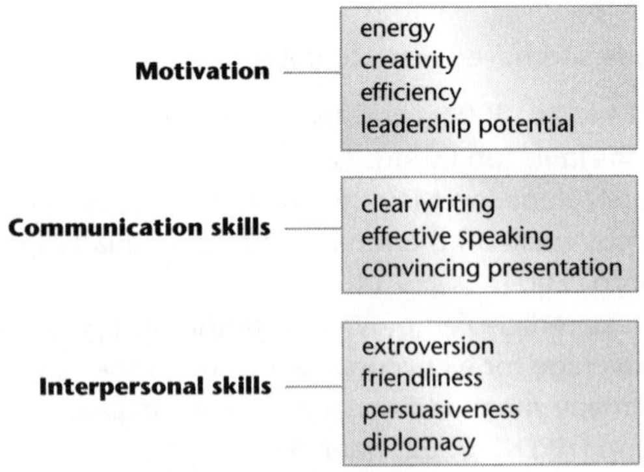

FIGURE 2 Requirements for a Technical Marketing Career

Motivation is essential for marketing work. Professionals must be energetic and able to function with minimal supervision. Career counsellor Anthony Meier describes the ideal candidates as people who can plan and program their own tasks, who can manage their time, and who have no fear of hard work (personal interview, May 11, 2004). Leadership potential, as demonstrated by extracurricular activities, is an asset.

Motivation alone provides no guarantee of success. Marketing professionals are paid to communicate the virtues of their products or services. This career therefore requires skill in communication, both written and oral. Documents for readers outside the organization include advertising copy, product descriptions, sales proposals, sales letters, and user manuals and online help. In-house writing includes recommendation reports, feasibility studies, progress reports, memos, and email correspondence. Increasingly, marketing professionals also need to incorporate digital images and digital video into their work (Meaux, 2004, p. 57).

Skilled oral presentation is vital to any sales effort, as Anthony Meier points out. Technical marketing professionals need to speak confidently and persuasively—to represent their products and services in the best possible light (personal interview, May 11, 2004). Sales presentations often involve public speaking at conventions, trade shows, and other similar forums.

Figure 18.3 An Analytical Report *(continued)*

Beyond motivation and communication skills, interpersonal skills are the ultimate requirement for success in marketing (Meier, 2004). Consumers are more likely to buy a product or service when they like the person selling it. Marketing professionals are extroverted, friendly, and diplomatic; they can motivate people without alienating them.

Advantages of the career. As shown in Figure 1, technical marketing offers diverse experience in every phase of a company's operation, from a product's design to its sales and service. Such broad exposure provides excellent preparation for countless upper-management positions.

In fact, sales engineers with solid experience often open their own businesses as "manufacturers' agents" representing a variety of companies. These agents represent products for companies that have no marketing staff of their own. In effect their own bosses, manufacturers' agents are free to choose, from among many offers, the products they wish to represent (Tostenson, 2004).

Another career benefit is the attractive salary—marketing professionals typically receive base pay plus commissions. National figures as of April 2003 indicate that technical sales specialists earned, on average, $19.38 per hour, while sales, marketing, and advertising managers earned an average of $28.06 per hour. The average for all occupations in the federal government's database was $16.91 per hour (Job Futures, 2003). These conservative government figures do not include sales commissions or performance bonuses.

Technical marketing is especially attractive for its geographic and job mobility. Companies nationwide seek recent graduates, especially on the east and west coasts. In addition, the interpersonal and communication skills possessed by marketing and sales professionals are highly portable (Meaux, 2004, p. 57).

Drawbacks of the career. Technical marketing is by no means a career for every engineer. Sales engineer Roger Cayer cautions that personnel might spend most of their time travelling to meet potential customers. Success requires hard work over long hours, evenings, and occasional weekends. Above all, the job is stressful because of constant pressure to meet sales quotas (phone interview, May 8, 2004). Anyone considering this career should be able to work and thrive in a highly competitive environment.

A Comparison of Entry Options

Engineers and other technical graduates enter technical marketing through one of four options. Some join small companies and learn their trade directly on the job. Others join companies that offer formal training programs. Some begin by getting experience in their

Figure 18.3 An Analytical Report (continued)

technical specialty. Others earn a graduate degree beforehand. These options are compared below.

Option 1: Entry-level marketing with on-the-job training. Smaller manufacturers offer marketing positions in which people learn on the job. Elaine Carto, president of ABCO Electronics, believes small companies offer a unique opportunity; entry-level salespersons learn about all facets of an organization and have a good possibility for rapid advancement (personal interview, May 10, 2004). Career counsellor Anthony Meier says, "It's all a matter of whether you prefer to be a big fish in a small pond or a small fish in a big pond" (personal interview, May 11, 2004).

Entry-level marketing offers immediate income and a chance for early promotion. A disadvantage, however, might be the loss of any technical edge one might have acquired in college.

Option 2: A marketing and sales training program. Formal training programs offer the most popular entry into sales and marketing. Mid-size to large companies typically offer two formats: (a) a product-specific program, focused on a particular product or product line, or (b) a rotational program, in which trainees learn about an array of products and develop the various skills outlined in Figure 1. Programs last from weeks to months.

Former trainees Roger Cayer, of Northland Products, and Bill Collins, of Ontarex, speak of the diversity and satisfaction such programs offer: specifically, solid preparation in all phases of marketing, diverse interaction with company personnel, and broad knowledge of various product lines (phone interviews, May 8, 2004).

Like direct entry, this option offers the advantage of immediate income and early promotion. With no chance to practise in their technical specialty, however, trainees might eventually find their technical expertise compromised.

Option 3: Prior experience in one's technical specialty. Instead of directly entering marketing, some candidates first gain experience in their specialty. This option combines direct exposure to the workplace with the chance to sharpen technical skills in practical applications. In addition, some companies, such as Roger Cayer's, will offer marketing and sales positions to outstanding staff engineers, as a step toward upper management (phone interview, May 8, 2004).

Although this option delays a candidate's entry into technical marketing, industry experts consider direct workplace and technical experience key assets for career growth in any field. Also, work experience becomes an asset for applicants to top MBA programs (Meaux, 2004, p. 58).

Figure 18.3 An Analytical Report *(continued)*

Option 4: Graduate program. Instead of direct entry, some people choose to pursue an MS degree in their specialty or an MBA. According to engineering professor Mary Stewart, MS degrees are usually unnecessary for technical marketing unless the particular products are highly complex (personal interview, April 2, 2004).

In general, job seekers with an MBA have a distinct competitive advantage. More significantly, new MBAs with a technical bachelor's degree and one to two years of experience command salaries from 10 to 30 percent higher than MBAs who lack work experience and a technical bachelor's degree. In fact, no more than 3 percent of job candidates offer a "techno-MBA" specialty, making this unique group highly desirable to employers (Meaux, 2004, p. 58).

A motivated student might combine graduate degrees. Deepak Amarjit, president of Northeast Systems, sees the MS/MBA combination as ideal preparation for technical marketing (phone interview, May 4, 2004).

One disadvantage of a full-time graduate program is lost salary, compounded by school expenses. These costs must be weighed against the prospect of promotion and monetary rewards later in one's career.

An overall comparison by relative advantage. Table 1 compares the four entry options on the basis of three criteria: immediate income, rate of advancement, and long-term potential.

TABLE 1 Relative Advantages among Four Technical-Marketing Entry Options

	Relative Advantages		
Option	Early, immediate income	Greatest advancement in marketing	Long-term potential
Entry level, no experience	yes	yes	no
Training program	yes	yes	no
Practical experience	yes	no	yes
Graduate program	no	no	yes

Figure 18.3 An Analytical Report *(continued)*

CONCLUSION

Summary of Findings

Technical marketing and sales involves identifying, reaching, and selling the customer a product or service. Besides a solid technical background, the field requires motivation, communication skills, and interpersonal skills. This career offers job diversity and excellent income potential, balanced against hard work and relentless pressure to perform.

College graduates interested in this field confront four entry options: (1) direct entry with on-the-job training, (2) a formal training program, (3) prior experience in a technical specialty, and (4) graduate programs. Each option has benefits and drawbacks based on immediacy of income, rate of advancement, and long-term potential.

Interpretation of Findings

For graduates with a strong technical background and the right skills and motivation, technical marketing offers attractive career prospects. Anyone contemplating this field, however, needs to be able to enjoy customer contact and thrive in a highly competitive environment.

Those who decide that technical marketing is for them can choose among the various entry options:

- For hands-on experience, direct entry is the logical option.
- For sophisticated sales training, a formal program with a large company is best.
- For sharpening technical skills, prior work in one's specialty is invaluable.
- If immediate income is not vital, graduate school is an attractive option.

Recommendations

Those whose interests and abilities match the requirements should consider these suggestions:

1. To get an involved opinion, seek advice from people in the field. A good place to start is by contacting professional associations such as the Canadian Professional Sales Association through its website, www.cpsa.com, or the Direct Sellers Association of Canada, www.dsa.ca/.
2. Any career in technical sales and marketing rests on thorough knowledge of the products and services sold, so a good starting point is a technical or scientific diploma or degree.
3. Each of the entry options has its advantages and disadvantages, so the fledgling marketer needs to match the chosen entry option to his/her career goals.

REFERENCES

[The complete list of references is shown and discussed in Figure 19.1, at the end of Chapter 19.]

[**Note:** References normally start on a new page. In this report, the REFERENCES page would be page 9.]

Figure 18.3 An Analytical Report

THE PROCESS OF WRITING REPORTS

The efficient writing process described in Chapter 3 certainly applies to writing lengthy reports. Also, the research advice in Chapters 15, 16, and 19 applies to gathering, recording, and documenting information for formal reports. To avoid unnecessary effort and to save time in writing a lengthy report, follow the advice in Chapters 3 and 15.

Using Outlines

You can use three types of outlines to write top-quality reports efficiently:

1. Use a *planning outline* to guide your research and initial planning. That outline will change as you gather material, but such an outline will continually remind you of the report's purpose and the analytical criteria to achieve that purpose. Figure 18.4, shows a planning outline for a recommendations report.
2. When you have chosen, evaluated, and analyzed the material for your report, write a detailed formal *working outline*, including:

ON THE JOB...

Visual Outlines

"For longer documents, I set up a graphics page with the sections of the report or proposal, almost like a flow chart. Then, I write the sections in turn, referring to my notes and rough paragraph outlines. It's a kind of outline system that's suited to my visual mind. Taking this organized approach has been especially useful in writing the training and user documentation for the software development and quality management systems I've been working on for the past few years. In both of those topic areas, the reader could take more than one path, which further necessitated visual planning of the entire document before I started to write it...."

—Jan Bath, civil engineering technologist and application developer

An essay's equivalent of a pre-summary statement is the essay's "thesis" or main point

- the report's *working title*
- a *purpose/audience* statement to remind yourself of the reason for the report
- a *pre-summary* statement to further remind yourself that everything in the report contributes to a "bottom-line" answer
- all *headings* and subheadings, named and formatted as they will be in the finished report's body
- a brief description of every *paragraph* in the finished report
- the name and number of each *illustration*, placed where it will appear in the report

This working outline will take some time to write because it forms a complete blueprint for the first draft, but a thorough, well-conceived outline will dramatically decrease the time required to compose, revise, and edit your first draft. Also, *each keystroke that goes into the working outline will appear in that first draft*; the headings and illustration labels will all be in place, and even the paragraph description phrases will likely end up in their respective paragraphs.

Project: Assess the CT83 Pit Jack Adapter's design and perhaps recommend improvements in (1) the weight and manoeuvrability of the jack adapter, (2) the choice of component materials, (3) the CT83's range of applications, and (4) the height.

R & D method:
- Consult the internet for competing products—automotive, heavy-duty equipment; transit vehicles.
- With assistance from our professors, assess the current design to evaluate the chosen materials, design components and stress points, and overall dimensions.
- Interview experts in the industry.
- Assess the gathered data and use the assessment as a basis for design modifications.
- Assess the cost of modifications; if necessary, redesign the adapter to decrease costs.
- Create drawings and models for engineering assessments and, later, tech sales material.
- If time allows, build and test a prototype.

Possible report topics:
- history of the CT83's development (?)
- problems/obstacles/design flaws—analysis after industry feedback
- solutions/design improvements
- cost analysis
- final recommendations (if any)

Information sources: Omega Lift website
Mott, R.L. (2002). *Applied strength of materials*, 4th ed. New Jersey: Pearson Education
Southern Tool Company website
Interviews with Bill Glaus, Bill Sand, Terry Lockhart, Henry Murphy

Figure 18.4 A Planning Outline

Compare the headings and paragraph descriptions in Figure 18.5 with the corresponding report in Figure 18.6.

3. As you use the working outline to compose the first draft, you can refer to your notes to establish the exact content of each paragraph, or you can write a brief, informal *paragraph outline* for each one. See page 418 for an example. Such "quickie" outlines don't have to be neat; they merely help you write coherent, unified paragraphs quickly. You may prefer to create a paragraph outline for each new paragraph as you come to it, or you may prefer to write outlines for several paragraphs in succession.

   Now, let's see this sequence of outlines at work.

The writers are mechanical engineering students engaged in a "real-life" project: the assessment and redesign of an industrial tool. Their reader, Dave Cochrane, owns CT Solutions, which designs and builds equipment used in the maintenance and repair of heavy equipment. He has commissioned this study in hopes of refining his CT83 Pit Jack Adapter so that it may become commercially viable.

The title emphasizes "recommended"

Title: Recommended Changes to the CT83 Pit Jack Adapter

This statement essentially poses the report's "question"

Purpose/Audience
This report will help Dave Cochrane decide whether it is feasible to modify the CT83 Pit Jack Adapter, to make it commercially viable, and, if so, what changes are needed.

And here's the answer to that question

Thesis (bottom-line) Statement
The CT83 has been transformed into an improved model, the CT04, which has enough promise to warrant making a prototype.

All headings use the font type and font size that will appear in the finished report

1.0 INTRODUCTION

1.1 Purpose
- purpose of report – improve CT Solutions CT83 Pit Jack Adapter

Figure 1 CT83 Pit Jack Adapter

1.2 Research and Development Method
- seven stages of process – numbered list

2.0 RESEARCH

Each bullet represents a planned paragraph

2.1 Interviews
- lead-in

2.1.1 Automotive Industry
- Bill Sand – no
- transition?

The writers will know if a transition paragraph is necessary when they write the first draft

2.1.2 Commercial Transit Industry
- Gerry Hanson – interested
- Hanson's recommendation
- key issue is versatility

2.1.3 Heavy-duty Industry
- Terry Lockhart – interested
- desires the same design criteria as Gerry

2.2 Examination of Products Available to Industry
- examined: transmission jacks, engineered stands, and heavy-duty engine stands

2.2.1 Transmission Jacks
- lead-in paragraph
- advantage of the column jack is height, but unstable

Each figure is named and inserted where it will appear in the report

Figure 2 Column-type transmission jack
- floor-type jack – larger maximum loading capacity and more stable
- drawback

Figure 3 Floor-type transmission jack

2.2.2 Engineered Stands
- very basic
- the CT83 Pit Jack Adapter falls into this category

Figure 4 Engineered jack stand

Figure 18.5 A Working Outline

(continued)

This paragraph likely requires a bulleted list

These specifications will be drafted directly from project notes

Figure 12 occupies a whole page, so its lead-in paragraph will ideally appear at the bottom of the previous page

2.2.3 Heavy-duty Engine Stands with Rotation Capabilities
- a recent innovation

Figure 5 Heavy-duty rotating engine stand

2.3 Problems and Obstacles
- four main problems: height adjustability, lack of versatility, incorrect material selection and optimization, cost efficiency

3.0 SOLUTIONS

3.1 Redesign Components
- transition paragraph

3.1.1 Casters
- reason for drop forged steel caster with polyurethane tread
- description

Figure 6 Semi-steel 2500 lb caster

3.1.2 Frame
- reasons for material choice

Figure 7 Frame
- design related to cost

3.1.3 Teleposts
- purpose and specifications (description)

Figure 8 Telepost height adjustment assembly

3.1.4 Mounting platform
- specifications – result in weight saving and usability (might be two paragraphs)

Figure 9 6061-T6 lightweight mounting platform

3.1.5 Mounting Plates
- specs
- how they will be used

Figure 10 Mounting plate
- introduce Figure 11

Figure 11 Illustration of quick-change mounting posts

3.2 Evolution in Design
- how the design meets the four design needs
- lead-in to Figure 12

Figure 12 CT04 engineered stand improvements

3.3 Room for Growth
- rotation and quick-change posts – why? (connect to Figure 13)

Figure 13 Illustration of concept for engine stand adapter compatible with CT04 frame

Figure 18.5 A Working Outline *(continued)*

3.4 Solution Specifications

- lead-in to Table 1

Table 1 Solution specifications for CT04 Modular Engineered Stand

4.0 COST ANALYSIS

4.1 Redesign

- two main variables
- resolving the cost/design paradox

4.2 Projected Cost Summary

- lead-in to Figure 14's main idea – cost is a factor of scale

Figure 14 Component costs of manufacturing the CT04 stand

- main point of Figure 14
- check with prototype builders re: cost saving
- introduce Figure 15

Figure 15 Total projected manufacturing cost

- assume a 35% markup
- caution re: figures (list them)

5.0 CONCLUSION AND RECOMMENDATION

- the CT04 addresses all apparent flaws with the CT83
- cannot recommend production because. . .
- should interview craftspeople
- excellent potential

APPENDIX A: Stress calculations

APPENDIX B: CT83 and CT04 engineering drawings and solid models

APPENDIX C: Materials quotations

Figure 18.5 A Working Outline

A description of the overall process used by the writers appears in page 1 of their report (Figure 18.6). Figure 18.4 is their planning outline, which they used to guide their research and development process.

After seven weeks of interviews, secondary research, design work, analysis, and computer modelling, the writers produce the detailed working outline presented in Figure 5.5. Such an outline is useful for any writer, but particularly important for a collaborative writing project—this outline keeps the team on track and speeds up the writing process.

When you compare this outline to the headings, order of topics, illustrations, and number of paragraphs in the final report, you'll notice that some aspects have

ON THE JOB...

Producing a Consultant Report

"A contract lists the expected scope of the project, the objectives, the tasks, the deliverables, the schedule, and the cost. We assign a project manager and a team who gather data, analyze it, write conclusions and recommendations, create supporting visuals, and add appendices. The project manager either writes or coordinates the writing. A completed draft is internally reviewed by people outside the project team, who follow a detailed set of guidelines to ensure quality control. Finally, we print and bind copies and make PDFs...."

—**Dr. Brian Guy, senior geoscientist, Summit Environmental Consultants**

changed during the writing process (a perfectly normal occurrence). For example, this outline lists 45 paragraphs, but the final report ended up with 52. Not all possibilities can be anticipated.

As an example of how the writing team works with its working outline, look at the second paragraph in the report section 4.1. The working outline's note in Figure 18.5 includes

- resolving the cost/design paradox

That note identifies the paragraph's basic idea; then, when it's time to draft the paragraph, the group might have created a simple paragraph outline, such as

- cost/design paradox resolved:

1. math stress analysis (Appendix A)
2. dimensions/material size affect mfg. cost & vice versa
3. repeat until all criteria met

Now, with the key elements in place, the team drafts a paragraph in the form of a process description (page 10 of the report in Figure 18.6):

> This situation created a cost/design paradox that could only be resolved through a process of iteration. Appendix A illustrates the mathematical stress analysis of the CT40's framework to derive the material selection and final sizing of the stand. The cost of manufacturing was then determined according to material size and dimensions, and allowed to change the dimensions and material sizing if a cost reduction was necessary. This procedure was repeated until we established a design that provided solutions to all criteria.

The three-stage series of outlines keeps the group organized and focused. The process also prevents duplicated effort—nearly every word in the working outline ends up in the final report. You might prefer to write your paragraph outlines in pen or pencil, perhaps in paragraph sequences, and then key in the paragraphs as you compose. Find the method that best suits your working style, but use outlines!

A FORMAL ANALYTICAL REPORT

Figure 18.6, on the following pages, presents the report produced from the working outline in Figure 18.5. To save space in this book, the report's 12 appendix pages have not been included.The formatting has been altered somewhat to fit it onto a 6.5" by 8.5" sample page, but the essential page design has been retained.

OUC
Okanagan University College **1000 K.L.O. Road, Kelowna, British Columbia V1Y 4X8**

April 19, 2008

Mr. Dave Cochrane
Owner, CT Solutions
6395 Star Road
Vernon, British Columbia
V1B 3J9

Dear Mr. Cochrane:

Re: The CT83 Pit Jack Adapter

In response to your request, we have completed an analysis of the potential of mass producing the CT83 Pit Jack Adapter. The results of that analysis are provided in the enclosed report, "The CT83/CT04 Pit Jack Adapter and Engineered Stand."

As the "CT04" part of the title suggests, we have modified the device to make it lighter, more versatile, and cheaper to produce. Those modifications have resulted from a process that has included consultation with industry, internet research, engineering analyses of the original design and its modifications, and cost analyses. All the engineering stress calculations point to a strong, versatile, usable piece of equipment. Also, our design modifications have been directed at producing the CT04 as inexpensively as possible. The projected manufacturing cost analysis for the CT04 shows a unit cost of $535.00, based on a mass production scale. That cost may be further reduced by consulting tradespeople and craftspeople involved in the production of the first few stands.

At this time, we do not have test data to recommend mass production of the CT04 Modular Engineered Stand. However, we recommend that CT Solutions manufacture a prototype and send it to a suitable testing facility. After the stand has been tested, you will be able to confirm whether the CT04 modular jack and stand should go into mass production, or undergo further design modifications.

We have enjoyed working on this project, and would be pleased to be involved in further development of the CT04 Pit Jack Adapter and Engineered Stand. As a result of our research, we believe the CT04 has strong potential for commercial success.

We would be happy to discuss the report and its recommendations with you, at your convenience. You can contact our group through me, at (250) 542-6654, or at vincible@shaw.ca. We look forward to hearing your reactions.

Yours sincerely,

Vince Cummings

Vince Cummings

Figure 18.6 A Formal Analytical Report—Transmittal Document *(continued)*

THE CT83/CT04 PIT JACK ADAPTER AND ENGINEERED STAND: ASSESSMENT AND PRODUCTION RECOMMENDATION

Prepared for Dave Cochrane
Owner, CT Solutions

Prepared by Vince Cummings, Joe Trainor,
Brandon Vidal, and Greysen Aby

Submitted:
April 19, 2008

Figure 18.6 A Formal Analytical Report *(continued)*

SUMMARY

An analysis of the potential of mass producing the CT83 Pit Jack Adapter has revealed four problems with the CT83 Pit Jack Adapter: a missing height adjustment, lack of versatility, incorrect material choice and usage, and low cost efficiency. The CT04 Modular Engineered Stand addresses all of these problems.

- Versatility and adjustability concern industry professionals. These problems were addressed by moving to a modular frame incorporating quick-change adapter posts and height-adjustable teleposts. Replacing the rigid mounting pillars of the CT83 Pit Jack Adapter with teleposts allows for a simple but effective height adjustment without the need for hand tools. The quick-change adapter posts featured on the frame increase versatility and will allow future expansion adapters compatible with the CT04 platform.

- The issue of incorrect material specifications has been addressed by a full stress analysis of the structure, followed by selecting the optimum materials and material sizes for the typical working environment of the CT04 Modular Engineered Stand.

- Closely tied to the material choice, a manufacturing cost analysis for the CT04 Modular Engineered Stand has been completed, along with the projected cost of manufacturing one, 50, and 500 units.

The CT04 Modular Engineered Stand has a footprint of 48"H X 36"W X 62"L, and a max loading capacity of 8000 lb. The stand is made out of a combination of AISI 1020 ANN, A-500 Grade "A" structural tubing, and 6061-T6 aluminum, and has a full assembly weight of 344 lb.

The projected manufacturing cost analysis for the CT04 shows that a per-unit cost based on a mass production scale is $535.00; however, it may be possible to further reduce this cost by consulting tradespeople and craftspeople involved in the production of the first few stands.

At this time, because of incomplete test data, we cannot yet recommend mass production of the CT04 Modular Engineered Stand, but CT Solutions should manufacture a prototype and send it to a suitable testing facility. After the stand has been tested for an appropriate period of time, it will be much easier to make a sound decision as to whether the CT04 Modular Engineered Stand should go into mass production, or undergo further design modifications.

Figure 18.6 A Formal Analytical Report *(continued)*

TABLE OF CONTENTS

Figure 18.6 A Formal Analytical Report *(continued)*

LIST OF ILLUSTRATIONS

FIGURES

TABLE

Figure 18.6 A Formal Analytical Report *(continued)*

1.0 INTRODUCTION

1.1 Purpose

This report determines how the original CT Solutions CT83 Pit Jack Adapter (Figure 1) can be improved to serve current industry needs. The original design bolted a floor-type transmission jack to the top of its frame, raising the jack off the shop floor by 36 inches. This elevation increase enabled service technicians to work on transport vehicles and heavy-duty equipment in an upright position either in a pit or with a hoist, increasing efficiency by up to 200%.

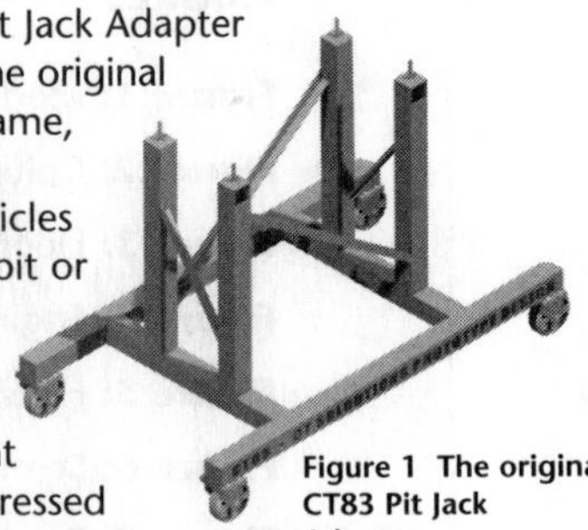

Figure 1 The original CT83 Pit Jack Adapter

The CT83 Pit Jack Adapter has generated positive feedback, including several manufacturing requests; however, the current design has some critical engineering defects that must be addressed before it can be manufactured. Therefore, this report investigates the detailed engineering changes necessary to produce the CT83. A recommended redesign of the original CT83 Pit Jack Adapter has resulted from the following process.

1.2 Research and Development Method

1. **Preliminary Research:** Most of the initial information came from a series of interviews and meetings with industry professionals. All interviewees were asked similar questions about their work requirements and where the current design for the jack adapter falls short. Also, we found various components and competing products on the internet.
2. **Analysis of Gathered Data:** After reviewing the data in a series of meetings, our engineering team created a preliminary list of all necessary design changes.
3. **Early Concept for Redesign of the CT83:** All aspects of the redesigned stand had to be combined into a complete, cohesive unit. As a result, the redesigning task was viewed as one large problem to be solved rather than several small problems. Addressing the problems and flaws uncovered by the research was handled collectively by the team, rather than in individually delegated tasks. By methodically attacking all key design faults together, all team members were able to provide input into the redesign of the jack adapter.
4. **Final Research:** Following the redesign stage, the potential prototype design was presented to the previously interviewed professionals for more feedback. This second series of meetings identified a few more minor issues that needed to be addressed.
5. **Final Concept for Redesign of the Adapter:** The second set of industry suggestions and comments helped lead to a final design for the jack adapter.
6. **Mathematical Analysis:** A mathematical analysis of the final adapter concept provided the data to determine material specifications, safety factors, and final dimensions.
7. **Cost Analysis:** Once material sizes and final dimensions were decided, an accurate cost for the new design was determined. The resulting comprehensive cost breakdown for the redesigned adapter for prototype and mass-scale production is provided in Section 4.0.
8. **Engineering Drawings and Solid Models:** The full set of detailed engineering drawings and production plans, as well as working assembly drawings for the adapter, are found in Appendix B and Appendix C of this report.

Figure 18.6 A Formal Analytical Report *(continued)*

2.0 RESEARCH

2.1 Interviews

Interviews were conducted within three targeted industries: the automotive industry, the commercial transit industry, and the heavy-duty industry.

2.1.1 Automotive industry

After having been shown models and engineering drawings of the CT83 Pit Jack Adapter, Bill Sand, the shop foreman at Cosworth Specialty Motors, could not see a plausible use for the CT83 in his maintenance environment. He believes that the CT83 Pit Jack Adapter is better suited to the heavy-duty use for which it was originally designed; the CT83 is too large for a general automotive setting: "Most likely, the CT83 would actually hinder maintenance times, and potential benefits we might achieve through extra capacity and stability wouldn't be realized. A regular floor-type or column-type transmission jack is suitable for any situation encountered in our maintenance shop" (personal interview, 2004, February 10).

Because a tool such as the CT83 would not benefit the automotive industry, Bill Sand was unable to provide suggestions for redesigning the CT83 Pit Jack Adapter.

2.1.2 Commercial transit industry

Gerry Hanson, the service manager of Bell Equipment, showed interest in the CT83 and was able to illustrate some scenarios where his facility would benefit from its use. He pointed out several possible design improvements (personal interview, 2004, February 19).

He recommended a height adjustment that would allow the CT83 to be used on a variety of jobs. Because not all maintenance shops have the same equipment, or emulate the exact same working environment, a height adjustment would enable the adapter to conform to the needs of different maintenance facilities.

For Mr. Hanson, another key issue is the versatility of the CT83. Having just recently purchased a heavy-duty engine stand capable of 360 degrees of rotation, he provided us with the idea of increasing versatility by enabling different attachments to be placed onto the CT83. For one thing, heavy-duty engine stands capable of rotation are very expensive—he had just paid $5000 for a Revolver model. If it could be made possible for the adapter to function both as an engine stand and as a jack adapter, it would not only increase versatility, but would also most likely be cheaper for maintenance facilities in the long run. This particular suggestion is explored and realized in further depth later in this report.

This interview illustrated quite clearly that addressing the versatility and ease of use of the CT83 could create serious potential for a modified jack adapter in the commercial transit industry.

Figure 18.6 A Formal Analytical Report *(continued)*

2.1.3 Heavy-duty industry

On February 23, 2004, Terry Lockhart, an instructor in the Heavy Duty Trades Department of Okanagan University College, showed a great deal of interest in the CT83 Pit Jack Adapter. He provided several possible scenarios where the OUC training facility could use such a tool.

Terry Lockhart desires the same design criteria as the professional in the commercial transit industry, especially the height adjustment. An added height adjustment could enable the CT83 to raise heavy equipment transmissions off the facility's concrete floor to a comfortable height, while providing a mobile working platform for the technician. The feedback received from Mr. Lockhart at OUC was very similar to the feedback received from Mr. Hanson at Bell Equipment. Both hope to use the CT83 for much more than just transmission removal.

2.2 Examination of Products Available to Industry

In order to conduct further research, and in an effort to determine whether or not the CT83 is a unique product, we examined three types of tooling currently being used in industry: transmission jacks, engineered stands, and heavy-duty engine stands (with rotational capabilities). Although engine stands with rotational capabilities are not directly related to this report, or to the CT83 Pit Jack Adapter, several of our research sources mentioned their growing popularity in industry.

2.2.1 Transmission jacks

Two primary types of transmission jacks are used in industry: the column type and the floor type. Both types of jacks have advantages and disadvantages.

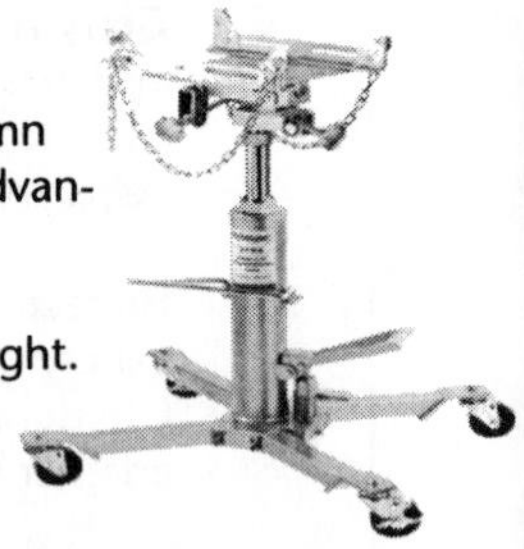

Figure 2 Column-type transmission jack (Omega)

As shown in Figure 2, the main advantage of the column jack is its height. The ability to work underneath heavy equipment and commercial transport vehicles in an upright position often increases the technician's efficiency. However, the increased working height makes the jack unstable due to a higher centre of gravity, and the decreased cross-section and inertia of the base result in a decreased maximum loading capacity.

Figure 3 Floor-type transmission jack (Omega)

The floor-type jack is shown in Figure 3. Its centre of gravity is much closer to the ground, which, coupled with the increased cross-section and inertia of its base, gives it a much larger maximum loading capacity than the column jack. Its lower operating centre of gravity also makes it much more stable than a column-type jack. The greater stability gives the jack higher maximum loading capacities, and also makes it safer for the technician.

The main drawback of the floor-type jack is the difficulty associated with working underneath heavy equipment so low to the ground. Using a creeper or a similar device becomes necessary, and in most circumstances the technician's mobility becomes severely limited. Its low working height and difficult working conditions compromise the technician's efficiency.

Figure 18.6 A Formal Analytical Report *(continued)*

2.2.2 Engineered stands

Engineered stands, like the one shown in Figure 4, are usually very basic tools used as support structures, often incorporating a height adjustment. They are rated by their design engineers for a maximum loading capacity and are used to support heavy equipment while it is being serviced.

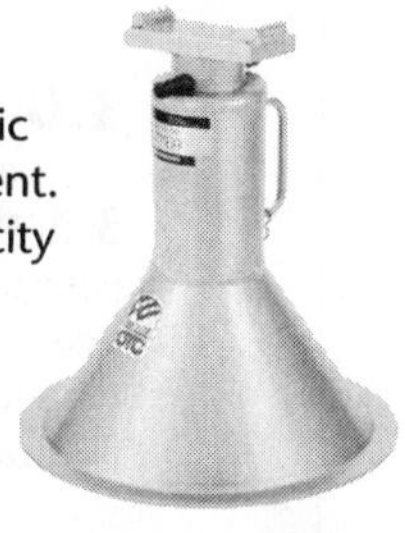

Figure 4 Engineered jack stand (Omega)

The CT83 Pit Jack Adapter falls into the category of engineered stands. A check of several websites for engineered stands similar to the CT83 Adapter revealed nothing similar being currently used in industry.

2.2.3 Heavy-duty engine stands with rotation capabilities

One of the primary redesign elements established in our evaluation of the CT83 was an increase in versatility. Although automotive stands with rotational capabilities have been commonplace for some time now, heavy-duty engine stands with rotational capabilities designed for the maintenance of extremely large diesel engines are a recent innovation. The type of stand illustrated in Figure 5 is gaining popularity every day in industry. The stable frame and high maximum loading capacity of the CT83 warrant an investigation into the possibility of assuming this capability.

Figure 5 Heavy-duty rotating engine stand (Omega)

2.3 Problems and Obstacles

Four main problems with the CT83 were determined through the industrial interviews and an examination of other industrial equipment.

- **Height adjustability:** Due to varying operating environments, and possible varying applications for the CT83, this device really must add height adjustability.
- **Lack of versatility:** An ability to accommodate different types of floor jacks, and possibly even adapters, is currently missing. The redesigned jack adapter must be more versatile than its predecessor. The final design must be able to conform to the existing equipment used at any given shop.
- **Incorrect material selection and optimization:** The CT83 was designed and fabricated with little regard for proper material selection and application. This approach has resulted in a heavy, over-designed adapter that would be expensive to produce. Proper material selection and use will provide the strength, safety, and cost effectiveness needed in order to move to a mass-producible version.
- **Cost efficiency:** Ultimately, the goal of this report is to determine whether CT Solutions can make money with this new product. A thorough redesign of the adapter must reduce cost while still ensuring that a high level of quality and safety is maintained.

Figure 18.6 A Formal Analytical Report *(continued)*

3.0 SOLUTIONS

3.1 Redesign Components

Feedback from industry showed that all aspects of the original pit jack adapter would need to be addressed in order to supply potential customers with a useful tool. A detailed explanation of all changes to the CT83 design, moving from the ground up, is illustrated in the following section.

3.1.1 Casters

In light of the environment that the pit jack adapter would be operating in, the following design seems the most suitable. Most maintenance shops will likely have rough, uneven floors with floor dry or dirt on the ground, so a caster with a high loading capacity and smooth manoeuvrability is needed. At first, a solid steel caster seemed to be the best choice due to its high loading capacity; however, the solid steel caster does not provide the pit jack adapter with the required manoeuvrability. Therefore, we chose a drop-forged steel caster with polyurethane tread.

Figure 6 Semi-steel 2500 lb caster

The drop-forged steel caster with polyurethane tread has a 6" diameter wheel, a 2" tread width, and a total capacity of 2500 lb. (Figure 6). Because four casters are required, the total capacity that all four casters can take is 10 000 lb. The semi-steel design greatly adds to the capacity of the caster, while the polyurethane tread ensures easy rolling of the pit jack adapter under maximum load. Ease of use is one of the key design considerations for the pit jack adapter, and the steel/poly casters greatly improve the usability while only marginally increasing the price. Suitable casters may be purchased for $21.00 each.

3.1.2 Frame

The frame of the design will end up taking the majority of the load, which will cause bending moments at the base of the load-bearing posts and at the points where the centre channels connect with the side rails. For the frame, our team contemplated changing to a less expensive steel than square tubing. We considered fabricating the frame from I-beam or wide flange; however, suitable sizes were not available and would not have greatly reduced weight or cost. The wall thickness of the tubing was reduced from 3/8" to 1/4" while retaining the maximum loading capacity required (Figure 7).

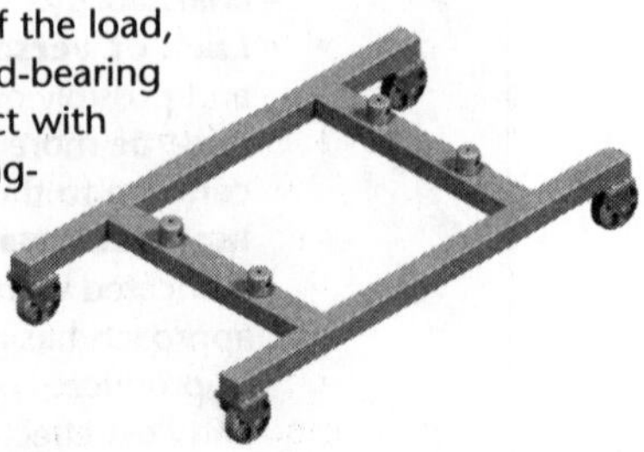

Figure 7 Frame

Figure 18.6 A Formal Analytical Report *(continued)*

The frame itself has a maximum loading capacity of 16 000 lb; however, for safety reasons, it should be rated at 8000 lb. The frame is constructed out of A-500 grade "A" structural tubing, the side rails are 3"H X 3"W X 1/4"T, and the centre channels are 3"H X 4"W X 1/4"T. With a maximum load rating of 8000 lb, the pit jack adapter should have a wide range of applications. For example, the frame should easily be able to support the back end of a city bus (half of the bus's net weight), and theoretically the frame should be able to support the entire weight of the bus without failing.

Cost is decreased by increasing the size of the centre channels. Changing from 3"H X 3"W square tubing to 3"H X 4"W rectangular tubing, we incorporated off-the-shelf teleposts to introduce a simple height adjustment.

3.1.3 Teleposts

With wider frame centre channels, teleposts were incorporated into the design as a simple height adjustment. Each post is rated at 8300 lb maximum loading capacity; with four posts, the total maximum loading capacity is 33 200 lb. A 33 200 lb capacity far surpasses what is required for the CT04 design. The posts provide a height range of 18"–33". The posts use a simple design featuring two pieces of round tubing; one piece has a diameter of 3", and the other has a diameter of 2-1/2" (Figure 8). The smaller diameter piece fits inside the larger diameter piece and can be secured at the desired height with the use of a shear pin. Each post comes equipped with a fine-tuning height adjuster, which can be used after the pin is secured to acquire the perfect height required for the job.

Since the teleposts arrive ready to use right off the shelf, the only extra costs incurred with this design would be for required bracing materials to be welded between each telepost. This would ensure safety and stability in off-centre loading or side-loading situations. Total costs for the teleposts are $20.50 each and $20.00 for the bracing materials when purchased on a mass-production scale.

Figure 8
Telepost height adjustment assembly

3.1.4 Mounting platform

The mounting platform was created to increase stability to the teleposts at higher adjustments (Figure 9). This design features all-aluminum construction. The weight savings and improved ease of use should more than make up for the extra cost incurred. The mounting platform is made from 6061-T6 aluminum, the side rails are 2"H X 1"W X 1/8"T, the mounting caps are 3" outside diameter X 2.5" inside diameter welded tubing, and the support plates are 3" diameter solid.

Figure 9 6061-T6 lightweight mounting platform

If the mounting platform were made from steel, its weight would be around 43 lb. Although this weight is not unmanageable for one person, the length of the platform would make it quite awkward for a single technician to handle. All-aluminum construction reduces the platform weight to about 15 lb, so it can easily be assembled and adjusted by a single operator.

Figure 18.6 A Formal Analytical Report *(continued)*

3.1.5 Mounting plates

The mounting plates will be used to bolt any existing floor-type transmission jack to the structure. We chose 4"W X 1/2"T C1018/1020 flat bar steel for the mounting plates (Figure 10). These plates require quite a bit of machining, and C1018/1020 is easily machined.

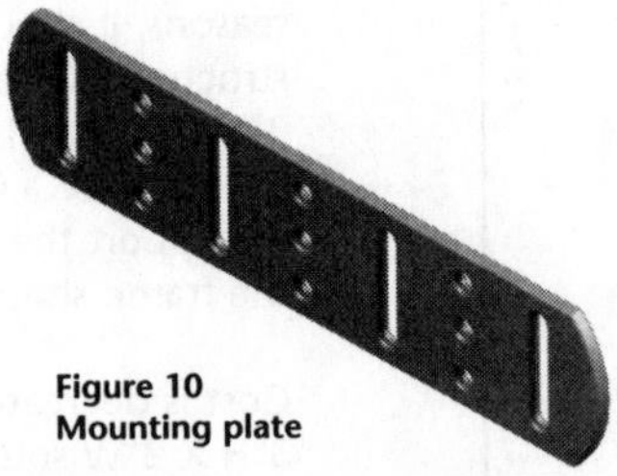

Figure 10
Mounting plate

There is no standard for how a floor-type transmission jack is designed, so each mounting plate will vary from use to use. Several different mounting plates, with different bolt patterns, must be available to accommodate the many existing name-brand floor-type transmission jacks. Providing customized mounting plates will affect the cost due to the machining that will be required for each different plate.

3.2 An Evolved Design

The final design addresses all of the four main pressing design issues: versatility, adjustability, proper material selection/optimization, and cost efficiency:

- Teleposts provide the design with a height adjustment, cost reduction, and increased usability.
- A modular assembly increases the versatility of the design by featuring the quick-change posts illustrated in Figure 11. The quick-change posts highlighted in the figure can easily adapt to different attachments without requiring hand tools. Adapters fit securely over the posts on the frame and are secured in place with a locking shear pin. For example, the mounting platform detailed in Figure 9 could be pinned directly to the frame to allow the user to work closer to the ground.

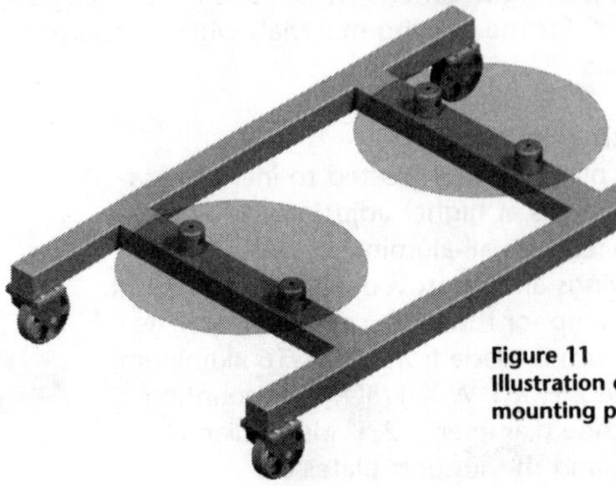

Figure 11
Illustration of quick-change mounting posts

The original pit jack adapter was designed for one specific job with no real engineering in its design. It is now more than just a pit jack adapter. Its increased versatility and adjustability gives this new design a wide range of capabilities. The CT04 Modular Engineered Stand is detailed in Figure 12 on the next page.

Figure 18.6 A Formal Analytical Report *(continued)*

Recommendation: CT83 Pit Jack Adapter / CT04 Engineered Stand

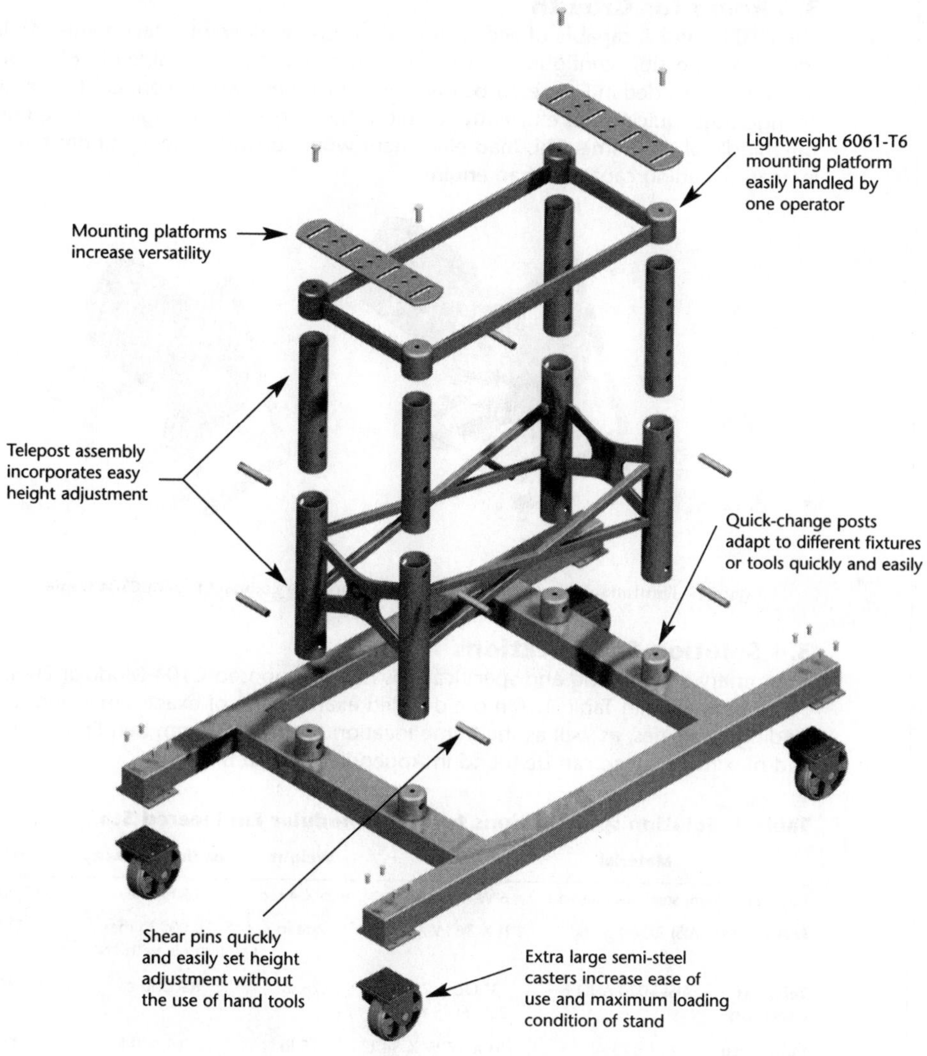
Lightweight 6061-T6 mounting platform easily handled by one operator
Mounting platforms increase versatility
Telepost assembly incorporates easy height adjustment
Quick-change posts adapt to different fixtures or tools quickly and easily
Shear pins quickly and easily set height adjustment without the use of hand tools
Extra large semi-steel casters increase ease of use and maximum loading condition of stand

Figure 12 Exploded view of the CT04 Engineered Stand's design improvements.

Figure 18.6 A Formal Analytical Report *(continued)*

3.3 Room for Growth

The CT04 stand is capable of accommodating several different attachments. An illustration of a possible configuration featuring an engine stand capable of 360 degrees of rotation is provided in Figure 13 below. This attachment would connect to the quick-change posts quickly and efficiently, keeping the weight of the engine centred over the middle of the frame. This load placement would provide stability under the increased loading capacity of an engine.

Figure 13 Illustration of concept for engine stand adaptor compatible with CT04 frame

3.4 Solution Specifications

A summary of the sizing and specifications of the proposed CT04 Modular Engineered Stand is detailed in Table 1. A more detailed examination of exact dimensions and loading capacities, as well as the frame location of the maximum bending moments and maximum shear, can be found in Appendices A and B.

Table 1 Solution specifications for CT04 Modular Engineered Stand

	Material	Size	Weight	Loading Capacity	Cost (CAD)
Casters	Semi-steel w/polytread	6"W X 2" tread	8 lb X 4 req.	2500 lb ea.	$17.70 x 4 req.
Frame	AISI A-500 grade "A" tube	3"H X 36"W X 62"L	204 lb	16 000 lb max 8000 lb with "N"	$150.00
Telepost Assembly	AISI 1020 ANN	3" OD x 2.5" 36"–60" range	73 lb	8800 lb ea.	$102.00
Mounting Platform	6061-T6 Al	2.5"H X 17"W X 34"L	15 lb	> 18 000 lb	$55.00
Mounting Plates	AISI C1018/1020	4"W X 18"L X 1/4"T	11 lb X 2 req.	> 18 000 lb	$20.00 avg.
Totals	**N/A**	**48"H X 36"W X 62"L***	**344 lb**	**8000 lb****	**$397.80*****

* Footprint size for a completely assembled unit.

** Based on a safety factor of two, and the maximum loading capacity of the frame (weakest section).

*** Cost is based on mass-production scale, and would be higher for prototype construction.

Figure 18.6 A Formal Analytical Report *(continued)*

4.0 COST ANALYSIS

4.1 Cost Analysis Procedure and Cost/Design Relationship

Two main variables needed to be eliminated in order to determine an actual manufacturing cost for the CT04:

- The relationship between the specifications and features of the redesigned stand and the stand's final cost is affected by current industry needs, and how much industry is willing to pay to satisfy those needs. Therefore, all research and final design content had to be complete before costs could be considered.
- Cost factors such as material choice and final product dimensions could not be properly determined until a full stress analysis had been completed; however, a stress analysis could not be completed until material and dimensions had been chosen.

This situation created a cost/design paradox that could only be resolved through a process of iteration. Appendix A illustrates the mathematical stress analysis of the CT40's framework to derive the material selection and final sizing of the stand. The cost of manufacturing was then determined according to material size and dimensions, and allowed to change the dimensions and material sizing if a cost reduction was necessary. This procedure was repeated until we established a design that provided solutions to all criteria.

4.2 Projected Cost Summary

The projected cost of manufacturing for the CT04 stand varies substantially according to the number of units planned for production. Figure 14 illustrates the projected cost to manufacture the stand for a one-prototype test unit, a 50-unit order, and a mass production order of 500 units.

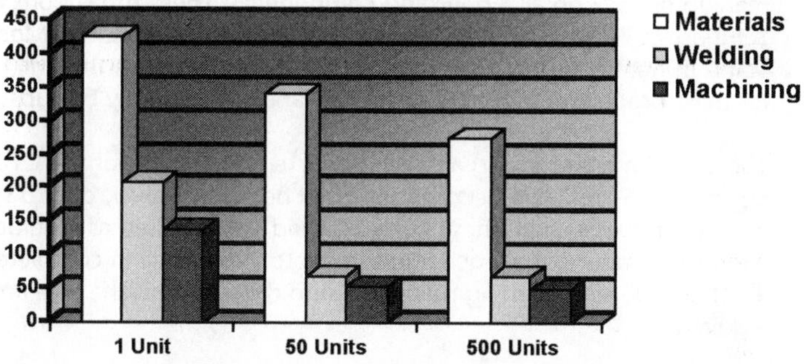

Figure 14 Component costs of manufacturing the CT04 stand

As detailed in Figure 14, the cost of labour to produce the stand is nearly as high as the cost of raw materials and components. Customized jigs and fixtures for the efficient production of the stand should seriously be considered in order to possibly further reduce the cost of the stand.

Figure 18.6 A Formal Analytical Report *(continued)*

Recommendation: CT83 Pit Jack Adapter / CT04 Engineered Stand

It may also be possible to determine which design factors increase the cost by interviewing tradesmen involved in the actual manufacture of the first prototype. They may well have alternate design suggestions that will reduce the production cost and thus increase the design's profitability.

The complete projected cost of manufacturing with, and without, CT Solutions' sales markup is summarized in Figure 15.

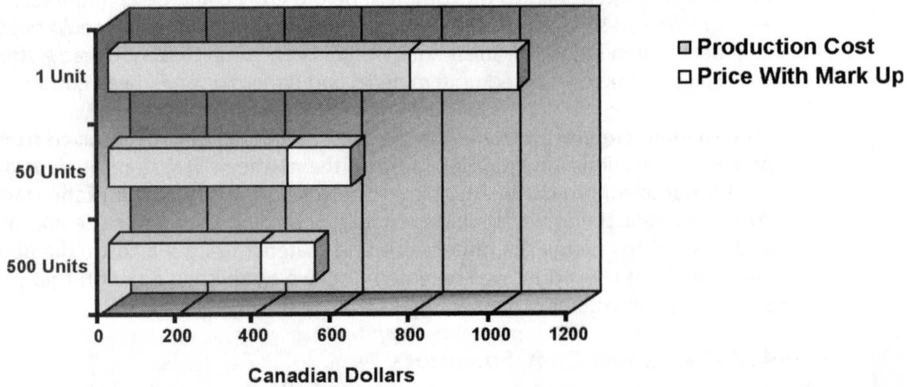

Figure 15 Total projected manufacturing cost

The projected cost of manufacturing, and the estimated sale price, assume a generic markup of 35% on all labour and components. These projections also assume that CT Solutions will manufacture all fabricated portions of the CT04 Modular Engineered Stand in-house, with no outsourcing of labour. Although this will probably be the case for mass production, the projected cost and markup may be substantially different.

The cost of manufacturing and the projected retail price for the CT04 Modular Engineered Stand have been summarized below; however, due to several of the reasons outlined in this section, these figures should only be used as a guide. It will be impossible to determine actual pricing until a prototype has been completed and we can evaluate the feedback regarding manufacturing difficulty and the true amount of labour required.

As Figure 15 shows,

- The cost for one prototype is $777.00 CDN; with the 35% mark up, **$1050.00** CDN.
- Cost for 50 units is $467.00 CDN; with 35% mark up, **$631.00** CDN.
- Cost for 500 hundred units is $397.00 CDN; and with 35% mark up, **$535.00** CDN.

Figure 18.6 A Formal Analytical Report *(continued)*

5.0 CONCLUSION AND RECOMMENDATION

The CT04 Modular Engineered Stand has started to receive positive industry feedback—the suggested design improvements address all apparent flaws with the CT83 as well as all known consumer requirements. The redesign is quite versatile and has the potential to accommodate virtually any adapter designed for its mounting scheme, as illustrated in Figure 11. The future expandability of the CT04 could make this design the foundation of a very large product line for CT Solutions.

At this time, we cannot recommend that the CT04 Modular Engineered Stand enter production because it hasn't been thoroughly tested. Although the design seems sound, modifications to the CT04 may be necessary to ensure customer safety and satisfaction. The next logical step in reaching CT Solutions' ultimate goal of mass production of the stand would be to manufacture a prototype of the CT04 and place it in a suitable testing facility where it would be subject to normal working conditions. After the testing phase, more interviews should be conducted with technicians who have worked with the CT04. Test data should be gathered and analyzed.

In addition, craftspeople involved in the manufacture of the prototype should be interviewed after the first stand has been completed. Their insight about any major difficulties encountered during the manufacturing process may be instrumental in making design changes capable of further reducing the manufacturing cost of the stand, and increasing profitability of the design.

After the test data have been analyzed, it will be much easier to make a sound decision about whether to put the CT04 Modular Engineered Stand into mass production or to further modify the design.

Whatever the outcome of the suggested testing phase may be, the CT04 Modular Engineered Stand has potential for a bright future, and could become one of the cornerstones of the CT Solutions line of high-end tooling.

Figure 18.6 A Formal Analytical Report *(continued)*

REFERENCE CITED

Omega Lift Equipment Incorporated. (n.d.). *Column Jack SCE1765*. Retrieved January 15, 2004, http://Omega.com/graphics/sce1765.html

Figure 18.6 A Formal Analytical Report *(continued)*

ADDITIONAL SOURCES CONSULTED

Jack-X-Change. (2004). *Catalog*. Retrieved on February 8, 2004, from www.jackxchange.com/products/42001

Mott, R.L. (2002). *Applied strength of materials* (4th ed.). New Jersey: Pearson Education, Inc.

OTC. (2004, January 2). Floor Jack 5078. Retrieved January 15, 2004, from http://otctools.com/graphics/5078.gif

Snap On Tools. (n.d.). Jack, Transmission, high-lift, 1/2 ton—Microsoft Internet Explorer. Retrieved January 15, 2004, from http://buy1.snapon.com/catalog/pro_det.asp?P65=&tool=all&item_ID=56290&group_ID=1720&store=snapon-store&dir=catalog

Southern-Tool Company. (copyright 2000). *Catalog*. Retrieved February 8, 2004, from www.southern-tool.com/store/catalog/transmission_jacks.html

Figure 18.6 A Formal Analytical Report

CHECKLIST FOR REVISING AND EDITING ANALYTICAL REPORTS

Use this checklist to refine the content, arrangement, and style of your report.

Content

- Does the report grow from a clear statement of purpose?
- Is the report's length adequate and appropriate for the subject?
- Are all limitations of the analysis clearly acknowledged?
- Are visuals used whenever possible to aid communication?
- Are all data accurate?
- Are all data unbiased?
- Are all data complete?
- Are all data fully interpreted?
- Is the documentation adequate, correct, and consistent?
- Are the conclusions logically derived from accurate interpretation?
- Do the recommendations constitute an appropriate response to the question or problem?

Arrangement

- Is there a distinct introduction, body, and conclusion?
- Are headings appropriate and adequate?
- Are there enough transitions between related ideas?
- Is the report accompanied by all needed front matter?
- Is the report accompanied by all needed end matter?

Style and Page Design

- Is the level of technicality appropriate for the stated audience?
- Is the writing style throughout clear, concise, and fluent?
- Is the language convincing and precise?
- Is the writing in the report grammatical?
- Is the page design inviting and accessible?

WEB CONNECT

The first site lists technical reports on a commercial website. The next two sites will take you to examples of technical reports, most of which have an analytical purpose. Then, the University of Calgary site provides general advice about report writing. The last site shows how the commercially available StyleWriter can be used "to edit any technical document to make it clear and readable."

www.hpl.hp.com/techreports/
www.cics.uvic.ca/climate/change/cimpact.htm
www.ec.gc.ca
www.efwr.ucalgary.ca/efwr/reportwriting
www.stylewriter-usa.com/productinfo.html

EXERCISES

Prepare an analytical report, using some sequence of these guidelines:

a. Choose a subject for analysis from the list your instructor provides, from your major, or from a subject of interest. Identify the problem or question so that you will know exactly what you are looking for.
b. Restate the main question as a declarative sentence in your statement of purpose.
c. Identify an audience—other than your instructor—who will use your information for a specific purpose.
d. Hold a private brainstorming session to generate major topics and subtopics.
e. Use the topics to make an outline based on the model outline in this chapter. Divide as far as necessary to identify all points of discussion.
f. Make a tentative list of all sources (primary and secondary) that you will investigate. Verify that adequate sources are available.
g. Write your instructor a proposal memo, describing the problem or question and your plan for analysis. Attach a draft bibliography.
h. Use your planning outline as a guide to research and observation. Evaluate sources and evidence, and interpret all evidence fully. Modify your outline as needed.
i. Read Chapter 17 and then submit a progress report to your instructor describing work completed, problems encountered, and work remaining. Attach a detailed working outline.
j. Compose an audience/purpose profile. (Use the sample on page 404 as a model, along with the profile worksheet on page 35.)
k. Write the report for your stated audience. Work from a clear statement of purpose, and be sure that your reasoning is shown clearly. Verify that your evidence, conclusions, and recommendations are consistent. Be especially careful that your recommendations observe the critical-thinking guidelines in Figure 18.1.

l. After writing your first draft, make any needed changes in the outline and revise your report according to the revision checklist. Include all necessary supplements.
m. Exchange reports with a colleague for further suggestions for revision.
n. Prepare an oral report of your findings for the class as a whole.

COLLABORATIVE PROJECTS

1. Divide into small groups. Choose a subject for group analysis—preferably, a campus issue—and partition the topic by group brainstorming. Next, select major topics from your list and classify as many items as possible under each major topic. Finally, draw up a working outline that could be used for an analytical report on this subject.
2. Prepare a questionnaire based on your work above, and administer it to members of your campus community. List the findings of your questionnaire and your conclusions in clear and logical form. (Review pages 321–26, on questionnaires and surveys.)

CHAPTER 19

Documenting Research Findings

LEARNING OBJECTIVES

After reading this chapter, you should be able to

- Understand the value of documenting information sources.
- Learn the basic principles of parenthetical documentation ("name/date") used by the APA system.
- Use the required documentation system correctly and consistently.

Documenting research findings means acknowledging one's debt to each information source. Proper documentation satisfies professional requirements for ethics, efficiency, and authority.

WHY YOU SHOULD DOCUMENT

Documentation is *ethical* in that the originator of borrowed material deserves full credit and recognition. Moreover, all published material is protected by copyright law. Failure to obtain permission to reproduce published material could make you liable to legal action, even if you have documented the source.

Documentation also is *efficient*. It provides a network for organizing and locating the world's recorded knowledge. If you cite a particular source correctly, your reference will enable interested readers to locate that source themselves.

Finally, documentation *provides authority*. In making any claim—for example, "A Honda Accord is more reliable than a Ford Taurus"—you invite challenge: "Says who?" Data on road tests, frequency of repairs, resale value, workmanship, and owner comments can help validate your claim by showing its basis in *fact*. A claim's credibility increases in relation to the expert references supporting it. For a controversial topic, you may need to cite several authorities who hold various views, as in this next example, instead of forcing a simplistic conclusion on your material:

> Opinion is mixed as to whether a marketable quantity of oil rests beneath Great Slave Lake. Edmonton geologist Mo Rajabully feels that extensive reserves are

Citing a balance of views

improbable ("Geologist Dampens Hopes" 3). Oil geologist Marta Silverlaug is uncertain about the existence of any oil in quantity at this location ("Northern Oil Drilling" 2). But the Canadian Geological Survey reports that the lake bed may overlay 3.5 billion barrels of oil (Ruston 8).

Readers of your research report expect the *complete* picture.

WHAT YOU SHOULD DOCUMENT

Document any insight, assertion, fact, finding, interpretation, judgment, or other "appropriated material that readers might otherwise mistake for your own" (Gibaldi and Achtert 155)—whether the material appears in published form or not. Specifically, you must document

- any source from which you use exact wording
- any source from which you adapt material in your own words
- any visual illustration: chart, graph, drawing, or the like

Sources that require documentation

You don't need to document anything considered *common knowledge:* material that appears repeatedly in general sources. In medicine, for instance, it is common knowledge that foods high in fat correlate with higher incidences of cancer, so in a report on fatty diets and cancer, you probably would not need to document that well-known fact. But you would document information about how the fat/cancer connection was discovered, subsequent studies (e.g., the role of saturated versus unsaturated fats), and any information for which some other person could claim specific credit. If the borrowed material can be found in only one specific source and not in multiple sources, document it. When in doubt, document the source.

HOW YOU SHOULD DOCUMENT

Borrowed material has to be cited twice: at the exact place that you use the material, and at the end of your document. Documentation practices vary widely, but all systems work almost identically: a brief reference in the text names the source and refers readers to the complete citation, which enables the source to be retrieved.

This chapter illustrates citations and entries for

- American Psychological Association (APA) style, for social sciences

APA DOCUMENTATION STYLE

APA style is useful when writers wish to emphasize the publication dates of their references. A parenthetical reference in the text briefly identifies the source, date, and page number:

Reference cited in the text

In a recent study, mice continuously exposed to an electromagnetic field tended to die earlier than mice in the control group (de Jager & de Brun, 1994, p. 224).

The full citation then appears in the alphabetic listing of "References," at the end of the report:

Full citation at the end of the document

de Jager, L., & de Brun, L. (1994). Long term effects of a 50 Hz electric field on the life-expectancy of mice. *Review of Environmental Health,* 10(3–4), 221–224.

APA style (or some similar author-date style) is preferred in the sciences and social sciences, where information quickly becomes outdated.

APA Parenthetical References

The APA citation includes the publication date; a comma separates the items in the reference; and "p." or "pp." precedes the page number (this is optional in the APA system). When a subsequent reference to a work follows closely after the initial reference, the date need not be included. Here are specific guidelines:

- If your discussion names the author, do not repeat the name in your parenthetical reference; simply give the date and page number:

Author named in the text

Researchers de Jager and de Brun explain that experimental mice exposed to an electromagnetic field tended to die earlier than mice in the control group (1994, p. 224).

When two authors of a work are named in your text, their names are connected by "and," but in a parenthetical reference their names are connected by an ampersand (&).

- If you cite two or more works in a single reference, list the authors in alphabetical order and separate the citations with semicolons:

Two or more works in a single reference

(Jones, 2003; Gomez, 1999; Leduc, 2004)

- If you cite a work with three to five authors, try to name them in your text, to avoid an excessively long parenthetical reference:

A work with three to five authors

Franks, Oblesky, Ryan, Jablar, and Perkins (1993) studied the role of electromagnetic fields in tumour formation.

In any subsequent references to this work, name only the first author, followed by "et al." For six or more authors, do this in all parenthetical references.

Two or more works by the same author in the same year

- If you cite two or more works by the same author published in the same year, assign a different letter to each work:

(Lamont, 2002a, p. 135)
(Lamont, 2002b, pp. 67–68)

Other examples of parenthetical references appear with their corresponding entries in the following discussion of the list of references.

How to space and indent entries

APA Reference List Entries

The APA reference list includes each source that you cited in your document. In preparing the list, key the first line of each entry flush with the left margin. Indent the second and subsequent lines five spaces (1.25 cm [$^1/_2$"]). Use one character space after any period, comma, or colon.

Following are examples of complete citations as they would appear in the "References" section of your document. Shown immediately below each entry is its corresponding parenthetical reference as it would appear in the text. Note the capitalization, abbreviation, spacing, and punctuation in the sample entries.

APA Entries for Books. Any citation for a book should contain all applicable information in the following order: author, date, title, editor or translator, edition, volume number, and facts about publication (city and publisher).

1. Book, Single Author—APA

Broadhead, R. (2000). *Canadian internet directory and research guide* (3rd ed.). Toronto: Stoddart Publishing.

Parenthetical reference: (Broadhead, 2000, p. 17)

Use only initials for an author's first and middle names. Capitalize only the first words of a book's title and subtitle and any proper names. Identify a later edition in parentheses.

2. Book, Two to Six Authors—APA

Aronson, L., Katz, R., & Moustafa, C. (1996). *Toxic waste disposal methods.* New Haven: Yale University Press.

Parenthetical reference: (Aronson, Katz, & Moustafa, 1996)

Use an ampersand (&) before the name of the final author listed in an entry. As an alternative parenthetical reference, name the authors in your text and include date (and page numbers, if appropriate) in parentheses.

3. Book, More Than Six Authors—APA

Fogle, S. T., et al. (1995). *Hyperspace technology.* Boston: Little, Brown.

Parenthetical reference: (Fogle et al., 1995, p. 34)

For more than five authors, name only the first, followed by "et al."

4. Multiple Books, Same Author, Same Year—APA

Chang, J. W. (1997a). *Biophysics.* Boston: Little, Brown.

Chang, J. W. (1997b). *MindQuest.* Chicago: John Pressler.

Parenthetical references: (Chang, 1997a) (Chang, 1997b)

Two or more works by the same author not published in the same year are distinguished by their respective dates alone, without the added letter.

5. Book, One or More Editors—APA

Gunn, J. M. (Ed.). (1995). *Restoration and recovery of an industrial region: Sudbury.* New York: Springer-Verlag.

Parenthetical reference: (Gunn, 1995, p. 34)

For more than five editors, name only the first, followed by "et al."

6. Anthology Selection or Book Chapter—APA

Terminello, V., & Reed, M. G. (2003). E-mail: The good, the bad, & the ugly. In *E-mail: Communicate effectively* (pp. 1–16), Saddle River, NJ: Pearson Education, Inc.

Parenthetical reference: (Terminello & Reed, 2003, p. 14)

The page numbers in the complete reference are for the selection cited from the anthology.

APA Entries for Periodicals. A citation for an article should give this information (as available) in this order: author, publication date, article title (without quotation marks), volume or number (or both), and page numbers for the entire article—not just the page cited.

7. Article, Magazine—APA

Johnston, A. D. (2004, May 24). The best and the brightest. *Maclean's, 117*, 35–48.

Parenthetical reference: (Johnston, 2004, p. 35)

If no author is given, provide all other information. Capitalize the first word in an article's title and subtitle, and any proper nouns. Capitalize all keywords in a periodical title. Italicize the periodical title. Then, list the volume number and page numbers, using commas to separate title, volume number, and page numbers (as above).

8. Article, Journal with New Pagination for Each Issue—APA

Ackerman, N. (1999). Landfill landscape. *Canadian Geographic, 119*(4), 56–63.

Parenthetical reference: (Ackerman, 1999, pp. 56–58)

Because each issue for a given year has page numbers that begin at "1," readers need the issue number ("4"). The "119" denotes the volume number, which is underlined or italicized.

9. Article, Journal with Continuous Pagination—APA

Norcliffe, G. (1999). John Cabot's legacy in Newfoundland. *Geography: An International Journal, 83*, 97–109.

Parenthetical reference: (Norcliffe, 1999, p. 104)

The "83" denotes the volume number. When page numbers continue from issue to issue for the full year, readers do not need the issue number, because no other issue in that year repeats these same page numbers. (You can include the issue number if you think it will help readers retrieve the article more easily.)

10. Article, Newspaper—APA

Mingail, S. (2004, April 23). Mix and mingle over the Internet. *The Globe and Mail,* natl. ed., p. C1.

Parenthetical reference: (Mingail, 2004, p. C1)

In addition to the year of publication, include the month and day. If the newspaper's name begins with "The," include it in your citation. Include "p." or "pp." before page numbers. For an article on non-consecutive pages, list each page, separated by a comma.

APA Entries for Other Sources. Miscellaneous sources range from unsigned encyclopedia entries to conference presentations to government documents. A full citation should give this information (as available): author, publication date, work title (and report or series number), page numbers (if applicable), city, and publisher.

11. Encyclopedia, Dictionary, Alphabetic Reference—APA

Communication. (1993). In *The business reference book.* Boston: Business Resources Press.

Parenthetical reference: ("Communication," 1993)

For a signed entry, begin with the author's name and publication date.

12. Report—APA

MacHutchon, A. Himmer, S., & Bryden, C.A. (1993, October). *Khatzeywateen Valley grizzly bear study: Final report.* Victoria: B.C. Ministry of Forests.

Parenthetical reference: (MacHutchon, Himmer, & Bryden, 1993, p. 29)

If the authors are named, list them first, followed by the publication date. When citing a group author; e.g., Canadian Professional Sales Association, include the group's abbreviated name in your first parenthetical reference; e.g., (Canadian Professional Sales Association [CPSA]), and use only that abbreviation in any subsequent reference; e.g., (CPSA). When the agency (or organization) and publisher are the same, list "Author" in the publisher's slot.

13. Conference Presentation—APA

Smith, A. A. (1996). Radon concentrations in molded concrete. In A. Hodkins (Ed.), *First British Symposium on Environmental Engineering* (pp. 106–121). London: Harrison Press.

Parenthetical reference: (Smith, 1995, p. 109)

The example shows a presentation included in the published proceedings of a conference. The name of the symposium is a proper name and so is capitalized. For an unpublished presentation, include the presenter's name, year and month, title of the presentation (underlined or italicized), and all available information about the conference or meeting: "Symposium held at . . ." Do not underline or italicize this information.

14. Interview, Personally Conducted—APA

Parenthetical reference: (D. Turner, personal communication, March 4, 2008)

This material is considered a non-recoverable source, and so is cited in the text only, as a parenthetical reference. If you name the interviewee in your text, do not repeat the name in your parenthetical reference.

15. Interview, Published—APA

Jable, C.K. (1997). The future of graphics [Interview with James Lescault]. In K. Prell (Ed.), *Executive Views of Automation* (pp. 216–231). Miami: Haber Press.

Parenthetical reference: (Jable, 1997, pp. 218–223)

Begin with the name of the interviewer, followed by the publication date, title, designation (in brackets), and publication information.

16. Personal Correspondence—APA

Parenthetical reference: (L. Nguyen, personal correspondence, May 15, 2006)

This material is considered non-recoverable data, and so is cited in the text only, as a parenthetical reference. If you name the correspondent in your text, do not repeat the name in your citation.

17. Brochure or Pamphlet—APA

This material follows the citation format for a book entry. After the title of the work, include the designation "Brochure" in brackets.

18. Lecture—APA

Jack, D. (2001, November 7). *Energy levels and spectrum of the hydrogen atom.* Lecture presented at Concordia University, Montreal, PQ.

Parenthetical reference: (Jack, 2001)

If you name the lecturer in your text, do not repeat the name in your citation.

19. Government Document—APA

British Columbia Ministry of Highways. (1999). *Standard specifications for bridge maintenance.* Victoria: Author.

Parenthetical reference: (British Columbia Ministry of Highways, 1999, p. 49)

If the author is unknown, present the information in this order: name of the issuing agency, publication date, document title, place, and publisher. When the issuing agency is both author and publisher, list "Author" in the publisher's slot.

20. Computer Software or Manual—APA

Rotellan, P. (2002). Forest inventory mapping control (Version 2.0) [Computer software]. Wakaw, Saskatchewan: Branch Services.

Parenthetical reference: (Rotellan, 2002, p. 17)

Do not reference standard software and programming languages such as Microsoft Word and Excel, Java, or AutoCAD. In the text, name the software and its version number ("this spring, AutoCAD 16 will be updated"). For specialized software, in limited distribution, use the above format.

APA Entries for Electronic Sources. APA documentation standards for electronic sources continue to be refined and defined. A sampling of currently preferred formats follows. Any citation for electronic media should enable the reader to identify the original source (printed or electronic) and provide an electronic path for retrieving the material.

21. Email—APA

Jerome Konecsni (personal communication, Oct. 21, 2001) comments on the use of email for messages sent locally, nationally, and internationally.

Provide a parenthetical reference for this personal communication; do not list the entry in the References section.

22. Message Posted to Internet Group (Newsgroup, Online Forum, or Discussion)—APA

Lewis, S. (2001, December 30). Checking out the geology when buying a house [Msg1]. Message posted to http://groups.google.com/groups?h1=en&group-sci.geo.geology.

Parenthetical reference: (Lewis, 2001, para. 1)

The basic form is the same for all types: Author(s). (Date of posting). Message subject line [Message ID]. Message posted to [group address].

23. Magazine or Journal Article from a Database—APA

Blackburn-Brockman, E., & Belanger, K. (2001, January). One page or two? A national study of CPA recruiters' preferences for resume length. *The Journal of Business Communication, 38*(1), 29. Retrieved June 20, 2001, from InfoTracCollege Edition database, Article No. A71327300.

Parenthetical reference: (Blackburn-Brockman, 2001, p. 29)

Name the author. In parentheses, give the publication date. Then, name the title of the article, followed by the italicized journal name and volume number, in title case (with the issue number in parentheses), and the page number(s). Provide the retrieval date and the database (with an article number, if given).

24. CD-ROM Reference Work—APA

Time almanac. (2001). Washington: Compact, 1999.

Parenthetical reference: (*Time almanac,* 2001)

If the work on CD-ROM has a print equivalent, APA prefers that it be cited in its print form.

25. Internet Article Based on a Print Source—APA

Gatehouse, J. (2001, November 5). Terror by mail [Electronic version]. *Maclean's, 114*(45), 22–24.

Parenthetical reference: (Gatehouse, 2001, November 5, p. 22)

Name the author or editor, if known. List the publication date (or write "n.d." for "no date"—if the date is unknown). Name the article's title and the publication medium. Name the magazine or journal, its volume and number, and the page numbers of the print version. (Add the date of retrieval and the URL only if you believe the electronic version differs from the print version.)

26. Article in Internet-only Magazine or Journal—APA

Kitts, K. (2001, March). Technical communication provides vital link. *Employment Review.Com,* March 2001. Retrieved November 7, 2001, from www.employmentreview.com/2001-03/features/Cnfeat04.asp

Parenthetical reference: (Kitts, 2001, March, para. 6)

Name the author and the publication date, then the title of the article. Place the journal's name in italics. Provide the volume and issue, if they're given. Provide the access date and the URL.

27. Newspaper Article, Searchable Electronic Version—APA

Garwood-Jones, A. (2001, June 23). Cattle battle. *The Globe and Mail.* Retrieved June 28, 2001, from www.globeandmail.com

Parenthetical reference: (Garwood-Jones, 2001, para. 3)

Name the author and the publication date, then the article title. Italicize the newspaper's name. Give the access date and the URL.

28. Internet Report—APA

Thompson, J., Baird, P., & Downie, J. (2001, October). Report of the committee of inquiry on the case involving Dr. Nancy Olivieri, the Hospital for Sick Children, the University of Toronto, and Apotex Inc. Retrieved June 28, 2001, from http://222.caut/ca/english/issues/acadfreedom/olivieri.asp

Parenthetical reference: (Thompson, Baird, & Downie, 2001, p. 45)

Name the author(s) and the publication date, then the report title. (If no author is named, name the sponsoring organization.) Give the access date and the URL.

29. Website Document, Author Named—APA

Coneybeare, S. (2001, October 24). *Papers 2001: Application of chlorine capping kits.* Retrieved October 28, 2001, from Alberta Water and Wastewater Association: www.awwoa.ab.ca/2001%20Papers.htm

Parenthetical reference: (Coneybeare, 2001, para. 6)

Name the author or editor, if known. Then give the revision or copyright date, if available. Next, give the page's title. List the access date, name the page publisher or site sponsor, provide the URL.

NOTE *APA recommends using a paragraph indicator (e.g., for parenthetical references when page numbers are not available for electronic sources).*

30. Website Document, Author Not Named—APA

National Sciences and Engineering Research Council. (Updated 2001, December 17). *Truck research hit the road.* Retrieved November 15, 2001, through the NSERC website, from www.nserc.ca/news/features/truck_e.htm

Parenthetical reference: (NSERC, 2001, para 6)

Name the website sponsor. Provide the latest revision date or copyright date, if either is available. Give the title of the hyperlinked document. Provide the access date and the URL.

31. Website Document (Non-periodical), Multi-page Not Dated, Author Not Named—APA

Tire Rack. (n.d.). *Tire test results: Building max performance that lasts.* Retrieved January 2, 2002, from within Tire Rack's website, http://222.tirerack.com/tires/tests/bs_s03_rd.jsp

Parenthetical reference: (Tire Rack tests, n.d., para. 4)

Name the sponsoring organization. Indicate that the article is not dated. Name the document or page title. Provide the access date and the URL.

32. Online Encyclopedia Article—APA

Bartleby.com. (2001). Phospholipid. Found in *The Columbia Encyclopedia,* 6th edition [Online]. Retrieved January 11, 2002, from www.bartleby.com/65/ph/phophol.html

Parenthetical reference: (Bartleby.com, 2001, para. 1)

Name the author, if known. If not, name the sponsoring organization—in the above example, Bartleby.com is the internet arm of Columbia University Press, which publishes the printed version. (Give the date or indicate that the article is not dated.) Name the hyperlinked document, the encyclopedia, and the edition, if known. Provide the access date and the URL.

APA Sample List of References

APA's References section is an alphabetic listing (by author) equivalent to MLA's Works Cited section. Like Works Cited, the reference list includes only those works actually cited. (A bibliography usually would include background works or works consulted as well.) One notable difference from MLA style is that the APA style calls for only "recoverable" sources to appear in the reference list. Therefore, personal interviews, email messages, and other unpublished materials are cited in the text only.

The list of references in Figure19.1 accompanies the report on technical marketing. In the left margin, blue numbers denote elements discussed on the page facing Figure 19.1.

1 **REFERENCES**

AllStarJobs.ca. (Copyright 1999–2004). Sales and marketing jobs. *AllStarJobs*. Retrieved May 26, 2004, from www.allstarjobs.ca/marketing/

2 CCHREI. (n.d.). Environmental sales and marketing. *EnviroCareers*. Calgary: Canadian
Council for Human Resources in the Environment Industry. Retrieved May 26, 2004,
3 from http://cchrei.ca/envirocareers/english/section5/profile05/profile.htm

4 Cornelius, H., & Lewis, W. (1983). *Career guide for sales and marketing* (2nd ed.). New York: Monarch Press.

5 HRDC. (2003, 12 June). 6221 technical sales specialists—wholesale trade. *National occupational classification*. Ottawa: Human Resources Development Canada. Retrieved March 12, 2004, from www23.hrdc-drhc.gc.ca/2001/e/groups/6221.shtml

———. (2002, 2 October). 6221 technical sales specialists—wholesale trade. *Ontario Job Futures*. Ottawa: Human Resources Development Canada. Retrieved May 27, 2004, from http://www1.on.hrdc-drhc.gc.ca/ojf/ojf.jsp?lang=e&section=Profile&noc=6221

Job Futures. (2003, 30 January). *Explore the world of work*. Ottawa: Government of Canada. Retrieved May 21, 2004, from http://jobfutures.ca/en/home.shtml

6

———. (2003, 24 April). *Sales, marketing, and advertising managers*. Ottawa: Government of Canada. Retrieved 27 May 2004, from http://jobfutures.ca/noc/0611p3.shtml

———. (2003, 24 April). *Technical sales specialists*. Ottawa: Government of Canada. Retrieved 27 May 2004, from http://jobfutures.ca/noc/6221.shtml

Meaux, A. (2004, January). The new tech sales gang. *Report on Business, 16*, 55–58.

7

Monster.ca. (2004, May 26). Technical sales and marketing. *Search Jobs*. Retrieved May 26, 2004, from http://jobsearch.monster.ca/

8 Nelson, J. (2001, Fall). Sales engineers. *Occupational Outlook Quarterly, 44*(3), 20–24. Retrieved March 15, 2004, from www.bls.gov/opub/ooq/ooqhome.htm

9 Tostenson, A. (2004, March). Alternate careers in marketing. Presentation at Electro '04 Conference in Halifax, NS.

Young, J. (1995, August). Can computers really boost sales? *Forbes ASAP*, 84–101.

Figure 19.1 A List of References (APA Style)

Discussion of Figure 19.1

1. Centre the References title at the top of the page, 1" to 2" from the top paper edge. Number pages consecutively with text pages. Include only recoverable data (material that readers could retrieve themselves); cite unpublished interviews and correspondence parenthetically in the text only. Double space within and between the entries for student assignments and APA journals. But single space within entries for workplace reports and proposals. Order the entries alphabetically.

2. The organization's title may be abbreviated if, later in the entry, it is included in full.

3. Do not add punctuation at the end of an electronic address.

4. For more than one author or editor, use ampersands (&) instead of spelling out "and." Use initials only for authors' first and middle names.

5. Do not enclose article titles in quotation marks. Italicize periodical, book, or website titles. Capitalize proper nouns and the first letter of the first word in article or book or website titles and subtitles. Capitalize all key words in newspaper, magazine, or journal titles and subtitles. For government reports, name the sponsoring agency and include all available information for retrieving the document. For electronic sources, name the article and the website titles.

6. For sources listed by the same author or sponsoring agency, list the entries alphabetically by the title of the article, book, website, or periodical. Write out names of all months.

7. Use a period and one space to separate a citation's three major items (author or sponsor, title, publication data). Leave one space after a comma or colon. Use commas to separate magazine title, volume/issue, and page numbers.

8. Use italics for a journal or magazine title, volume number, and the interceding comma. Include the volume number *and* issue number for a journal with new pagination in each issue.

9. Treat an unpublished conference presentation as a recoverable source; include it in your list of references instead of only citing it parenthetically in the text.

WEB CONNECT

A tour of the following sites reveals that documentation "experts" have not yet agreed about formats for citing electronic information sources. I recommend the Guffey site, the first listed.

www.westwords.com./guffey/documentation.html
www.columbia.edu/cu/cup/cgos/idx_basic.html
www.bedfordstmartins.com/online/citeappxa.html

This Colorado State University site has a well-organized guide to CBE style.

http://writing.colostate.edu/references/sources/cbe/index.cfm

This University of Toronto site covers IEEE engineering style documentation format.

www.ecf.utoronto.ca/~writing/handbook-docum1b.html

EXERCISES

1. Locate the style manual for your discipline. (Ask the faculty in your major or a librarian). Redesign Figure 19.1 according to the guidelines in this manual. Submit your document along with a memo outlining the main differences in the two documentation styles. If your discipline stipulates no particular style, use the *APA Manual* for this assignment.
2. Locate the latest updates for MLA and APA documentation of electronic sources at the following websites:
   - www.wisc.edu/writing/Handbook/DocMLA.html
   - www.westwords.com/guffey/students.html
   - www.apastyle.org/elecref.html

COLLABORATIVE PROJECT

Work in groups of three. Examine the documentation format each of you has used in your major report assignment to confirm that you have correctly used the documentation system stipulated by your project supervisor.

CHAPTER 20

Designing Visuals

LEARNING OBJECTIVES

After reading this chapter, you should be able to

- Appreciate the value of visuals in business and technical documents.
- Select appropriate visuals for specific purposes and audiences.
- Follow guidelines for designing readable, useful tables.
- Employ appropriate types of graphs and charts for specific dramatic and illustrative purposes.
- Integrate text and visuals.

Visuals clarify concepts, emphasize particular meanings, illustrate points, or analyze ideas or data. Besides saving space and words, visuals help audiences process, understand, and remember information. They offer powerful new ways of looking at data, so visuals reveal trends, problems, and possibilities that otherwise might remain buried in lists of facts and figures. In printed or online documents, in oral presentations or multimedia programs, visuals are a staple of communication today. This chapter covers four main types of visuals: tables, graphs, charts, and illustrations.

WHY VISUALS ARE ESSENTIAL

Readers expect more than just raw information; they want the information processed for their immediate understanding. Visuals help us answer many of the questions asked by readers as they process information:

TYPICAL READER QUESTIONS IN PROCESSING INFORMATION

- Which information is most important?
- Where, exactly, should I focus?
- What do these numbers mean?
- What should I be thinking or doing?
- What should I remember about this?
- What does it look like?
- How is it organized?
- How is it done?
- How does it work?

More receptive to images than to words, today's readers resist pages of mere printed text. Visuals help diminish a reader's resistance in several ways:

- Visuals enhance comprehension by displaying abstract concepts in concrete, geometric shapes. "How does the metric system work?" (Figure 20.1).
- Visuals make meaningful comparisons possible. "Which industrial sectors report the largest on-site releases of environmental pollutants?" (Figure 20.2). "How does one pound compare with one kilogram?" (Figure 20.1).
- Visuals depict relationships. "How does seasonal change affect the rate of construction in our city?" (Figure 20.10). "What is the relationship between Fahrenheit and Celsius temperature?" (Figure 20.1).
- Visuals serve as a universal language. In the global workplace, carefully designed visuals can transcend cultural and language differences and thus facilitate international communication (Figure 20.1).
- Visuals provide emphasis. To emphasize the change in death rates for heart disease and cancer since 1970, a table (Table 20.1) or bar graph (Figure 20.4) would be more vivid than a prose statement.
- Visuals condense and organize information, making it easier to remember and interpret. A simple table, for instance, can summarize a long and difficult printed passage, as in Table 20.1.

Technical data in printed form can be hard to interpret

Assume that you are researching recent death rates for heart disease and cancer. From various sources, you collect these data:

1. In 1970, 471.2 males and 267.4 females per 100 000 people died of heart disease; 227.6 males and 151.6 females died of cancer.
2. In 1980, 392.1 males and 213.5 females per 100 000 people died of heart disease; 240.3 males and 148.3 females died of cancer.
3. In 1990. . .

In the written form above, numerical information is repetitious, tedious, and hard to interpret. As the amount of numerical data increases, so does our difficulty in processing this material. Arranged in Table 20.1, these statistics become easier to compare and comprehend.

Along with your visual, analyze or interpret the important trends or the essential message you want your readers to see:

A caption explaining the numerical relationships

As Table 20.1 indicates, both male and female death rates from heart disease decreased from 1970 to 2003, but males showed a slightly larger decrease. Cancer deaths during this period decreased slightly for both males and females.

Besides their value as presentation devices, visuals help us analyze information. Table 20.1 is one example of how visuals enhance critical thinking by helping us identify and interpret crucial information and discover meaningful connections.

Table 20.1 Data Displayed in a Table

Death Rates for Heart Disease and Cancer, 1970–2003

Number of Deaths (per 100 000) Population

	Heart Disease		Cancer	
Year	**Male**	**Female**	**Male**	**Female**
1970	471.2	267.4	227.6	151.6
1980	392.1	213.5	240.3	148.3
1990	267.5	150.6	246.6	153.2
1992	255.8	141.4	244	152.8
1997	230.8	129.7	229.7	148.5
2003	178.9	98.2	215.3	148.1
Percent change, 1970–1997	–62.0	–54.3	–5.4	–2.3

Based on Statistics Canada Catalogue no. 82-221-XDE, Statistics Canada's 2001 Canada Yearbook, p. 14, and Statistics Canada Catalogue no. 84F0209.

WHEN TO USE A VISUAL

Translate your writing into visuals whenever they make your point more clearly than the prose. Use visuals to *clarify* and to enhance your discussion, not to *decorate* it. Use a visual display to direct the audience's focus or to help them remember something, as in the following situations (Dragga and Gong 46–48):

Use visuals in situations like these

- when you want to instruct or persuade
- when you want to draw attention to something immediately important
- when you expect the document to be consulted randomly or selectively (e.g., a manual or reference work)
- when you expect the audience to be relatively less educated, less motivated, or less familiar with the topic
- when you expect the audience to be distracted

WHAT TYPES OF VISUALS TO CONSIDER

Different types of visuals serve different functions. The following overview sorts visual displays into four categories: tables, graphs, charts, and graphic illustrations. Each type of visual offers readers a new way of seeing—a different perspective.

Tables Display Organized Lists of Data. Tables display data (as numbers or words) in rows and columns for comparison. Use tables to present exact numerical values and to organize data so that readers can sort out relationships for themselves. Complex tables usually are reserved for more specialized readers.

Numerical tables present data for analysis, interpretation, and exact comparison.

TABLE 1 **Charting the Lesson**

Lesson	Page	Page	Page
A	1	3	6
B	2	2	5
C	3	1	4

Prose tables organize verbal descriptions, explanations, or instructions.

TROUBLESHOOTING

Problem	Cause	Solution
• power	• cord	• plug-in
• light	• bulb	• replace
• flicker	• tube	• replace

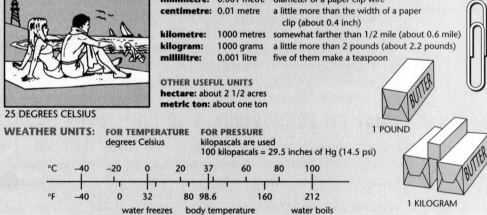

All You Need to Know about Metric
(For Your Everyday Life)

10

Metric is based on the decimal system

The metric system is simple to learn. For use in your everyday life you will need to know only ten units. You will also need to get used to a few new temperatures. Of course, there are other units which most persons will not need to learn. There are even some metric units with which you are already familiar; those for time and electricity are the same as you use now.

BASIC UNITS

METRE: a little longer than a yard (about 1.1 yards)
LITRE: a little larger than a quart (about 1.06 quarts)
GRAM: a little more than the weight of a paper clip

(comparative sizes are shown)

1 METRE

1 YARD

COMMON PREFIXES
(to be used with basic units)

milli: one-thousandth (0.001)
centi: one-hundredth (0.01)
kilo: one thousand times (1000)
For example
1000 millimetres = 1 metre
100 centimetres = 1 metre
1000 metres = 1 kilometre

1 LITRE

1 QUART

MILK MILK

25 DEGREES FAHRENHEIT

OTHER COMMONLY USED UNITS

millimetre:	0.001 metre	diameter of a paper clip wire
centimetre:	0.01 metre	a little more than the width of a paper clip (about 0.4 inch)
kilometre:	1000 metres	somewhat farther than 1/2 mile (about 0.6 mile)
kilogram:	1000 grams	a little more than 2 pounds (about 2.2 pounds)
millilitre:	0.001 litre	five of them make a teaspoon

OTHER USEFUL UNITS
hectare: about 2 1/2 acres
metric ton: about one ton

25 DEGREES CELSIUS

WEATHER UNITS: **FOR TEMPERATURE**
degrees Celsius

FOR PRESSURE
kilopascals are used
100 kilopascals = 29.5 inches of Hg (14.5 psi)

°C	−40	−20	0	20	37	60	80	100
°F	−40	0	32	80	98.6	160		212

water freezes body temperature water boils

BUTTER

1 POUND

BUTTER

1 KILOGRAM

Figure 20.1 Visuals That Clarify and Simplify

Source: National Institute of Standards and Technology, 1992.

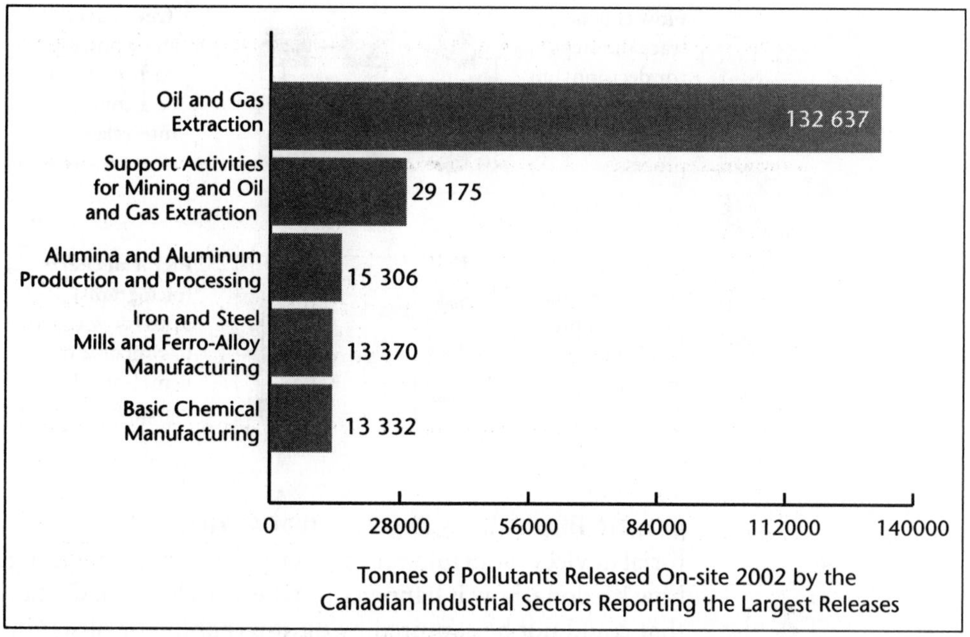

Figure 20.2 A Graph Displaying the "Big Picture"
Source: Environment Canada's National Pollutant Release Inventory—National Overview 2002. Found at www.ec.gc.ca/pdb/npri/2004N_Overview/2002FactSheet_e.cfm

Graphs Display Numerical Relationships. Graphs translate numbers into shapes, shades, and patterns by plotting two or more data sets on a coordinate system. Use graphs to sort out or emphasize specific numerical relationships for readers. The visual representation helps readers grasp, at a glance, the approximate values, the point being made about those values, or the relationship being emphasized.

Bar graphs often show comparisons.

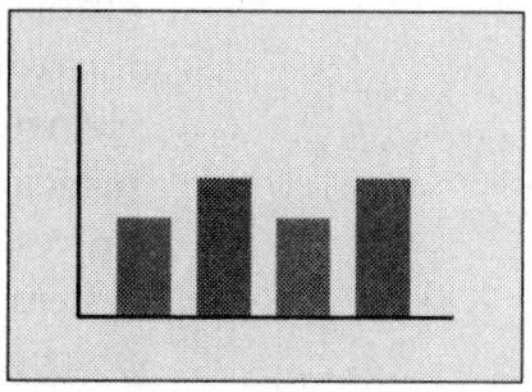

Line graphs often show changes over time.

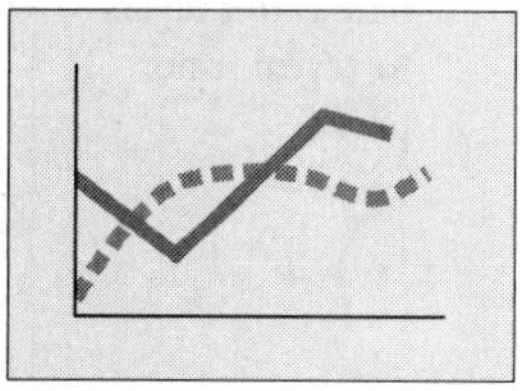

Charts Display the Parts of a Whole. Charts depict relationships without the use of a coordinate system by using circles, rectangles, arrows, connecting lines, and other designs.

Pie charts show the parts or percentages of a whole.

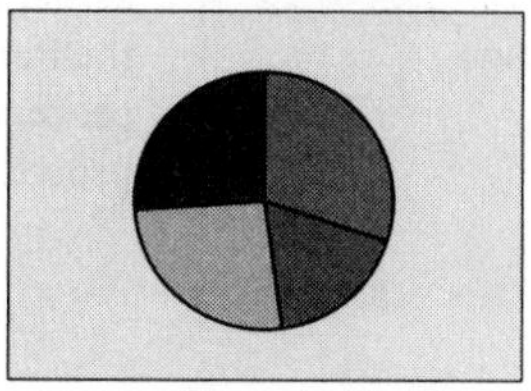

Organization charts show the links among departments, management structures, or other elements of a company.

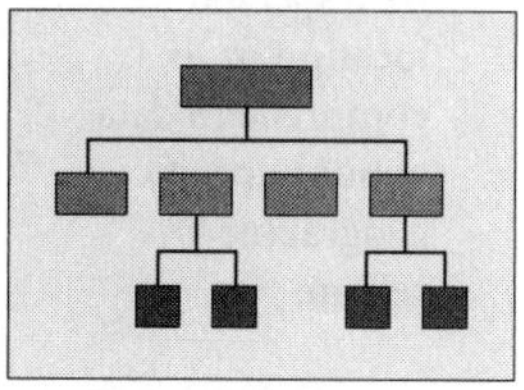

Flow charts trace the steps (or decisions) in a procedure or stages in a process.

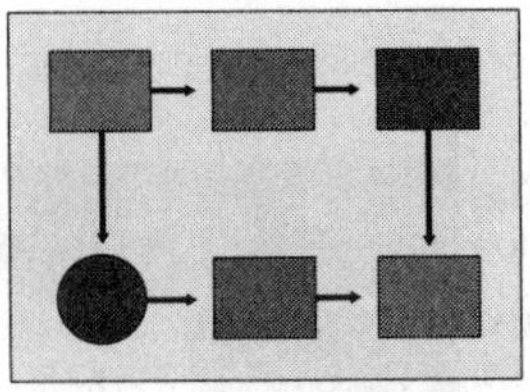

Tree charts show how the parts of an idea or a concept interrelate.

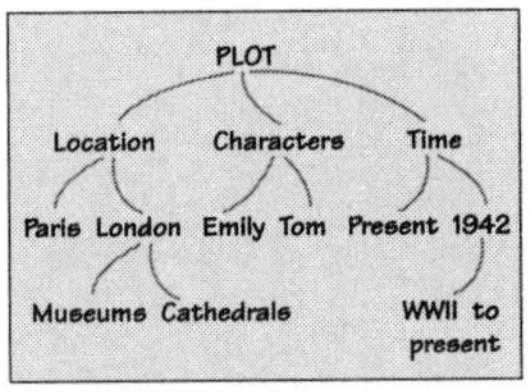

Gantt charts show when each phase of a project is to begin and end.

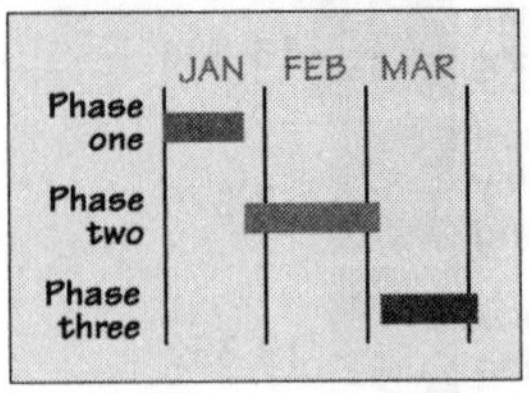

Pictorial charts (pictograms) use icons (or isotypes) to symbolize the items being displayed or measured.

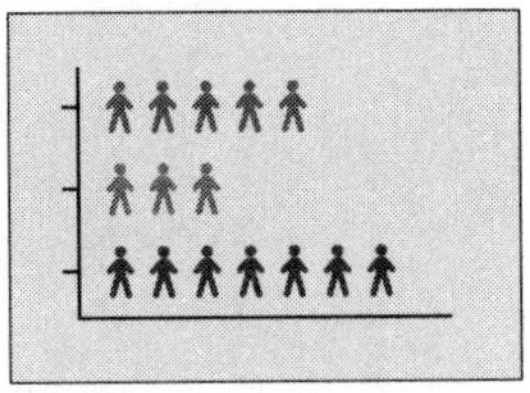

Graphic Illustrations Depict Actual or Virtual Views. Graphic illustrations are pictorial devices for helping readers visualize what something looks like, how it works, how it's done, how it happens, or where it's located. Certain diagrams present views that could not be captured by photographing or observing the object.

Representationa l diagrams present a realistic but simplified view, usually with essential parts labelled.

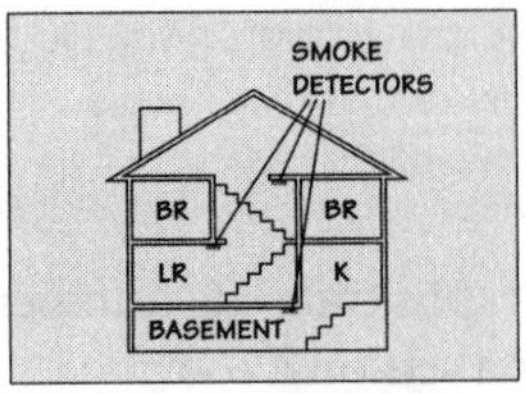

Exploded diagrams show the item pulled apart, to reveal its assembly.

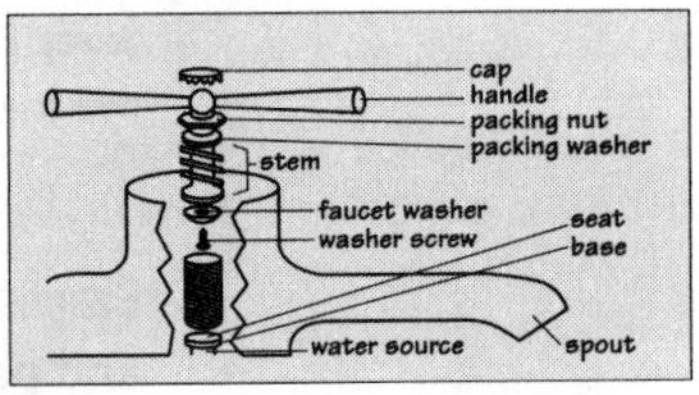

Cutaway diagrams eliminate outer layers to reveal inner parts.

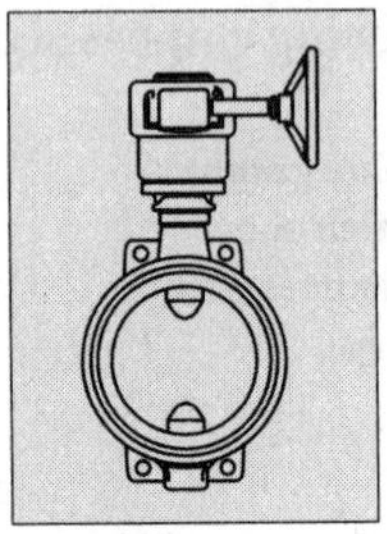

Block or schematic diagrams present the conceptual elements of a principle, process, or system to depict *function* instead of appearance.

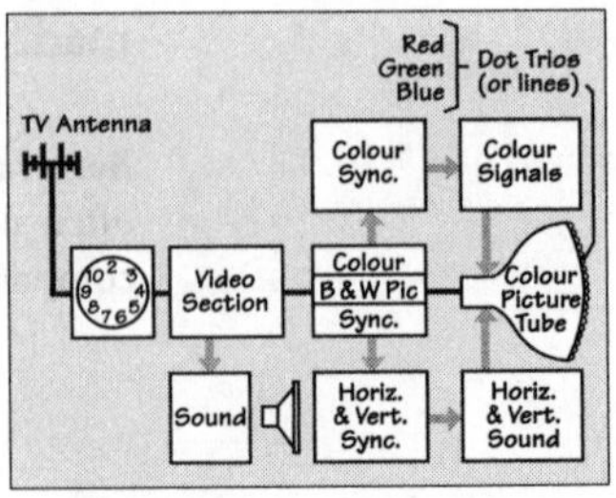

Maps enable readers to visualize a specific location or to comprehend data about a specific geographic region.

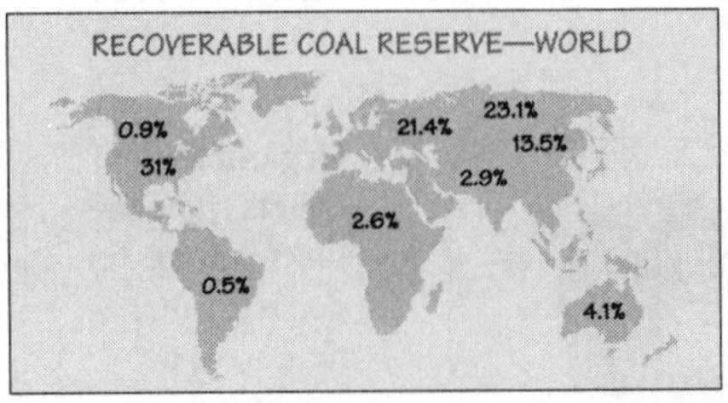

Photographs present an actual picture of the item, process, or procedure.

HOW TO SELECT VISUALS FOR YOUR PURPOSE AND AUDIENCE

You usually will have more than one way to display information in a visual format. To select the most effective display, consider carefully your specific purpose and the abilities and preferences of your audience.

QUESTIONS ABOUT A VISUAL'S PURPOSE AND INTENDED AUDIENCE

What is my purpose?

- What do I want the audience to do or think (know facts and figures, follow directions, make a judgment, understand how something works, perceive a relationship, identify something, see what something looks like, pay attention, other)?
- Do I want viewers to focus on one or more exact values, compare two or more values, or synthesize a range of approximate values?

Who is my audience?

- What is their technical background on this topic?
- What is their level of interest in this topic?
- Would they prefer the raw data or interpretations of the data?
- Are they accustomed to interpreting visuals?

Which type of visual might work best in this situation?

- What forms of information should this visual depict (numbers, shapes, words, pictures, symbols)?
- Which visual display would be most compatible with the type of judgment, action, or understanding I seek from this audience?
- Which visual display would this audience find most accessible?

Here are a few examples of the choices you must consider in selecting visuals:

Choices to consider in selecting visuals

- If you just want the audience to know facts and figures, a table might be sufficient, but if you want them to make a particular judgment about these data, a bar graph, line graph, or pie chart might be preferable.
- The operating parts of a mechanism might be better shown by an exploded or cutaway diagram than by a photograph.
- Expert audiences tend to prefer numerical tables, flow charts, schematics, and complex graphs or diagrams they can interpret for themselves.
- General audiences tend to prefer basic tables, graphs, diagrams, and other visuals that direct their focus and that interpret key points extracted from the data.

Although several alternatives might be possible, one particular type of visual (or a combination) usually is superior for a given purpose and audience. None of the above examples is, of course, immutable. Your particular audience or organization may express its own preferences. Or your choices may be limited by lack of equipment (software, scanners, digitizers), insufficient personnel (graphic designers, technical illustrators), or insufficient budget. In any case, your basic task is to enable the intended audience to interpret the visual correctly.

PREFERRED DISPLAYS FOR SPECIFIC VISUAL PURPOSES

Purpose	Preferred Visual
Organize numerical data	Table
Show comparative data	Table, bar graph, line graph
Show a trend	Line graph
Interpret or emphasize data	Bar graph, line graph, pie chart, map
Introduce an unfamiliar object	Photo, representational diagram
Display a project schedule	Gantt chart
Show how parts are assembled	Photo, exploded diagram
Show how something is organized	Organization chart, map
Give instructions	Prose table, photo, diagrams, flow chart
Explain a process	Flow chart, block diagram
Clarify a concept or principle	Block or schematic diagram, tree chart
Describe a mechanism	Photo, representational diagram, or cutaway diagram

Tables

Tables can display exact quantities, compare sets of data, and present information systematically and economically. Numerical tables such as Table 20.1 present *quantitative information* (data that can be measured). In contrast, prose tables present *qualitative information* (brief descriptions, explanations, or instructions). Table 20.2, for example, names pollutant facilities, lists pertinent numerical data, and gives each facility's explanation for that data.

Table 20.2 A Prose Table

Reporting the Largest Increase in On-site Releases from 1998 to 1999

Facility	NPRI Pollution Reported Releases	Comments Provided by Facility
Safety-Kleen Ltd Corunna, ON	Lead (and its compounds) ◆ increase of 2 211.74 tonnes (+4 264.9%)	The increased disposal numbers are due to variation in waste management business.
Agrium Fort Saskatchewan, AB	Ammonia (total) ◆ increase of 751.3 tonnes (+86.3%)	The increase in underground injection is due to remediation activities. The materials injected are from previous activities.
Petro-Canada Edmonton Refinery Edmonton, AB	Ammonia (total) ◆ increase of 447.62 tonnes (+28.9%)	No comments provided by facility.

Source: Environment Canada's 1999 National Pollution Release Inventory. Available: www.ec.gc.ca/pdb/npri/documents/National_FS_E.pdf.

No table should be overly complex for its intended audience. An otherwise impressive-looking table, such as Table 20.3, is difficult for non-specialists to interpret because it presents too much information at once. We can see how an unethical writer might use a complex table to bury numbers that are questionable or embarrassing (R. Williams 12). Readers need to understand how the table

Table 20. 3 A Complex Table

NPRI Pollutants Released On-site in the Largest Quantities (values in tonnes) 1999

Substance	Air	Underground Injection	Water	Land	Total
Hydrogen sulphide	7 976.5	119 871.8	18.8	0.0	127 868.7
Ammonia (total)	17 314.1	8 397.7	11 154.6	409.7	37 280.4
Methanol	20 566.7	4 238.2	1 844.7	111.4	26 775.2
Zinc (and its compounds)	709.8	0.1	206.9	15 744.6	16 669.5
T Calcium fluoride	19.5	0.0	0.0	13 035.7	13 056.2
Hydrochloric acid	11 630.6	0.0	20.8	9.6	11 665.8
Sulphuric acid	9 369.2	0.0	62.6	19.8	9 456.8
Toluene	7 191.4	72.0	2.4	10.5	7 289.5
Xylene (mixed isomers)	6 909.7	46.3	3.6	5.4	6 977.9
Nitrate ion in solution at pH >= 6.0	71.8	191.9	6 274.1	230.1	6 769.8
Methyl ethyl ketone	5 079.7	790.0	0.0	0.0	5 876.3
Carbon disulphide	4 245.1	0.0	0.0	0.0	4 246.1
Manganese (and its compounds)	143.3	0.0	790.2	3 196.3	4 141.9
T Hydrogen fluoride	3 541.0	0.0	0.0	0.0	3 542.0
T Lead (and its compounds)	481.5	0.0	14.3	2 995.2	3 495.3
n-Hexane	3 405.2	15.3	0.4	1.8	3 428.9
Ethylene glycol	283.7	532.3	28.1	1 804.2	2 653.2
T Dichloromethane	2 387.5	0.0	0.0	0.0	2 388.9
Ethylen	1 267.4	0.0	0.0	0.0	2 168.5
Styrene	2 093.0	0.4	0.0	0.0	2 097.9
Isopropyl alcohol	1 953.3	8.4	0.9	0.0	1 970.4
T Asbestos (friable form)	0.0	0.0	.0	1 725.1	1 725.7
T Formaldehyde	1 610.7	4.7	36.4	2.4	1 656.3
2-Butoxyethanol	1 566.0	0.0	0.0	0.0	1 567.9
T Benzene	1 424.4	93.0	1.1	0.6	1 523.1
Largest On-site Releases	**112 141.0**	**134 262.0**	**20 459.7**	**39 302.4**	**306 292.1**
National Total	**127 311.8**	**135 562.2**	**20 789.7**	**43 833.5**	**327 694.9**
% of National Total	**88.1**	**99.0**	**98.4**	**89.7**	**93.5**

T CEPA-toxic or Carcinogenic Pollutant

Source: Environment Canada's 1999 National Pollutant Release Inventory. National Overview. Available: www.ec.gc.ca/pdb/npri/ documents/National_FS_E.pdf.

is organized, where to find what they need, and how to interpret the information they find (Hartley 90).

Tables are constructed with various tools: (1) tab markers and tab keys on a word processor, (2) row-and-column displays in a spreadsheet program, (3) the "Table" command in better word-processing programs. The "Table" command option offers a full range of table editing features: cut and paste, adjust spacing, insert text between rows, add rows or columns, adjust column width, and so on.

Table Guidelines. Whichever table options you employ, use the following general guidelines:

Guidelines for using tables

- Use a table only when you are reasonably sure it will enlighten—rather than frustrate—readers. For non-specialized readers, use fewer tables and keep them simple.
- Try to limit the table to one page. Otherwise write "continued" at the bottom, and begin the second page with the full title, "continued," and the original column headings.

- If the table is too wide for the page, turn it 90 degrees (landscape) and place its top toward the inside of the binding. Or divide the data into two tables. (Few readers may bother rotating the page to read the table broadside.)
- In your discussion, refer to the table by number, and explain what readers should be looking for; or include a prose caption with the table. Specifically, introduce the table, show it, and then interpret it.

For more specific information about creating tables, see the Table Construction Guidelines accompanying Table 20.4.

Table 20.4 Table Construction Guidelines

How to Construct a Table

TABLE 1 ■ Science and Engineering Graduates in 1999 and 2000: 2001 Career Status

STUB HEAD — COLUMN HEADS

DEGREE AND FIELD	Graduates 1999 and 2000 (1000)	2001—PERCENT DISTRIBUTION: In school[a]	Employed: In S&E[b]	Employed: In other	Not employed	Median salary ($1000)
All science fields	**649**	**24**	**11**	**59**	**6**	**34**
Computer science/math	61.5	13	32	51	4	51
Life sciences	159.4	37	10	47	5	29
Physical sciences	32.2	39	27	30	4	34
Social sciences	218.7	X	5	67	7	30
All engineering fields[c]	**109.2**	**13**	**64**	**20**	**4**	**49**
Civil	16.8	13	67	17	3	42
Electrical/electronics	34.2	11	64	21	4	54
Industrial	6.9	9	59	28	3	49
Mechanical	25.8	12	66	17	4	48

[a]Full-time grad. students. [b]Science & engineering. [c]Other fields not shown. (X) Not available.
Source: National Science Foundation/SRS, *National Survey of Recent College Graduates: 2001*. *Statistical Abstract of the United States: 2001* (121st edition). Washington: GPO: 611.

1. Number the table in its order of appearance and provide a title that describes exactly what is being compared or measured.
2. Label stub, row, and column heads (*Degree and Field, Median salary, Computer science*) so readers know what they are looking at.
3. Stipulate all units of measurement using familiar symbols and abbreviations ($, hr., no.). Define specialized symbols or abbreviations (*Å* for *angstrom*, *dB* for *decibel*) in a footnote.
4. Compare data vertically (in columns) instead of horizontally (in rows). Columns are easier to compare than rows. Try to include row or column averages or totals, as reference points for comparing individual values.
5. Use horizontal rules to separate headings from data. In a complex table, use vertical rules to separate columns. In a simple table, use as few rules as clarity allows.
6. List the items in a logical order (alphabetical, chronological, decreasing cost). Space listed items so they are not cramped or too far apart for easy comparison. Keep prose entries as brief as clarity allows.
7. Convert fractions to decimals, and align decimals vertically. Keep decimal places for all numbers equal. Round insignificant decimals to the nearest whole number.
8. Use *X*, *NA*, or a dash to signify any omitted entry, and explain the omission in a footnote ("Not available," "Not applicable").
9. Use footnotes to explain entries, abbreviations, or omissions. Label footnotes with lowercase letters so readers do not confuse the notation with the numerical data.
10. Cite data sources beneath any footnotes. When adapting or reproducing a copyrighted table for a work to be published, obtain written permission from the copyright holder.

Tables work well for displaying exact values, but for easier interpretation, readers prefer graphs or charts. Geometric shapes (bars, curves, circles) generally are easier to remember than lists of numbers (Cochran et al. 25).

Any visual other than a table usually is categorized as a *figure,* and so titled ("Figure 1 Aerial View of the Panhandle Site"). Figures covered in this chapter include graphs, charts, and illustrations.

Like all other components in the document, visuals are designed with audience and purpose in mind (Journet 3). An accountant doing an audit might need a table listing exact amounts, whereas the average public stockholder reading an annual report would prefer the "big picture" in an easily grasped bar graph or pie chart (Van Pelt 1). Similarly, an audience of scientists might find Table 20.3 perfectly appropriate, but a less specialized audience (say, environmental groups) might prefer the clarity and simplicity of Figure 20.2.

GRAPHS

Graphs translate numbers into pictures. Plotted as a set of points (a *series*) on a coordinate system, a graph shows the relationship between two variables.

Graphs have a horizontal and a vertical axis. The horizontal axis carries categories (the independent variables) to be compared, such as years within a period (1990, 1995, 2000). The vertical axis shows the range of values (the dependent variables) for comparing or measuring the categories, such as the number of people who died from heart failure in a specific year. A dependent variable changes according to activity in the independent variable (e.g., a decrease in quantity over a set time, as in Figure 20.3). In the equation $y = f(x)$, x is the independent variable and y is the dependent variable.

Graphs are especially useful for displaying comparisons, changes over time, patterns, or trends. When you decide to use a graph, choose the best type for your purpose: bar graph or line graph.

Bar Graphs

Easily understood by most readers, bar graphs show discrete comparisons, as on a year-by-year or month-by-month basis. Each bar represents a specific quantity. Use bar graphs to help readers focus on one value or compare values that change over equal time intervals (expenses calculated at the end of each month, sales figures totalled at yearly intervals). Use a bar graph only to compare values that are noticeably different. Otherwise, all the bars will appear almost identical.

Simple Bar Graphs. The simple bar graph in Figure 20.3 displays one relationship taken from the data in Table 20.1, the rate of male deaths from heart disease. To aid interpretation, you can record exact values above each bar—but only if readers need exact numbers.

Multiple-bar Graphs. A bar graph can display two or three relationships simultaneously, each relationship plotted as a separate series. Figure 20.4 displays two comparisons from Table 20.1, the rate of male deaths from both heart disease and cancer.

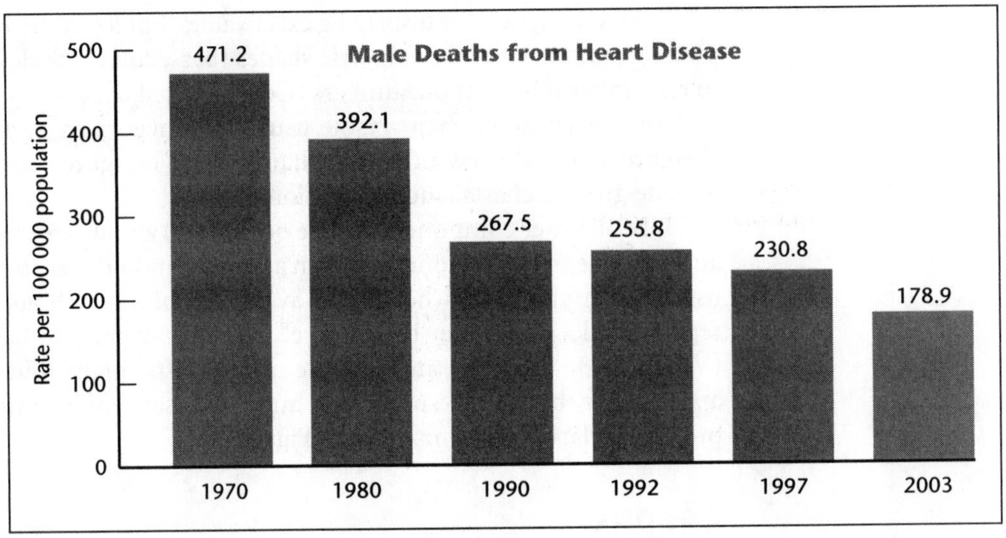

Figure 20.3 A Simple Bar Graph

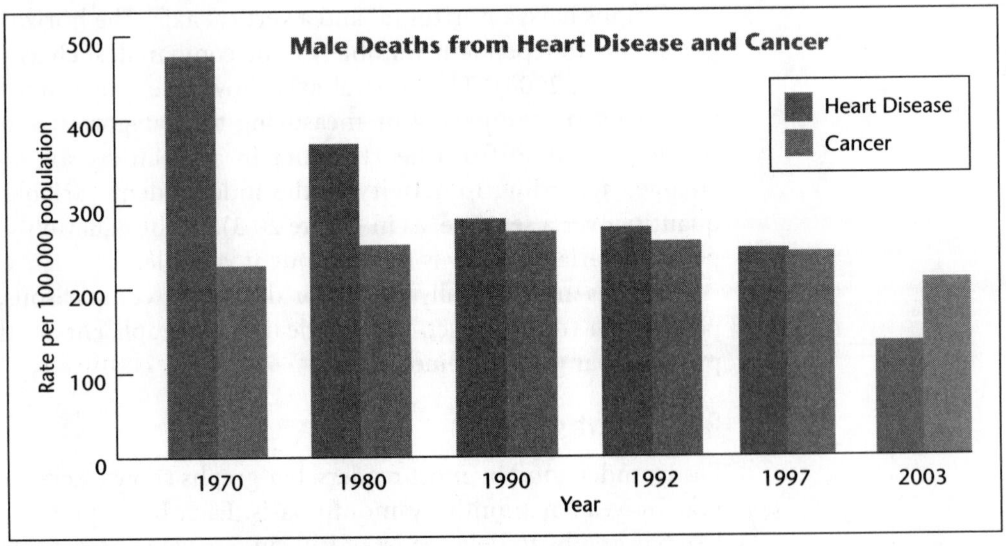

Figure 20.4 A Multiple-bar Graph

Whenever a graph shows more than one relationship (or series), each series of numbers is represented by a different pattern, colour, shade, or symbol, and the patterns are identified by a *legend.*

The more relationships a graph displays, the harder it is to interpret. As a rule, plot no more than three series of numbers on one graph.

Horizontal-bar Graphs. To make a horizontal-bar graph, turn a vertical-bar graph (and scales) on its side. Horizontal-bar graphs are good for displaying a large series of bars arranged in order of increasing or decreasing value, as in Figure 20.5. The horizontal format leaves room for labelling the categories horizontally ("Manufacturing," etc.). A vertical-bar graph leaves no room for horizontal labelling.

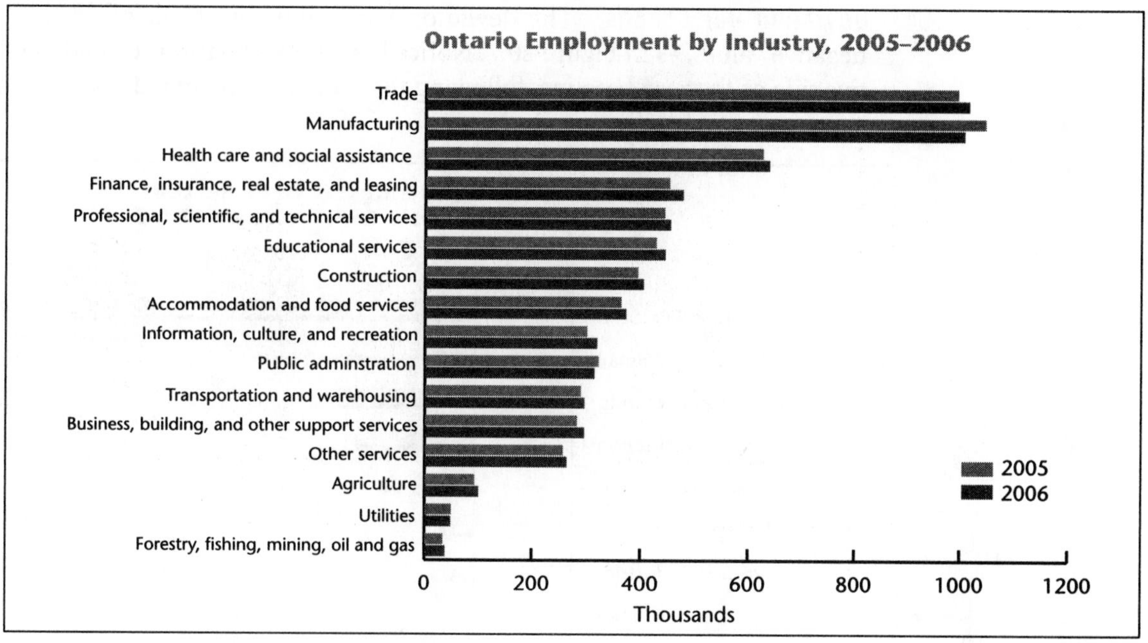

Figure 20.5 A Horizontal-bar Graph
Source: Statistics Canada, Labour Force Survey 2006, February 2007.

Stacked-bar Graphs. Instead of side-by-side clusters of bars, you can display multiple relationships by stacking bars. Stacked-bar graphs are especially useful for showing how much each item contributes to the whole. Figure 20.6 displays other comparisons from Table 20.1.

Display no more than four or five relationships in a stacked-bar graph. Excessive subdivisions and patterns create visual confusion.

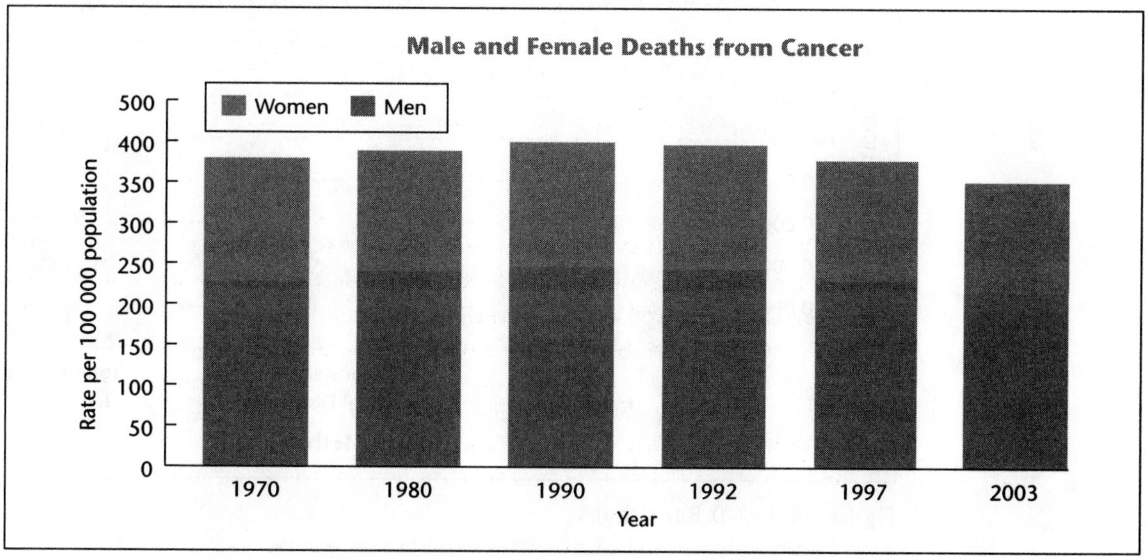

Figure 20.6 A Stacked-bar Graph

Deviation Bar Graphs. The deviation bar graph can display both positive and negative values, as in Figure 20.7. Notice how the vertical axis extends to the negative side of the zero baseline, following the same incremental division as above the baseline.

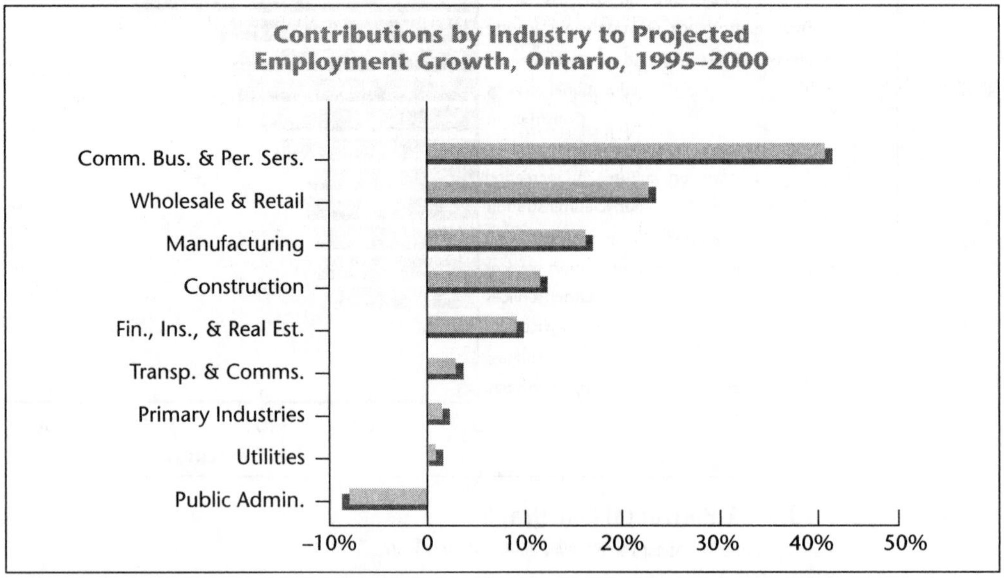

Figure 20.7 Deviation Bar Graph

Source: Adapted from FOCUS-Ontario and PRISM-Ontario models, the Institute for Policy Analysis, University of Toronto.

3-D Bar Graphs. Graphics software enables you to shade and rotate images and produce three-dimensional views. The 3-D perspectives in Figure 20.8 engage our attention and add visual emphasis to the data.

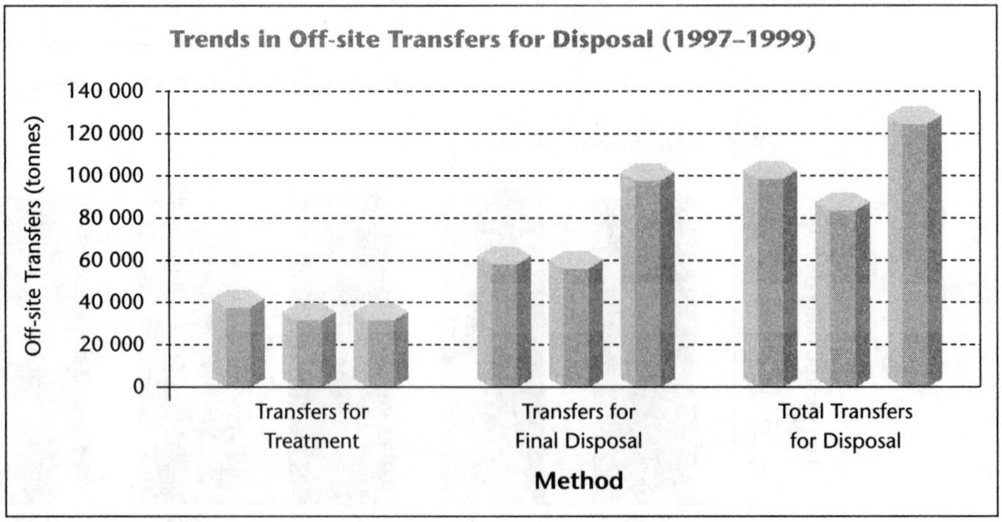

Figure 20.8 3-D Bar Graphs

Source: Environment Canada's 1999 National Pollutant Release Inventory. Available: www.ec.gc.ca/pdb/npri/documents/National_FS_E.pdf.

Although 3-D graphs can enhance and dramatize a presentation, an overly complex graph can be almost impossible to interpret. Never sacrifice clarity and simplicity for the sake of visual effect.

Bar Graph Guidelines. Once you decide on a type of bar graph, use the following suggestions for presenting the graph to your audience.

Bar graph guidelines

- Keep the graph simple and easy to read. Avoid plotting more than three types of bars in each cluster. Avoid needless visual details.
- Number your scales in units the audience will find familiar and easy to follow. Units of 1 or multiples of 2, 5, or 10 are best (Lambert 45). Space the numbers equally.
- Label both scales to show what is being measured or compared. If space allows, keep all labels horizontal for easier reading.
- Use *tick marks* to show the points of division on your scale. If the graph has many bars, extend the tick marks into *grid lines* to help readers relate bars to values.

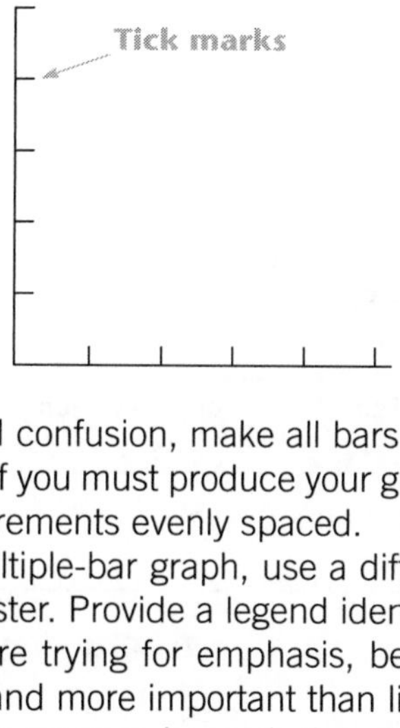

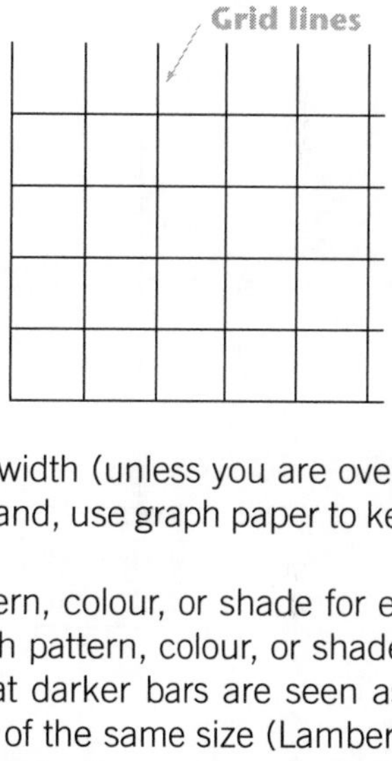

- To avoid confusion, make all bars the same width (unless you are overlapping them). If you must produce your graphs by hand, use graph paper to keep bars and increments evenly spaced.
- In a multiple-bar graph, use a different pattern, colour, or shade for each bar in a cluster. Provide a legend identifying each pattern, colour, or shade.
- If you are trying for emphasis, be aware that darker bars are seen as larger, closer, and more important than lighter bars of the same size (Lambert 93).
- Cite data sources beneath the graph. When adapting or reproducing a copyrighted graph for a work to be published, you must obtain written permission from the copyright holder.
- In your discussion, refer to the graph by number ("Figure 1"), and explain what readers should be looking for; or include a prose caption along with the graph.

Many computer graphics programs automatically employ most of the design features discussed above. Anyone producing visuals, however, should know all the conventions.

Line Graphs

A line graph can accommodate many more data points than a bar graph (e.g., a 12-month trend, measured monthly). Line graphs help readers synthesize large bodies of information in which exact quantities need not be emphasized. Whereas bar graphs display quantitative differences among items (cities, regions, yearly or monthly intervals), line graphs display data whose value changes over time, as in a trend, forecast, or other change during a specified time (profits, losses, growth). Some line graphs depict cause-and-effect relationships (e.g., how seasonal patterns affect sales or profits).

Simple Line Graphs. A simple line graph, as in Figure 20.9, uses one line to plot time intervals on the horizontal scale and values on the vertical scale. The relationship depicted here would be much harder to express in words alone.

Multiple-line Graphs. A multiple-line graph displays several relationships simultaneously, as in Figure 20.10. For legibility, use no more than three or four curves in a single graph. Explain the relationships readers are supposed to see.

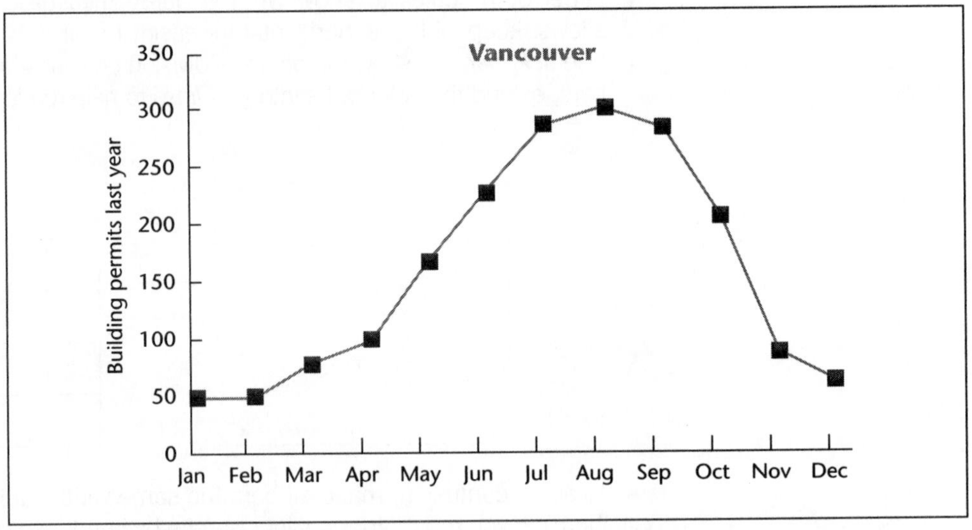

Figure 20.9 A Simple Line Graph

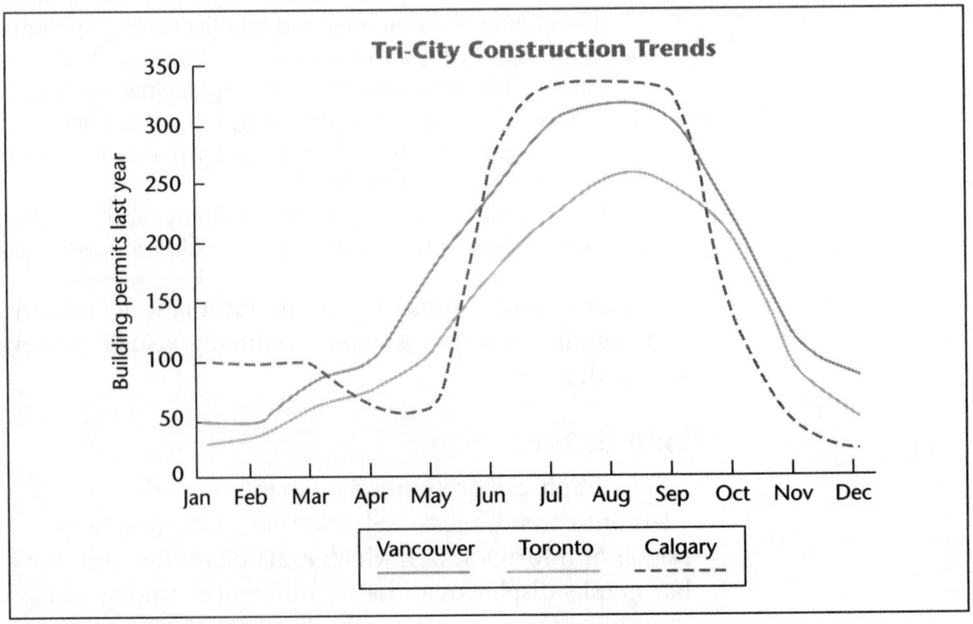

Figure 20.10 A Multiple-line Graph

A caption explaining the visual relationships

Building permits in all three cities increased steadily as the weather warmed, but Calgary's increase was more erratic. Its permits declined for April–May, but then surpassed Vancouver's and Toronto's for June–September.

Band or Area Graphs. For emphasis and appeal, fill the area beneath each plotted line with a pattern. Figure 20.11 is a version of the Figure 20.9 line graph.

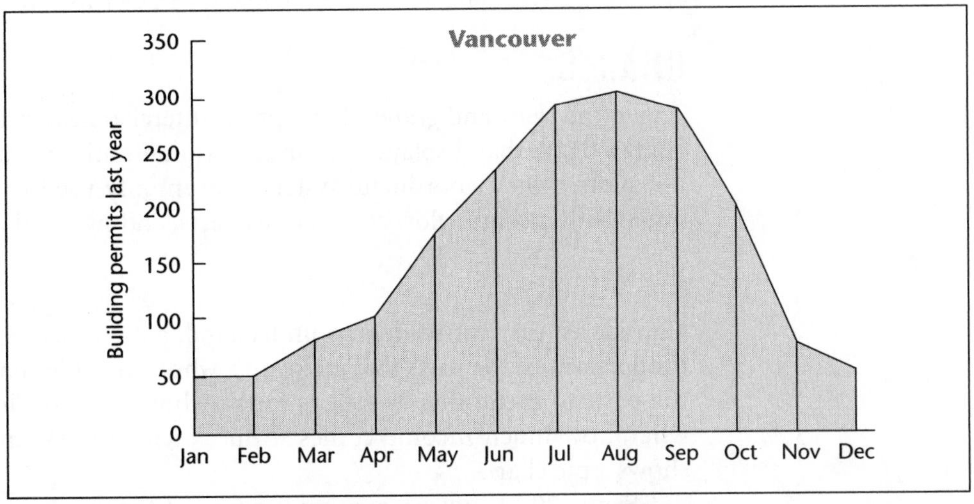

Figure 20.11 A Simple Band Graph

The multiple bands in Figure 20.12 depict relationships among sums instead of the direct comparisons depicted in the equivalent Figure 20.10 line graph.

Despite their visual appeal, multiple-band graphs are easy to misinterpret. In a simple band graph, each line depicts its own distance from the zero baseline. But in a multiple-band graph, the very top line depicts the *total*, each band below it being a part of that total (like stacked-bar graph segments). Always clarify these relationships for viewers.

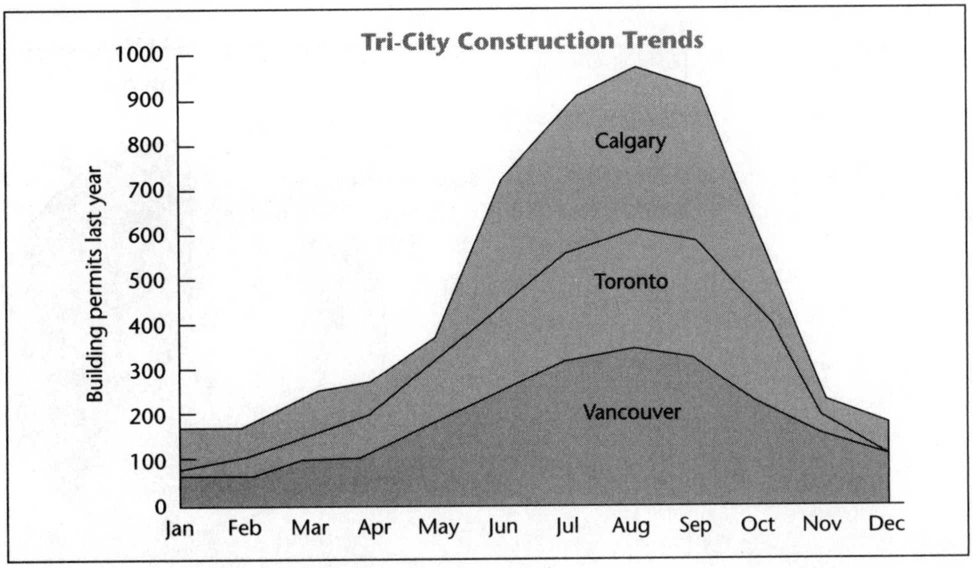

Figure 20.12 A Multiple-band Graph

Line Graph Guidelines. Follow bar graph guidelines, with these additions:

Line graph guidelines

- Display no more than three or four lines on one graph.
- Mark each individual data point used in plotting each line.
- Make each line visually distinct (using colour, symbols, etc.).
- Label each line so readers will know what it represents.
- Avoid grid lines that readers could mistake for plotted lines.

CHARTS

The terms *chart* and *graph* often appear interchangeably. But a chart is more precisely a figure that displays relationships (quantitative or cause-and-effect) that are not plotted on a coordinate system. Commonly used charts include pie charts, organization charts, flow charts, tree charts, and pictorial charts (pictograms).

Pie Charts

Considered easy for readers to understand, a pie chart depicts the percentages or proportions of the parts that make up a whole. In a pie chart, readers can compare the parts to each other as well as to the whole (to show how much was spent on what, how much income comes from which sources, and so on). Figure 20.13 shows a pie chart.

Figure 20.14 shows two other versions of the pie chart in Figure 20.13. Version (a) displays dollar amounts and version (b), the percentage relationships among these dollar amounts.

Pie Chart Guidelines. For constructing pie charts, follow these suggestions:

Pie chart guidelines

- Be sure the parts add up to 100 percent.
- If you must produce your charts by hand, use a compass and protractor for precise segments. Each 3.6-degree segment equals 1 percent. Include any number from two to eight segments. A pie chart containing more than eight segments is difficult to interpret, especially if the segments are small (Hartley 96).

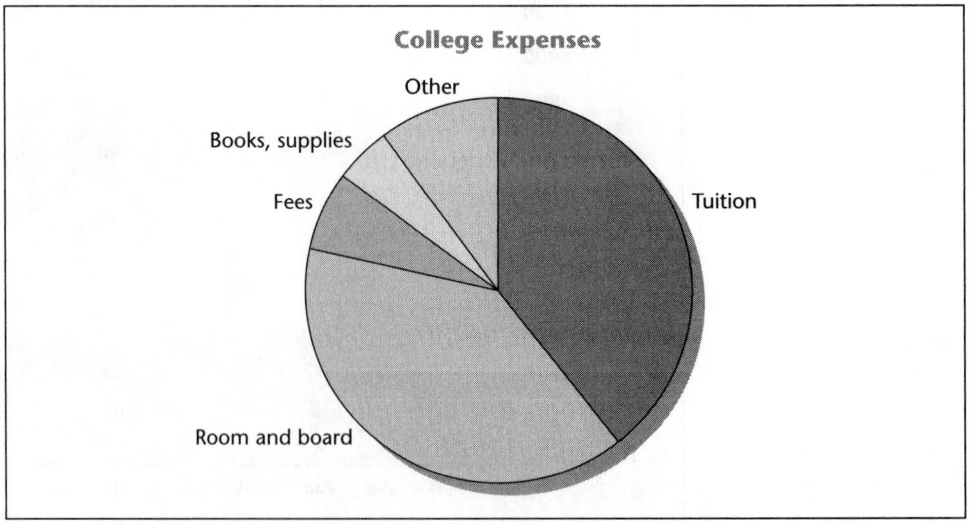

Figure 20.13 A Simple Pie Chart

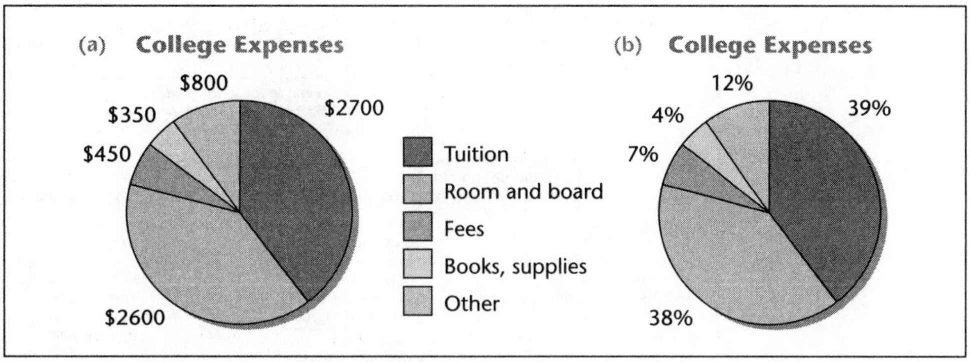

Figure 20.14 Two Other Versions of Figure 20.13

- Combine small segments under the heading "Other."
- Locate your first radial line at 12 o'clock and then move clockwise from large to small (except for "Other," usually the final segment).
- For easy reading, keep all labels horizontal.

Organization Charts

An organization chart divides an organization into its administrative or managerial parts. Each part is ranked according to its authority and responsibility in relation to other parts and to the whole, as in Figure 20.15.

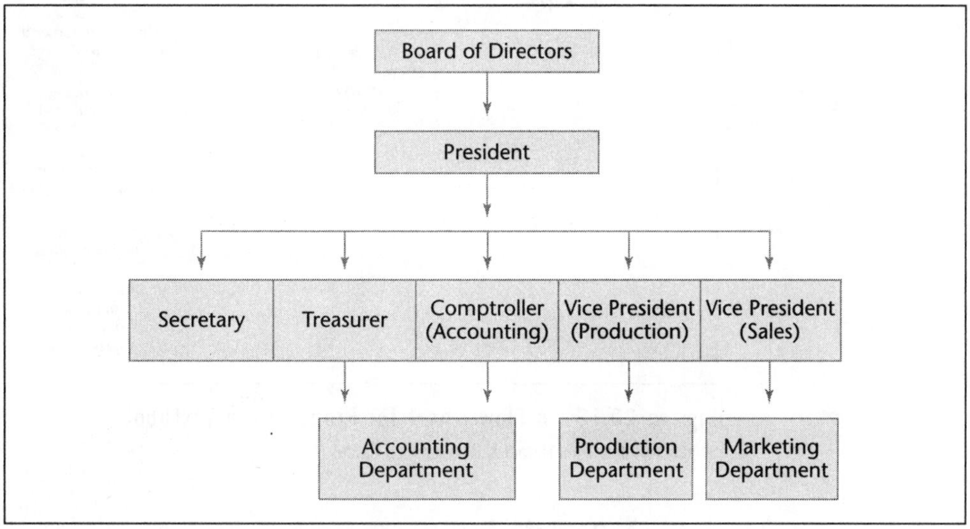

Figure 20.15 An Organization Chart for One Corporation

Flow Charts

A flow chart traces a procedure or process from beginning to end. In displaying the steps in a manufacturing process, the flow chart would begin at the raw materials and proceed to the finished product. Figure 20.16 on the following page traces the procedure for producing a textbook. (Other flow chart examples appear on page 14 and elsewhere throughout the text.)

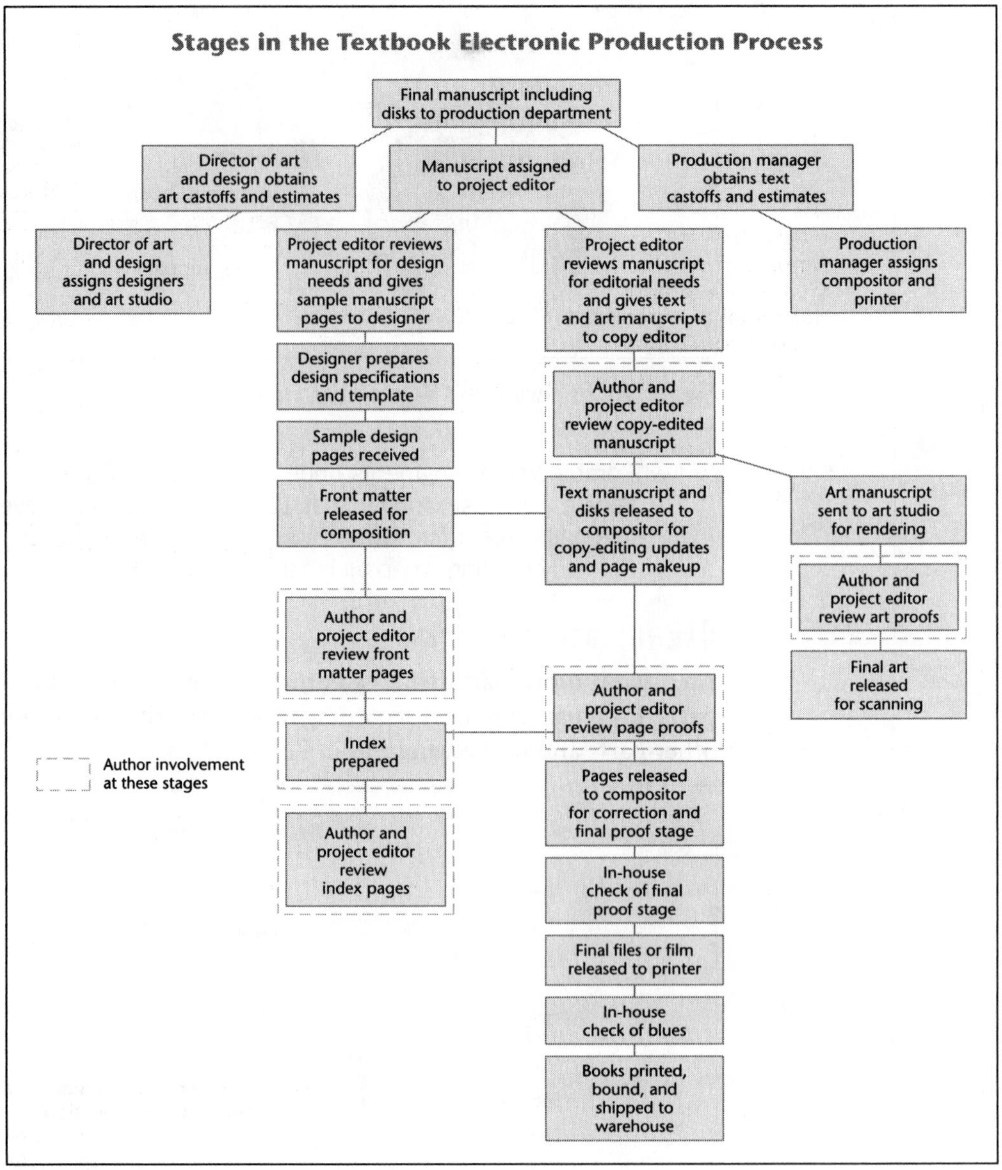

Figure 20.16 A Flow Chart for Producing a Textbook
Source: Adapted from Harper & Row Author's Guide.

Tree Charts

Whereas flow charts display the steps in a process, tree charts show how the parts of an idea or concept relate to each other. Figure 20.17 displays the parts of an outline for this chapter so that readers can better visualize relationships. The tree version seems clearer and more interesting than the prose listing.

Pictograms

Pictograms depict numerical relationships with icons or symbols (cars, houses, smokestacks) of the items being measured, instead of using bars or lines. Each

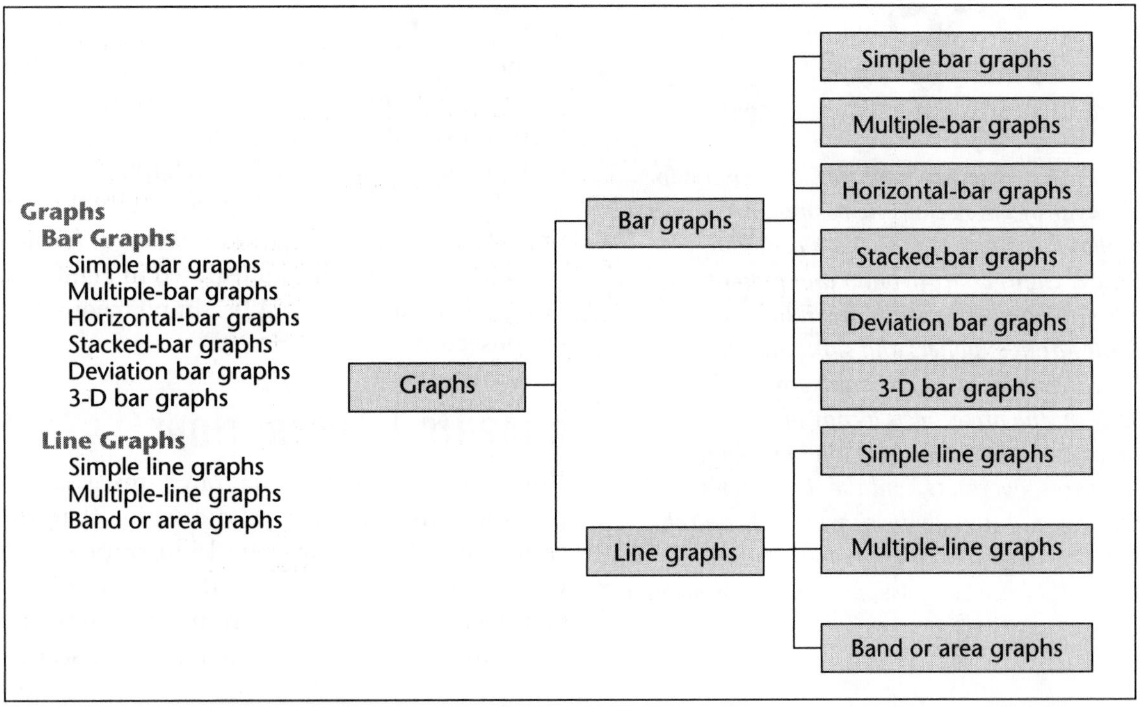

Figure 20.17 An Outline Converted to a Tree Chart

symbol represents a stipulated quantity, as in Figure 20.18. Many graphics programs provide an assortment of pre-drawn symbols.

Use pictograms when you want to make information more interesting for non-technical audiences.

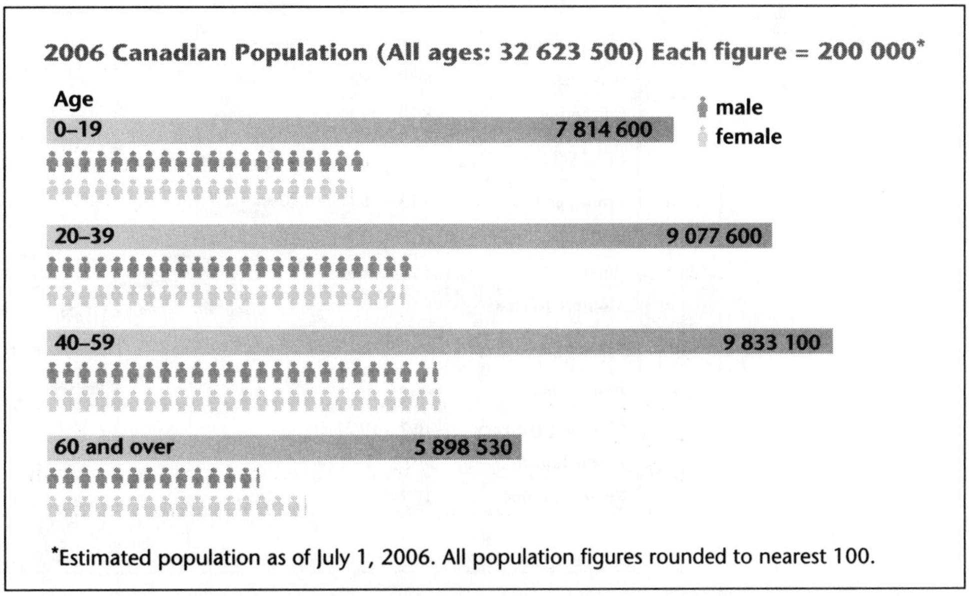

Figure 20.18 A Pictogram

Source: Based on data from Statistics Canada, CANSIM table 051-0001

ON THE JOB...

Gantt Charts in Project Management

"I use MS Project to produce Gantt charts for all my projects. A chart helps present the initial proposal (emailed to the client as a PDF); I use a Gantt chart to build and present cost estimates and time estimates; it helps me get quotes from suppliers and subcontractors; and I use the chart to schedule the project. Everybody on the project gets a copy of the complete chart, and as a result I get total buy-in from labourers, operators, and the developer. On a big project, I update the chart weekly and the chart becomes a kind of progress report...."

—Ken Langedyk, consulting civil engineer

Gantt Charts

Named for engineer H.L. Gantt, a Gantt chart depicts progress as a function of time. A series of bars or lines (timelines) indicates start-up and completion dates for each phase or task in a project, relative to the other phases or tasks. Gantt charts are especially useful for planning a project (as in a proposal) and tracking it (as in a progress report). The Gantt chart illustrated in Figure 20.19 shows tasks whose timelines can be simultaneous, overlapping, or consecutive.

GRAPHIC ILLUSTRATIONS

Illustrations consist of diagrams, maps, drawings, and photographs depicting relationships that are physical rather than numerical. Good illustrations help readers understand and remember the material (Hartley 82). Consider this information from a government pamphlet, explaining the operating principle of the seat belt:

> The safety-belt apparatus includes a tiny pendulum attached to a lever, or locking mechanism. Upon sudden deceleration, the pendulum swings forward, activating the locking device to keep passengers from pitching into the dashboard.

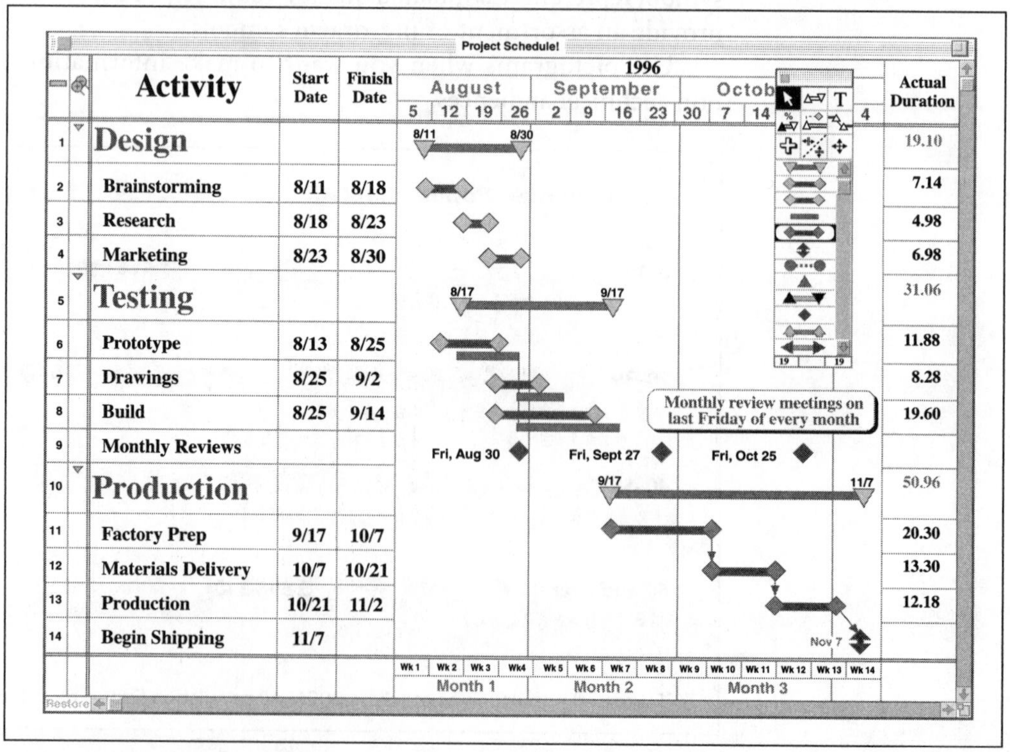

Figure 20.19 A Gantt Chart

Source: Courtesy of AEC Software, ©1996.

Without the illustration in Figure 20.20, the mechanism would be difficult to visualize. Clear and uncluttered, a good diagram eliminates unnecessary details and focuses only on material useful to the reader. The following pages illustrate some commonly used diagrams.

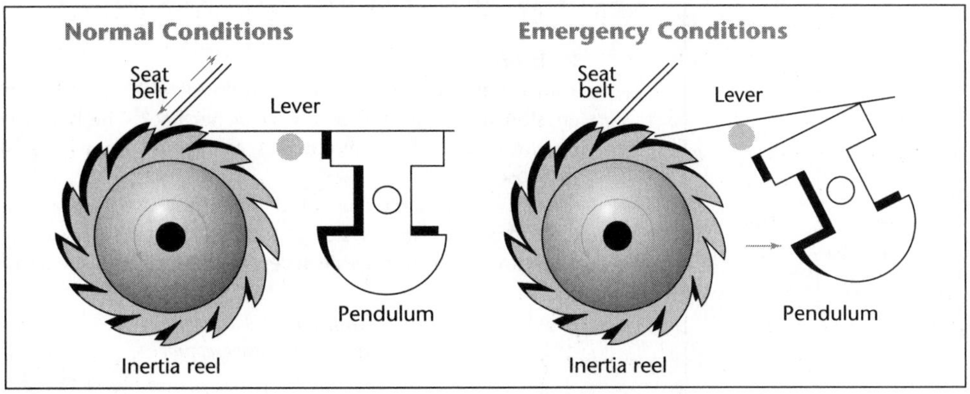

Figure 20.20 A Diagram of a Safety-belt Locking Mechanism

Source: Safety Belts. U.S. Department of Transportation.

Diagrams

Exploded diagrams, like that of a brace for an adjustable basketball hoop in Figure 20.21, show how the parts of an item are assembled; they often appear in repair or maintenance manuals. Notice how all parts are numbered for the reader's easy reference in the written instructions.

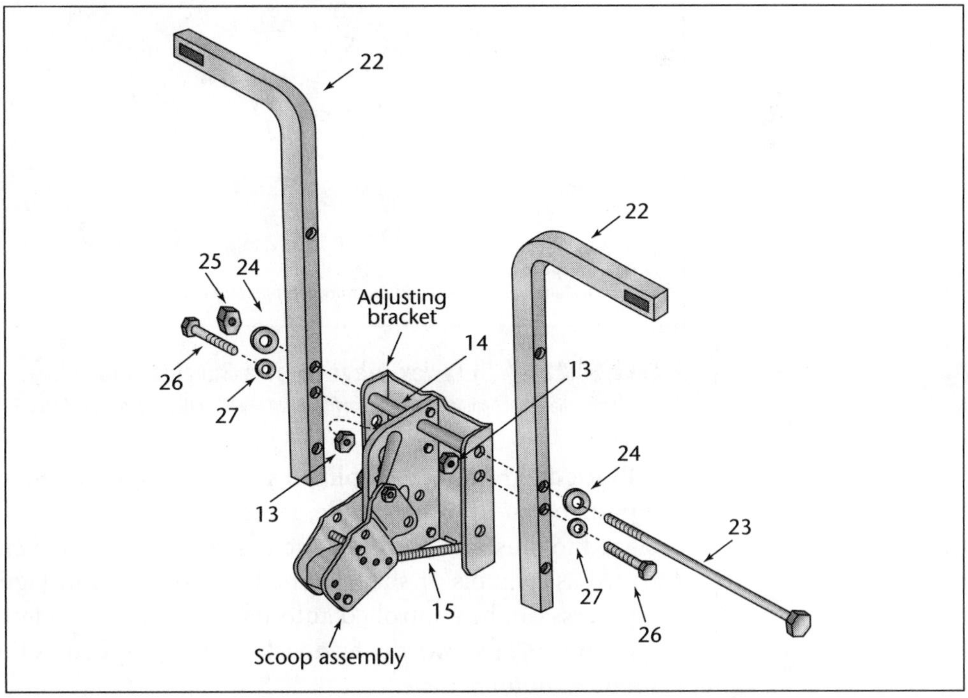

Figure 20.21 An Exploded Diagram of a Brace for a Basketball Hoop

Source: Courtesy of Spalding.

Cutaway diagrams show the item with its exterior layers removed in order to reveal interior sections, as in Figure 20.22. Unless the specific viewing perspective is immediately recognizable (as in Figure 20.22), define for readers the angle of vision: "top view," "side view," and so on.

THE OPERATION

Incision

Transsphenoidal surgery is performed with the patient under general anesthesia and positioned on his or her back. The head is fixed in a special headrest, and the operation is monitored on a special x-ray machine (fluoroscope).

In the approach illustrated here (not used by all surgeons), a small incision is made in one side of the nasal septum **(Fig. 2)**. Part of the septum is then removed to provide access to the sphenoid sinus cavity **(Fig. 3)**.

Figure 2
Incision into nasal septum

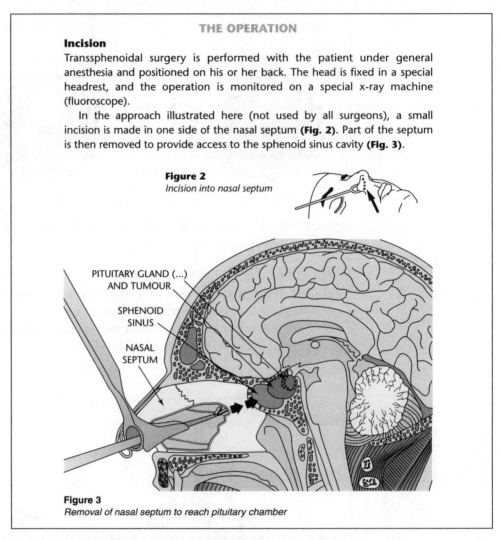

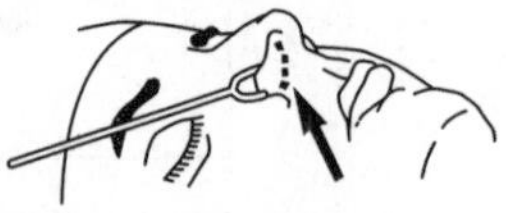

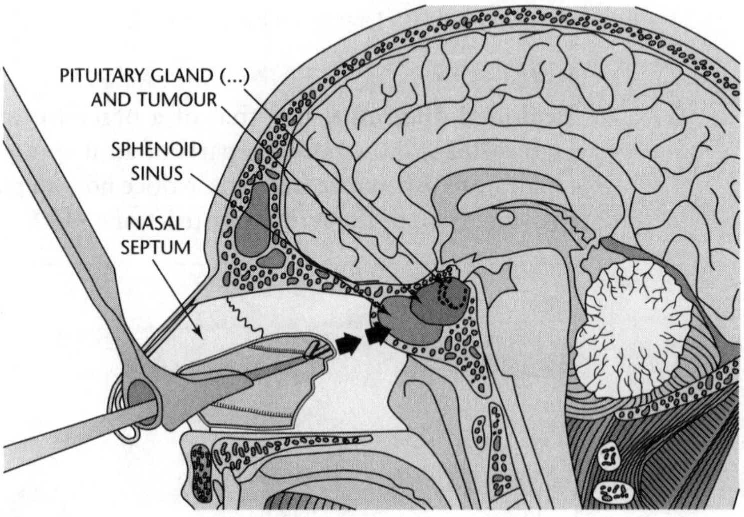

Figure 3
Removal of nasal septum to reach pituitary chamber

Figure 20.22 A Cutaway Diagram of a Surgical Procedure

Source: Transsphenoidal Approach for Pituitary Tumor. ©1986 by the Ludann Co., Grand Rapids, MI.

Block diagrams are simplified sketches that represent the relationship between the parts of an item, principle, system, or process. Because block diagrams are designed to illustrate *concepts* (such as current flow in a circuit), the parts are represented as symbols or shapes. The block diagram in Figure 20.23 illustrates how any process can be controlled automatically through a feedback mechanism.

Figure 20.24 shows the feedback concept applied as the cruise-control mechanism on a motor vehicle.

Increasingly available are electronic drawing programs, clip-art programs, image banks, and other resources for creating visuals or downloading pre-drawn images. Specialized diagrams, however, often require the services of graphic artists or technical illustrators. The client requesting or commissioning the visual provides the art professional with an *art brief* (often prepared by writers and editors) that spells out the visual's purpose and specifications for the visual.

For example, part of the brief addressed to the medical illustrator for Figure 20.22 might read as follows:

An art brief for Figure 20.22

Purpose: to illustrate transsphenoidal adenomectomy for laypersons

- View: full cutaway, axial
- Range: descending from cranial apex to a horizontal plane immediately below the upper jaw and second cervical vertebra
- Depth: medial cross-section
- Structures omitted: cranial nerves, vascular and lymphatic systems
- Structures included: gross anatomy of bone, cartilage, and soft tissue—delineated by colour, shading, and texture
- Structures highlighted: nasal septum, sphenoid sinus, and sella turcica, showing the pituitary embedded in a 1.5 cm tumour invading the sphenoid sinus via an area of erosion at the base of the sella

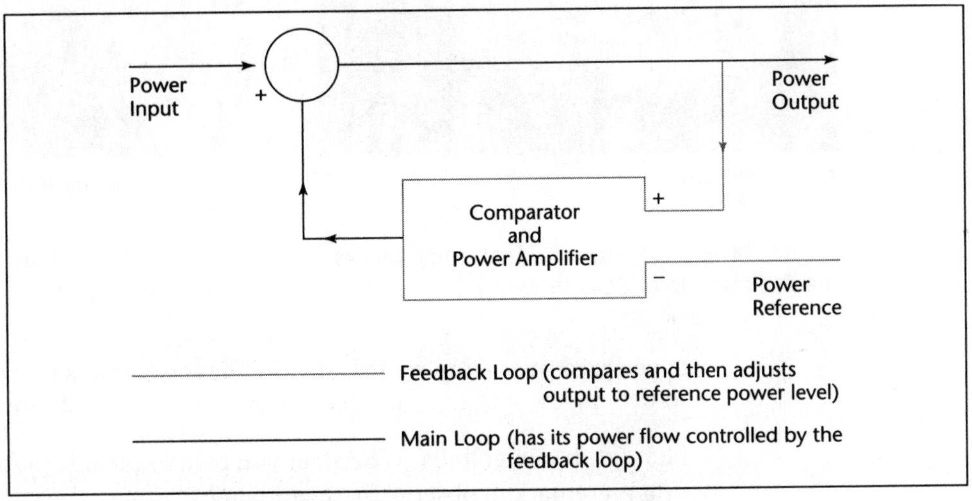

Figure 20.23 A Block Diagram Illustrating the Concept of Feedback

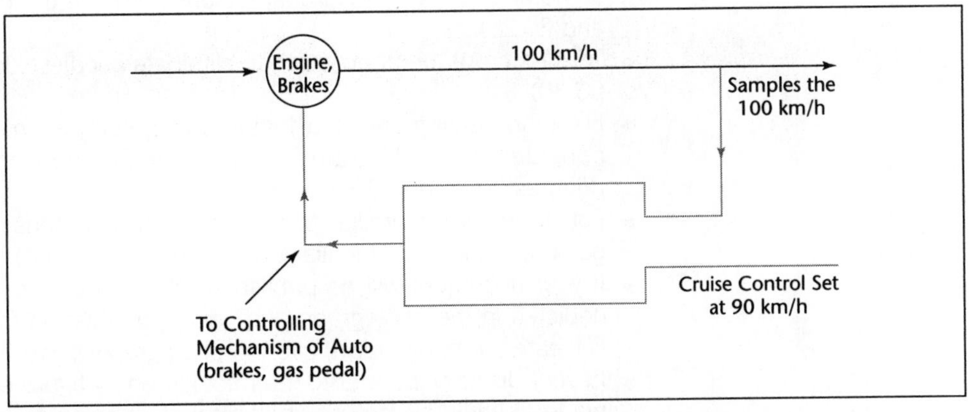

Figure 20.24 A Block Diagram Illustrating a Cruise-control Mechanism

Photographs

Photographs are especially useful for showing what something looks like (Figure 20.25) or how something is done (Figure 20.26).

No matter how visually engaging, a photograph is difficult to interpret if it includes needless details or fails to identify or emphasize the important material. One graphic design expert offers this practical advice for technical documents:

> To use pictures as tools for communication, pick them for their capacity to carry meaning, not just for their prettiness as photographs… [but] for their inherent significance to the [document]. (White, *Great Pages* 110, 122)

A Fixed-Platform Oil Rig
Source: SuperStock.

Figure 20.25 A Photograph That Some Shows the Appearance of Something

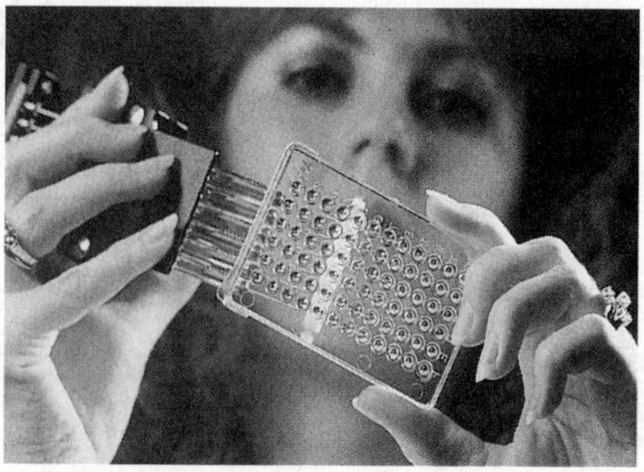

Antibody Screening Procedure
Source: SuperStock.

Figure 20.26 A Photograph That Shows How Something Is Done

Specialized photographs often require the services of a professional who knows how to use angles, lighting, and special film to obtain the desired focus and emphasis.

Photograph Guidelines. Whenever you plan to include photographs in a document or a presentation, observe these guidelines:

Guidelines for using photographs

- Try to simulate the approximate angle of vision readers would have in identifying or viewing the item or, for instructions, in doing the procedure (Figures 20.27 and 20.28).
- Trim (or crop) the photograph to eliminate needless details (Figures 20.29 and 20.30).
- For emphasizing selected features of a complex mechanism or procedure, consider using diagrams in place of photographs or as a supplement (Figures 20.31 and 20.32).
- For an image unfamiliar to readers, provide a sense of scale by including a person, a ruler, or a familiar object (such as a hand) in the photo.
- If your document will be published, obtain a signed release from any person depicted in the photograph and written permission from the copyright holder. Beneath the photograph, cite the photographer and the copyright holder.
- In your discussion, refer to the photograph by figure number and explain what readers should be looking for; or include a prose caption.

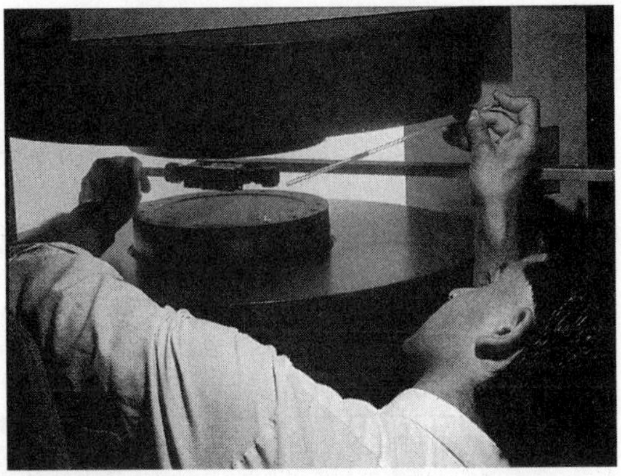

Titration in Measuring Electron-spin Resonance
Source: SuperStock

Figure 20.27 A Photograph That Shows a Realistic Angle of Vision

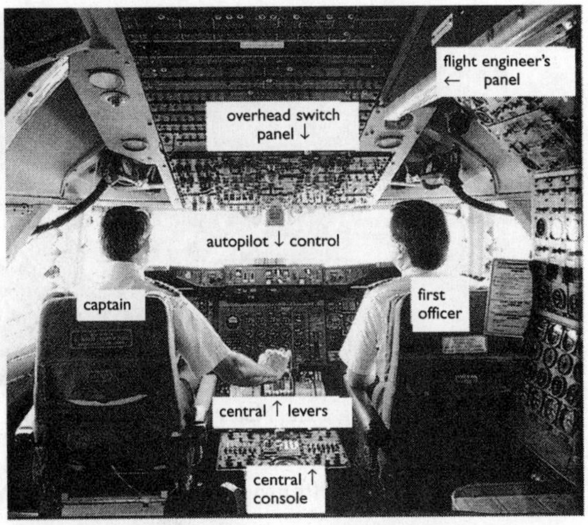

Standard Flight Deck for a Long-range Jet
Source: SuperStock.

Figure 20.28 A Photograph with Essential Features Labelled

Replacing the Microfilter Activation Unit
Source: SuperStock

Figure 20.29 A Photograph That Needs to Be Cropped

Source: SuperStock

Figure 20.30 The Cropped Version of Figure 20.29

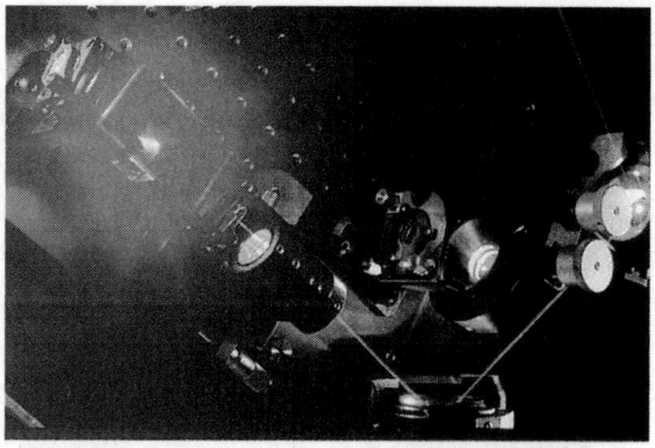

Sapphire Tunable LaserMajor Parts of the Laser
Source: SuperStock.

Figure 20.31 A Photograph of a Complex Mechanism

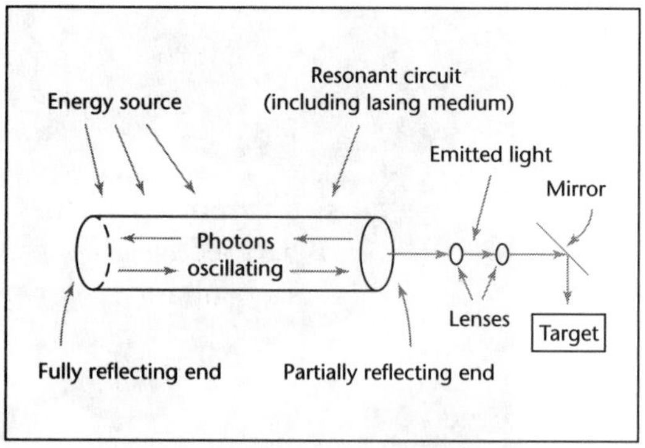

Major Parts of the Laser

Figure 20.32 A Simplified Diagram

Digital-imaging technology allows photographs to be scanned and stored electronically. These stored images then can be retrieved, edited, and altered. Such capacity for altering photographic content creates unlimited potential for distortion and raises questions about the ethics of digital manipulation (Callahan 64–65).

COMPUTER GRAPHICS

Computer technology transfers many of the tasks formerly performed by graphic designers and technical illustrators to individuals with little formal training in graphic design. In whatever career you anticipate, you probably will be expected to produce high-quality graphics for conferences, presentations, and in-house publications.

Today's computer systems create sophisticated, multicolour graphic displays and multimedia presentations. Among the virtually countless types of computer-generated visuals are these examples:

- With an electronic stylus (a pen with an electronic signal), you can draw pictures on a graphics tablet to be displayed on the monitor, stored, or sent to other computers.
- You can create three-dimensional effects, showing an object from different angles through the use of shading, shadows, on-screen rotation, background lighting, or other techniques.
- You can re-create the visual effect of a mathematical model, as in writing equations to explain what happens when high winds strike a tall building. (As the wind deforms the structure, the equations change. Then you can take those new equations and represent them visually.)
- You can create a design, build a model, simulate the physical environment, and let the computer forecast what will happen with different variables.
- You can integrate computer-assisted design (CAD) with computer-assisted manufacturing (CAM), so that the design will direct the machinery that makes the parts themselves (CAD/CAM).
- You can create animations, to see how bodies move (as in a car crash or in athletics).
- You can practise dealing with toxic chemicals, operating sophisticated machines, or making other rapid decisions in medical or technical environments, without the cost of or danger in actual situations.

- Through various types of scientific visualization, you can do "what-if" projections and explore countless ways of conceptualizing and understanding your data. Because the computer can generate and evaluate many possibilities rapidly, it enables you to test hypotheses without doing the calculations.

Computer graphics systems allow you to experiment with scales, formats, colours, perspectives, and patterns. By testing design options on the screen, you can revise and enhance your visual repeatedly until it achieves your exact purpose.

Using Clip Art

Clip art includes collections of ready-to-use images (of computer equipment, maps, machinery, medical equipment, etc.), all stored electronically. Clip-art packages enable you to import images like the one in Figure 20.33. Through a drawing program, you can enlarge, enhance, or customize it, as in Figure 20.34.

Figure 20.33 A Clip-art Image
Source: Desktop Art®; Business 1 © Dynamic Graphics, Inc.

Figure 20.34 A Customized Image
Source: Professor R. Armand Dumont.

Although a handy source for images, clip art often looks generic or crude and it makes a document appear unprofessional.

One form of clip art that's useful in technical writing is the *icon* (an image with all non-essential background removed). Icons convey a specific idea visually, as in Figure 20.35. Icons appear routinely in computer documentation and in other types of instructions because the image provides readers with an immediate signal of the desired action.

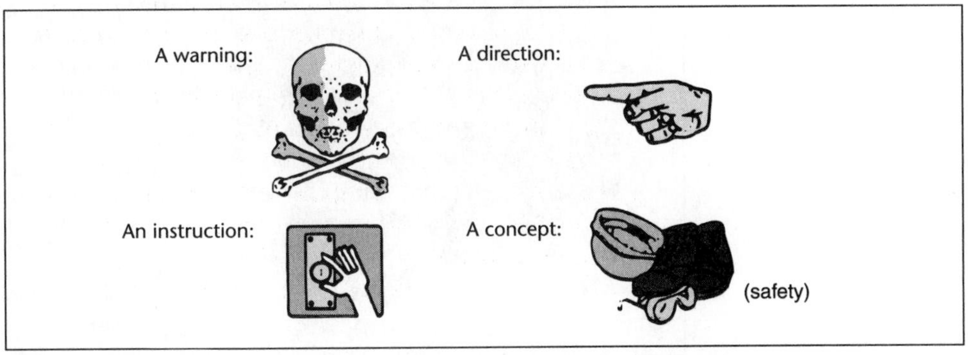

Figure 20.35 Icons
Source: Desktop Art®; Business 1 and Health Care 1, © Dynamic Graphics, Inc.

Whenever you use an icon, be sure it is "intuitively recognizable" to your readers ("Using Icons" 3). Otherwise, readers are likely to misinterpret its meaning—in some cases with disastrous results.

Keep in mind that certain icons have offensive connotations in certain cultures. Hand gestures are especially problematic: some Arab cultures consider the left hand unclean. A pointing index finger—on either hand—as in Figure 20.35, is a sign of rudeness in Venezuela and Sri Lanka (Bosley 5–6).

Using Colour or Shading

Colour or shading often makes a presentation more visually interesting. But colour and shading serve purposes beyond visual appeal. Used effectively in a visual, they draw and direct readers' attention to various elements. Colour or shading can help clarify a concept or dramatize how something works, as shown in Figure 20.36: the bright colours against a darker, duller background enable readers to *visualize* concepts, as does the use of dark shading against light.

Along with shape, type style, and position of elements on a printed page, colour or shading can guide readers through the material. Used effectively on a printed page, colour and shading help organize the reader's understanding, provide orientation, and emphasize important material.

Use Colour and Shading to Organize. Readers look for ways of organizing their understanding of a document (Figure 20.37). Colour or shading can reveal structure and break up material into discrete blocks that are easier to locate, process, and digest:

- A colour or shaded background screen can set off elements such as checklists, instructions, or examples.
- Horizontal rules can separate blocks of text, such as sections of a report or areas of a page.
- Vertical rules can set off examples, quotations, captions, and so on.

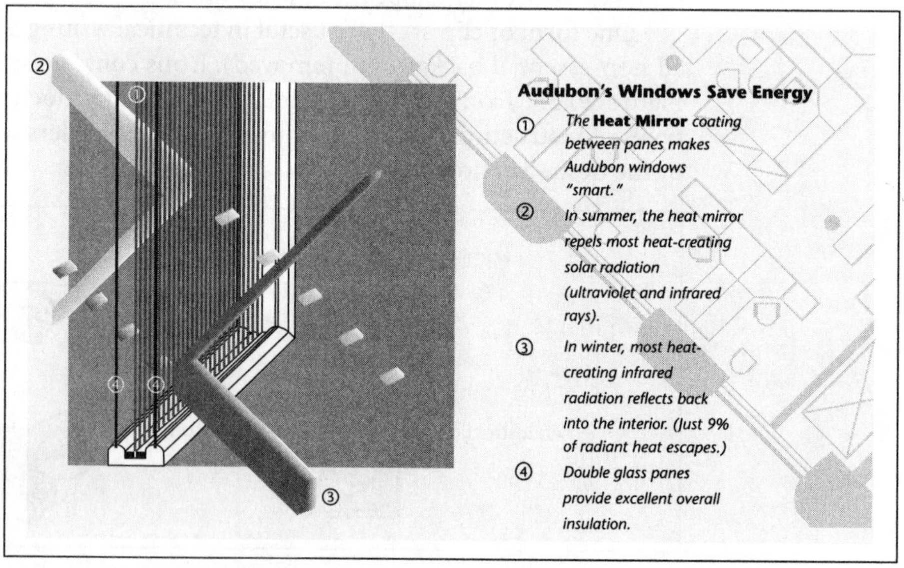

Figure 20.36 Colour Used as a Visualizing Tool
Source: Courtesy of National Audubon Society.

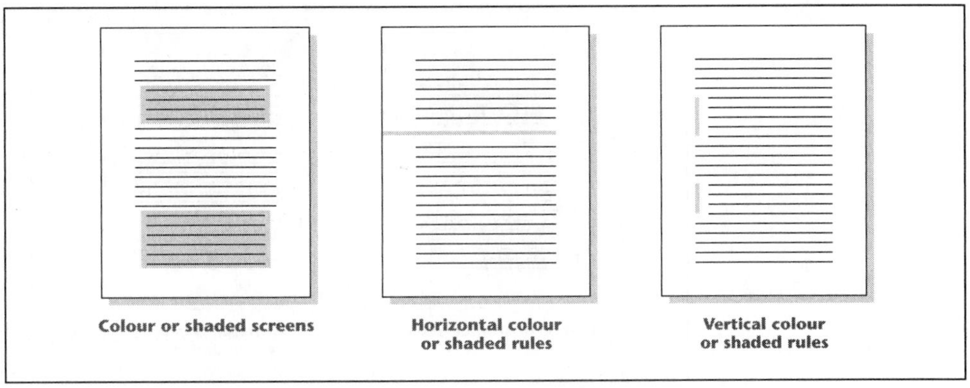

Figure 20.37 Colour or Shading Used to Organize Page Elements

Use Colour or Shading to Orient. Readers look for clear bearings and signposts that help them find their place and find what they need (Figure 20.38):

- Colour or shading can help headings stand out from the text and differentiate major from minor headings.
- Coloured or shaded tabs and boxes can serve as location markers.
- Coloured or shaded sidebars (for marginal comments), callouts (for labels), and leader lines (for connecting a label to its referent) can guide the eyes.

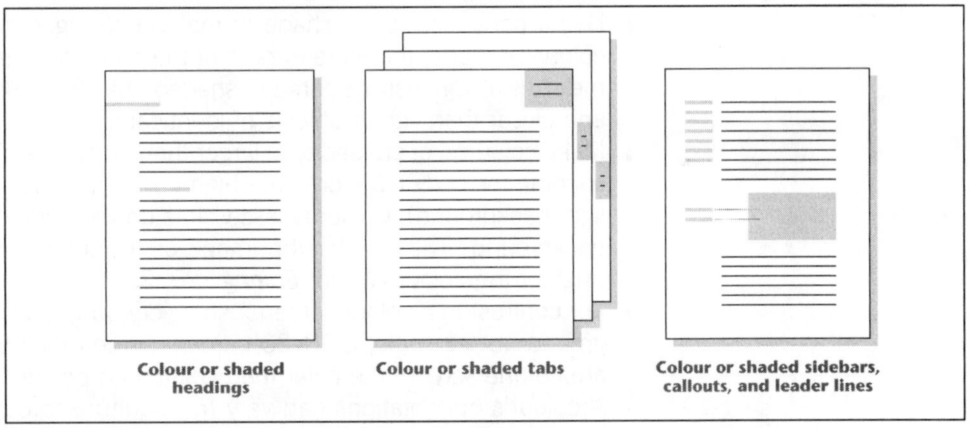

Figure 20.38 Colour or Shading Used as an Orientation Device

Use Colour or Shading to Emphasize. Readers look for places to focus their attention in a document (Figure 20.39):

- Colour or shaded typefaces can highlight key words or ideas.
- Colour or shading can call attention to cross-references.
- A coloured or shaded ruled box can frame a warning, caution, note, or hint.

Colour or Shading Guidelines. Whichever colour or shading options you use, employ the following general guidelines:

Guidelines for using colour or shading

- Colour or shading gains impact when it is used selectively. It loses impact when it is overused (*Aldus Guide* 39). Use colour or shading sparingly, and use no

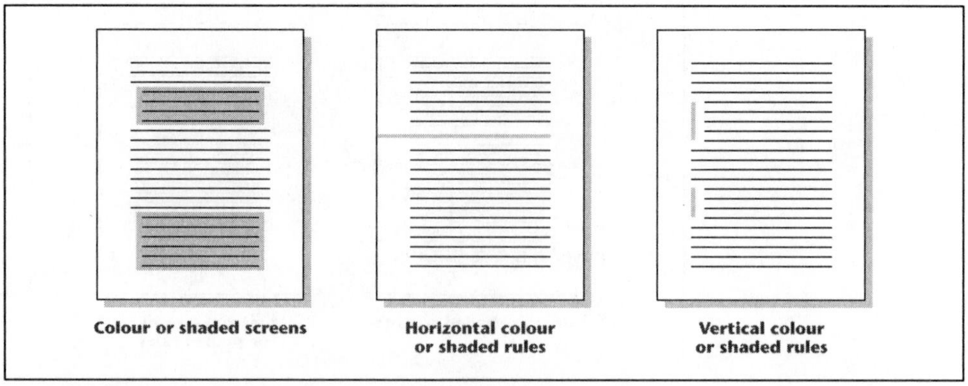

Figure 20.39 Colour or Shading Used for Emphasis

more than three or four distinct colours when using colour—including black and white (White, *Great Pages* 76).

- Apply colour or shading consistently to elements throughout your document. Inconsistent use of colour or shading can distort readers' perception of the relationships (Wickens 117).
- Make colour redundant. Be sure all elements are first differentiated in black and white: by shape, location, texture, type style, or type size. Different readers perceive colours differently or, in some cases, not at all. A sizable percentage of readers have impaired colour vision (White, *Great Pages* 76).
- Use a darker colour or shade to make a stronger statement. The darker the colour or shade, the more important the material. Readers perceive differently the sizes of variously coloured or shaded objects. Darker items can seem larger and closer than lighter objects of identical size.
- Make coloured or shaded type larger than body type. Try to avoid colour or light shading for body type, or use a high-contrast colour or shade (dark against a light background). Colour is less visible on the page than black ink on a white background. The smaller the image or the thinner the rule, the stronger or brighter the colour (White, *Editing* 229, 237).
- For contrast in a colour screen, use a very dark type against a very light background, for example, a 10–20 percent screen (Gribbons 70). The bigger the area of the screen, the paler the background colour (Figure 20.40).
- A colour's connotations can vary from culture to culture. In North America, for example, red signifies danger and green traditionally signifies safety. But in Ireland, green and orange carry political connotations in certain contexts. In Muslim cultures, green is a holy colour (Cotton 169).

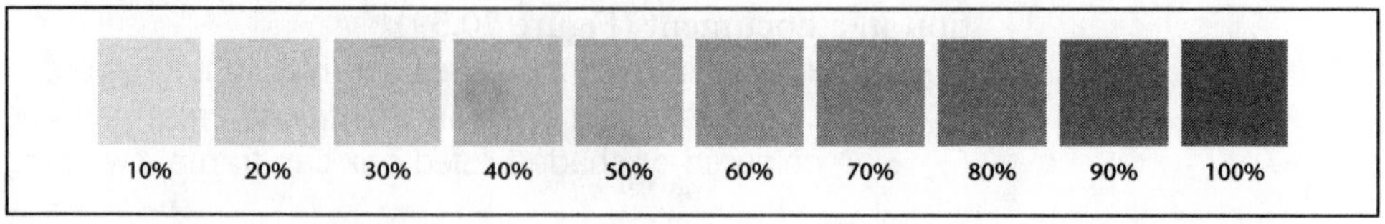

Figure 20.40 A Colour-density Chart

Using Websites for Graphics Support

The World Wide Web offers a growing array of visual resources. Following is a sample of useful websites and gateways (Martin 135–36).

- *Clip art:* For a comprehensive, updated directory, go to **www.clipart.com**.
- *Photographs*: Vintage photos of people, places, and things can be found at **www.classicphotos.com**. You can find links to all sorts of photography sites at **www.photolinks.com**.
- *Art images* (paintings, sculpture, etc.): Go to **www.artresources.com** for a search engine and links to art sites worldwide.
- *Maps:* National Geographic has links to local, global, and political maps at **www.nationalgeographic.com/maps/index.html**.
- *Audio and video*: For examples, instructions, and software for adding audio and video to your own website, go to **www.streamingmediaworld.com/**.

Be extremely cautious about downloading visuals (or any material, for that matter) from the web and then using it. Review the copyright law (pages 335–36). Originators of **any** work on the web own the work and the copyright.

HOW TO AVOID VISUAL DISTORTION

Although you are perfectly justified in presenting data in its best light, you are ethically responsible for avoiding misrepresentation. Any one set of data can support contradictory conclusions. Even though your numbers may be accurate, their visual display could be misleading.

Present the Real Picture

Visual relationships in a graph should portray accurately the numerical relationships they represent. Begin the vertical scale at zero. Never compress the scales to reinforce your point. Notice how visual relationships in Figure 20.41 become distorted when the value scale is compressed or fails to begin at zero.

In version A, the bars accurately depict the numerical relationships measured from the value scale. In version B, item *Z* (400) is depicted as three times *X* (200).

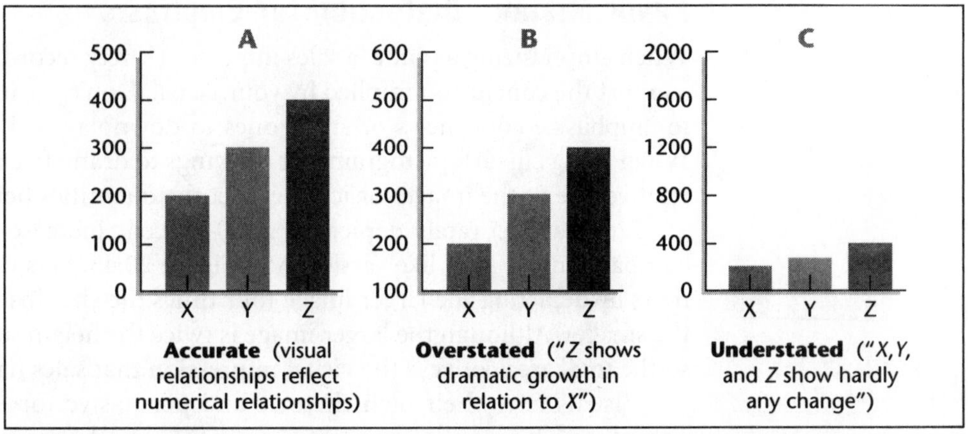

Figure 20.41 An Accurate Bar Graph and Two Distorted Versions

In version C, the scale is overly compressed, causing the shortened bars to understate the quantitative differences.

Deliberate distortions are unethical because they imply conclusions contradicted by the actual data.

Present the Complete Picture

Without bogging down in needless detail, an accurate visual includes all essential data. Figure 20.42 shows how distortion occurs when data that would provide a complete picture are selectively omitted. Version A accurately depicts the numerical relationships measured from the value scale. In version B, too few points are plotted. Decide carefully what to include and what to leave out of your visual display.

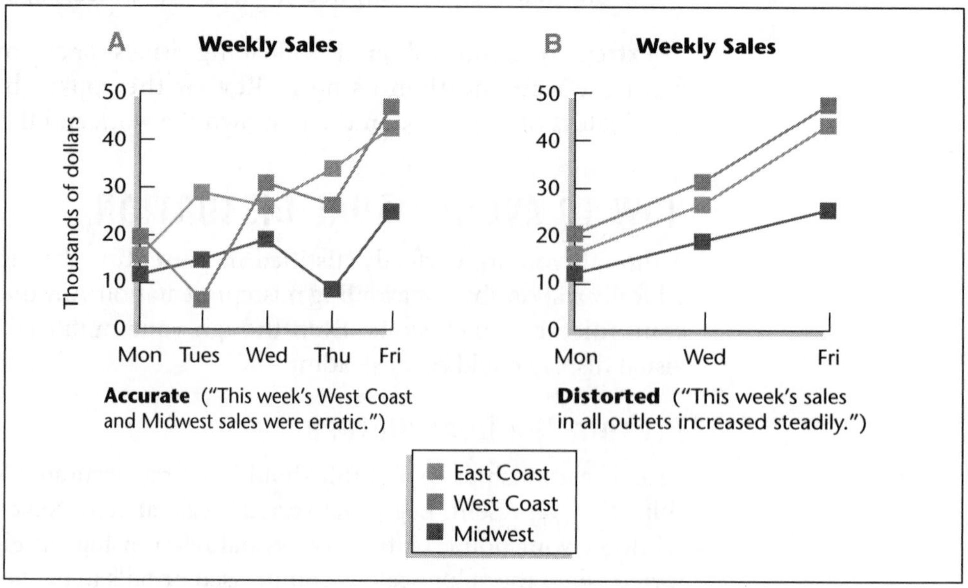

Figure 20.42 An Accurate Line Graph and a Distorted Version

Never Mistake Distortion for Emphasis

When emphasizing a point (a sales increase, a safety record, etc.), be sure your data support the conclusion implied by your visual. Don't use inordinately large visuals to emphasize good news or small ones to downplay bad news (R. Williams 11). When using clip art, pictograms, or drawings to dramatize a comparison, make the relative size of the images or icons reflect the quantities being compared.

A visual accurately depicting a 100 percent increase in phone sales at your company might look like version A in Figure 20.43. Version B overstates the good news by depicting the larger image four times the size, instead of twice the size, of the smaller. Although the larger image is twice the height, it is also twice the *width*, so the total area conveys the visual impression that sales have *quadrupled*.

Visuals have their own rhetoric and persuasive force, which we can use to advantage—for positive or negative purposes, for the reader's benefit or detriment (Van Pelt 2). Avoiding visual distortion is ultimately a matter of ethics.

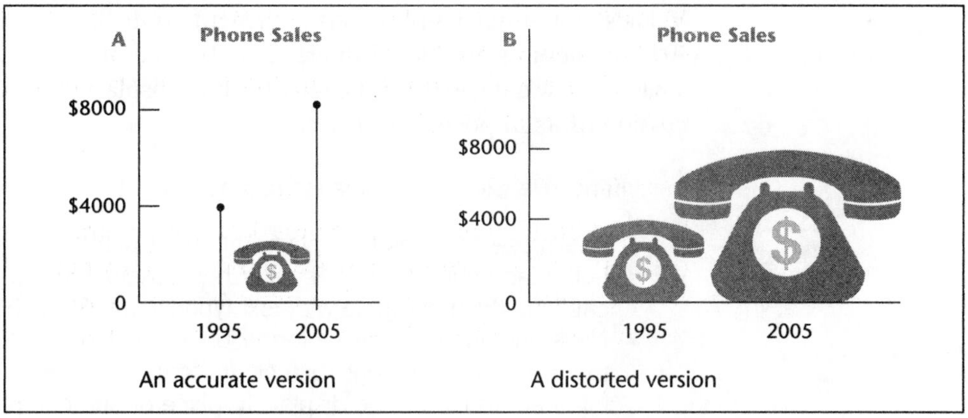

Figure 20.43 An Accurate Pictogram and a Distorted Version

HOW TO INCORPORATE VISUALS WITH THE TEXT

An effective visual enables readers to locate and extract the information they need. To simplify the reader's task, visual and verbal elements in a document should complement each other. For example, a visual should be able to stand alone in meaning—even when isolated from the verbal text.

Visual and Verbal Element Guidelines. Following are specific guidelines for incorporating visual and verbal elements effectively.

Guidelines for fitting visuals with text

- Place the visual where it will best serve your readers. If it is central to your discussion, place the visual as close as possible to the material it clarifies. (Achieving proximity often requires that you ignore the traditional "top or bottom" design rule for placement of visuals on a page.) If the visual is peripheral to your discussion or of interest to only a few readers, place it in an appendix so that interested readers can refer to it as they wish. Tell readers when to consult the visual and where to find it.
- Never refer to a visual that readers cannot easily locate. In a long document, don't be afraid to repeat a visual when you discuss it again later.
- Never crowd a visual into a cramped space. Set your visual off by framing it with plenty of white space, and position it on the page for balance. To save space and to achieve proportion with the surrounding text, consider carefully the size of each visual and the amount of space it will occupy.
- Number the visual and give it a clear title and clear labels. Your title should tell readers what they are seeing. Label all of the important material.
- Match the visual to your audience. Don't make it too elementary for specialists or too complex for non-specialists. Be sure your intended audience will be able to interpret the visual correctly.
- Introduce and interpret the visual.

Informative	Table 2 shows that operating costs have increased 7 percent annually since 1999.
Uninformative	See Table 2.

Visuals alone make ambiguous statements (Girill, *Technical Communication and Art* 35); pictures need to be interpreted. Instead of leaving readers to struggle with a page of raw data, explain the relationships displayed. Follow the visual with a discussion of its important features:

Informative This cost increase means that. . .

- Use prose captions to explain important points made by the visual. Captions help readers interpret a visual. When possible, use a smaller type size so that captions don't compete with text type (*Aldus Guide* 35).
- Never include excessive information in one visual. Any visual that contains too many lines, bars, numbers, colours, or patterns will overwhelm readers, causing them to ignore the display. In place of one complicated visual, use two or more straightforward ones.
- Be sure the visual's meaning can stand alone. Even though it repeats or augments information already in the text, the visual should contain everything readers will need to interpret it correctly.

The following Checklist for Revising Visuals will help ensure that your visuals enhance your meaning.

CHECKLIST FOR REVISING VISUALS

Use this checklist to revise your visuals.

Content

- Does the visual serve a legitimate purpose (clarification, not mere ornamentation) in the document?
- Is the visual titled and numbered?
- Is the level of complexity appropriate for the audience?
- Are all patterns in the visual identified by label or legend?
- Are all values or units of measurement specified?
- Are the numbers accurate and exact?
- Do the visual relationships represent the numerical relationships accurately?
- Are explanatory notes added as needed?
- Are all data sources cited?
- Has written permission been obtained for reproducing or adapting a visual from a copyrighted source in any type of work to be published?
- Is the visual introduced, discussed, interpreted, integrated with the text, and referred to by number?
- Can the visual itself stand alone in meaning?

Arrangement

- Is the visual easy to locate?
- Are all design elements (title, line thickness, legends, notes, borders, white space) positioned for balance?
- Is the visual positioned on the page to achieve balance?
- Is the visual set off by adequate white space or borders?
- Does the top of a wide visual face the inside binding?
- Is the visual in the best report location?

Style

- Is this the best type of visual for your purpose and audience?
- Are all decimal points in each column vertically aligned?
- Is the visual uncrowded and uncluttered?
- Is the visual engaging (patterns, colours, shapes), without being too busy?
- Is the visual in good taste?
- Is the visual ethically acceptable?

WEB CONNECT

The following websites deal with graphics and are less commercial than most:

www.arcm.com/illustra.html
http://members.aol.com/macbloom/
www.wcdd.com/dd/ddindex.html

EXERCISES

1. The following statistics are based on data from three colleges in a large western city. They give the number of applicants to each college over six years.
   - In 2003, X College received 2341 applications for admission, Y College received 3116, and Z College 1807.
   - In 2004, X College received 2410 applications for admission, Y College received 3224, and Z College 1784.
   - In 2005, X College received 2689 applications for admission, Y College received 2976, and College 1929.
   - In 2006, X College received 2714 applications for admission, Y College received 2840, and Z College 1992.
   - In 2007, X College received 2872 applications for admission, Y College received 2615, and Z College 2112.
   - In 2008, X College received 2868 applications for admission, Y College received 2421, and Z College 2267.

   Illustrate these data in a line graph, a bar graph, and a table. Which version seems most effective for a reader who (1) wants exact figures, (2) wonders how overall enrollments are changing, or (3) wants to compare enrollments at each college in a certain year? Include a caption interpreting each of these versions.
2. Devise a flow chart for a process in your field or area of interest. Include a title and a brief discussion.
3. Devise a pie chart to depict your yearly expenses. Title and discuss the chart.
4. Obtain enrollment figures at your university or college for the past five years by sex, age, race, or any other pertinent category. Construct a stacked-bar graph to illustrate one of these relationships over the five years.
5. Keep track of your pulse and respiration at 30-minute intervals over a four-hour period of changing activities. Record your findings in a line graph, noting the times and specific activities below your horizontal coordinate. Write a prose interpretation of your graph and give it a title.
6. In textbooks or professional journal articles, locate each of these visuals: a table, a multiple-bar graph, a multiple-line graph, a diagram, and a photograph. Evaluate each according to the revision checklist, and discuss the most effective visual in class.
7. Anywhere on campus or at work, locate at least one visual that needs revision for accuracy, clarity, appearance, or appropriateness. Look in computer manuals; lab manuals; newsletters; financial aid or admissions or placement brochures; student, faculty, or employee handbooks; newspapers; or textbooks. Use the Checklist for Revising Visuals as a guide to revise and enhance the visual. Submit to your instructor a copy of the original, along with a memo explaining your improvements. Be prepared to discuss your revision in class.

COLLABORATIVE PROJECT

Compile a list of 12 websites that offer graphics support by way of advice, image banks, design ideas, artwork catalogues, and the like. Provide the address for each site, along with a description of the resources offered and the cost. Report your findings in a format stipulated by your instructor.

CHAPTER 21

Adding Document Supplements

LEARNING OBJECTIVES

After reading this chapter, you should be able to

- Choose which supplements should be included in a report.
- Understand how to write clear and accurate titles.
- Complete the supplements required in an assigned report.

Supplements help make a long report or proposal more accessible. According to their needs, readers can refer to one or more of these supplements or skip them altogether. All supplements, of course, are written only after the document itself has been completed.

Some companies and organizations require a full range of supplements for any long document; others do not. When your audience has not stipulated its requirements, select only those supplements that enhance the informative value of your particular document. Avoid using supplements merely as decoration.

PURPOSE OF SUPPLEMENTS

Document supplements address these workplace realities to reach varied readers:

- *Confronted by a long document, many readers will try to avoid reading the whole thing.* Instead they look for the least information they need to complete the task, make the decision, or take some other action.
- *Different readers often use the same document for different purposes.* Some look for an overview; others want details; others want only conclusions and recommendations, or the "bottom line." Technical personnel might focus on the body of a highly specialized report and on the appendices for supporting data (maps, formulas, calculations). Executives and managers might read only the transmittal letter and the executive summary. If the latter read any parts of the report proper, they are likely to focus on conclusions and recommendations.

Report supplements can be classified into two groups:

Front matter

1. *supplements that precede your report*: transmittal document, cover, title page, summary, table of contents, list of illustrations, acknowledgements
2. *supplements that follow your report* (back matter): glossary, appendices, footnotes, endnote pages

COVER

Use covers only for long documents. Use a sturdy, plain cover with page fasteners. With the cover on, the open pages should lie flat.

Centre the report title and your name 10–13 cm (4–5") below the upper edge of your page (many workplace reports include a company name and logo instead of the report author's name).

TRANSMITTAL DOCUMENT

In university and college reports, the transmittal document (memo or letter) sometimes follows the title page and is bound as part of the report. However, workplace reports usually do not bind the transmittal document in the report, but present it separately. A transmittal letter or memo included with a formal report or proposal addresses a specific reader; it adds a note of courtesy and allows for personal remarks. For instance, your transmittal document might

What to include in a transmittal document

- acknowledge those who helped with the report
- refer to sections of special interest: unexpected findings, key visuals, major conclusions, special recommendations, and the like
- discuss the limitations of your study, or any problems gathering data
- discuss the need and approaches for follow-up investigations
- describe any personal (or off-the-record) observations
- suggest some special uses for the information
- urge the reader to immediate action

The transmittal document can be tailored to a particular reader, as is Richard Larkin's in Figure 21.1. If a report is being sent to a number of people who are variously qualified and bear various relationships to the writer, the information may instead be included within the following basic structure:

Introduction. Open with a reference to the reader's original request. Briefly review the reasons for your report or include a brief descriptive abstract. Maintain a confident and positive tone throughout.

Body. In the body, include appropriate items from the above list of possibilities.

Conclusion. State your willingness to answer questions or discuss findings. End positively, and, where appropriate, suggest follow-up actions.

7409 Trinity Court
Niagara Falls, ON L2H 3A6

June 2, 2008

Ms. Mimi Lim
Placement Director
Seneca College
1750 Finch Avenue East
North York, ON M2J 2X5

Dear Ms. Lim:

Here is my analysis to determine the feasibility of a career in technical marketing. In preparing my report, I've learned a great deal about the requirements and modes of access to this career, and I believe my information will help other students as well.

Although committed to their specialities, some technical and science graduates seem interested in careers in which they can apply their technical knowledge to customer and business problems. Technical marketing may be an attractive choice of career for those who know their field, who can relate to different personalities, and who are good communicators.

Technical marketing is competitive and demanding, but highly rewarding. In fact, it is an excellent route to upper-management and executive positions. Specifically, marketing work enables one to develop a sound technical knowledge of a company's products, to understand how these products fit into the marketplace, and to perfect sales techniques and interpersonal skills. This is precisely the kind of background that paves the way to top-level jobs.

I've enjoyed my work on this project, and would be happy to answer any questions.

Sincerely,

Richard B. Larkin

Richard B. Larkin

Figure 21.1 A Letter of Transmittal for a Formal Report

TITLE PAGE

Back matter

The title page (see Figure 21.2) lists the report title, author's name, name of person(s) to whom the report is addressed or the name of the organization to which it is addressed, and date of submission.

How to prepare a title page

Title. Your title announces the report's purpose and subject. The previous title (given as an example for the cover) is clear, accurate, comprehensive, and specific. But even slight changes can distort this title's signal.

An unclear title

A TECHNICAL MARKETING CAREER

The version above is unclear about the report's purpose. Is the report *describing* the career, *proposing* the career, *giving instructions* for career preparation, or *telling one person's career story*? Insert descriptive words (*analysis*, *instructions*, *proposal*, *feasibility*, *description*, *progress*) that accurately state your purpose.

To be sure that your title forecasts what the report delivers, write its final version *after* completing the report.

Placement of Title Page Items. Do not number your title page but count it as page i of your preliminary pages. Centre the title horizontally, 8–10 cm (3–4") below the upper edge. Place other items in the spacing and order shown in Figure 21.2, the title page to a report. Or devise your own system, as long as your page is balanced.

SUMMARY

Chapter 5 defines varieties of summary writing, including the summary (or executive summary) that *accompanies* a formal report or proposal (illustrated in Figure 18.6 on page 421). Many readers who don't have the time or willingness to read your entire report will consider the summary to be the most useful part of the material you present.

Chapter 5 also recommends a step-by-step process that will help you find and condense the elements of a good summary:

- the issue or need that led to the report
- the report's key facts, statistics, findings, and, in some cases, illustrations—this is the material your reader *must* know
- the report's conclusions and recommendations

When you write and edit a summary, make clear connections between the report's data and interpretations. If you find yourself unable to do this in the summary, you'll probably need to revise the original report.

Follow these guidelines for the report summary:

- Make the summary about one-tenth the length of the original, but remember that summaries rarely are shorter than three-quarters of a page or longer than five pages.
- Where appropriate, use a table to summarize key facts and findings.

FEASIBILITY OF A CAREER
IN TECHNICAL MARKETING

for
Mimi Lim
Placement Director
Seneca College
North York, Ontario

by
Richard B. Larkin,
English 266 Student

June 2, 2008

Figure 21.2 A Title Page for a Formal Report

- Add no new information. Simply give the report's highlights.
- Use the same order of topics in the summary as in the original.
- Adjust the vocabulary to suit the intended reader. An executive summary, for example, includes little technical jargon. When you send report copies to readers with varying levels of expertise, write a different summary for each type of reader.
- Include a graph or other figure in the summary *only* if the illustration is absolutely necessary in understanding the report.

TABLE OF CONTENTS

How to prepare a table of contents

The table of contents (Figure 21.3) serves as a road map for readers and a checklist for you. If you are using a high-end word-processing program, you can generate a table of contents automatically, provided that you have assigned styles or codes to all of the headings in your report. If your word-processing program does not have this feature, compose the table of contents by assigning page numbers to headings from your outline. Keep in mind, however, that not all levels of outline headings appear in your table of contents or your report. Excessive headings can fragment the discussion.

Follow these guidelines:

- List front matter (summary, list of illustrations), numbering the pages with small Roman numerals. (The title page, though not listed, is counted as page i.) List back matter such as glossary, appendices, and endnotes. Number these pages with Arabic numerals, continuing the page sequence of your main report.
- Include in the table of contents only headings or subheadings that are in the report; the report may, however, contain subheadings not listed in the table of contents.
- Phrase headings in the table of contents exactly as in the report.
- List various levels of headings with varying typefaces and indentations.
- Use *leader lines* (.........) to connect the heading text to the page number. Align rows of dots vertically, each above the other.

LIST OF FIGURES AND TABLES

Following the table of contents is a list of figures and tables, if needed. When a report has three or more visuals, place this table on a separate page. List the figures first, then the tables. Figure 21.4 shows the list of figures and tables for Larkin's report. Also see the extensive list of illustrations in Figure 21.6.

DOCUMENTATION

As Chapter 19 demonstrates, reference pages are organized according to the format required by your workplace or academic discipline. APA format requires references to be listed in alphabetical order on a Works Cited page or References page. IEEE and CBE formats list sources in the same numerical order as they are cited in the report.

TABLE OF CONTENTS

Figure 21.3 A Table of Contents for a Formal Report

FIGURES AND TABLES

Figure 21.4 A List of Figures and Tables for a Formal Report

Whichever documentation format you use, consider including a separate list of sources you consulted but did not cite under the heading "Additional Sources Consulted." Thus, you will

- show your reader that you have indeed covered all the bases,
- acknowledge that certain sources influenced your thinking, even if you didn't have reason to cite them specifically, and
- serve the reader who wishes to explore the topic further.

GLOSSARY

A glossary alphabetically lists specialized terms and their definitions, following or preceding your report. Specialized reports often contain glossaries, especially when written for both technical and non-technical readers. A glossary makes key definitions available to non-technical readers without interrupting the flow of the report for technical readers. If fewer than five terms need defining, place them in the report introduction as working definitions, or use footnote definitions. If you use a separate glossary, inform readers of its location: "(see the glossary at the end of this report)." Note, though, that some readers prefer the glossary in the front matter, just before the introduction.

Follow these guidelines for a glossary:

How to prepare a glossary

- Define all terms unfamiliar to a general reader (an intelligent layperson).
- Define all terms that have a special meaning in your report (e.g., "In this report, a small business is defined as").
- Define all terms by giving their class and distinguishing features, unless some terms need expanded definitions.
- List your glossary and its first page number in your table of contents.

- List all terms in alphabetical order. Boldface each term. You may use a colon to separate the term from its single-spaced definition. This is not necessary if you use a tabular format.
- Define only terms that need explanation. In doubtful cases, over-defining is safer than under-defining.

Figure 21.5 shows part of a non-tabular glossary for a comparative analysis of two techniques of natural childbirth, written by a nurse practitioner for expectant mothers and student nurses. Figure 21.6 illustrates a partial tabular glossary.

GLOSSARY

Analgesic: a medication given to relieve pain during the first stage of labour.

Cervix: the neck-shaped anatomical structure that forms the mouth of the uterus.

Dilation: cervical expansion occurring during the first stage of labour.

Episiotomy: an incision of the outer vaginal tissue, made by the obstetrician just before the delivery, to enlarge the vaginal opening.

First stage of labour: the stage in which the cervix dilates and the baby remains in the uterus.

Induction: the stimulating of labour by puncturing the membranes around the baby or by giving an oxytoxic drug (uterine contractant), or both.

Figure 21.5 A Non-tabular Glossary (Partial)

GLOSSARY

Analgesic	A medication given to relieve pain during the first stage of labour.
Cervix	The neck-shaped anatomical structure that forms the mouth of the uterus.

Figure 21.6 A Tabular Glossary (Partial)

APPENDICES

An appendix follows the text of your report. It expands items discussed in the report without cluttering the report text. Figure 21.7 shows an appendix to a budget proposal. Typical items in an appendix include

What an appendix might include

- complex formulas
- details of an experiment
- interview questions and responses
- long quotations (one or more pages)
- maps or photographs
- material more essential to secondary readers than to primary readers
- related correspondence (letters of enquiry, and so on)
- sample questionnaires and tabulated responses
- sample tests and tabulated results
- some visuals occupying more than one full page
- statistical or other measurements
- texts of laws and regulations

The appendix lists items that are important but difficult to integrate within your text.

Do not stuff appendices with needless information. Do not use them unethically for burying bad or embarrassing news that belongs in the report proper. Follow these guidelines:

How to prepare an appendix

- Include only material that is relevant.
- Use a separate appendix for each major item.
- Title each appendix clearly: "Appendix A: Projected Costs."
- Limit an appendix to a few pages, unless more length is essential.
- Mention your appendix early in your introduction, and refer readers to it at appropriate points in the report: "(see Appendix A)."

Use an appendix for any material that is essential but might harm the unity and coherence of your report.

APPENDIX A

Table 1 Allocations and Performance of Five College Newspapers

	Prairie College	**Drake College**	**Kelsey College**	**Hollander College**	**Northern College**
Enrollment	1600	1400	3000	3000	5000
Fee paid (per year)	$65.00	$85.00	$35.00	$50.00	$65.00
Total fee budget	$88 000.00	$119 000.00	$105 000.00	$150 000.00	$334 429.28
Newspaper budget	$10 000.00	$6 000.00	$25 300.00	$37 000.00	$21 500.00 $25 337.14[a]
Yearly cost per student	$6.25	$4.29	$8.43	$12.33	$4.06 $5.20[a]
Format of paper	Weekly	Every third week	Weekly	Weekly	Weekly
Average no. of pages	8	12	18	12	20
Average total pages	224	120	504	336	560 672[a]
Yearly cost per page	$44.50	$50.00	$50.50	$110.11	$38.25 $38.69[a]

[a]These figures are next year's costs for the Northern *Torch.*

Source: Figures were quoted by newspaper business managers in April 2005.

Figure 21.7 An Appendix

WEB CONNECT

These sources discuss the common types of document supplements that usually appear in formal reports. The University of Toronto site, the first one listed, is the most useful of the four sites.

http://www.ecf.utoronto.ca/~writing/handbook.html
http://www.coba.unt.edu/mgmt/pitre/mgmt3330/Parts%20of%20Formal%20Report.pdf
http://www.dc-uoit.ca/assets/Learner~Support~Centre/PDF/Formal_Report_Writing.pdf
http://core.ecu.edu/engl/snyderh/3880/reports.html

EXERCISES

1. These titles are intended for investigative, research, or analytical reports. Revise each inadequate title to make it clear and accurate.
   a. The Effectiveness of the Prison Furlough Program in Our Province
   b. Drug Testing on the Job
   c. The Effects of Nuclear Power Plants
   d. Woodburning Stoves
   e. Interviewing
   f. An Analysis of Vegetables (for a report assessing the physiological effects of a vegetarian diet)
   g. Wood as a Fuel Source
   h. Oral Contraceptives
   i. Lie Detectors and Employees
2. Prepare a title page, transmittal document (for a definite reader who can use your information in a definite way), table of contents, and informative abstract for a report you have written earlier.
3. Find a short but effective appendix in one of your textbooks, in a journal article in your field, or in a report from your workplace. In a memo to your instructor and colleagues, explain how the appendix is used, how it relates to the main text, and why it is effective. Attach a copy of the appendix to your memo. Be prepared to discuss your evaluation in class.

COLLABORATIVE PROJECT

Collect samples of various document supplements. As a group, critique the format and content of the supplements.

PART III

CHAPTER 22

Introduction

Often during my four decades of teaching technical communications, I've surveyed business people about the communications skills required for success in their industry or profession. When I've asked what skills and knowledge should be taught in post-secondary English and Communications courses, they've responded with comments such as the following:

- "Our employees need to analyse who reads their correspondence and reports because different readers look for different information and analysis."
- "I like to see short paragraphs and sentences in our company documents, so that they're easy to read and understand."
- "When we hire employees, we look for people who can write clear, concise sentences. We can't afford ambiguity in our instruction manuals and online prompts."
- "We spend more money on communications training than on technical training—it's too bad that our employees don't leave college or university with better communications skills."

The most common response, often accompanied by impassioned, "colourful" language, reads something like this: "Please, please, **PLEASE** make your students pay attention to spelling, punctuation, and grammar! We require correct English in all our documents."

Thriving businesses emphasize language basics because they realize that business success depends on clear, readable, persuasive communications. They also know that they are judged by the quality of the documents they produce, not just by their products and services. Successful business operators know that sloppily-written workplace reports, proposals, and correspondence will fail, even if those documents are technically accurate and well-designed.

Here's a portion of an actual letter sent by the owner of a construction firm to local businesses affected by upcoming roadworks:

> T.G. Jones Contracting will be doing Roadworks on 35th Street+36th. Ave starting Sept.17th until Aprx.. Nov.23rd in conjuction with the city of .... + Rogers head Office. Their will be no parking on 35th. Street, please advice your clients, we will have traffic control, barricades, flashers on the street at all times they must find alternate

parking. We will be doing new sewer connections on your properties in which you will be notified 1 day in advance having replacement the same day.

What is your impression of the above document? Based on the quality of the letter, would you be tempted to pre-judge the quality of work done by the writer's construction firm? Might such judgments affect your decision to hire such a firm for a future contract? If you manage a business affected by the road and sewer construction, what concerns might you have? And, most of all, do you understand what the writer is trying to convey?

Grammar at Work responds to a need for supplementary material and exercises to help writers improve their skills—this workbook focuses on grammar, sentence structure, vocabulary and usage, and mechanics such as spelling, punctuation, and numbers. The book provides self-directed instruction and exercises that students can use to improve their mastery of business and technical English. *Grammar at Work* can operate in conjunction with the 4th Canadian edition of *Technical Communication* or as a stand-alone workbook.

Please understand that this book does not present complete coverage of grammar, usage, and mechanics. More exhaustive coverage is available in a handbook such as the *Simon & Schuster Handbook for Writers*, 4th Canadian Edition or the *Prentice Hall Canada Reference Guide to Grammar and Usage*, 2nd edition.

This workbook progresses in three stages:

- On pages 511–514, a **Diagnostic Test** provides exercises that test your current knowledge and skill levels. You can then use the self-evaluated results to determine which skill areas you most need to improve.
- Leading into each group of improvement exercises, a **Review of Basic Principles** provides advice and examples that you will find useful in preparing to complete the practice exercises and the self-improvement exercises.
- The **Self-improvement Exercises** appear in the following order:
    - Basic grammar: parts of speech (nouns, pronouns, verbs, prepositions, conjunctions, interjections, and articles)
    - Sentence grammar
    - Punctuation
    - Mechanics (spelling, capitals, numbers)
    - Vocabulary and style

Following the review of principles in each of the five groups listed above, the exercises help you improve your English grammar, mechanics, and usage. First, a set of practice exercises helps you determine how well you understand those principles and what you need to improve. Next, a more extensive group of improvement exercises contains errors that you will need to avoid or eradicate in workplace writing. Finally, a document critique will sharpen your proofreading and editing skills. Page 643 lists the Correction Symbols that you'll need to complete the document critiques.

Starting on page 617, you will find answer keys for the exercises in this workbook.

Grammar at Work: Good Grammar is Valuable

"I didn't enjoy studying grammar at school, and I still cringe when I hear that word [grammar], but in my business, our letters, emails, proposals, and bills need to be grammatically perfect and free of spelling errors and punctuation errors. So I guess good grammar is a necessary evil!"

—**Gary Sedlick,** *owner and manager of Okanagan Audiolab, which tests hearing at industrial and service locations*

CHAPTER 23

Diagnostic Test of English Skills

Use the following test to learn whether you need to work on grammar, punctuation, mechanics or vocabulary. After answering the questions, score the test by comparing your answers to the answer key on page 617. Then, use the *Skills Assessment* form on page 514 to record your number of correct answers for each section.

The following choices apply to items 1 through 10. In each blank, write the letter of the choice that best describes each sentence.

A. incomplete sentence
B. run-on sentence (phrases or clauses are incorrectly strung together)
C. modifying elements misplaced or left dangling
D. structure not parallel
E. nothing wrong

____ 1. Stop here.
____ 2. This system can recognize voice commands, respond to those commands, and also displaying current settings.
____ 3. While the flag rose, the cheering increased.
____ 4. Running quietly on a pedestal, I didn't notice the machine at all.
____ 5. The printer, an advanced laser jet model, is quite reliable.
____ 6. Measuring the stream output, the main function.
____ 7. When it's convenient, file your report.
____ 8. Several problem areas have been identified, unfortunately, they will all be difficult to solve.
____ 9. Running your own business is to face the risk of go bankrupt.
____ 10. Smoking is only permitted in designated areas on this campus.

The following choices apply to items 11 through 20. In each blank, write the letter of the choice that identifies the underlined word(s) in each sentence.

A. subject
B. verb
C. object
D. modifier
E. conjunction or preposition

____ **11.** Run this part over to the loading dock.
____ **12.** On Thursday, the Leafs lost another game.
____ **13.** Bombardier Inc. has moved some of its aerospace operations to Northern Ireland.
____ **14.** Running quietly, the new machine doesn't disturb our conversations.
____ **15.** The printer is proving quite reliable.
____ **16.** Measuring electronic output is the main function of this multimeter.
____ **17.** When the job's complete, carefully report your findings.
____ **18.** We have found an assistant for you.
____ **19.** Your business needs a complete communications audit.
____ **20.** Smoking is permitted but not encouraged at this job site.

In the blanks for items 21 through 30, write the letter of the word or phrase that properly completes each sentence.

____ **21.** McDonald's (A. is **or** B. are) experiencing stiff competition.
____ **22.** There (A. is **or** B. are) several reasons for the U.S. dollar's slide.
____ **23.** Every worker who wants to control (A. their **or** B. his or her) own pension plan must complete form W-256.
____ **24.** Not one of them (A. was **or** B. were) on time for the presentation.
____ **25.** An important factor affecting that firm's performance is that (A. they try **or** B. it tries) to retain key personnel.
____ **26.** Once they (A. saw **or** B. seen) the annual report, changes came quickly.
____ **27.** The number of hooking penalties called in the NHL (A. has **or** B. have) increased since the crackdown on interference.
____ **28.** If I (A. was **or** B. were) younger, I'd study robotics engineering.
____ **29.** The receptionist (A. lay **or** B. laid) the drawings on the counter.
____ **30.** Either Hewlett Packard or Dell (A. has **or** B. have) won the bid.

For items 31 through 40, in the provided blank write the letter of the choice that best describes the corresponding sentence.

A. all punctuation used correctly
B. some punctuation used incorrectly or incorrectly omitted

____ **31.** McDonald's which is a huge enterprise, is not easy to manage.
____ **32.** Look for evidence of slippage, shown by deep scratches in the surface.
____ **33.** Could you complete form W-256 each time an application is successful.

____ **34.** The project engineer, Susan Marsh, said that, "it's just a matter of time before the bridge fails."

____ **35.** Cross Canada Engineering has offices in Halifax, Nova Scotia, Ottawa, Ontario, Brandon, Manitoba, and Kelowna, British Columbia.

____ **36.** After checking his assistant learned that three turbines had failed.

____ **37.** Do you have a clear idea of the company's "rules of conduct?"

____ **38.** One main option, then, remains: the turbine must be replaced.

____ **39.** Not all the spawning beds in Delorme Creek have been contaminated, however, we should continue to monitor the situation.

____ **40.** Hewlett Packard, Dell, and Acer—these three firms have met the bid requirements.

The following choices apply to items 41 through 50. In each blank, write the letter of the choice that best describes each sentence.

A. error in punctuation
B. error in use of abbreviations or symbols
C. error in use of numbers
D. error in capitalization
E. no errors

____ **41.** This year's salmon run is high in the Adams river, despite adverse spawning conditions.

____ **42.** Kovalev, Andrei Kostitsen, & Markov have scored all the team's goals in the past three games.

____ **43.** Bombardier Inc. has moved some of its aerospace operations to northern Ireland.

____ **44.** This semester, I'm studying physics, English, and mathematics.

____ **45.** The printer can print 12 pages per minute, in colour or in black and white.

____ **46.** The Johnsrude 389B multimeter—last year's model, has four function ranges.

____ **47.** When the job's complete carefully report your findings.

____ **48.** We have found an assistant for you; please explain our operating procedures to him.

____ **49.** Sale prices of houses in Saskatoon rose by an average of 27% last year.

____ **50.** Seven smelters will soon appear at this job site, which will necessitate stringent air quality monitoring.

In the blanks for items 51 through 60, write the letter of the word or phrase that properly completes each sentence.

____ **51.** The McDonald's and Wendy's chains will soon have to modify (A. their **or** B. they're) menus to include low carb items.

____ **52.** The main (A. effects **or** B. affects) of global cooling will soon appear.

____ **53.** Our ethics guidelines operate on the (A. principal **or** B. principle) of "no harm, no foul."

____ **54.** We have four (A. prospective **or** B. perspective) candidates for the vacant position.

____ **55.** Good team members (A. complement **or** B. compliment) each other's talents; they do not compete for status within the team.

____ **56.** If we (A. loose **or** B. lose) this contract, our company will have to lay off nearly half of its employees.

____ **57.** After we hear the last of the six competing proposals, the four members of our committee should discuss the proposals (A. among **or** B. between) ourselves.

____ **58.** Set the pallets of paving tiles (A. besides **or** B. beside) the brick wall.

____ **59.** He has advanced the engineering designs (A. farther **or** B. further) than we had thought possible.

____ **60.** Neither Hewlett Packard or Dell has shown that (A. its **or** B. it's) bid is superior.

SKILLS ASSESSMENT

In the space provided below, record the number of questions you answered correctly.

Questions	Number You Got Correct	Skill Area
1–10	________	Sentence structure
11–20	________	Grammar: Parts of speech
21–30	________	Grammar: Verbs and agreement
31–40	________	Punctuation
41–50	________	Punctuation and mechanics
51–60	________	Vocabulary

CHAPTER 24

Basic Grammar

First, let's define this book's version of the term *grammar*. Often, people use the word to refer to all aspects of writing mechanics—correct use of the parts of speech, sentence structure, spelling, punctuation, capitalization, spacing, verb tense, numbers, and abbreviations. And, people often carry emotional (connotative) meanings for the word—*grammar* is often associated with rules, rules, and more rules, many of which don't seem to make sense. That feeling usually results from mechanical teaching and rote learning of the "rules" of grammar. It's no wonder that school kids often recoil at the thought of a grammar lesson.

This book looks at grammar in three main ways:

- Grammar should be **descriptive** rather than prescriptive—we should try to understand which word combinations help make our meanings clear; we shouldn't focus on memorizing a host of rules. We should also realize that English is a living, changing language and we need to react accordingly—when enough people use the noun *access* as a verb, we can follow suit. We don't have to write the ungainly phrase, "gain access to the library;" we can simply write, "access the library." Eventually, the dictionaries catch up to common usage. For example, the 2006 editions of the Oxford English and Merriam-Webster dictionaries added *google* as a transitive verb, following the amazing success of Google Inc.'s search engine.[1]
- In this book, *grammar* refers to **parts of speech** (nouns, pronouns, verbs, adjectives, adverbs, prepositions, conjunctions, interjections) and how they function to convey meaning. Punctuation, mechanics (spelling, capitalization, abbreviation, numbers), and vocabulary usage are treated separately. For example, the difference between *its* and *it's* is considered a spelling/punctuation issue, not a grammar issue.
- In *Grammar at Work*, a separate section called **sentence grammar** displays the structures that make some sentences clearer and easier to read than others.

1. Google's trademark lawyers have actively discouraged using *google* as a verb because they argue the practice devalues the Google brand. They don't want their company name to become a generic term like *thermos* or *aspirin*. On October 25, 2006, Google pleaded with the public to "please only use 'Google' when you're actually referring to Google Inc. and our services." ("Do You 'Google'?" posted by Michael Krantz of the Google Blog Team, at *http://googleblog.blogspot.com/2006/10/do-you-google.html*)

Also, in this book, the term *grammatical* denotes effective, well-formed phrases and sentences. In other words, *grammatical* reflects a judgment call, a positive evaluation of the way words have been strung together.

NOTE *The above distinctions among grammar, sentence grammar, punctuation, mechanics, and usage help make this book easy to use because you can focus on one aspect of language at a time. Still, these elements do not operate in isolation, and so this workbook's exercises appear as sentences or paragraphs that test those five components of clear, effective writing.*

NOUNS AND NOUN PHRASES

One of language's most basic functions is to name elements of our experience, whether that experience results from our senses (sight, hearing, and so on) or from our minds—our feelings and our ideas. Therefore, any given dictionary page displays more nouns than verbs or other parts of speech. Some nouns are concrete; they can be experienced directly through our senses (rocks, music, bread, automobile), or they can be identified and measured (kilogram, velocity, calories). Abstract nouns (truth, reconciliation, clarity, element) express our ideas.

Proper and Common Nouns

All the nouns in the above paragraph are **common nouns** that name general classes. A common noun such as "automobile" is not capitalized. But the name of a particular brand of automobile, such as an Acura RDX, is capitalized. These names of specific items are known as **proper nouns**. Similarly, "music" refers to a general class of things, while a specific song such as "Stairway to Heaven" is capitalized. The sub-classes within a class (rock music or bluegrass or hip hop) are not capitalized.

Nouns as Subjects and Objects

At the heart of English expression, nouns often denote the person, place, thing, feeling, or idea that forms the **subject** of the sentence. Nouns also function as **objects** of verbs or prepositions. In the following sentence, the nouns are underlined.

> In its corporate blog, Google Inc. asked the public to preserve the value of Google's brand.

The above 16-word sentence uses six nouns, one as a subject (Google Inc.), two as objects (public, value) of verbs (asked, to preserve) and two as objects (blog, brand) of prepositions (in, of). The sixth noun (Google's) appears in the possessive form and essentially acts as an adjective.

Here's a simpler sentence whose subject (engineer) is in a state of being (expressed by the adjective, "uncertain"). This sentence also contains two noun objects (causes, landslide) of prepositions (about, of).

> The engineer is uncertain about the causes of the landslide.

The point here is that each type of word has a job to do, a function to perform. Nouns (and verbs) perform primary functions; English, like all Indo-European languages, absolutely requires nouns and verbs to express basic meaning. The other parts of speech support nouns and verbs—pronouns stand in for nouns; adjectives and adverbs add detail and colour; prepositions, conjunctions, and interjections help complex sentences flow smoothly.

When a noun is not a noun. Let's remember that certain words can function as nouns or as adjectives, or even as verbs:

> These *steel* (adjective) bolts are made of an extremely expensive alloy of *steel* (noun), so *steel* (verb) yourself for the cost of the 1,000 bolts required for the deck supports.

Plural Nouns

Nouns can be singular: computer, law, battlefield, textbook. Or they can be plural: computers, laws, battlefields, and textbooks demonstrate the most common way of making a noun plural—we simply add an *s*.

However, we have several other ways of forming plural nouns:

- ox ⟶ oxen
- father-in-law ⟶ fathers-in-law
- child ⟶ children
- medium ⟶ media
- life ⟶ lives
- box ⟶ boxes
- sheep ⟶ sheep
- company ⟶ companies
- woman ⟶ women
- datum or data ⟶ data
- cactus ⟶ cacti
- criterion ⟶ criteria
- mouse ⟶ mice
- crisis ⟶ crises
- appendix ⟶ appendixes or appendices

Why does English have so many ways of forming plural nouns? The short answer is that English has been forged from one root language (Anglo-Saxon, an early form of German) and four modifying languages (French, Latin, Greek, and Norse). So, for example, the plural form of *goose* is *geese* because those words came from the original German, but by the time the words *caboose* and *moose* came into English, plurals were being formed by adding an s sound, or in the case of moose, with no change in the word. Words that have come from Latin (*medium, datum*) and Greek (*crisis, criterion*) brought their native plural forms with them.

Possessive Nouns

Most English nouns add *'s* to denote ownership:

> Steven Carr's Jaguar　　　　my sister's apartment

However, the "ownership" doesn't have to be legal:

the van's motor each worker's locker a dollar's worth

Here are the usual conventions for using apostrophes to indicate possession:

- For singular nouns, including nouns ending in *s*, acronyms, and indefinite pronouns, add *'s*:

  Mark's laptop Chris's laptop OPEC's oil revenues everyone's answers

- For plural nouns ending in *s*, add only the apostrophe:

  the Joneses' trust fund three players' equipment

- For plural nouns not ending in s, add *'s:*

  women's opportunities men's privileges

- For compounds, add *'s* only to the last word:

  someone else's idea my mother-in-law's advice the Prime Minister's veto

- To indicate individual ownership, add *'s* to each name:

  the engineer's and the technologist's drawings Tom's and Rhianna's desks

- To indicate joint ownership, add 's only to the last name or to each name:

  Tom and Rhianna's car Tom's and Rhianna's car

Noun Phrases

A noun phrase contains a noun and one or more modifiers:

the old bypass road several responsible biologists the woefully late report

A noun phrase might appear as a subject:

The old bypass road should be upgraded to handle the construction traffic.

It might function as an object:

Jeannine silently slid *the woefully late report* under her professor's door.

Or, it might function as a complement:

Norma Cross, the lab director, is one of the *several responsible biologists* whose reputations have been tarnished by allegations of careless sampling methods.

Practice Session—Nouns

Underline the preferred choice within each set of parentheses in the following sentences. You will find answers for these exercises on page 618.

1. Our firm's (*specialtys, specialties*) are in data gathering and statistical analysis.
2. Water temperature exceeded 34 degrees (*celsius, Celsius*) for the second day in a row.
3. Place the heavier equipment on the lower (*shelfs, shelves*).
4. Send your company newsletter items to the (*editor-in-chief's, editor's-in-chief, editor-in-chiefs*) email address.
5. Our shop guarantees its repairs to (*RVs and boats, RV's and boat's, RVs and boat's*) for three months.
6. Despite his heavy workload this spring, (*Ryan Collins', Ryan Collin's, Ryan Collinses, Ryan Collins's*) reports have all been submitted on time.
7. George McAvoy, the acting (*pit boss, Pit Boss, pit Boss*), entered the mine just as the support beams collapsed.
8. (*Bill and Wanda's, Bill's and Wanda's*) reports recounted quite different versions of the meeting with the city's solicitors.
9. A thorough analysis of the stream flow (data, datas) showed very little evidence to support the conservation society's accusations.
10. Our company has been in business in Fredericton since the early (*1980s, 1980's, 1980,s*).

Improvement Exercises—Nouns

In items 1 through 5, underline the common nouns and circle the proper nouns. You will find answers for these exercises on page 618.

1. Each of the consultants wrote a report about Riverbend Dam's projected cost overruns.
2. In this book, "grammatical" refers to effective, well-formed phrases and sentences.
3. Grammar studies the rules governing the use of language, as Dr. Benson has stated many times.
4. Written technical communication is not the only subject covered in *Technical Communication*, a book designed for present and future technical communicators.
5. Brick walls can withstand considerably higher temperatures than concrete board walls.

In items 6 through 10, underline the subjects and circle the objects. You will find answers for these exercises on page 618.

6. Each of the consultants wrote a report about Riverbend Dam's projected cost overruns.
7. In this book, the term "grammatical" refers to effective, well-formed phrases and sentences.
8. Grammar studies the rules governing the use of language, as Dr. Benson has stated many times.

9. Written technical communication is not the only subject covered in *Technical Communication*, a book designed for present and future technical communicators.
10. Brick walls can withstand considerably higher temperatures than concrete board walls.

In items 11 through 20, underline inappropriate noun plurals and possessives and write the correct form(s) in the space provided. You will find answers for these exercises on page 618.

11. __________ Rollover rates for SUVs are nearly twice that of sedans, and 30 percent higher than that of pickup truck's.
12. __________ Please pay attention to all the criterions listed in the test procedure bulletins.
13. __________ Sundins career as a Toronto Maple Leaf appears to be ending.
14. __________ His partner's offers were insufficient to resolve the companies debt load.
15. __________ Plagiarism may be more prevalent than ever, but so is detection softwares.
16. __________ Revenue Canada requires more stringent accounting procedure than our firm can afford.
17. __________ According to Rene Corbeils report, the bridge is no longer safe.
18. __________ Every one of the seven stimuluses introduced in the test sequence provoked abnormally high levels of radiation.
19. __________ Don't expect your cellular phone's to receive strong signal's in the far northern Arctic.
20. __________ Who knows which shoreline's will be most affected by global warming?

Document Critique—Nouns

The following document may contain errors in grammar, capitalization, punctuation, or spelling. Underline all errors and identify them using standard proofreading marks. (See the Correction Symbols list on page 643.) You will find answers for this exercise on page 619.

MEMO

To: Harlan Devonshire, Field Supervisor
From: Arjun Atwal, Accounting Office
Date: June 24, 2009
Subject: Expense Claims

We have had difficultys establishing the accurcy of recent expense claims submitted by your exploration group. Especially this past month.

Would you please review all your team members expense claims before they are sent to are office? Im sure that you no when claims are excessive and you'll be able to correct them before we have to deal with them.

As an example of what I mean, I've attached Rose Francis' claim for this May. I find it hard to belief that she could spend $900 on camp supply's in addition to the food allowance!

PRONOUNS

In order to create smooth phrasing and to avoid repeating nouns, writers (and speakers) use pronouns.

> Each Monday morning, the department heads report the previous week's production in their sections of the plant; *they* fret about these reports because *their* bonus pay is based on these production figures.

The pronouns *they* and *their* stand in for the noun *heads*, which is the antecedent of the pronouns; heads is the antecedent of *they* and *their*. When the antecedent is plural, the replacement pronoun(s) must be plural, to avoid confusing the reader. However, when the antecedent is singular, the replacement pronoun must be singular:

> When Canwood Furniture announced *its* closure, 91 employees lost *their* jobs.

In the above example, it's clear that Canwood Furniture is a single entity, so the pronouns *it* or *its* logically substitute for that proper noun. The plural pronoun *their* substitutes for the plural noun *employees*.

However, the issue may not be so clear with a noun phrase such as the *Montreal Canadiens*. At first glance, *Canadiens* looks like a plural word and if one is thinking of the many people in the Canadiens organization, the correct pronoun replacements would be *they* or *their*. On the other hand, if one is thinking of the organization itself, the logical pronouns would be *it* or *its*. Just to be sure about that point, let's consider these examples:

> The Canadiens may finish in top spot in the league for the first time in many years, as *they* rely on *their* young players to provide scoring punch. The team has continued to be financially successful; now *its* on-ice performance matches *its* corporate performance.

Plural Antecedents

A pronoun might have more than one antecedent:

> Ricky Ruiz and Elma deLoos had their laptops stolen from their lockers on Wednesday.

Each of *Ricky Ruiz* and *Elma deLoos* would be a singular antecedent, if used alone. However, in the above sentence they form a plural antecedent, so the plural pronoun must be used.

Unclear Antecedents

Sometimes, a pronoun's antecedent is unclear:

> Elma deLoos told Marcie Harper about the change to *her* work schedule; *she* was unhappy about the changes, because *she* had already arranged for babysitting.

How would a reader understand the references to *her* and *she* in the above sentence, unless the reader already knows the situation? The acronym COIK has been coined for such unclear references—"clear only if known!"

Such a sentence can be made clear by repeating nouns where necessary:

> Elma deLoos told Marcie Harper about the change to *Marcie's* work schedule; *Marcie* was unhappy about the changes, because *she* had already arranged for babysitting.

Or,

> Elma deLoos told Marcie Harper about the change to *Elma's* work schedule; *Elma* was unhappy about the changes, because *she* had already arranged for babysitting.

Pronoun Case

Grammar handbooks normally identify three pronoun *cases*, the term used for forms in which pronouns are employed: subject, object, possessive. To those three, we could also add the reflexive case, because increasingly the pronoun *myself* is mistakenly used instead of *I* and *me*. The following table lists the singular and plural forms of these cases.

Subjective pronouns perform the action or precede a statement of being:

> *He* ran the samples through a spectrometer. *She* is happy to be here.

Subjective pronouns can also follow a linking verb, as the following two examples demonstrate:

> Are you certain that it will be *she* who is assigned to the Samuel Plains project?
> Who is there? It is *I*.

It can be tricky to choose whether to use the subjective or objective case when words are omitted in comparative statements.

Table 24.1 Pronoun Cases

	Subjective		**Objective**		**Possessive**		**Reflexive**	
	Singular	*Plural*	*Singular*	*Plural*	*Singular*	*Plural*	*Singular*	*Plural*
First person	I	we	me	us	my, mine	our, ours	myself	our selves
Second person	you	you	you	you	your, yours	your, yours	your self	your selves
Third person	he she it	they they they	him her it	them them them	his her, hers it, its	their, theirs their, theirs their, theirs	himself herself itself	themselves themselves themselves

NOTE *The* subjective *case is sometimes called the* nominative *case.*
Later, this section discusses the subjective, objective, and possessive relative pronouns, who, whom, whoever, whomever *and* whose.

She is more intelligent than *I*. [The omitted words here are "am intelligent".]

Professor Magellan likes you more than *me*. [The omitted words are "more than he likes".]

In the first case above, a subject is needed—"*I* am intelligent."
The second sentence requires an object—"...more than he likes *me*."

Problems with Pronouns

In many situations, you will know whether to use the objective, subjective, or possessive form of a pronoun, but some pronoun problems do plague writers (and readers).

1. Who and *whom* versus *that*

Recently, speakers (and writers, too) have been using *that* instead of *who* or *whom*, perhaps because many people don't know that *who* operates in the subjective case and *whom* is designed to receive action (objective case). Or, perhaps many people are just lazy and they don't want to think about the distinction. Or, more likely, we simply mimic what we hear, without thinking about it much. However, careful writers should use "that" to refer to inanimate objects, animals that are not named, and ideas.

Remember that *who* and *whom* are for humans or for animals that have been given names.[2]

The young man *who* retrieved the record-breaking home run ball *that* Barry Bonds hit has offered to sell the ball; he believes that the "finders/keepers" rule entitles him to the cash. Others say that the baseball belongs in the Major League Baseball hall of fame in Cooperstown. *Whom* do you support in this controversy? And what if Dusty the Bloodhound, *who* hangs out regularly at TriCom Park, had "fetched" the ball? Should Dusty be able to trade the ball for a 20-year supply of Dog Chow and a plush dog house?

But how do you tell when to use *who* and when to use *whom*? The down and dirty technique identifies the key clause and then decides whether it needs a subject, which would equate to *who*, or an object that would require *whom*. For example, the clause "who/whom should be Prime Minister?" requires a subject—if you substituted *he* or *him* for *who* or *whom*, you would write, "**he** should be Prime Minister." In other words, the correct version of the above example would be "**who** should be Prime Minister?"

How about this example: "who/whom do you want to lead the country?" In this case, the key thought is "do you want _________?" The clause requires an

2. Mignon Fogarty, a.k.a. the **Grammar Girl**, who speaks entertainingly about grammar, prefers the traditional rule outlined above. However, she points out that "it's more of a gray area than some people think, and if you have strong feelings about it, you could make an argument for using *that* when you're talking about people. But my guess is that people who use *who* and *that* interchangeably do it because they don't know the difference." See the transcript of her podcast Episode 24, posted November 4, 2006 at *http://grammar.quickanddirtytips.com/who-versus-that.aspx*

object such as *him* (do you want **him**?), so the correct version of the above example would be "**whom** do you want to lead the country?"

Additional examples follow:

- Who/whom saw Elvis at the car wash? (**he** saw Elvis)
- The professor glowered at whoever/whomever spoke out of turn. (**he** spoke out of turn)
- Who/whom did you see at the rally? (you saw **him**)
- I will hire whoever/whomever the hiring committee recommends. (the committee recommends **him**)
- I will hire the person who/whom is best qualified. (**he** is best qualified)

2. Unclear reference pronouns

To help readers understand the relationship between a pronoun and the noun it replaces, make sure that your pronoun refers to a noun that is mentioned nearby and not merely implied. To further help your reader, place that pronoun as close as possible to the noun it replaces.

Unclear reference: Jason gave Roger his keys to the company van.
[Are these Jason's keys or Roger's keys?]

Clear reference: Jason gave his keys to the company van to Roger.
[The possessive pronoun *his* is now closer to the noun it references.]

Also, don't use the vague *it* or *they* if such words do not refer to a specific word or phrase. In some cases, you will need to reword a sentence in order to include the noun or phrase you had in mind.

Unclear: Our office recycles as much paper as possible because *it* helps the environment.
[Does *it* refer to the paper, or to the office, or to something that's not even in the sentence?]

Clear: Our office recycles as much paper as possible because *such efforts* help the environment.

Unclear: When we asked the company whether *they* would follow the new guidelines for capturing plant emissions, *they* did not respond.
[Who are *they*? And does the writer have persons in mind for each of the two *they*s?]

Clear: When we asked the company whether *it* would follow the new guidelines for capturing plant emissions, *its Public Relations Office* did not respond.

Unclear: Negotiators announced an expanded health plan, a reduction in dental coverage, and on-site child-care facilities. *This* caused employee protests.

> **Remember:**
> The pronouns *this*, *that*, *these*, and *those* provide clear references only when they are immediately followed by a noun or a noun phrase.

[Does *this* refer to the health plan, the reduced dental coverage, or the child-care facilities?]

Clear: Negotiators announced an expanded health plan, a reduction in dental coverage, and on-site child care facilities. *This* reduction in dental coverage caused employee protests.

Unclear: The beach sand has eroded away, leaving a rocky beach. *This* has made the property less desirable for tourist campers.
[Does *this* refer to the erosion, or to the rocky beach, or to the cause-effect relationship?] The three following edits express what the writer really meant to say.

Clear: The beach sand has eroded away, leaving a rocky beach. *This erosion* has made the property less desirable for tourist campers.
Clear: The beach sand has eroded away, leaving a rocky beach. *This property* is now less desirable for tourist campers.
Clear: The beach sand has eroded away, leaving a rocky beach, *which* has made the property less desirable for tourist campers. [*Which* refers to everything that precedes it.]

3. Misuse of reflexive pronouns

Reflexive pronouns, which are sometimes called *intensive* pronouns, reflect or intensify the nouns or pronouns they invoke:

I finished it *myself.* Give *yourself* some credit! They have only *themselves* to blame.

However, they should not be used as subjects:

No: *Myself* and three others spoke at the meeting.
Yes: Three others and *I* spoke at the meeting.

Nor should they be used as objects:

No: The credit was given to *myself* and Janus Czorzinski.
Yes: The credit was given to Janus Czorzinski and *me.*

4. Lack of pronoun agreement

Pronouns should agree in number, person, and gender with their antecedents:

The students handed in their assignments, confident that *their* work would be graded fairly.
For the third day in a row, Grant called in to say that *he* was sick.

The above two examples are quite straightforward, but compound antecedents pose more of a challenge. So, when two parts of a compound antecedent are joined by *and*, use a plural pronoun:

Television and radio commercials often express *their* pitches in colloquial language.

A compound antecedent that is preceded by *each* or *every* requires a singular pronoun:

> Every period, comma, colon, and semi-colon has *its* useful function.

When the parts of a compound antecedent are joined by *or* or *nor*, the pronoun agrees with the nearest antecedent:

> Neither the company nor the union members would revise *their* bargaining positions.

5. Possessive pronouns

Remember that not one of the possessive pronouns requires an apostrophe. Not one of them! Let's repeat that point—*its, his, hers, my, mine, our, ours, their, theirs, your, yours, whose*—none of these pronouns uses an apostrophe. The apostrophe is used with nouns to indicate possession.

6. The relative pronouns, *that* and *which*

The issue of whether to use *that* or *which* has plagued writers for generations, but luckily there's a straightforward rule of thumb: *that* introduces essential phrases or clauses, while *which* leads into nonessential phrases and clauses.

> The car *that* he sold to me is in better shape than I thought.
> [The *that* clause in this sentence is essential to the meaning.]

> The Honda Civic, *which* has been the best selling car in Canada for the past three years, suits my transportation needs perfectly.
> [The *which* clause is not essential to the meaning; this clause presents extra information.]

7. Generic pronouns

English has masculine pronouns (he, him, his) and feminine pronouns (she, her, hers), but the language doesn't have gender-neutral singular pronouns. Until recently, English speakers used masculine forms for either masculine or feminine expressions. In a post-feminist world, that usage is deemed to be a gender bias and is therefore unacceptable. In the 1970s, there was a concerted effort to introduce the words *tey*, *tem*, and *ter* as gender-neutral pronouns, but that initiative failed, as have previous attempts to introduce generic singular pronouns.

To avoid sexist language, we need some way of dealing with sentences such as the following:

> A student will succeed in a writing class only if *he* completes all *his* assignments.

A writer might be tempted to use the words she and her, perhaps in an attempt to compensate for centuries of male sexism:

> A student will succeed in a writing class only if *she* completes all *her* assignments.

However, that solution is no better than the male version, is it? Many people now hijack the plural forms, *they*, *them*, and *their*, but that solution has its limitations, also:

> A student will succeed in a writing class only if *they* complete all *their* assignments.

Apparently, that single student has been cloned! *They* and *their* do not agree in number with their antecedent, *a student*. Still, ever-increasing usage of this illogical approach may soon crown this solution as the winner. Here's one advocate for the practice:

> I will state for the record that I am a firm believer that someday *they* will be the acceptable choice for this situation. English currently lacks a word that fits the bill, and many people are already either mistakenly or purposefully using *they* as a singular generic personal pronoun; so it seems logical that rules will eventually move in that direction. (Mignon Fogarty, transcript of podcast Episode 29 posted December 8, 2006 at *http://grammar.quickanddirtytips.com/he-they-generic-personal-pronoun.aspx*)

Here are some other ways to use a pronoun to refer to an unknown gender or to refer to both males and females:

- Use the awkward combinations of *he or she* or *his or hers*

  A student will succeed in a writing class only if *he or she* completes all *his or her* assignments.

- Recast the antecedents and pronouns into the plural form:

  Students will succeed in a writing class only if *they* complete all *their* assignments.

- **Reword the sentence to avoid the problem altogether:**

  Success in a writing class depends on completing all the assignments.

In most cases, rewording is not only possible, but preferable.

Grammar at Work: "they" should not replace "he or she" in software documentation

"I always rewrite or use "he or she"; singular "they" is not in the company style guide largely because I wouldn't allow it. I understand the reasoning behind it and I agree the language is likely to evolve to make it a non-controversial solution, but it hasn't evolved that far yet. When I read singular "they" I always notice it, feel that it is inaccurate, and wince.... I'll just point out that if you're writing for translation, as technical writers often do, those pronouns should absolutely be left in. As grammatical markers they aid translators by eliminating any possible syntactical ambiguity."

—**Tom Storer,** *writing in response to a* Grammar Girl *podcast and blog post re: generic pronouns Available at http://grammar.quickanddirtytips.com/he-they-generic-personal-pronoun.aspx*

Practice Session—Pronouns

Underline the preferred choice within each set of parentheses in the following sentences. You will find answers for these exercises on page 619.

1. Return that spectrometer to Gordon Burns or (*myself, me*) when you've finished using it.
2. Despite the strong Canadian dollar and low U.S. demand for lumber, Foreman Brothers Ltd. is increasing (*their, its*) production of framing lumber.
3. He is a basketball player (*that, who*) can rebound, run the floor, and shoot three-balls.
4. Everyone has (*his or her, their*) email address posted on the class message board.
5. Our shop guarantees (*its, their*) repairs for three months.
6. After the environmental assessment board tabled (*its, their*) report, three mining firms disputed the board's conclusions.
7. When you challenged the security officer's dispersal order after the pep rally, did you know to (*who, whom*) you were speaking?
8. (*Myself, I*) and Toni Colette were the first observers to recognize the SARS symptoms.
9. Let's be honest—(*who, whom*) really knows how global warming will affect the East Coast?
10. Every collector bottle, pipette, and Petri dish has (*its, their*) function in this experiment.

Improvement Exercises—Pronouns

In items 1 through 5, replace the underlined nouns with the correct pronouns. You will find answers for these exercises on page 619.

1. Each of <u>the consultants</u> wrote a report about Riverbend Dam's projected cost overruns.
2. To <u>which government agent</u> will you send the gas well report?
3. The Environmental Protection Board has issued <u>the Environmental Protection Board's</u> assessment of Alberta's gas-powered power generators.
4. After examining the project files closely, can you tell <u>which person's</u> drafting errors contributed to the failed earth dam?
5. The engineering firm submitted <u>the firm's</u> proposal three days early.

In each of items 6 through 10, write the correct pronoun in the space provided. You will find answers for these exercises on page 619.

6. Each of the consultants wrote a report about _________ (*his or her, their*) view of Riverbend Dam's projected cost overruns.
7. Make sure to include _________ (*you're, your*) receipts when you submit this month's travel expense claim.
8. _________ (*We, Us*) technologists know what will work, not the project engineers.

9. Bring the design to __________ (*myself, me*) for final approval.
10. Much of the time, our __________ (*company's, companies*) equipment is inadequately maintained.

The following 15 sentences may contain errors in pronoun usage, spelling, or punctuation. Rewrite those sentences, correcting the errors. If a sentence is already correct, write ***C*** in the space following the sentence. You will find answers for these exercises on pages 619–620.

11. Myself and all the team at EBS look forward to hearing from you.
12. These dense patches of forest are not a vulnerable ecosystem, it is in generally good condition, but they are found on steep slopes and would be best left undisturbed by development.
13. In order to create a new water intake at Lambeau lake, a new structure will have to be built below the current water level of 112 feet. In order to accomplish this, the lake level has to be dropped to allow construction at an elevation of about 92 feet.
14. The housing used to protect the stream meters is a 2-inch galvanized pipe, that rests flush with the riprap boulders on the left bank.
15. The system includes two cigar-sized dataloggers which contain both pressure transducers and temperature recorders. These are housed in protective casings.
16. Canadian National Railways (CN) has mapped the location of all known streams that are crossed by their railways, on a GIS-based railway Information System.
17. Box type concrete culverts were constructed with a concrete skirt (Figure 15) downstream of the outlet. The reason for this was to reduce scour below the skirt, which would block fish passage.
18. To transfer vinyl records to MP3 files, it must meet certain specifications.
19. Just between you and I, our network specifications will not meet Microsoft's standards.
20. Martin Technologies has just announced who they have chosen as their main supplier of cable and peripherals.
21. Its time for the company to review all its' recruiting practises.
22. Each of Frances and Donna have told their clients about the new line of excavators.
23. Austin St. Pierre of St. Johns Ambulance Services will explain their new billing policy.
24. In Calgary. officials ended their (intersection) red light camera program after statistics showed a 40 percent drop in ticketable offenses.
25. I found that in researching this report it was useful in learning about management techniques.

Document Critique—Pronouns

The following document may contain errors in grammar, capitalization, punctuation, or spelling. Underline all errors and identify them using standard proofreading marks. (See the Correction Symbols list on page 643.) You will find answers for this exercise on page 620.

Concept Architectural Designs
MEMO

To:	Devin Marchand, Architectural Technologist
From:	Shirley Tostenson, Managing Partner
Date:	April 16, 2009
Subject:	Preliminary Research for Potential project

We are in the preliminary stages of preparing a proposal to design Halifaxes potential Seaport Redevelopment project. I am assigning yourself to conduct reserch that will place our proposal in context.

Please review all the available literature on the folowing group of Waterfront developments, Granville island, Vancouver, the Distillery district, Toronto, the custard Factory, Birmingham, England, the forks, Winnipeg, make note of its capitalization, scope, end uses, community involvement, sources of capital, architectural themes, blend of commercial, retail, arts and crafts and residential.

Complete the survey by April 25 and bring the results directly to myself. This is a high priority so drop everything else which you are doing. Don't discuss this outside of the office, we don't this leaking out to who might be also submitting a proposal.

VERBS

Verbs describe action (active verbs):

The department heads *report* the previous week's production.

And verbs express a state of being (linking verbs):

My feet *are* my only mode of transportation.
(Bob Marley used more colourful, albeit ungrammatical, phrasing when he sang, "My feets is my only carriage.")

Here are some of the more common active verbs you'll use in technical writing:

observe	report	perform	measure	conclude	recommend
contain	develop	agree	reduce	use	include

Nearly all linking verbs are forms of *to be*:

am, is, are, was, were, will be, have been

However, *sounds*, *seems*, *looks*, and *appears* are sometimes used to express a state of being:

This winter *seems* like the worst one we've had in the past 20 years.
He *looks* tired. You *look* tired.
The road *appears* to have been repaired since last month's floods.
Their praise of employee performance *sounds* insincere.

To be and the other four linking verbs connect the words that precede them with what follows in the sentence. That link provides a useful function in many sentences, but sets up semantic pitfalls. For example, a statement such as "She is the best writer on the research team" contains two potential problems.

1. It appears to state a fact, but only expresses an opinion, and in this case the opinion is not easy to verify.
2. It sets up a static judgment by using the present tense of the linking verb. Statements that feature *is* or *are* lead to the assumption that people are consistent and unchanging. She may not always submit the best pieces of writing!

Linking verbs often contribute to another phrasing problem—their presence can result in wordy phrasing. See the Vocabulary and Style section of this workbook (page 597) for advice on how to reduce wordiness by replacing linking verbs with active verbs.

Verb Tenses

The concept of past, present, and future time is built into English:

Past: We *reported* that there's been no change in caribou migration patterns for the past 12 years.

Present: They need to *report* the findings concerning caribou herd enhancement.

Future: We *will report* current methods of identifying and culling the herd's disease carriers.

The past, present, and future simple verb tenses have predictable forms. The regular verbs (which constitute the majority of all verbs) end the past tense in *ed* while the future tense verbs are preceded by *will* or *shall.* Present tense forms can be slightly more complex, as Table 24.2 shows.

Table 24.2 Present Tense Verb Forms

	First Person	Second Person	Third Person
Singular	I report	you report	he/she/it reports
Plural	we report	you report	they report

The verb's root form, *report,* adds an *s* when preceded by *he, she,* or *it.*
Here are other forms of a regular verb such as *report:*

Table 24.3 Additional Verb Tenses

	First Person	Second Person	Third Person
Present perfect	I/we have reported	you have reported	they have reported
Past perfect	I/we had reported	you had reported	they had reported
Future perfect	I/we will have reported	you will have reported	they will have reported

When actions occur at the same time, keep verbs in the same tense:

Each time the protestors *moved* forward, the riot police *raised* their shields.
The project manager *has reported* that he *has found* safety infractions.

However, when actions occur at different times, change case accordingly:

The project manager *reported* that he *has fired* two workers for safety infractions.
If the tests *show* abnormalities, they *will confirm* our suspicions that the cattle *have been ingesting* tainted feed.

Irregular Verbs

Not all verbs follow the patterns shown above. Here's a sampling of irregular verbs:

Present	Past	Past Participle
run	ran	run
become	became	become
go	went	gone
grow	grew	grown
make	made	made
take	took	taken

The most irregular of all verbs is *to be*:

Table 24.4 Tense Forms *of* to *be*

	Singular	Plural
Present	I am/you are/he is/she is/it is	we are/you are/they are
Past	I was/you were/he was/she was/it was	we were/you were/they were
Future	I will be/you will be/he, she, it will be	we/you/they will be
Present perfect	I have been/you have been he/she/it has been	we/you/they have been
Past perfect	I /you/he/she/it had been	we/you/they had been
Future perfect	I/you/he/she/it will have been	we/you/they will have been

Transitive and Intransitive Verbs

Transitive verbs transfer action to an object; intransitive verbs express an action, but do not transfer it to an object. Here are some examples that show three sets of verbs (lie/lay, sit/set, and rise/raise) that often pose problems for writers:

Table 24.5 Transitive and Intransitive Verbs

Intransitive	Transitive
Even though the Varsity Blues team has lost 12 games in a row, don't expect the Blues to *lie* down and let the Mustangs roll over them.	Just *lay* that rebar beside the driveway.
Don't *sit* in the General Manager's chair!	Please *set* the cases of beer on the floor behind the bar.
We can expect the Bombardier's stock to *rise* quickly, now that the company won the bid to supply all those trains to France.	When you *raise* the issue of tainted water, I will call forhas a full inquiry.

Remember that *lie* and *lay* are different verbs, but the present tense of *lay* and the past tense of *lie* are spelled and pronounced the same.

Present	**Past**	**Past Participle**
I lie	I lay	I have lain
I lay (something down)	I laid (something down)	I have laid (something down)

To further confuse matters, an alternate meaning for *to lie* (to tell an untruth), uses *lied* as its past tense and past participle forms!

Subject-Verb Agreement

Clear phrasing often depends on agreement between subject and verb, in person (first, second, third) and in number (single or plural). Simple clauses like "my watch keeps perfect time" present few difficulties, but here's a more complex sentence that might prove vexing:

> Symptoms of lymphocytic bronchitis include shortness of breath.

Although the singular word *bronchitis* is close to the verb and may seems to be the subject of the sentence, the actual subject, *symptoms*, is plural and it requires a corresponding plural verb.

In cases where the subject may be singular or plural, you need to examine the surrounding sentence to decide which verb form to use. In the following examples, the subject is underlined and the verb is italicized. Explanations appear in brackets.

> Almost <u>all</u> of the paragraphs, especially the first one, *require* a clearer topic sentence. [The plural subject requires a plural verb; *almost* and *of the paragraphs* modify *all.*]

> Either the <u>Director</u> or the research team <u>members</u> *have* issues that must be resolved. [When subject words are joined by *either...or*, *neither...nor*, or *not only...but also*, the verb agrees with the closer subject.]

Running a marathon *requires* tremendous willpower.
[When a whole clause or phrase is the subject, use a singular verb.]

Each speaker must *talk* no longer than 10 minutes.
Each of the computers *has* a serial number engraved on the back wall of its chassis.
[Indefinite words such as *every*, *each*, and *any* require a singular verb when they act as a subject or precede a subject word.]

McCains *is* hiring plant workers for the summer months.
Surprisingly, *Seven Canadian Truisms* *has* higher sales figures in the U.S. than in Canada.
"Felicitations" *is* a phrase he often uses when greeting people.
[Names of companies, titles of books, and words used as terms require a singular subject.]

Twenty spelling errors *is* excessive in a five-page document.
Did you know that 20 scientists *are planning* to move to the U of S research facility?
[Quantities that refer to a total amount require a singular verb, while quantities that refer to individual, countable units require plural verbs.]

The staff *prefer* to eat lunch away from the office.
[When you perceive an apparently singular subject as a countable collection of individuals, use a plural verb.]

The log *book* and the test *report* are in my office.
A compound subject requires a plural verb.]

The news media *are* very interested in the global warming issue.
[A plural subject requires a plural verb.]

Active and Passive Voice

In the active voice, the subject performs the action of the verb. In passive voice, the subject receives the action.

Passive: The report was written by me. [Weak and wordy]
The experiment was conducted by our group.
The project has been completed.
Active: I wrote the report. [Stronger and more concise]
Our group conducted the experiment.
The field engineers have completed the project.
Passive: All doors in this building will be locked by 8 p.m.
Active: The commissionaire will lock all doors in this building by 8 p.m.
[Change in emphasis, change in responsibility]
Passive: While conducting these experiments, the rats were seen to become excited when food was brought in. [Passive voice helps contribute to the dangling modifier]

Although the passive voice usually leads to wordy, less powerful phrasing than the active voice, the passive voice does have its uses:

- Passive voice can place emphasis on the action, rather than on the doer of the action.

  The project has been completed on time and on budget.

- Sometimes a writer doesn't know, or doesn't want to say, who performed the action.

  Seven of the golf course's greens were damaged by vandals on Tuesday evening.
  The project was completed three weeks behind schedule.

Practice Session—Verbs

Underline the preferred choice within each set of parentheses in the following sentences. You will find answers for these exercises on page 621.

1. One hundred dollars (*is, are*) far too much to pay for a DVD.
2. Mary, Barry, and Larry (*has, have*) gone to look at computer programs.
3. Which one of those guys (sings, sing) in the choir?
4. *No Alternatives* (*was, were*) very tense reading.
5. One of the boys (*was, were*) supposed to meet you at the train station.
6. Every one of these buildings (*need, needs*) a new roof.
7. Everyone has (*his or her, their*) email address posted on the class message board.
8. The measles (*was, were*) thought to be eradicated until new cases developed in the 1990s.
9. Recommendations for mitigating potential impacts (*are, were*) presented.
10. Someone has inadvertently (*lain, laid*) the specimen case on the van's roof.

Improvement Exercises—Verbs

In items 1 through 5, rewrite the sentences so that they use the active voice. **However**, if you believe a sentence should be left in the passive voice, say so, and then explain your decision. You will find answers for these exercises on page 621.

1. The experiment was conducted by our group.
2. A final report will be prepared upon receipt of your comments.
3. A list of upcoming squash games has been posted on the bulletin board.
4. Following a storm in March 2008, woody debris, boulders, and gravel were removed from the site.
5. The firm's proposal was submitted by the engineering firm three days early.

In items 6 through 10, replace linking verbs with active verbs.

6. The following report is a summary of the project's progress to date.
7. Also included in the report are comments intended to give an estimate of ecosystem richness and the presence of invasive alien species.

8. Successive approximations is a method of converting analogue to digital signals, in which comparing the unknown input against a known input produced by the D/A converter.
9. Their software is used by our firm for tracking traffic on our website.
10. Seeking reliable data on who utilizes open source software, Freeware.com provides the best option.

The following 18 sentences may contain errors in subject-verb agreement or in verb tense. Or, linking verbs might help bury the action in nouns or adjectives. Rewrite sentences where necessary, correcting grammatical and/or stylistic errors. If a sentence needs no improvement, write ***C*** in the space following the sentence. You will find answers for these exercises on pages 621 and 622.

11. In March 2009, Northern Nurseries and Landscaping began their reconstruction of the banks of MacDonald Creek.
12. A new crib wall construction was done in July 2008.
13. It is my opinion that online gambling is a threat to small local casinos.
14. The test method and the answer key is faulty.
15. The system is two cigar-sized dataloggers, each of which is containing a pressure transducer and a temperature recorder. These are housed in protective casings.
16. As instructor of this course, it is my role to be facilitative and provide learning opportunities.
17. I will be graduating from George Brown College's Health Informatics program on May 26.
18. No work program was plan for at the time of this environmental assessment.
19. By allowing the engine to breathe easier typically is producing 15 more horsepower.
20. The structure of the following analysis is a combination of an assessment, a comparison, and an eventual recommendation for doubling next year's research budget.
21. Every time I suggested an alternative plan, my boss was raising objections of a budget nature.
22. The rough draft of the guidance document is recommending that pharmaceuticals would be labelled if they would pose an environmental risk when released into the water supply.
23. He must have grew four inches over the summer holidays!
24. The Accident Prevention Board like to hold informal sessions that include all stakeholders.
25. The Accident Prevention Board is comprised of seven members from a wide range of industrial occupations.
26. There (is, are) some oranges in the fruit bowl.
27. Each of the winners receive $500 and their choice of Corel software.
28. The media has its own agenda regarding the Kyoto Accord.

Document Critique—Verbs

The following document may contain errors in grammar, capitalization, punctuation, or spelling. Underline all errors and label them using standard proofreading marks. (See the Correction Symbols list on page 643.) You will find answers for this exercise on page 622.

Concept Architectural Designs

MEMO

To:	Shirley Tostenson, Managing Partner
From:	Devin Marchand, Architectural Technologist
Date:	April 22, 2009
Subject:	Preliminary Research for Potential project

As you have request, I have been engaging in research of several waterfront developments. As you will see in the attached research Overview, some very exciting developments have happen in canada. England, too.

I guess you should be knowing where I found the information about the respective water front developments. Well, I have got a lot of info from the internet, but most of it is being supply by the development corporation themself. So, its suspect. That's why I then went to newspaper archives for the Vancouver, Toronto, Birmingham, and winnipeg daily Papers. Especially the bisiness sections.

Also, I was able to get documents from the planning offices in the city of Vancouver and also the city of winnipeg. I had a friend in City hall in Toronto, so she is able to give me background details of the proposals submitted to the City for the Distillery District development, that I received last week. I have phoned the City CLERK in Birmingham, he promised to send a package of materials which will have described the whole Custard Factory development, complete with construction costs. I hope it come because as you see there was not much else available.

Thanks for having been assigning myself this research project which had been very interesting.

ADJECTIVES AND ADVERBS

Adjectives and adverbs describe or add information about other words in phrases and clauses.

An **adjective** modifies the meaning of a noun or a pronoun. In other words, adjectives provide additional information so that the reader or listener gets a clearer, more complete idea of what the noun or pronoun signifies. Here are some examples that modify nouns:

complete coverage   *heavy* load   *blue* uniform   *inexact* measurement

These adjectives modify pronouns:

lucky you   I am *late*   they look *angry*   he was *brilliant*

Most adjectives that modify pronouns follow linking verbs, as in "Each type of error is avoidable."

Adverbs modify the meaning of verbs, verbals, adjectives, or other adverbs, as in the following examples (all adverbs are in italics):

adverbs that modify verbs –	run *swiftly*	write *carefully*	jumped *gracefully*
adverbs that modify verbals –	to aim *correctly*	to advance *slowly*	
adverbs that modify adjectives –	*so* tall	*very* slow	*extra* careful
adverbs that modify adverbs –	*very well*	*too carefully*	*too highly* placed

Types of Adjectives

Several types of purposes are served by adjectives:

adjectives that **describe** –	*red* earth	*large* fish	*knotted* rope
adjectives that **limit** –	*two* collisions	*occasional* crashes	*my* problem
adjectives that **emphasize** –	the *very* one	*perfect* success	*complete* idiot

English has several word sources for adjectives. Some words function only as adjectives:

tall *splendid* *large* *empty* *strong* *rich*

Others can also function as nouns:

cold *rough* *computer* *wool* *car* *football*

Still others spend part of their time as adverbs:

well *late* *early* *hard* *near* *daily*

Some adjectives are taken from the participle form of verbs:

washing machine *parking* meter *whistling* wind *running* water

Other adjectives take hyphenated forms:

last-minute orders *up-to-date* equipment *well-built* truck *10-year* employee

Articles as adjectives Many grammarians classify the articles *a*, *an*, and *the* as adjectives because these useful little words limit the meaning of nouns. The definite article *the* specifies a particular, identifiable noun as in *the causeway* or *the apple*, while the indefinite articles *a* and *an* refer to nouns in nonspecific ways, as in *a causeway* or *an apple*.

Types of Adverbs

Most adverbs are formed by adding *ly* to adjectives or by dropping or changing the final letter and then adding *ly*:

Adjective	Adverb
sad	sadly
efficient	efficiently
cold	coldly

slow	slowly
quick	quickly
due	duly
empty	emptily
busy	busily

But some adverbs do not end in *ly*:

very *soon* *too* *much* *often* *well*

Some adverbs are formed as phrases, not as single words:

> They displayed the waveform *on an oscilloscope.* [the preposition phrase *on an oscilloscope* is used as an adverb to modify *displayed*]
>
> I'm writing this book *to showcase* effective grammar. [the infinitive phrase *to showcase* is used as an adverb to modify *writing*]

Occasionally, the adverb appears as a clause that contains a subject and a verb:

> We reported the incident *after we returned to the office.*
> [*After we returned to the office* modifies *reported* by indicating <u>when</u> the report happened.]

Comparative Forms of Adjectives and Adverbs

Both adjectives and adverbs can be used to compare items. Grammarians use the terms *positive, comparative,* and *superlative* to denote the three degrees of comparison. Table 24.6 lists adjectives and adverbs in these three degrees.

NOTE *Some grammarians use the term simple instead of positive.*

Table 24.6 Comparative Forms

	Positive	Comparative	Superlative
Adjectives	hard	harder	hardest
	tall	taller	tallest
	rich	richer	richest
	good	better	best
	little	less	least
	some	more	most
	acceptable	more acceptable	most acceptable
	daunting	more daunting	most daunting

Table 24.6 Comparative Forms (continued)

	Positive	Comparative	Superlative
Adverbs	fast	faster	fastest
	well	better	best
	badly	worse	worst
	slowly	more slowly	most slowly
	aggressively	more aggressively	most aggressively
	smoothly	less smoothly	least smoothly

NOTE *Most adverbs use* more *and* most *or* less *and* least *to create their comparative forms.*

Usage Hints

The following advice is designed to help you use adjectives and adverbs effectively.

1. **Use *a* and *an* properly**
   Use *a* when the following word starts with a consonant sound:

   a bracket   *a* design   *a* software program   *a* CBC podcast

   Use *an* when the following word starts with a vowel sound:

   an amateur   *an* honour   *an* SOS signal [the *S* here is sounded as "es"]

   Until recently, *an* was used with unaccented syllables beginning with *h*, as in "*an* historical epic"; however, current usage is switching to *a* history or *a* historical epic.

2. **Be careful with comparative adjectives and adverbs**
   Most one-syllable adjectives use *-er* and *-est* endings for comparatives:

   quick   *quicker*   *quickest*

   Some two-syllable adjectives take *-er* and *-est*; others use *more* and *most*:

   windy   *windier*   *windiest*
   grateful   *more grateful*   *most grateful*

   Adverbs most often use *more* and *most* or *less* and *least* to form comparatives:

   clearly   *more clearly*   *most clearly*

Three-syllable adjectives and adverbs almost always use *more* and *most* or *less* and *least* to form comparatives:

honourable	*more honourable*	*most honourable*
cheerfully	*more cheerfully*	*most cheerfully*

Avoid double comparisons in which both *-er* and *more* (or *-est* and *most*) are used:

The ~~*more*~~ *windier* city the ~~*most*~~ *richest* dessert on the table

3. **Avoid double negative adverbs**
Truly effective negative adverbs such as *neither, nor, no, not, scarcely*, and *seldom* don't need help in conveying negation. So, avoid statements such as the following (especially if you want to seem educated):

I *don't* want *no* more materials delivered to the Spadina worksite.
[Write," I *don't* want *any* more material.." or "I want *no* more materials..."]

They *couldn't hardly* cross the road because of the heavy traffic.
[Write, "They *could hardly* cross.." or "They *couldn't* cross ..."]

Raphael scarcely paid attention to neither one of the inspectors.
[Write," Raphael *scarcely* paid attention to the inspectors." or "Raphael paid attention to *neither* of the inspectors]

4. **Be aware of the pitfalls with *well, good, bad, badly, real,* and *really***
Well can function as an adjective or as an adverb. And, in conversation, many people don't pay attention to the distinctions between *good* and *well* and between *bad* and *badly*. Here are some examples of ungrammatical usage:

You did really *good* on the Martin Brothers project.
[Correct usage: "You did really *well*..."]

Marta performed *bad* on her job interview.
[Correct usage: "Marta performed *well*..."]

The lobster tasted *badly* because of the rancid garlic butter.
[Correct usage: "The lobster tasted *bad*..."]

He uses spreadsheets *good* and accounting software *not bad.*
[Correct usage: "He uses spreadsheets *well* and accounting software *not badly.*"]

He's been feeling *good* since his kidney transplant.
[Correct usage: "He's been feeling *well* ..."]

You look *well* in that black dress.
[Correct usage: "You look *good* ..."]

Real and *really* are often used incorrectly in casual conversation:

He has a *real* good attitude.
[Correct usage requires an adverb: "He has a *really* good attitude."]

Remember that *real* is an adjective and *really* is an adverb.

5. **Do not pile up noun modifiers**
Nouns can function as adjectives in such phrases as *horse farm* or *atom bomb,* but when noun modifiers pile up, they can obscure meaning. For example, how long would it take a reader to decipher this phrase: *duplicate cross-contaminant groundwater well samples*? Four nouns pile up in front of *samples,* and two of those nouns used as adjectives are compound nouns. The poor reader looks at such a phrase and thinks, "Come on, give me a break!" Here are two more examples taken from actual workplace documents:

The *2007 hydrology survey access* information contained no surprises.
[In this sentence, four nouns all help modify *information.* Four!]

The board created a *downtown community access and decision* structure to deal with the burgeoning rabbit population. [This sentence appeared in a newspaper account of a CityCouncil's creation of a committee. Yes—*committee* was what they meant by all those words.]

6. **Know when to use commas to separate adjectives**
When more than one adjective precedes a noun, commas can be very useful in signalling the writer's exact meaning:

They discovered toxic, non-recoverable traces of pharmaceuticals in the water supply. [*Toxic* and *non-recoverable* independently modify *traces*; *toxic* does not modify *non-recoverable.*]

They discovered toxic pharmaceutical elements in the water supply.
[Here, *pharmaceutical* modifies *elements* and *toxic* modifies *pharmaceutical.*]

Hint:
If you could change the order of the adjectives with no real change in meaning, these adjectives are acting independently and require commas:

Several *industrious, motivated, high-achieving* students received scholarships.

But if reversing the order would change the meaning, you shouldn't use a comma:

Our *extended equipment* warranty does not cover damage caused by negligence.

Practice Session—Identify Adjectives and Adverbs

Underline the adjectives and circle the adverbs in the following sentences. You will find answers for these exercises on page 623.

1. Two dedicated teams desperately want to win the Vanier Cup, which is awarded annually to the champion of CIS football.
2. Biodiesel has a higher cetane level than petroleum diesel.
3. The Canadian cement industry claims that it has steadily improved energy efficiency in its manufacturing processes.
4. Improved indoor air quality probably reduces the number of sick days claimed by workers.
5. Despite urgent requests from the local health authorities, the mine repeatedly refused to install modern water treatment methods.
6. He has done well with the aging equipment at his disposal.
7. The Earth Home system provides fully integrated, self-sufficient buildings.
8. Compressed earth bricks are environmentally sustainable because they require comparatively little energy to produce and very little energy to transport.
9. The sales manager will work closely with the plant manager to plan just-in-time deliveries.
10. Someone has inadvertently left the specimen case on the loading dock.

Improvement Exercises—Adjectives and Adverbs

In items 1 through 10, repair errors in the use of adjectives and adverbs. If a sentence contains no errors, write ***C*** in the space provided. You will find answers for these exercises on page 623.

1. Don't think bad of me because I tried to improve our working conditions.
2. According to Bobbie Cruz in the IT department, every computer, hard drive eventual fails.
3. They advised us to move slow and careful when working with those volatile chemicals.
4. We must conserve depleted scarce non-renewable resources or face the consequences.
5. Reported, rollover rates for vans and SUVs are considerably higher than for sedans.
6. He was clearly the strongest of the two of them.
7. The maple syrup harvest is way more early than usual this year, perhaps because of global warming.
8. The researchers made a honest mistake when they miscalculated the size of the honey bee population in Ontario.
9. Global cooling sure is more likely than global warming in the next 50 years.
10. Windows Vista arrived on the market with more glitches than I was prepared to accept.

Each of the sentences 11 through 20 contains an underlined adjective or adverb. In the space below the sentence,

a. identify whether the word is being used as an adjective or as an adverb, and
b. write a sentence that uses that word as the other type of modifier. (If the highlighted word is an adjective, use it as an adverb; if the word is an adverb, use it as an adjective in the sentence that you write.) If necessary, consult a dictionary's list of meanings for the word.

See pages 623–624 for sample answers.

11. In March 2009, Northern Landscaping discovered a near collapse of the Arduin Reservoir dike.
12. He is usually late for meetings that require him to present a project update.
13. Please report daily about the progress of labour contract negotiations.
14. Three times this season he has been reprimanded for playing fast and loose with the fishery regulations.
15. She responded to the dissident workers' grievances very well, don't you agree?
16. Please submit the monthly production figures by the second day of the following month.
17. Do you think that our boss is a well woman?
18. The early indications are that the real estate bubble is about to burst.
19. Just how hard did you try to make the exam questions difficult?
20. *The Globe and Mail*'s weekly "Career" section has recently focused on the changing demographics of the Canadian work force.

Document Critique—Adjectives and Adverbs

The following document may contain errors in grammar, capitalization, punctuation, or spelling. Underline all errors and label them using standard proofreading marks. (See the Correction Symbols list on page 643.) You will find answers for this exercise on page 624.

Christopher Metals

MEMO

To:	Shift Foremen
From:	Augusta Brown, General Manager
Date:	May 22, 2009
Subject:	Reducing Toxic Emmisions At Our Plant

As you have might have heard, we received a D^- from Environment Canada following their December site visit. Apparently we have 6 months to clean up are act—the inspecters will be here again in November. If are sulphur and hydrochloric acid readings have not been reduced by 50 percent, they'll move to close us down.

To be honest, I don't think we've bin doing that bad. For example, are culvert mill and are lead coating facility doesn't have no more free-flowing smoke stacks—the emission capture equipment diverts the gases to the holding chamber wear the gases is chilled and the toxic elements are filtered out. But that's not good enough for the government, I guess.

I'm attaching some literature on equipment thats supposed to reduce sulphuric and hydrochloric acid emmisions. Would you please read the descriptions and look at the diagrams of the equipment to see whether we could fit such devices into are existing setups? I mean, you know you're areas inside out, so youll know if the equipment will work in are plant.

Pay particuler atention to the rugged low-cost low-maintenance air pollution control equipment sold by Herring Engineering. How much of it would we need? Can we cut into are ductwork to install it? The price looks right, so look at the Herring stuff real carefully

Lets discuss this next Tuesday in are regular production meeting.

CONJUNCTIONS, PREPOSITIONS, AND INTERJECTIONS

Three kinds of helping words are discussed in this section: conjunctions, prepositions, and interjections help complete the patterns of meaning conveyed by nouns, pronouns, and verbs.

Conjunctions

These connecting words reveal three kinds of relationships—*coordinating, correlative,* or *subordinating.*

> Ricky Ruiz *and* Elma deLoos had their laptops stolen *because* the computers were not properly stored. Perhaps that's why *neither* Ricky *nor* Elma has yet claimed for insurance.

Coordinating conjunctions such as *and* join equivalent sets of nouns, pronouns, verbs, adjectives, adverbs, prepositions, phrases, and clauses. (See pages 554 to 557 for definitions of clauses.)

Correlative conjunctions such as *neither* and *nor* work in pairs to establish a connection.

Subordinating conjunctions such as *because* introduce dependent (a.k.a. subordinate) clauses.

Table 24.7 Conjunctions and their uses

Coordinating	Relationships They Express
and	addition
but, yet	contrast
for	cause or reason
so	effect or result
or	choice
nor	negative choice
Correlative	**Relationships They Express**
both...and not only...but	addition
either...or whether...or	contrast
neither...nor	negative choice

Table 24.7 Conjunctions and their Uses (continued)

Subordinating	Relationships They Express
because	cause or reason
in order that, so, so that, that	effect or result
after, before, since, until, once, when, whenever, while	time
if, even if, provided that, unless	condition
although, even though, whereas	contrast
where, wherever	location
than, whether	choice

NOTE *See page 564 in the "Sentence Grammar" section for examples of appropriate and inappropriate coordination and subordination.*

Conjunctive adverbs create logical connections within sentences. At the same time, they modify verbs, adjectives, or other adverbs within the sentence. Table 24.8 lists conjunctive adverbs.

Table 24.8 Conjunctive Adverbs

Words	Relationships They Express
also, furthermore, moreover, besides	addition
however, still, nevertheless, conversely, nonetheless, instead, otherwise	contrast
similarly, likewise	comparison
therefore, thus, consequently, accordingly, hence, then	result or summary
next, then, subsequently, meanwhile, finally	time
indeed, certainly	emphasis

Conjunctive adverbs such as *however* can effectively operate at the beginning, in the middle, or at the end of sentences:

> *However*, people with the HIV virus find their weakened immune system significantly improved by this treatment regimen.
>
> People with the HIV virus, *however*, find their weakened immune system significantly improved by this treatment regimen.
>
> People with the HIV virus find their weakened immune system significantly improved by this treatment regimen, *however.*

Prepositions

Most prepositions convey relationships in time or space, between nouns or pronouns and other words. Typical examples of prepositions appear in the following phrases:

in a year	*in* a few minutes	*in* the morning	*at* noon	*on* Friday
in town	*in* Nova Scotia	at the ballpark	*on* the road	*on* Main Street

Here are some other prepositions:

about, across, after, along, among, against, apart from, as, behind, beneath, between, beyond, down, from, in front of, into, on, onto, past, round, through, toward, until, up, with, without

Prepositional phrases essentially function as adjectives or as adverbs:

I'll return his call *in* a few minutes. [adverb—indicates **when**]

The picture *above* your desk [adjective—indicates **where**]
reminds me *of* my lake cottage. [adverb—indicates **what**]

Preposition usage hints Conventions for using prepositions and prepositional phrases have evolved through centuries of usage. One of those "rules," which prohibits placing prepositions at the end of sentences, has been relaxed because some expressions are downright silly when that rule is strictly enforced. Winston Churchill dramatized that silliness in his famous lampoon line, "This is something up with which I will not put!" Churchill knew that "This is something I won't put up with" or "I won't put up with this" are more natural and less pedantic. Still, we should try to avoid ending sentences with prepositions, especially if that final preposition is not really needed, as in

Where was Roger going ~~*to*~~? What are you thinking ~~*of*~~?

Superfluous prepositions at the beginning or in the middle of sentences can safely be deleted:

He fell off ~~*of*~~ the Ferris wheel at the CNE. ~~*Like*~~, he couldn't help ~~*from*~~ showing off.

Many distinctive English idiomatic expressions[3] include prepositions:

above the fray	*under* the weather	*behind* the 8-ball	*down* to the wire
by all means	*by* a country mile	*at* the drop of a hat	*against* the grain

3. Wayne Magnuson's comprehensive and entertaining *English Idioms: sayings and slang* (Calgary: Prairie House Books, 2001) is a very useful compendium of English idioms, with special emphasis on North American sayings.

Writers may confuse these pairs of prepositions and phrases:

- ***among*** and ***between***—*between* refers to two (the road *between* the poplar bluff and the creek), while among refers to three or more (share the research load *among* George, Paula, and Syd)
- ***in*** and ***into***—in refers to static positions (the dump truck *in* the yard); *into* refers to movement toward a position (despite the tight opening, we crawled *into* the cave)
- ***as if*** and ***like***—*as if* comes before a clause (it's not *as if* he has seniority)
- ***beside*** and ***besides***—*beside* means "next to" (place the barrels *beside* the loading dock); *besides* means "in addition to" (we have other alternatives *besides* declaring bankruptcy)
- ***different than*** and ***different from***—both these phrases are widely used, especially in speech and in informal writing, but *different from* is generally preferred in formal writing
- ***differ from*** and ***differ with***—*differ from* means to be unlike something (the 2008 Acura MDX *differs from* the previous model in its styling and its engine); *differ with* means to disagree (I *differ with* his interpretation of the landslide's causes)
- ***like*** and ***such as***—*like* refers to the similarities between two or more compared items (the Honda Accord, *like* the Acura TL, uses a V-Tec 6-cylinder engine); *such as* often replaces *for example* in order to achieve smoother phrasing (natural disasters *such as* hurricanes are becoming more frequent)

Interjections

These words exclaim; they present emotion:

> *Oh,* I don't think I want to buy that car. *Oh, no!* We have another broken hex bolt.
>
> *Bravo!* We needed to win that job, and you've secured the contract with your well-written proposal.

When interjections appear on their own, typically they're followed by an exclamation point. When they appear in a sentence, usually they're set off by one or more commas. Note, however, that interjections don't appear very often in technical writing.

Practice Session 1—Identify Prepositions

Underline the prepositions in the following sentences. Then, circle the complete phrase in which each preposition appears. You will find answers for these exercises on page 625.

1. The Vanier Cup is awarded annually to the champion of CIS football.
2. Improved indoor air quality probably reduces the number of sick days claimed by workers.
3. Despite urgent requests from the local health authorities, the mine repeatedly refused to install modern water treatment methods.
4. The news media are very interested in the global warming issue.
5. Someone has inadvertently left the specimen case on the loading dock.

Practice Session 2—Identify Conjunctions

Using the supplied form, list and name all the conjunctions in the following passage and describe the relationship each one expresses. An example is provided. (See Table 24.7) You will find answers for these exercises on page 625.

New research and increased understanding of natural cycles suggest that longer autumns may be diminishing the ability of northern forests to fight global warming. Trees absorb carbon dioxide from the atmosphere as they grow, but they release CO_2 when they burn or decompose. Spring warming trends have increased tree growth, so more CO_2 is being absorbed than "normal." However, autumns have been warming at an even greater rate than springs, so more CO_2 is being released than normal because soil microbes are more active in the warmer weather and their activity releases carbon dioxide.

Conjunction	Type of Conjunction	Relationship Expressed
and	coordinating	Connects the compound subject, "research and understanding"

Practice session 3—Identify Prepositional Functions

Using the supplied form, identify the prepositional phrases and the nature of their modifying functions in the following passage. An example is provided in the form. You will find answers for these exercises on page 626.

The day after a burrowing owl captured media attention in Ottawa, a 6000-name petition was tabled yesterday in the House of Commons. The petition supports plans for a national park in the South Okanagan. The petition was submitted by B.C. Southern MP

Alex Atamanenko, prior to a meeting with representatives of the National Park Network. Atamanenko said that he and his staff have worked closely with Parks Canada officials to facilitate a dialogue between groups that hold opposite points of view regarding the grasslands park proposal.

Prepositional Phrase	Type of Modifying Phrase	Word or Phrase Modified
in Ottawa	adverb	Says where the owl "captured media attention"

Improvement Exercises—Conjunctions and Prepositions

In items 1 through 10, repair errors in the use of conjunctions and prepositions. (You may also have to fix punctuation or spelling errors.) If a sentence contains no errors, write ***C*** in the space that follows the sentence. You will find answers for these exercises on page 626.

1. Where is the new computer projection system at?
2. Clearly, we have to improve the communication between the production team, the sales people and the shipping people.
3. Either the transmission bolt threads are stripping when the engine torque increases because they're made of too soft steel; the engine might also be too powerful for this type of transmission.
4. Michelle damaged the portable oscilloscope when she tried to jam it in a metal container that wasn't large enough.
5. Please remember to not place the GPS receiver besides equipment that emits a strong magnetic field.

6. The maple syrup harvest involves like way more work than most people realize.
7. Way to go, that set of schematics represents the best work you've done for our firm.
8. Big hybrid SUVs, like the Toyota Highlander, the Chevrolet Tahoe, and the GMC Yukon, are now getting up to 30 miles per Imperial gallon.
9. Neither the diehard Ottawa football fans or the corporate community believe that a CFL football team can flourish in Ottawa.
10. A large body of evidence supports the contention that global warming results primarily from sun spot activity, not from fossil fuel emissions, however.

Document Critique—Prepositions and Conjunctions

The following document may contain errors in grammar, capitalization, punctuation, or spelling. Underline all errors and label them using standard proofreading marks. (See the Correction Symbols list on page 643.) You will find answers for this exercise on page 627.

Christopher Metals

MEMO

To:	Shift Foremen
From:	Augusta Brown, General Manager
Date:	June 2, 2009
Subject:	Reducing Toxic Emmisions At Our Plant

Thank you for you're useful coments in yesterdays meeting. I know we differ with each other on some points, but overall are experience point to ward either of three alternative.

Alternative 1—upgrade are the emission capture equipment. I thought that are existing equipment is state of the-art, however, as Jim reported, its already showing signs of aging and needs new filtering and storage addons. This alternative is probably the least expensive.

Alternative 2—shut down the galvanizing facility. This section of the plant requires the most expensive work, still it generates 65 percent of are income. So I don't want to shut it down.

Alternative 3—shut down the culvert mill, sell its equipment, and use the sale funds to expand and modernize are galvanizing facility. Not only would this strategy get rid of the culvert mill, that is bearly coverring operating costs and it would allow us to expand production of galvanized pipe, that is in high demand. Beside these benefits, Jeanine pointed out that new ways of capturing and storing galvanizing by-products have been develop.

Their seems to be more research to do, as we look in this issue. Lets meet again on Monday.

CHAPTER 25

Sentence Grammar

The previous chapter, "Basic Grammar," focuses on the role of individual words and small groups of words in conveying meaning. This chapter studies the word patterns that effectively describe, explain, and persuade. Make no mistake about it—good technical writing depends on these patterns as much as it depends on the words themselves.

As in the previous chapter, our discussion of sentence grammar is descriptive, not prescriptive, as this book passes on the wisdom and techniques learned by technical writers. Countless writers have learned the hard way that too many long, complex sentences make readers weary, that dangling modifiers confuse readers, or that lack of parallelism leaves readers scratching their heads. This chapter covers those three topics and more, but first let's look at main structural principles that make English sentences work.

SENTENCE BUILDING BLOCKS

At the heart of the English sentence are **subjects** and **predicates.** If a group of words contains both of those elements, we call the grouping a **clause.** A one-word subject mated with a one-word predicate (such as *he runs* or *commerce rules*) qualifies as a clause, but such two-word sentences are rather rare, especially in technical writing.

More often, subjects and predicates also contain adjectives, adverbs, conjunctions and/or phrases that contribute to more detailed information and to more complex thought.

Grammar at Work: Clear Communication Saves Money and Reputations

An event planner sent information about a national conference to all the members, vendors and speakers attending the conference, but she wrote the wrong start date of the conference in her message. As a result, her company had to pay nearly $20,000 in airline change fees and other penalties. Such mistakes can cost time and money and can erode a company's credibility.

"In addition to credibility issues, the wrong dollar amount in a contract or letter of agreement may force one party to honor the wrong price.... The wrong address or phone number can delay or prevent contact or correspondence. These errors may be considered 'minor' but they can potentially be costly and embarrassing." (Ronnie Moore, in *Why Did I Say That? Communicating to Keep Your Credibility, Your Cool, and Your Cash!)*

—Based on "Sloppy Writing at Work Has Dire Consequences," a report by Rachel Zupek, *Careerbuilder.Com* Writer, Posted March 3, 2008 at *http://jobs.aol.com/article/_a/sloppy-writing-at-work-has-dire/20071115155809990001*

Subjects

Grammarians distinguish between a **simple subject** (a key word or group of words that acts, or describes a state of being, or is acted upon) and a **complete subject** (the simple subject and its modifiers). In each of the following sentence, the complete subject is italicized and the simple subject is underlined.

> *Every <u>scientist</u> at the research station* has resigned.

Our language's amazing versatility is reflected in the variety of forms that subjects can take:

Single noun:	*Music* soothes the soul.
Single pronoun:	*She* repaired the fuel line.
Compound subject:	The white van and the *Hummer* crashed head on.
Noun phrase:	*Corporate responsibility* has tilted toward satisfying the shareholders.
Gerund (a present participle form of a verb):	*Running* gives me time by myself.
Gerund phrase (a gerund and other words combine to act as a subject):	*Running a drag line* requires specialized training.

NOTE *Commands such as* Sweep the deck or Submit the proposal by Monday morning *usually don't include the subject,* you, *which is understood to be present. In rare cases, the subject is inserted in a command sentence:* <u>Ladies and gentlemen</u>, please rise and remove your hats for the singing of the national anthem.

Predicates

In a sentence, the predicate contains the verb, which expresses what the subject is experiencing or doing, or what is being done to the subject. A **simple predicate** contains only the verb:

Our team leader is *ill.* The train *stopped.* Surprisingly, the Canadian dollar *rose.*

A **complete predicate** contains the simple predicate and one or more modifiers:

Our team leader is *very ill.* The train *stopped abruptly at the station.*

A **compound predicate** contains two or more verbs:

The coach *waved* her arms and *whistled* in a vain attempt to get the point guard's attention.
Our latest ice storm *damaged* trees and *downed* power lines.

Clauses

The above examples of sentences show **independent clauses**, patterns of thought that stand alone as complete sentences. Although **dependent clauses** also contain a subject and a predicate, they rely on being attached to an independent clause to complete their meaning. In the following sentence, the dependent clause (in italics) comes first, followed by the independent clause that could have operated on its own:

After he left university, Raoul joined an oil exploration firm.

In the next example, the independent (or main) clause comes first, followed by the dependent (or subordinate) clause:

Sarah won a Kohlman bursary *because her grades were well above the norm.*

Dependent clauses that perform an adverbial function usually start with a subordinate conjunction such as *because, until, after,* or *when.* For a more complete list of subordinate conjunctions, see Table 24.7.

TYPES OF SENTENCES

Grammarians recognize four types of sentences:

- simple sentences contain a single independent clause;
- compound sentences have two independent clauses;
- complex sentences contain one independent and one or more dependent clauses; and
- compound-complex sentences feature two or more independent and one or more dependent clauses.

Simple Sentences

Good technical writing contains a high percentage of straightforward sentences. One study[4] found that readable prose consists of a minimum of 75.5 percent simple sentences, either in **subject-verb-object** (SVO) order or in **subject-verb-complement** (SVC) order.

SVO sentences are easy to follow, especially if the subject (underlined below) appears at the very beginning of the sentence, followed immediately by the verb (italicized below):

Regina *will host* the 2010 Grey Cup game.
He *won* the first match with a devastating serve.

Both the above examples feature simple subjects, but sentences with more complete subjects are also quite easy to understand:

Actually, Regina, the home of the Saskatchewan Roughriders, *will host* the 2010 Grey Cup game.
Later that afternoon, he easily *won* his second match with a finesse game, proving his adaptability.

These embellished sentences now begin with a transitional word or phrase that helps maintain a smooth flow of ideas within a paragraph. The first sentence also inserts a noun phrase (*the home* of *the Saskatchewan Roughriders*) that adds some texture to the sentence. The second sentence adds an adverb (*easily*) and a verbal phrase (*proving his adaptability*). Still, these augmented SVO sentences remain easy to follow.

Most **SVC sentences** are also easy to read—the complementary bits follow the core subject and verb. The complement could say more about the subject, or more about the verb, or both.

- An adjective or phrase could function as an adjective, following a linking verb:

Our boss is *unhappy.* [*unhappy* modifies *boss]*
Martine is *under the weather.* [The prepositional phrase *under the weather* modifies *Martine.)*

- Adverbs or adverbial phrases might follow an active verb:

Denman works *hard at his chosen profession, for six 12–hour days a week.*
[The adverb *hard* modifies *works.* The prepositional phrase *at his chosen profession* further modifies *works.* The phrase *for six 12–hour days a week says* **when** Denman works.]

- A string of complementary phrases might combine adverbial and adjectival functions:

---

4. Dr. Francis Christensen, an English professor at the University of Southern California, reported his findings in "Notes Toward a New Rhetoric," in *College English*, October 1963 (pp. 7–18). His data and conclusions remain relevant today.

> On Sundays, Denman remains *happily at home with his collection of exotic birds.* [The adverb *happily* modifies *remains.* Two adverbial prepositional phrases complement the subject-verb core of this sentence: *at home and with his collection.* Both say **where** Denman *remains.* The adjectival phrase *of exotic birds modifies collection.* This **cumulative** building of meaning works well because it keeps the core meaning at the beginning of the sentence, and it rhythmically adds information.]

The previous example uses a short prepositional phrase, *on Sundays,* to lead into the sentence. Such transitions perform a useful function and they don't impede the reader's understanding of the sentence's meaning.

The following paragraph illustrates SVO and SVC sentences at work in a technical document:

> On Lake Superior, Environment Canada annually samples water at 94 stations. This sampling requires a sturdy vessel to navigate the lake and gain access to remote spots along the shore. In addition, 25 surveillance cruises have gathered data on Lake Superior between 1976 and 2006. During these cruises, scientists sampled for nutrients, major ions, organic contaminants, and biological and physical trends. The results have been startling.

The above passage packs a considerable amount of information into its 66 words. However, it's readable because all five sentences use an SVO or SVC pattern, and the sentences are linked together with transitions such as "this sampling," "in addition," and "during these cruises." To further aid readability, the average sentence is only 13.2 words long, the average number of words before the subject is only 2.0, and the verbs immediately follow those subjects.

> **The Good News:**
> You don't have to be a great stylist to be an effective technical writer; you just have to write lots of clear SVO and SVC sentences, linked by transitional words and short transitional phrases.

Compound Sentences

At some point in your writing career, you've probably been told that you need to write a variety of sentence types, including compound and complex sentences. That advice doesn't necessarily hold for technical writing, but sometimes your thoughts will require longer, more involved sentence structures such as compound sentences. Here are two compound sentences, one with two independent clauses and one with three:

> Servers must operate continuously and reliably, so efficient, trustworthy fans must be used for ventilation.

> Some popular operating systems for servers are derived from the UNIX operating system and Unix has been a logical choice for many servers, but *the market share of the Windows Server product line has been growing steadily.*

The above 15-word sentence doesn't present a reading challenge, but the 37-word sentence demands close attention, and perhaps even a second reading. Writers of such sentences need to plan them carefully to ensure that the thought pattern develops logically.

Complex Sentences

Essayists who espouse complex philosophies often need complex modes of expression—the complex sentence, with its single independent clause and one or more dependent clauses, can serve that need. However, sentences such as the following are relatively rare in technical writing:

> Although electrical signals propagate along a cable very quickly, they weaken as they travel, so that electrical interference from nearby devices such as fluorescent lights can scramble the signal.

The independent clause, "they weaken as they travel," is at the heart of the above complex sentence. Now, are you ready for an even more complicated collection of words?

Compound-Complex Sentences

This type of sentence contains two or more independent clauses and one or more dependent clauses, as in

> A single shared cable can serve as the basis for a complete Ethernet network and several machines can be connected to the network, although there are practical limits on the size of the Ethernet network in this case, and the length of the shared cable must be considered.

So, here we have 4 clauses and 48 words in one sentence. The sentence requires your full commitment, doesn't it? Would you feel better if the sentence were broken up? Do you find the following arrangement easier to read?

> A single shared cable can serve as the basis for a complete Ethernet network and several machines can be connected to the network. However, this case imposes practical limits on the size of the Ethernet network. In particular, the length of the shared cable must be considered.

Now, the four clauses occupy three sentences and 47 words. Flow has been maintained by using transitions.

Grammar at Work: Write Short, Crisp Sentences

"Avoid the pitfall of using excessive technical jargon or complex sentences. Keep the sentences short, crisp and simple. Also, don't jam too much thought content into one post. Instead, add another post later."

—**"Common Mistakes to Avoid,"** *posted June 19, 2007 at the Blogging Strategies website, http://www.bloggingstrategies.com/*

SENTENCE ERRORS AND CHALLENGES

Relatively short, uncomplicated sentences help readers navigate technical and business documents, but these sentences can still be sabotaged by the following kinds of mistakes.

Packed Sentences

Technical writers may be tempted to overfill sentences with descriptive or analytical detail:

> The Nokian WR all-season tire's features provide important safety benefits: a high dispersion silica compound provides excellent grip, longer mileage, and better rolling resistance while the arrowhead tread pattern effectively expels water, snow, and slush, and the Haka siping creates "rubber studs" in the tread that result in better grip and high stability during high-speed driving.

I defy you to grasp that 57-word statement the first time you read it. Perhaps a bulleted list would make the sentence easier to swallow.

> The Nokian WR all-season tire features important safety benefits:
>
> - a high dispersion silica compound provides excellent grip, longer mileage, and better rolling resistance;
> - the arrowhead tread pattern effectively expels water, snow, and slush; and
> - the Haka siping creates "rubber studs" in the tread that result in better grip and high stability during high-speed driving.

Words Before the Subject

Subjects can be hard to find in sentences that open with long phrases.

> In a city where careers are made and broken in the time it takes to grill a hot dog, *Pink's* is one of Hollywood's few constants—a place where families, struggling actors and the show-biz elite temporarily unite in the common pursuit of hot dogs.

The above statement trots out 19 words before getting to the subject of the sentence, *Pink's*. Elaborate openings might be fine for popular journalism—the above sentence appeared in an MSN story about America's best hot dog joints—but readers of technical writing don't expect to be entertained; they want plain English and they want sentences to place the subject at or near the beginning, as in this sentence:

> The Nokian WR all-season tire features important safety benefits:
>
> - a high dispersion silica compound provides excellent grip, longer mileage, and better rolling resistance;
> - the arrowhead tread pattern effectively expels water, snow, and slush; and
> - the Haka siping creates "rubber studs" in the tread that result in better grip and high stability during high-speed driving.

Compare the above list to this mess, which presents 52 words before naming the subject:

> Because of excellent grip, longer mileage, and better rolling resistance resulting from a high dispersion compound, together with an the arrowhead tread pattern that effectively expels water, snow, and slush and Haka siping that creates "rubber studs" in the tread that result in better grip and high stability during high-speed driving, *the Nokian WR all-season tire* rolls out important safety benefits.

Here's a good rule of thumb: the sentences in a given passage should average no more than three words before naming the sentence's subject. In other words, get to the point as soon as possible.

Words Between the Subject and the Verb

Again, the rule of thumb uses the number *3*. On average, no more than three words should come between the subject and the verb in clauses. If you use more, you increase reading difficulty. When you make material hard to read, you lose your readers.

> Employment portfolios, which might contain supporting documents, work samples, lists of accomplishments, records of community service, photo documentation, certainly a targeted resume, and maybe even video evidence, can be very useful in job searches.

After ploughing through the 25 words that separate the subject and the verb, the reader might well forget what the subject of the sentence is. A better approach would reunite the subject and verb at the beginning of a two-sentence statement:

> Employment portfolios can be very useful in job searches. These portfolios might contain supporting documents, work samples, lists of accomplishments, records of community service, photo documentation, a targeted resume, and maybe even video evidence.

And why not break the second statement into a bulleted list?

> Employment portfolios can be very useful in job searches. These portfolios might contain
>
> - supporting documents and photo documentation,
> - work samples,
> - lists of accomplishments,
> - records of community service,
> - a targeted resume, and
> - video evidence.

Sentence Fragments

A phrase or a dependent clause that is presented as if it were a sentence is called a sentence fragment. Editors pounce on these fragments because complete thoughts are not provided. Still, fragments have their place in, for example, advertising messages:

> Come ski at the Rocking Donkey Resort. *The best powder in B.C. No lift lines. And best bang for your buck!*

The above example would lack punch if the ad read, "We have the best powder in B.C. along with virtually no lift lines. Therefore, we offer excellent value." No. That approach doesn't work in ad copy. However, completed thought is exactly what's needed in workplace writing, which needs to describe and explain, not entertain. Here's an example of the problem with sentence fragments in workplace writing:

> Pollutants can enter a watercourse through a particular entry such as a drainpipe. *Flowing directly into a stream or lake. Point source pollution.* That's its name, and its main sources are sewage treatment plants and industrial waste discharges. *Including toxic chemicals and human waste.*

In the above paragraph, the three fragments are italicized. Each lacks an element that would clarify what the writer intended to convey. It's hard to tell if that first fragment is meant to say more about the preceding noun, *drainpipe*, or whether *flowing directly into a stream or lake* is meant to be tied to the phrase, *point source pollution*. The third fragment might be intended to modify *discharges*, or it might be a modifying phrase for a statement that didn't make it to the page. The following edited version adds a clause that can show the relevance of *toxic chemicals and human waste*.

> Pollutants can enter a watercourse through a particular entry such as a drainpipe that flows directly into a stream or lake. Known as point source pollution, its main sources are sewage treatment plants and industrial waste discharges. Point source pollutants include toxic chemicals and human waste.

Let's quickly review. Phrases and dependent clauses aren't particularly useful by themselves. For example, *because atmospheric pollution comes from many diffuse sources* is incomplete, even though it contains a subject and a predicate. The conjunction *because* has hinted at something that would complete the thought, but we don't know what that something is. We could guess that the intended complete sentence would read, *Because atmospheric pollution comes from many diffuse sources, it is difficult to control.* However, guesswork isn't good enough for technical and business documents.

Run-on Sentences

Complete sentences need to be separated by periods, semi-colons, or colons. These punctuation methods receive full treatment in the "Punctuation Exercises" section of this workbook, so here we focus on what's wrong with **comma splices** and **fused sentences.**

> Come ski at the Rocking Donkey Resort, it has the best powder in B.C. and no lift lines.

I've underlined the sequence of words where the two independent clauses are ineffectively *spliced* together with a comma. The first clause ends at *Resort.* The second clause begins at *it*. That comma doesn't help us at all. Now here are four possible interpretations of the writer's intention:

1. Come ski at the Rocking Donkey Resort *because it* has the best powder in B.C. and no lift lines.
2. Come ski at the Rocking Donkey *Resort, which* has the best powder in B.C. and no lift lines.
3. Come ski at the Rocking Donkey *Resort. It* has the best powder in B.C. and no lift lines.
4. Come ski at the Rocking Donkey *Resort; it* has the best powder in B.C. and no lift lines.

These four versions have slightly different meanings. Version 1 emphasizes the cause-effect relationship. Version 2, like Version 1, also turns the second clause into a dependent clause, but now the reasons for going to the Resort are less important than going there. The second clause is no longer essential to the sentence. Versions 3 and 4 separate the two clauses, but the period in Version 3 prompts the reader to pause a little longer than indicated by the semi-colon in Version 4. Also, Version 3's semi-colon suggests a closer relationship between the two clauses than the period does in Version 4.

Yes, the distinctions are rather subtle, but they do exist. Moreover, one of the four versions almost certainly expresses exactly what the reader intended. The comma splice doesn't even come close!

Fused sentences don't even bother with a comma:

> All our networked computers are checked for viruses every month an IT technician carefully searches each computer's hard disk drives.

So what exactly did the writer mean? Did he or she mean to emphasize that all the computers are checked every month, or did the writer mean to say that every month an IT technician searches the hard disk drives? In practical terms, it amounts to the same thing. Or does it? Probably, the IT department would like the emphasis placed on what the IT technicians do, especially if this sentence appears in a proposal to hire more technicians. So, there's more at stake here than issues of correctness and rules about when to use periods or semi-colons. The real problem with fused sentences is that it's hard to tell what the writer meant.

Misplaced Modifiers

Often, a modifying word or phrase can dramatically change the meaning of a sentence by its placement:

The Act *only allows* engineers to approve designs.	[but it doesn't <u>require</u> engineers to do so]
Only the Act allows engineers to approve designs.	[only the "Act," not any other document]
The Act allows *only engineers* to approve designs.	[just engineers, not technologists or foremen]

The Act allows engineers to *only approve* designs.	[they can approve but not create the designs]

One of the above versions reflects what the writer meant.

Sometimes, the writer clearly has misplaced the modifier and, although we can decipher what was meant in such cases, the process takes time and the writer loses credibility:

> *Rising from every one of the seven dead trees*, we saw the eagles taking flight. [The eagles rose; we didn't.]
>
> Stéphane Dion delivered a ringing endorsement of federalism, *determined to seem strong in Québec*. [Here, the modifying phrase should immediately precede the subject because Dion is the one who wants to appear strong in *La Belle Province*.]

Dangling Modifiers

In some cases, a modifying word or phrase has nothing in the sentence to modify, perhaps with comic effect:

> Jogging along the road, a car swerved and nearly hit me. [Can cars *jog?]*
>
> **Better:** *As I was* jogging along the road, a car swerved and nearly hit me.

Jogging along the road is known as a **dangling modifier**. In the following sentence, a modifier vaguely implies a connection with something or someone not identified in the sentence:

> Speaking with Joe Burns, he said that only the 2007 group of contractors would be considered for 2008 haul licences. [Joe wasn't talking to himself.]
>
> **Better:** Joe Burns told me that only the 2007 group of contractors would be considered for 2008 haul licences.
>
> ***Or,*** When I spoke with Joe Burns, he told me that. . . .

Disruptive Modifiers

Inserting a modifying phrase between a subject and verb, or between parts of a verb phrase, interrupts the natural progression from subject to verb that readers expect:

> Campbell expected the protestors to *fairly quickly* go home.
> Workers will, *if they are abused too long*, rebel in one way or another.
> The transits, *because we've moved to GPS readings*, were discarded last fall.
> He bought *with his first pay cheque* a secondhand car.

Instead, place the phrase either before the subject or after the verb:

> Campbell expected the protestors to go home *fairly quickly.*
> *If they are abused too long,* workers will rebel in one way or another.

Faulty Coordination

Using conjunctions such as *and*, *but*, *so*, *or*, *for*, and *nor* to join two independent clauses works well as long as the two clauses are closely related or equivalent as in the following examples:

As an engineer he is responsible for ethical designs *and* he takes that responsibility seriously.
The timing belt broke *and* the engine immediately stopped running.
Most engines will simply stop running when the timing belt breaks, *but* "interference" engines will experience major damage when a moving piston strikes an open valve.

The first example contains two clauses closely linked by their emphasis on an engineer's responsibility. Example three also describes a close relationship between the two clauses. The second example shows a cause-effect relationship between the two clauses.

These examples of faulty coordination neither express a cause-effect relationship nor a close thematic connection. In each case, the writer needs to choose which clause is subordinate.

Faulty: Each year the creek overflows its banks and the creek has several sizeable sand bars.
This control box is connected to each sensor and it sends information about each room to the building's main climate control computer.
PharmaHeal Inc. is a private company in Cambridge, Ontario and it started in 2001.

Better: Each year the creek, which has several sizeable sand bars, overflows its banks.
This control box, which is connected to each sensor, sends information about each room to the building's main climate control computer.
PharmaHeal Inc., a private company in Cambridge, Ontario, started in 2001.
Or, PharmaHeal Inc., which started in 2001, is a private company in Cambridge, Ontario.
Or, A private company in Cambridge, Ontario, PharmaHeal Inc. started in 2001.

Faulty Parallelism

Balanced sentences join matching grammatical forms:

The timing belt *broke* and the engine immediately *stopped* running.
[*Broke* and *stopped* are **parallel words**, both of which are past tense verbs.]

Short sentences *reduce word counts* and *improve readability*.
[The two **verbal phrases** use **parallel phrasing**.]

As the head engineer, *he oversees all the designs* and *he takes that responsibility* seriously. [The two **clauses** use **parallel phrasing**.]

Readers may be confused when equivalent words, phrases, or clauses are not phrased in parallel ways:

The proposed upgrades include:

- *Upgrading* the electrical service from 15 amps to 30 amps;
- *Replacement and an upgrade* of the water pipes on the property; and
- *An upgrade of* the existing drain field is anticipated.

The list helps readability, but the italicized words in the three listed items should use the same grammatical form. In this case, the present participle would work well:

The proposed improvements include:

- *upgrading* the electrical service from 15 amps to 30 amps,
- *replacing and upgrading* the water pipes on the property, and
- *upgrading* the existing drain field.

Here's another list that requires parallel structure:

Selecting the priority watersheds to be studied focused on two main considerations:

- *significance of the watersheds* (*high fisheries* or *domestic water* supply values), and
- *restoration projects must have* a high probability of success.

Yes, the reader can eventually figure out what this relatively short list entails, but that task would be easier if both the bulleted items (and the bracketed phrase) were parallel and if the two bracketed adjectival phrases were also phrased in parallel:

Selecting the priority watersheds to be studied focused on two main considerations:

- *the watersheds must be significant* (they must have *high fishery* or *domestic water* supply values), and
- *proposed restoration projects must have* a high probability of success.

Parallelism is also important within standard sentences. The following lack parallel structures:

Getting to the interview stage can sometimes be more satisfying than *to do well at the interview* itself. [The parallel phrases should be *getting to* and *doing well*]

Differing data gathering methods *can not only result in* spotty data collection but *also lead to* difficulties in interpreting the data.
[The parallel phrases should be *not only result in* and *can also lead to*]

Practice Session 1—Identify Subjects and Predicates

Underline the complete subject in each of the following sentences and circle the simple subject. Double underline each complete predicate and circle each simple predicate. You will find answers for these exercises on page 627.

1. You will need to return that spectrometer to Gordon Burns.
2. Will the ratepayers pay the development costs for the proposed riverside trail system?
3. Some air toxins come from natural sources such as forest fires and soil erosion.
4. Air toxins pose a serious threat to human health in all parts of the world.
5. The ozone layer in southern Canada thinned by an annual average of about 6 percent in the late 1990s.

Practice Session 2—Identify Sentence Types

In the space provided, name the type of sentence for that item (simple, compound, complex, compound-complex). You will find answers for these exercises on page 628.

6. Although the ozone layer is an important defence against UV penetration, several other factors can have an effect. ____________
7. The air is cleaner and cooler in the Arctic region. ____________
8. Both greenhouse warming and the thinning of the atmospheric layer result partially from human activities, but those activities have had less impact than natural phenomena, whose impact has not been recognized by the orthodox scientific community. ____________
9. Government agencies have focused on gathering data and lobby groups have used that data to push their own agendas, while the oil industry carries on like there's no tomorrow. ____________
10. The Kyoto Accord will not survive in its present form. ____________

Practice Session 3—Identify Sentence Errors

Underline each example of a comma splice (CS), fused sentence (FS), dangling modifier (DM), misplaced modifier (MM), sentence fragment (frag), disruptive modifier (DisM), faulty coordination (coord), or faulty parallelism (//) in the following sentences. In the space above the underlined error, write the appropriate symbol (CS, DM, etc.) You will find answers for these exercises on page 628.

11. The Ekati mine has cost Dia Met about $536 million and is 70% complete.
12. When grading the site, two-way radios, which allow surveyors to communicate from a distance, are used.
13. Most people like to relax after a hard day's work in front of the TV.
14. After completing the project under budget, the head engineer rewarded me with a promotion.
15. The employee persuaded his boss to grant a pay raise with logical arguments.
16. Many municipalities created, for the benefit of local farmers, policy that provided for minimal monitoring of animal waste runoff.

17. The Integration comparator is also quite popular, it is used most commonly in digital multimeters.
18. When manufacturing a car chassis, materials need to be strong and lightweight.
19. The objectives of this assessment were to ascertain whether the completed work is in compliance with the prescriptions and that the drainage along the road might have been improved.
20. The lake will be temporarily drained during the drawdown it will then increase in size during the re-wetting phase of the project.

Improvement Exercises—Sentences

The following 30 sentences may contain errors in sentence structure, pronoun usage, adjectives and adverbs, conjunctions, prepositions, spelling, or punctuation. Rewrite those sentences, correcting the errors. If a sentence is already correct, write *C* in the space following the sentence. You will find answers for these exercises on pages 628 and 629.

1. Storm water pond construction did not cause negative environmental impacts and was completed following best management practices.
2. The plan area includes about 390 ha and is bound by Powers Creek to the east, Highway 97 to the north, the District of Peachland to the west, and Okanagan Lake to the south.
3. If the native trees are lost or damaged during the construction process, we'll plant three trees for every one that needs replacing. This will ensure an 80 percent survival of shrubs and a 100 percent survival of trees after three years.
4. Watering of theses plants twice weekly for the first two weeks, reduced to once a week for four weeks thereafter, weather dependant, will ensure quick root growth.
5. Myself and all the team at ESB look forward to hearing from you.
6. One of his finer projects was the Penticton Channel recreation area, he helped design and he oversee the construction of this project.
7. This proposal outlines the proposed research that will need to be conducted, as well as, the solution to the problem that we will implement.
8. By erecting a breakwater wall, the currents will be diverted, thereby eliminating beach erosion.
9. Facial expressions are raising or lowering the eye brows, squinting, clenching the jaw, as well as many others.
10. pH measures the acidity or alkalinity of water and many organisms that live in the water are sensitive to changes in pH.
11. These steps, keep sun exposure to a minimum, especially between 10 a.m. and 3 p.m. and wear wide-brimmed hats and wear sunscreen with Sun Protection Factor of 15 or greater and reapply the sunscreen frequently, will help protect you from the sun's harmful rays.
12. Fearing the dilution of its trademark, remembering what happened to brand names like Kleenex and aspirin and trampoline, and seeing the word entrenched in dictionaries such as the Oxford English Dictionary, and noting the increasing popularity of the word, Google inc. tried to persuade members of the public to refrain from using "google" as a verb.

13. A post-development/construction report summarizing the development, outlining the degree of compliance with the above measures and demonstrating that the SPEA is protected will also be produced and submitted on the RAR database.
14. The proposed "F" shaped dock will be made of perforated material and consists of a 1.8 m wide mainstem.
15. None of the species are recently reported in the area, and it is not likely that the storage of wood waste on the subject property will significantly affect any of these species.
16. The average person spends 3,220 hours stuck in traffic, but only minutes planning their retirement.
17. Client A has not attended regularly, nevertheless, he continues to make contact with our counsellors.
18. Smoking is only allowed in the gazebos at this campus.
19. Because each of us has a responsibility to the organization.
20. Trying their very best in the aptitude tests, we observed the clients at the Centre.
21. If you know the answer, it is easy, however, not everyone knows the answer.
22. After sending the message, the following screen will appear.
23. Specialty NiCd batteries have a niche market in the area of cordless and wireless telephones, emergency lighting, model airplanes, as well as power tools.
24. With a relatively low internal resistance, a NiCd battery can supply high surge currents. This makes them a favourable choice for remote controlled electric model aeroplanes, boats, and cars, as well as cordless power tools and camera flash units.
25. This workshop series has three objectives, including:

    - The development of a strategies for structuring documents.
    - learning how to proofread and edit other's documents
    - as well as improving ones' efficiency in writing.

26. Please feel free to contact myself if you require further clarification.
27. This is the first tier of the assessment process and is completed by the supplier.
28. Roughly 100 pharmaceuticals have now being identified in rivers, lakes, and coastal waters throughout Europe and in north America. In concentrations that have alarmed environmental protection agencies.
29. The Europeane medicines Agency recommend additional testing of drugs to learn how they break down when they enter surface or underground water supplies.
30. One worry for pharmaceutical companies is that increased amount of testing could costly translate into delays for the release of new drugs.

Document Critique—Sentences

The following email may contain errors in sentence structure, grammar, capitalization, punctuation, or spelling. Underline all errors and identify them using standard proofreading marks. (See the Correction Symbols list on page 643.) You will find answers for this exercise on page 630.

NOTE *Do not comment on the tone of the email; simply identify errors.*

Corrine Maltais

From:	Billie Cochrane < bcochrane@on.gc.ca
To:	Corrine Maltais <cmaltais@on.gc.ca
Sent:	Friday, June 27, 2008 11.19 AM
Subject:	Conflicting responsibilities for The Georgian bay Project

As my project leader, I hope your can answer my question about what Im suposed to be doing on the boat. When I took this on as my summer student placement, I thot that myself and the other student wood just be observing procedures and collecting data, not doing all the grunt work on the boat. Isnt that what sailors are for?

Here's what been happening –

- On Monday, myself and Jeannie (shes the other student) had to coil all the ropes and check for flaws in the ropes, that's very hard work, let me tell you, those ropes are heavy and some of them are dirty too.
- Then on Tuesday the captain made us clean the decks, he said that were the ones getting the deck dirty with all our fish samples and because we came on board with muddy boots after checking the mud flats at 3 Moon bay. That's a big boat actually and we had to use mops and then hand scrub with those hard sponge things. Why doesn't they have proper motorized cleaning equipment on board?
- Wedensday we sailed to parker Point to get water samples and to check for fish mortality. Remember we had heard reports that fish were washing up on shore we didn't see any though, maybe the reports were for another point. That was a good day, we collected samples from 17 lakeshore locations and 5 deep water locations we observed three outflow pipes and took samples from those outflows, one of them I think it was the pulp mill around the corner from Parker Point was really disgusting – the colour was muddy red and it smells like sulphur and diesel fuel which is a really foul combination for sure.
- Yesterday as you know we spent in the lab with your techs as they checked the samples for toxic substances they found very high levels of dieldrin and lindane which was surprising because I thot that those pollutants were in decline, at least that's what Professor Gorsline said.
- This morning Jeannie and myself went down to the boat to retreive some equipment and the captain said that we had to clean the cabin and the storage lockers down below. Whoa I said, that's not what I came here for. Im a forth year biology student, I said, and Im gonna tell Dr Maltais whats going on and he said go right ahead I don't care but its my boat and youll do what I tell you when your on board That's what he said. Well I came right up to see you but you were in a meeting so Jeannie said I better write to you right away.

Thanks for listening. Can you talk to the captain?

CHAPTER 26
Punctuation

On a recent drive through a Montana mountain pass, I grudgingly followed a truck whose back doors screamed, "Car's RV's Boats We repair Them All!" in letters two feet high. What possessed the perpetrator of this crime to place the apostrophe in the plural form of *car*? And why, I wondered through clenched teeth as I followed the truck through swirling snow, were *them* and *all capitalized*? This type of response to faulty punctuation appears in the witty, ruthless exposé of mismanaged punctuation in Lynne Truss's book, *Eats, Shoots* & *Leaves.*[5]

Truss makes a case for paying close attention to the punctuation we employ:

> . . . all our thoughts can be rendered with absolute clarity if we bother to put the right dots and squiggles between words in the right places. Proper punctuation is both the sign and the cause of clear thinking. (Truss, p. 202)

Punctuation marks were introduced to the written language during the age of printing by print setters who wanted to approximate the pauses, tonal emphasis, and musical pitch that we easily use when we speak. In the intervening half millennium, punctuation methods and styles have changed, but the key punctuation marks have survived. This chapter examines periods, commas, colons and semicolons, question marks and exclamation points, apostrophes, dashes, hyphens, italics, and underlining.

END PUNCTUATION

Conventional usage places a period, a question mark, or an exclamation point at the end of a sentence:

> That laptop is yours to use this semester.
> Is that your laptop?
> Your laptop is amazingly light!

---

5. Truss, Lynne. *Eats, Shoots* & *Leaves.* London: Gotham Books, 2003.

Colons and semicolons often appear at the end of independent clauses as in the following examples:

I've ordered a laptop that has all the features you requested:

- a 17" widescreen LCD,
- an MP camera,
- 3 GB RAM,
- a 300 GB hard disk drive, and
- a dual processor.

The laptops will be here Thursday; please install networking software as soon as they arrive.

You'll need a wireless router: an SMC Barricade 2804BR would fit your system.

COLONS AND SEMICOLONS

Colons point at things, as if to say, "here, look at these words." As the examples at the bottom of the previous page illustrate, colons can appear at the end of independent clauses. However, a colon should not be placed at the end of an incomplete thought, such as a phrase or dependent clause.

If we have a labour stoppage next week, do not enflame the situation by actions such as

- crossing the picket lines,
- sharing your feelings about the strike with reporters, or
- conducting classes at a location outside the College.

> **Hint:**
> When the lead-in words at the end of an independent clause are *including, consists of, like,* or *such as,* do not use a colon. You can use a colon if the lead-in words are *as follows* or *the following.*

You can use a colon to introduce a **quotation** or an **example**:

Truss believes we should resist the erosion of standard punctuation: "The reason to stand up for punctuation is that without it there is no reliable way communicating meaning."
(Truss, p. 20)

Some punctuation marks are overworked: for example, Lynne Truss lists seven discrete uses for the apostrophe.

After an independent clause, you can use a colon to introduce an **appositive**, a word or collection of words that renames a noun or pronoun.

The Mitsubishi i-car has a major competitive advantage; the design of this diminutive vehicle allows four passengers to ride in comfort.

Semicolons also have several uses:

- A semicolon can separate independent clauses if the writer wants to show that the two ideas are closely related (as shown by a pause rather than by a full stop):

Whirlpool Corporation has been busy acquiring brand names; its stable of brands now includes Amana, Whirlpool, Maytag, Inglis, Admiral, Jenn-Air, Magic Chef, and KitchenAid.

- If the second independent clause starts with a conjunctive adverb or transitional expression, a semicolon could be placed between the two clauses:

  The Maytag dishwasher has a distinctive, independent brand name; however, its replacement parts come directly from Whirlpool.

- When each of the items in a series is comparatively long, or if each item contains commas, the items might be separated by semicolons rather than commas:

  The Canadian Olympic Committee's responsibilities include athletic, cultural, and educational programs promoting Olympic values in Canada; grassroots programs in communities across the country; and selection of Canadian cities to host Olympic, Olympic Winter, and Pan American Games.

Grammar at Work: The One Million Dollar Comma

In August 2006, the Canadian Radio and Television Commission (CRTC) ruled that Aliant Inc. could terminate a contract with Rogers Communications Inc. and thus increase the rates charged to Rogers for stringing cable TV wires along New Brunswick power poles. The ruling would effectively cost Rogers an extra $2.3 million, which was later reduced to $1 million by New Brunswick's public utility board. The ruling hinged on the presence of a second comma in this sentence: "...this agreement shall be effective from the date it is made and shall continue in force for a period of five (5) years from the date it is made, and thereafter for successive five (5) year *terms, unless* and until terminated by one year prior notice in writing by either party." Had that second comma not been there, said the CRTC, Rogers would have had a valid five-year deal at the lower rate, at least for the first five years.

The French language version of the contract used slightly different phrasing and punctuation, which Rogers Communications argued expressed the true spirit of the contract. Rogers appealed the CRTC verdict and in August 2007 the CTRC reversed its judgment, although the CRTC did not indicate how Rogers might get its money refunded!

—Based on the following reports:
Crosariol, Beppi. "Tiny Punctuation Mark, Big Legal Lesson." *The Globe and Mail,* 16 Aug. 2006: B6.
Robertson, Grant. "A $2 Million Dollar Comma? Au Contraire, Rogers Tells Aliant." *The Globe and Mail,* 16 Oct. 2006: B1.
Ruby, Peter. "The Comma Case Redux." Goodmans Update, online law review, accessed 30 Mar. 2008 at *http://goodmans.ca/docs%5CLitigationCommaRedux.pdf*

COMMAS

Commas precede nonrestrictive elements (elements that are not essential to the meaning):

The Rogers/Aliant comma controversy, *which cost Rogers millions,* was totally avoidable.

Commas do not precede restrictive elements (elements essential to the meaning):

I was very interested in the Rogers/Aliant comma controversy *that The Globe and Mail reported.*

Commas separate items in a series (three or more elements constitute a *series*):

Recent Antarctic ice breakups may affect sea levels, ocean temperatures, and Antarctic weather patterns.

Creating bronze statues requires specialized equipment, skill, patience, and expensive materials.

The practice of burning yard debris in suburban neighbourhoods has implications for people with breathing problems, for bylaw officers, and for those responsible for municipal landfills.

Note that a comma appears before the coordinating conjunction (*and, or*) that precedes the last item in a series:

Health problems might include eye irritation, headaches, *asthma, or bronchitis.*

If a comma does not appear before the coordinating conjunction in the above sentence, *asthma or bronchitis* can be interpreted as a single phrase, not as two separate items.

A comma does not appear within an item that incorporates *and*:

You have a choice of an omelette, *ham and eggs,* or a Denver sandwich.

Commas may set off parenthetical expressions:

Residents of Sooke (a suburb of Victoria, B.C.) have complained about backyard burning.

Residents of *Sooke, a suburb of Victoria,* B.C., have complained about backyard burning.

A total of $148 million in capital spending, *mostly housing projects,* is planned for the spring.

Commas may set off quoted words from explanatory or lead-in words:

Ross Grieve, CEO of PCL Constructors Inc., *said,* "*Employee* stock ownership is a good way to compensate people and tie them to the company."

However, a comma is not needed when the quoted words blend into the grammatical structure of a sentence:

Ross Grieve believes that "*Employee* stock ownership is a good way to compensate people and tie them to the company."

Commas may appear in dates:

March 28, 2008 Friday, March 28, 2008

Commas don't appear when they don't have to separate numbers:

March 2008 28 March 2008

Commas with numbers:

The metric system doesn't require commas in numbers that have more than four digits:

98 429 124 654 190

However, many people still use commas: 5,397 98,420 124,654,190

Commas with names, places, and addresses:

Here are some examples of comma usage with names, places, and addresses:

Maxwell Sandestin, M.D.

Saskatoon, Saskatchewan

I sent the parcel to 26 Prince Andrew Place, Don Mills, Ontario M3C 2T8.
[Notice the comma usage when an address is part of a sentence]

Do not use a comma in a name such as *Martin Luther King Jr.* or *Davis Love III.*

Commas in correspondence:

Emails and informal letters place a comma after the salutation:

Hello Mr. Konecsni,

Dear Judy,

Formal letters use a colon after the salutation, or after an attention line:

Dear Ms. Ramage:

Attention: Ms. Frances Ramage

Complimentary closes in letters or formal emails require a comma:

Yours truly,

Sincerely,

Best regards,

> **Hints For Inserting Commas:**
>
> Inserting a comma where <u>you</u> would pause during speech provides one way of knowing when to use a comma, but not everyone thinks or breathes in the same patterns, so equating commas to your speech pauses is not necessarily useful. A better strategy is to place a comma where you would like your <u>reader</u> to momentarily pause.
>
> If you're unsure, circle the point where you think a comma might be useful, and later check the advice provided in a grammar handbook. (And remember that *Grammar at Work* provides only that advice needed to guide you in this book's exercises—the 2½ pages of advice and examples in this workbook do not offer the level of detail that you'll find in a grammar handbook.)

APOSTROPHES

The apostrophe came into English in the 16th century, when its sole purpose was to stand in for dropped letters (as in Shakespeare's use of *'tis* instead of *it is*). Since then, it has been given much more work to do, starting in the 17th century when printers inserted the apostrophe in singular possessive nouns (such as *the printer's mistake*).

These days, the apostrophe indicates the following kinds of possession:

- **Possessive form of singular nouns**

  John's wedding   the duck's wing   Sandra's banquet Ross's car

- **Possessive form of plural nouns**

  printers' conventions   politicians' indiscretions   the Browns' house
  the Joneses' house   the Rosses' car

- **Possessive form of compound words and phrases**

  my father-in-law's response   Member of Parliament's expense account

- **Possessive form of individual nouns in a phrase**

  John's and Karla's wedding rings   the student's and the professor's interpretations

- **Form of the last noun in a joint or group possession**

  John and Karla's house   John and Karla's two dogs

- **Form of possessive indefinite pronouns**

  No one's phone has been tapped.   Someone's phone is ringing.

NOTE *Do not use apostrophes with possessive pronouns such as my, your, hers, his, and its.*

The apostrophe also indicates when one or more letters have been omitted in **contractions:**

aren't   can't   didn't   don't   I'm   she's

Apostrophes are <u>not</u> used for the possessive forms of pronouns such as *my, mine, your, yours, his, hers, its, our, ours, their, theirs,* and *whose.* So, do not confuse the following possessive pronouns and contractions that sound alike:

Possessive pronoun	**Contraction**
its	it's (it is)
your	you're (you are)
their	they're (they are)
whose	who's (who is)

Recent practice has discouraged using the apostrophe in forming **plurals of numerals, years, acronyms, and symbols.** The following sentences illustrate current usage as defined by the Modern Languages Association (MLA):

How many *8s* appear in that sequence of numbers?

In the early *1900s*, very few motor cars were evident in Canada.

At last count, 237 *MPs* favoured a major overhaul of the income tax system.

I use very few @s and &s in my writing.

DASHES

Dashes let you interrupt sentences to add information or to temporarily take the sentence in a different direction. A dash can operate by itself, but more often dashes work in pairs. A dash is longer than a hyphen; in word processing software you can control the length of the dash in many ways. For example, in MSWord click on the *Insert* pull-down menu, and select *Symbols,* where you will find dashes and shortcut keys for adding them.

Here are some examples of dashes in action:

Canadian NHL teams—*Montreal, Toronto, Edmonton, Calgary, Vancouver*—have all welcomed the strong Canadian dollar.

What could be more appropriate—*or more profitable*—than boosting the provincial royalties on oil and gas production?

Her P.R. best work—*and I say this with all sincerity*—has resulted from happy accidents, not from careful planning.

HYPHENS

Hyphens have several applications:

- They separate compound words such as the following:

self-assured   president-elect   well-dressed   three-year plan anti-government

However, they <u>do not</u> separate compound words in phrases such as the following:

poorly managed project   most appropriate solution   a half week's work
a more sensible approach

- They appear after the prefixes *all-*, *ex-*, *quasi-*, and *self-*:

all-inclusive   ex-army officer   quasi-official   self-employed

They <u>do not</u> appear after the prefixes *re, un,* and *inter*:

revamp   unconventional   interplay

- They are used when a prefix or suffix is added to a number or to a proper noun:

post-2001   pre-Raphaelite   Harper-like   pro-Canadian

- They are used when the vowel at the end of a prefix or suffix is the same as the first letter of the root word:

re-entry   anti-inflammatory

PARENTHESES AND BRACKETS

Like dashes, parentheses allow you interrupt a sentence to insert information. However, dashes emphasize surrounding statements, while parentheses provide interesting asides, examples, or short explanations. Here are some examples:

This grammar workbook (*the first of its type*) is designed to supplement the 4th Canadian edition of *Technical Communication.* [an aside]

Other grammar workbooks (*such as Grammar Unplugged*) focus on exercises, with little advice or direction about how to complete the exercises. [an example]

This workbook has been printed in black and white (to save costs) in an 8½ X 11 inch format (to accommodate the exercises). [explanations]

Legal writing often places parentheses around a numeral that follows a spelled-out number (*for a period of five (5) years*), but technical writing does not use this practice.

Brackets (also known as square brackets) have very few uses, mainly in academic writing. Academics use brackets to insert words into quotations. For example, here's a quotation used in this workbook:

"Everyone makes mistakes, but a "minor" slip-up in writing—such as the start date of an important conference—can cost companies time, money and credibility."

Here's how one might incorporate part of that quote into a sentence:

Author Ronnie Moore notes that "Everyone makes mistakes [that] . . . can cost companies time, money and credibility." [The conjunction *that* is inserted to help the sentence flow smoothly.]

You've no doubt noticed that this book uses brackets to insert explanatory notes following certain examples, as in the one above.

Brackets are also used to enclose the Latin term *sic* when you want to inform the reader that an error in a quote is in the original document you're quoting:

The review board was uncertain about its' [*sic*] role in resolving the dispute. [Like all foreign words, sic is italicized in the above example.]

UNDERLINING AND ITALICS

In the good old days of typewriters, **underlining** was used to highlight the names of books and other publications. Headings were also underlined. In the age of electronic word processing, those functions have been superseded by italics. The only job left for underlining these days is to emphasize words or phrases:

The earth's ozone layer is in <u>very deep</u> trouble.

The earth's <u>stratospheric</u> layer of ozone protects us from the sun's harmful ultraviolet rays.

The "ozone hole" refers to <u>a large and rapid decrease</u> in the numbers of ozone molecules.

As you can see in this book or in any book, magazine or newspaper, **bold type** has replaced underlining for headings. Meanwhile, *italics* have taken over many of the other tasks once assigned to underlining. Here are some of the uses for italics.

- Italics grace the names of ships, airplanes, and trains:

  the *Orient Express* the *Titanic* *Spirit of St. Louis* [the plane flown by Charles Lindbergh in the first transatlantic flight]

- Italics signal the titles of books, magazines, newspapers, films, television programs, CDs, and websites:

  Technical Communication *Maclean's* *The Globe And Mail* *Corner Gas*
  Music For the Hard of Thinking *The Weather Network*

- Italics accompany foreign words and the scientific names of plants and animals:

  laissez-faire *ad infinitum* *canis lupus* *iris versicolor Linné*

- Italics are used for words, letters, and numbers referred to as words:

  Words like *groovy* and *cool* no longer have the in-crowd clout they once had.
  Here's a hint: the letter *s* appears in the word four times.
  Out of respect for the great players who had made the numbers *9*, *99*, and *66* famous, Crosby chose *87*.

- Italics can also be used to emphasize certain words:

  None of his designs could be considered great work, *except* for his work on the Ford Mustang.

> **Caution:**
> If you use italics for purposes other than emphasis in a document, you should not use italics to emphasize certain words. Instead, you should underline the words or use bold face.

QUOTATION MARKS

Quotation marks enclose short bursts of quoted material, which is one of several uses for these marks. The following descriptions include advice and examples:

- Quotation marks surround words that are quoted exactly as they appear in the original document:

  Lynne Truss believes that the comma has become "a kind of scary grammatical sheepdog." (Truss, p. 79)

  She also says that, "As we will shortly see, the comma has so many jobs . . . that it tears about on the hillside of language. . . . " (Truss, p. 79)

  Note that the first sentence leads into the quotation without a comma and starts the quotation with a lower case letter, because Truss's partial sentence fits into the flow of the containing sentence. The second quotation is preceded by a comma and begins with a capital *A*, which is standard practice for quoting a full sentence. Note also that part of that second quotation has been deleted, and the omitted words have been replaced by **ellipses points** (. . .).

- Quotation marks do not enclose a longer quotation, which is sometimes defined as 50 words or longer (APA (American Psychological Association) style) and sometimes identified as longer than four lines (MLA style). These quotations are indented and single spaced, and do not use quotation marks:

  Lynne Truss makes a fierce case for paying attention to punctuation:

  > But after journeying through the world of punctuation, and after seeing what it can do, I am all the more convinced we should fight like tigers to preserve our punctuation, and we should start now. Who wants a blank map, for heaven's

> sake? There is more at stake than the way people read and write. Note the way the *Washington Post* news story explained the benefits of emailing: it "increased employees' productivity by 1.8 hours a day *because they took less time to formulate their thoughts.*" (Truss, p. 201)

The above quotation can use quotation marks within the quoted passage to denote words that Lynne Truss is quoting. However, if your short quote cites an internal quotation, you need to use the following technique, which employs regular quotation marks for the full McCourt quote and partial quotation marks for the bit he quotes:

> McCourt cites Lynne Truss's combative spirit: "Then she flings down the gauntlet: '. . . he would be ill-advised to repeat this ploy once my punctuation vigilantes are on the loose.' (Notice my masterly use of the ellipsis . . .)." Clearly, McCourt admires Truss's feisty nature. (Truss, p. xiii)

Right! Had enough? If so, proceed to the following exercises.

Practice Session—Punctuation

Circle the letter of the preferred choice in the following pairs or groups of sentences. You will find answers for these exercises on page 631.

1. a. Three persons attended the conference: Garth Barton, shipping and receiving department;
   Marcie Jones, Marketing Division; and Rita Kohlmann, general manager.
   b. Three persons attended the conference: Garth Barton, shipping and receiving department, Marcie Jones, Marketing Division, and Rita Kohlmann, general manager.
2. a. Our biggest challenge is: how to increase the bore size while retaining wall strength.
   b. Our biggest challenge is how to increase the bore size while retaining wall strength.
3. a. Attention, Mr. Francis
   b. Attention: Mr. Francis
   c. Attention—Mr. Francis
4. a. Four weeks is a long time to wait for the test results: Our competition might win the mineral rights in the interim.
   b. Four weeks is a long time to wait for the test results, our competition might win the mineral rights in the interim.
   c. Four weeks is a long time to wait for the test results; our competition might win the mineral rights in the interim.
5. a. I wonder, should we hire the experienced candidate?
   b. I wonder: should we hire the experienced candidate?
6. a. Mel's and Doug's laptops both need new hard drives.
   b. Mel and Doug's laptops both need new hard drives.
7. a. We are able to supply desktop computers, servers, monitors, printers, and maintenance and service.

b. We are able to supply desktop computers, servers, monitors, printers, and maintenance, and service.

8. a. Do you still watch Hockey Night In Canada, or do you find it boring?
   b. Do you still watch <u>Hockey Night In Canada</u> or do you find it boring?
   c. Do you still watch *Hockey Night In Canada*, or do you find it boring?
9. a. No one notices when we do excellent work, I wonder if they know we're here.
   b. No one notices when we do excellent work I wonder if they know we're here.
   c. No one notices when we do excellent work; I wonder if they know we're here.
10. a. Grammar used to be my most hated subject but that was before I took this course.
    b. Grammar used to be my most hated subject, but that was before I took this course.
    c. Either **a** or **b** would be acceptable; your choice is a matter of preference.

Improvement Exercises—Punctuation

The following sentences may contain errors in grammar, punctuation, and spelling. Underline each error and, in the space provided, correct the error. If a sentence contains no errors, write ***C*** in the space provided. You will find answers for these exercises on pages 631 and 632.

1. The Trackstick has over 1 MB of memory it can store months of travel information.
2. The Trackstick can record your exact routes, when you bike, hike or run.
3. The Trackstick has several applications, employee monitoring, vehicle tracking, speed control, photo tours, public safety, law enforcement
4. CEO Hernan Hesse says that the Trackstick II offers: "Upgraded features and accuracy compared to the original device.
5. The device receives signals from 24 orbiting Satellites, that precisely calculates its position on this planet.
6. The property is owned by Northern Tent Vacations, and the president carlo DeValero, the Company has authorized Green Consultants to make applications, for environmental approvals as required for development
7. Don't worry about the condition of it's transmission; the rest of the car is in really good shape.
8. The proposed wharf will be the same length and appearance it will use the same materials as the the adjacent wharf.
9. She orchestrated, and wrote, a major update of a maintenance manual.
10. Shortly after he graduated with a engineering diploma he develops a process for evaluating the quality of concrete as it is poured.
11. Prominent scientists, such as Henri Casselle have questioned the popular beliefs about global warming.
12. Art Burns' designs won the Granby Award for high density housing projects this year.
13. Well, their the ones who own the fishing rights so we should back off.
14. The Canadian dollar—as strong as it is has hurt U.S. exports that are paid in U.S. dollars.

15. The Leafs post 2005 regular season records leave a lot to be desired.
16. The rocket burst into flames upon re-entry into the earth's atmosphere.
17. Generation Y workers are not all that different from any other "generation" of workers; according to workplace analyst Barbara Moses.
18. This grammar workbook [which supplements your *Technical Communication* textbook] provides hundred's of exercises.
19. The Spanish say, hasta mañana and thats' exactly how I feel about wanting tomorrow to be here now!
20. On 10 June, 2004 a British Airways Boeing 777 suffered a serious fuel leak as it took of from heathrow airport.
21. Lack of documentation [or poor documentation] costs your company money.
22. The total cost of a single call answered by a help desk technician is, $20 or more depending on the length of the call.
23. Innovatia reports on the costs of distributing poorly written documentation on their website.
24. The Regional Aquatics Monitoring Program (r.a.m.p.) is an industry funded multi-stakeholder initiative.
25. The Athabasca river has high year to year fluctuations in its flow patterns.
26. "I'd be shocked if we learned that the cause of the flooding was one of the valves installed last week" Said Roger Desroches Managing Director.
27. Unconscious bias may cause some doctors to more likely recommend knee replacement surgery to men than to women according to a recent study.
28. Compared with men, women have the surgery when their arthritis is at a more advanced stage, this perhaps explains why women tend to do more poorly than men after knee replacement.
29. The water quality in the Athabasca river in the fall, 2005, was better than in the previous year.
30. On March 25 2008 The Globe and Mail carried a story about Biovails involvement in a series of frauds that distorted reports of earnings, and revenue.
31. The US Securities an Exchange Commission said Biovail executuives were "obsessed with meeting quarterly and annual earnings guidance" and, engaged in a "corrupt strategy" to do so.
32. In the United States Sirius Satellite Radio Inc. has taken over its rival XM satellite radio holdings inc. which means that the Canadian subsidiaries will also merge.
33. Montreals waterfront district once a bustling scene of shipping and manufacturing has almost become a ghost town however current plans for private and public investment promises to rejuvenate the area.
34. The Canadian fashion industry is not centered in one location rather its found in Winnipeg, Montreal Toronto and Vancouver and of all places in Vernon British Columbia, the home of Far West and Valhalla Pure.
35. Several media networks including traditional media companies like Forbes Inc. are trying to lure advertisers away from google inc. and yahoo Inc. by offering onestop shopping for ad placement.
36. Each of the consultants wrote a report about Riverbend Dams projected cost overruns
37. In this book the term "grammatical" refers to effective well formed phrases and sentences.

38. Rollover rates for SUVs are nearly twice that of sedans, and 30 percent higher than that of pickup truck's.
39. Brick walls can withstand considerably higher temperatures than concrete board walls.
40. Sundins career as a Toronto Maple Leaf appears to be ending which is really two bad.
41. Don't expect your cellular phone's to receive strong signal's in the far northern Arctic.
42. According to Rene Corbeils report the bridge is no longer safe but we knew that.
43. Blogging has real advantages for company's that possess clear goals and a workforce who's ambitions align with the companys'.
44. Guerrilla email [*www.guerilla-mail.com*] supplies disposable email addresses which expires after 15 minutes so you can register a software program or service but not receive spam later on.
45. A study by York university professor Dr Robert Kozinets shows that consumers of technology are governed partly by their view of the role that technology plays in they're lives and in society.

Document Critique—Punctuation

The following document may contain errors in grammar, capitalization, punctuation, or spelling. Underline all errors and identify them using standard proofreading marks. (See the Correction Symbols list on page 643.) You will find answers for this exercise on page 641.

NOTE *The following email responds to an email that appears on page 569 of this workbook.*

Billie Cochrane

From:	Corrine Maltais <cmaltais@on.gc.ca
To:	Billie Cochrane <bcochrane@on.gc.ca
Sent:	Monday, June 30, 2008 7.48 AM
Subject:	Conflicting responsibilities for The Georgian bay Project

Thank you for drawing my attention to your experiences on the great lake queen our research vessel I have spoke with captain Blair whose denying the accusation made by yourself and Jeannie Brock.

Let me respond to each of youre comments;

- On Monday, you say that captain Blair forced yourself and Jeannie to coil all the ropes and check for flaws. He says that he asked you to help himself and the two sailors but only for 15 minutes that's because they had a particularly difficult time with the anchor rope that somehow become kinked. He said that after you helped with the anchor rope which he appreciated by the way he saw you coiling some dock lines however he says he didnt order you to do that.
- He said that on Tuesday all six of you including himself cleaned the deck.

- On Friday, when you went to retrieve the collection equipment according to captain Blair he asked you to clean the cabin because you had left a number of items lying around during Wednesdays trip to parker point also he claims that you and Jeannie didn't clean up the galley after you prepared lunch, by the way the captain said that him and the crew appreciated you're offer to cook lunch on Wednesday and it was good too he said.

So heres where were at, I think we [you Jeannie myself and the captain] need to get together to discuss your formal roles in the research team, while your on board the great lake queen. We also need to talk about the things that team member do to help each others out and to work as a team – often these things go beyond the formal defined roles you know. Ill set up a meeting for this Wednesday before you sail to The Ramsey shoals. Watch for a email later today which will set the time we should meet on the boat I think.

By the way, you mentioned that your Professor had said that dieldrin and lindane are in decline in the great lakes. Probably his comments were based on a flawed study conducted by the Michigan Fish and Game league. Their results have since been shown to been based on a too small sample and solely on levels of those chemicals found in one fish species.

CHAPTER 27

Mechanics

Mechanical aspects of written documents—capitalization, abbreviations, numbers, spelling, spacing, graphics, punctuation—quietly help readers navigate pages, paragraphs, and sentences. Punctuation is discussed in this work book's previous section ; this section covers spelling, capitalization, abbreviations, and numbers.

Grammar at Work and Play: spelling does matter!

Tobi Gutt, a 21-year-old German, left his German home on December 30, 2006 for Australia, dressed in T-shirt and shorts for the Australian summer and looking forward to seeing his girlfriend. Unfortunately, he had typed in "Sidney" instead of "Sydney" on an online booking form. He ended up in Sidney, Montana, 13,000 kilometres off course, with stops in Portland, Oregon and Billings, Montana.

After three cold days in his summer clothes, he received €600 from home and he was able to book a new ticket to Australia.

SPELLING

English includes words from many sources. Here's the result of one attempt to determine the percentages of English words derived from the contributing sources of our language:

> . . . the result of a computerized survey of roughly 80,000 words in the old *Shorter Oxford Dictionary* (3rd edition) was published in *Ordered Profusion* by Thomas Finkenstaedt and Dieter Wolff (1973). They reckoned the proportions as follows:

- Latin, including modern scientific and technical Latin: 28.24%
- French, including Old French and early Anglo-French: 28.3%

- Old and Middle English, Old Norse, and Dutch: 25%
- Greek: 5.32%
- No etymology given: 4.03%
- Derived from proper names: 3.28%

(Source: ***AskOxford.com.*** Accessed April 1, 2008 at *http://www.askoxford.com/asktheexperts/faq/aboutenglish/proportion?view=uk)*

Each one of the above sources brought its spelling conventions and sound combinations, so it's no wonder that English can be difficult to spell. For example, the "eau" in bureau is pronounced the same as "oe" in *hoe* and the same as "ow" in *grow*, and the same as "o" in *holocaust* or *oration*. Those words come, respectively, from French, Germanic, Greek and Latin origins. But words can have the same origin and still require wide variations in the letters chosen to represent sounds. For example consider the "ough" combination, which is pronounced differently in *through* (oo), *trough* (off), *rough* (uff), *bough* (ow), and *bought* (ott)! All five of those words have Germanic origins.

Unlike most other European languages, English does not employ phonetic spelling, despite attempts to introduce "logic" to spelling English. (Noah Webster did have limited success, starting with his dictionary in 1828. Through his efforts, American spelling includes *plow*, *threw*, and *check*, among others.) The real problem with English spelling, though, is that we use a 26-letter alphabet (originally created for Latin) that needs to somehow represent 40 distinct English sounds.

So, there's no easy answer for spelling English, especially for Canadians who waver between British spelling (*programme* and *centre*) and American spelling (*program* and *center*). Spell check helps to some extent, particularly if you set the default language to Canadian English. (In MS Word, click on "Tools," then on "Language," and finally on "Set Language," which will let you choose from among several variations of English.)

We can teach ourselves the correct spelling of many key words. The following lists are designed to guide your efforts.

Commonly Misspelled Words

acceptable	category	dumbbell	height
accidentally	cemetery	embarrass (ment)	hierarchy
accommodate	changeable	equipment	humorous
acquire	collectable	exhilarate	ignorance
acquit	column	exceed	immediate
a lot	committed	existence	independent
amateur	conscience	experience	indispensable
apparent	conscientious	fiery	inoculate
argument	conscious	foreign	intelligence
atheist	consensus	gauge	its/it's
believe	definite(ly)	grateful	jewellery
bellwether	discipline	guarantee	judgment
calendar	drunkenness	harass	kernel (colonel)

leisure	minuscule	possession	relevant
liaison	mischievous	precede	restaurant
library	misspell	principal/principle	rhyme
license	neighbour	privilege	rhythm
lightning	noticeable	pronunciation	schedule
maintenance	occasionally	publicly	separate
manoeuvre	occurrence	questionnaire	sergeant
medieval	pastime	receive/receipt	supersede
memento	perseverance	recommend	their/they're/there
millennium	personnel	referred	
miniature	playwright	reference	

Commonly Confused Words

adverse unfavourable, bad	**averse** strongly disliking or opposed to
assure pledge an outcome	**ensure** make an outcome certain **insure** secure the payment of money
affect make a difference to	**effect** a result (or cause a result)
ambiguous open to interpretation	**ambivalent** having mixed feelings
amoral not concerned with morality	**immoral** not conforming to accepted moral standards
appraise assess	**apprise** inform
augur sign of a likely outcome	**auger** a tool used for boring or conveying (as in a grain auger)
censure express strong disapproval	**censor** suppress unacceptable parts of (a book, film, etc.)
climactic forming a climax	**climatic** relating to climate
complacent smug and self-satisfied	**complaisant** willing to please
complement enhance by extra features	**compliment** an expression of praise or congratulation
continuous without interruption	**continual** happening frequently, with intervals between
council an administrative or advisory body	**counsel** advice or guidance
councillor a member of a council	**counsellor** counsels re: personal or psychological problems
credible believable, convincing	**creditable** deserving acknowledgement and praise
definite certain, sure	**definitive** decisive and with authority
defuse remove a fuse or reduce the danger or tension	**diffuse** spread over a wide area
desert a waterless area	**dessert** the sweet course
discreet careful not to attract attention	**discrete** separate, distinct
envelop wrap up, cover, or surround completely	**envelope** used to enclose a letter or document
fawn a young deer, light brown colour	**faun** a Roman deity that is part man, part goat

grisly causing horror or revulsion	**grizzly** from *grizzled*; refers to the bear's white-tipped fur
hoard a store of something valuable	**horde** a disparaging term for a large group of people
its possessive form of it	**it's** short for either **it is** or **it has**
loath reluctant, unwilling	**loathe** dislike greatly
loose unfasten or set free	**lose** cease to have or become unable to find
luxuriant rich and profuse in growth	**luxurious** very comfortable and extravagant
marital of marriage	**martial** of war
ordinance an authoritative order	**ordnance** guns or munitions
palate the roof of the mouth	**palette** an artist's board for mixing colours
pedal move by means of pedals	**peddle** a verb meaning sell (goods)
principal first in order of importance	**principle** a basis of a system of thought or belief
proscribe condemn or forbid	**prescribe** issue a medical prescription; recommend an action
stationary not moving or changing	**stationery** paper and other writing materials
story a tale or account	**storey** is a floor of a building
tortuous full of twists and turns	**torturous** characterized by pain or suffering
who's contraction of *who is* or *who has*	**whose** possessive form of *who*
you're contraction of *you are*	**your** possessive form of *you*

Commonly Misused Words and Phrases

alot	There's no such word; use *much* or many. However, there is a word spelled *allot*, which means assign, allocate, distribute. A *lot* is considered slang.
could of	The phrase should be *could have*. (Use the helping verb *have* with would, should, might, and could.)
decimate	This word means reduce by one-tenth. If you mean destroy or reduce to nothing, use the words *destroy* or *obliterate*.
disinterested	This word means unbiased and impartial. If you mean bored or having no interest, use the word *uninterested*.
irregardless	There's no such word. Use *regardless*.
less	Use less for uncountable quantities such as *less time* or *less water*. Use fewer for countable quantities: *fewer* birds, *fewer* pages, *fewer fans at the game*.
media	The plural form of the singular, *medium*. Don't write, "The media is trying to improve his chances of becoming our next Prime Minister," as if the word *media* represents a single entity.

real	This adjective should not be used as an adverb, as in he's *real* intelligent. Use the adverb *really* to modify another adjective.
reason is because	Use *The reason* is *that* I've become very interested in grammar.
since, as, for the reason that	*Since, as,* and *for the reason that* are often substituted for because, especially at the beginning of sentences. *For the reason that* is wordy and awkward, so it should not be used. *Since* and *as* are poor substitutes for *because*; each word has other, much more prominent meanings. *Since* is a preposition and conjunctive adverb that helps state time relationships (*since* I left college; *since* Thursday afternoon). *As* operates as a preposition, conjunction, or pronoun to express comparisons or processes (*as* you know; *as* he walked along the beach; *as* far *as* I can see; as a matter if fact; such provinces *as* Alberta). **Here's a sensible suggestion: whenever you mean *because*, write *because*, no matter where it appears in the sentence.**

Capitalization

Capitals appear at the beginning of these word groups:

- **Complete sentences**:

  In English, all sentences begin with a capital letter.

- **Formal statement following a colon:**

  She tries to instil a strong work ethic in her children, by often declaiming her favourite saying: *If* it's worth doing, it's worth overdoing.

- **Complete sentence quoted within a sentence:**

  He retorted with a stern command: *Do* not even think about leaving this office until you have completed the entire report.

- **Proper nouns and adjectives**:

  For a full list of capitalized proper nouns and adjectives, consult a grammar handbook such as the *Simon & Schuster Handbook for Writers.*Here's a sampling of capitalized words and phrases:

Queen Elizabeth II	*Grammar at Work*	Member of Parliament Fred McMurray	
Norwegian skiers	Eastern Canada	the Maritimes	Hockey Canada

Selkirk Mountains	planet Earth	Hospital for Sick Kids		McDonald's
Acura RDX	Physics 111	Humboldt Broncos		Passover
World War III	the Quiet Revolution	the Koran	NAFTA	MS Word
Wood Products Division		Acer computers (but Acer Inc.)		

NOTE *Some words pertaining to the World Wide Web (which has retained its status as a proper noun along with its capitalization) seem to have lost their proper noun status. Examples include internet and web (when used in phrases such as* internet search, *web presence* and *web page). The term Web site seems to have morphed into website. However, the Web retains the capital letter when it acts as an abbreviated version of the* World Wide Web.

Abbreviations

Although abbreviations often appear in tables, lists, charts and forms, you should use them sparingly in sentences. Here are a few common abbreviations:

- **Titles:**

  Mr. (Mister) Mrs. or Ms. (Mistress) Dr. (Doctor) Miller Ltd. (Limited)

- **Initials used as names:**

  RCMP NATO UNICEF PVR RRSP

- **Names of provinces and states:**

  Postal code designations for provinces and states use Canada Post's abbreviations (BC, AB, SK, WA, and so on). Note, however, that the Canadian branch of the IEEE (Institute of Electrical and Electronics Engineers, Inc.) prefers standard abbreviations (B.C., Alta., Sask., Wash., and so on) within documents. Better yet, write out the name of the province or state.

Numbers

IEEE Canada's rule of thumb for numbers is to write out the numbers one through nine, and to use Arabic numerals for 10 and above. That rule works well for any technical document.

Here are some other usage hints.

- When a number appears at the beginning of a sentence, write the number:

  Forty-four cartons of 18-year-old single malt whiskey have disappeared from our warehouse.

- Use numerals for numbers one through nine if they're part of a list with larger numbers:

  The results pleased the instructor: the final grades included 4 marks of 90 percent or better, 12 marks from 80 percent to 89 percent, and 14 marks from 63 percent to 79 percent.

- Use numerals for percentages. Write percent in normal text, but use % in tables, forms, and charts.

  Sales have jumped 45.5 percent compared to last June's figures.

- When two numbers appear next to each other in a sentence, spell out the first number and use an Arabic numeral for the second:

  We've installed fourteen 8-foot rolls of C350 turf reinforcement mat.

  Some style guides and business organizations prefer to use a numeral for the figure that is larger or more difficult to spell:

  Along the Corman Spillway's banks, Melrose Environmental has installed 274 eight-foot rolls of C350 turf reinforcement mat.

- Use numerals for dates, page numbers, ages, times with a.m. or p.m. designations, monetary figures, mileage figures, and addresses (but write out the names of streets numbered less than 100):

  29 March 2009 page 3 12.35 a.m. $3.09 123 kilometres
  1245 Monroe Avenue 78A Forty-fifth Street

- Use numerals for decimals and precise measurements:

  456.995 56.1 milligrams 87.16 kilos 16 3/4

- Use decimal points for dollar amounts only if cents are included:

  $23.78 $24 $1.48 million $328,098 $16,453.98

Proofreading Hints

Errors are not necessarily easy to detect, even when you know how to spell the words you're using or you know how to use commas effectively. Grammatical errors and unclear phrasing are particularly hard to identify when we've just finished phrasing a document. The following hints try to compensate, then, for our natural tendencies to miss certain kinds of errors, inconsistencies, and poor phrasing.

1. Delay the revision/editing/proofreading process as long as possible, so that you can return to the document with a fresh perspective. Even a 10-minute break will help you detect errors that you will not see at the moment you complete a draft.

2. Proofread more than once.
3. Have others proofread your material.
4. Proofread and revise content and structure first. Then, look at grammar, sentence structure, punctuation, and mechanics.
5. Isolate the spelling and other mechanics from context. (For example, read backwards or highlight random sections.)
6. If you have a tendency to misspell (or miss-key) a certain word, use your word processor's search function to find every placement of that word in the document. Also, use that search function to locate every time the word *this* appears; then ensure that every placement of *this* is followed by a noun or noun phrase. (In MS Word, click on the *Edit* pull-down menu and select *Find*. Then, key in the word or phrase you wish to find, and click on *Find All* and every instance of that word or phrase in the document will be highlighted. It's magic!)
7. Highlight paragraphs or other short sections on a computer screen.
8. Don't trust automated proofreading software, which wouldn't notice if you've used *their* instead of *they're.*
9. How to detect errors:
   - Use a grammar handbook to check all aspects of grammar, punctuation, and mechanics that you are not certain you know well.
   - Use a thesaurus and dictionary to find exactly the right word for each meaning.
   - Use lists of commonly misspelled words, commonly confused words, and commonly misused words (pages 586–588 in this workbook) to help with word choices and spelling.

Practice Session—Mechanics

The following sentences may contain errors in grammar, punctuation, spelling, capitalization, abbreviations, and numbers usage. Underline each error and, in the space provided, correct the error. If a sentence contains no errors, write ***C*** in the space provided. You will find answers for these exercises on page 634.

1. Great chef's can prepare Low Calorie meals that taste evrey bit as good as meals loaded with calories.
2. 14 students came late to the exam they where denied entrance to the exam hall.
3. Boy Im glad I didnt have to study latin in school.
4. The concensus amoung my friends is that we should take off the 2009–2010 year so that we can live and work at the whistler resort during the 2010 olympic games.
5. I went to see a councillor about my grades, that were to low. Theyt said that I should just work harder.
6. Whole areas of Thailands beach front tourist resorts and locals homes were wiped out by the soonamee in December, 2004.
7. The Thai government reported eitght thousand four hundred and fifty-seven confirmed deaths in the wake of the soonamee caused by the 2004 Indian Ocean earthquake on 26 December, 2004.
8. More than three years after the massive earthquake and subsequent soonamees on 26 December, 2004, that devastated countries around the Indian Ocean, recovery programmes undertaken by Red Cross and it's partner national

societies continue to provide assistance to those communities most affected by the disaster.

9. Canadians were particululaly generous in providing aid to the countries affected by that disaster.
10. The R.C.M.P. face criticism for several resent insidents which have eroded trust in our national police force.

Improvement Exercises—Mechanics

The following sentences may contain errors in grammar, punctuation, spelling, capitalization, abbreviations, and numbers usage. Underline each error and, in the space provided, correct the error. If a sentence contains no errors, write ***C*** in the space provided. You will find answers for these exercises on pages 635 and 636.

1. This MP3 player has over three MB of memory it can store thousands of songs.
2. 46% of all hockey games that go to Overtime are settled in the first 5 minutes of the 1st Overtime period.
3. The Acura mdx offers a three-hundred Horsepower motor.
4. The office has ordered 3 Dell Inspiron one five-two-five laptops for field work.
5. Dell offer twenty-four technical support fore all its' products.
6. Although dell is the most prominent of the On-line computer sales company's there are several other similar outfits in operating in Canada.
7. The client responded with a very negative assessment of our proposed approach: this proposal fails to meet even our most basic requirements.
8. Since the Royal Banke Cup was inaugurated in 1996, two teams have only won the cup twice; the Aurora Tigers (2007 and 2004) and the Vernon Vipers (1996 and 1999).
9. The North American Free Trade Agreement (nafta) has supporters and detractors in all 3 countries Canada, the United States and Mexico.
10. Dr. Judy diSantos, MD is a leading expert on the affects of workplace second-hand smoke.
11. He is a prime candidate for our quality control position, as he had similar experience in the steel industry.
12. The structure was completely decimated when the roof beams gave way under the snow load.
13. They should of reported the cracks that were developing in the support beams.
14. The 3 main principals of successful road construction are illustrated by the Howth project.
15. Always insure that the lock down lever has been properly set at the three o'clock position.
16. In Canada there are four hundred and thirty-four post-seconadry colleges and universities accredited by provincial governments.
17. Beside the public funded and accredited institutions, 49 for profit institutions have been authorized to grant specific credentials.
18. If you know wear to look youll find all kinds of scholarships and burrsories available to Canadian and foreign students too.

19. The AUCC [association of universities and colleges of Canada] administer more than 150 scholarships, fellowship and internship programs.
20. Canadian's standard of living has long depended on its competitiveness in a International trading economy where our natural resources afford an advantage
21. Insuring that postsecondary educational opportunities are affordable and that no qualified individual is denied access because of financial circumstances.
22. For the reason because of greater competition perhaps editing rates are considerably less in the United Staes than in Canada.
23. Universities have received roughly $11 billion in federal research funding since 1997, most of that flowing through research granting councils.
24. In 2006 The University of Toronto enrolled over sixty-four thousand full time students.
25. The highest 2007–2008 college and university tuition fees were at BCs Trinity Western University at $16500.
26. York University's course handout kits are classified carbon neutral, that means they are produced using environmentally-responsible printing practices that include incorporating locally produced papers manufactured using sound forestry practices and increased recycled fibre content.
27. A carbon footprint measures the impact our activities have on the environment in terms of the amount of greenhouse gases we produce, measured in carbon dioxide units.
28. Virtually anybody can make biodiesel, as it is so easy you can even make it in your own kitchen.

Document Critique—Mechanics

The following draft document may contain errors in grammar, capitalization, punctuation, abbreviations, numbers, or spelling. Underline all errors and identify them using standard proofreading marks. (See the Correction Symbols list on the page 643.) You will find answers for this exercise on page 636.

NOTE *The following propaganda piece responds to material found at the* Carbon Footprint *website, http://www.carbonfootprint.com/index.html. Assume that the following draft is being prepared to discredit* Carbon Footprint *and other players in the movement that seeks to convince Canadians that climate change is caused by human activity.*

Disclaimer:
The opinions in this sample document are not necessarily those of the author or publisher of this grammar handbook.

Lets examine some of the claims made by environmental opportinists like Carbon Footprint, a company that makes money from selling carbon offsets.

Claim number one:

> "At Carbon Footprint, our belief is that climate change will only be addressed if each and every one of us takes responsible steps to **REDUCE** their CO_2 emissions."

I've been looking for evidence that CO_2 emmissions one, actually cause global warming and that two, global warming is necessarily a bad thing. Here's what I've found at their website: I see scientific evidence that temperatures have been rising (point seven degrees celcuis in the past 100 years, world wide) and that glaciers have been melting (twenty-thousand square kilometres of Arctic ice in 30 years). But I don't see any evidence that released CO_2 has had anything to do with it. Yes, the increase in CO_2 emissions has been linked with warming, with evidence of those patterns going back four hundred thousand years but where's the connection? One has to prove **correlation**; not just timing. I mean you could just as easily say that periodic global warming cause greater CO_2 emmissions and that interspersed global cooling caused lower CO_2 emmissions.

Claim number two:

> "Even though the hole in the ozone layer doesn't contribute to global warming We should still be concerned about the affects of increased UV light."

Irregardless of their claims Carbon Footprint hasn't proved this either. Why should we just take their word for it? The company doesn't provide no evidence at their website that the "hole in the ozone layer doesn't contribute to global warming". None, Zilch.

The important thing to remember about Carbon Footprint:

> "From this web site only—you can offset your CO_2 emissions while you shop on-line. Every purchase you make on-line via the links on this page will count towards our carbon offset programme—including reforestation and clean energy projects globally."

So, we see what Carbon Fooprints all about—money! When they make you feel guilty enough, then you buy their services and you shop with their partners, like eBay and Amazon books and napster. Or buy their Ultra bright windup Eco Torch.

Don't be fooled by what the media gives you; don't be fooled by outfits Carbon Footprint in the business of selling guilt about global warming. Let's put are energy into dealing with the impacts of warming instead of sucumbing to the arrogant human asumption that we can cause a whole planet to change it's climate.

CHAPTER 28

Vocabulary and Style

The headline in a news story reads, "Mad Students Target Teacher." The story is about nine grade three students who hatched a plot to kidnap and possibly kill their teacher, all because the teacher scolded one of them for standing on a chair. Were they indeed "mad" (i.e. insane) or just angry? Legally, the distinction is extremely important, of course. Possibly the headline writer deliberately used the slang version of *mad* to appeal to readers, or perhaps the headline writer does not know the differences between *mad* and *angry*.

In technical writing, word choice can dramatically affect the reader's perception of the message. Key words also provide critical information, so writers should choose their words carefully. At the same time, technical writers must write concise, focused prose: wordy, flamboyant phrasing does not impress the readers of proposals, reports, manuals, and business correspondence.

CHOOSING THE RIGHT WORDS

Let's be clear about why people read business and technical writing. Workplace readers seek pertinent information, logical analysis, and sensible conclusions and recommendations. That's all. They don't expect entertainment or in-depth philosophy.

Grammar at Work: clear communication is critical

"When I was a student, I remember my instructors telling us about the importance of concise and accurate communication. Despite this good advice, I didn't attempt to develop good oral or writing skills, always letting interest in other areas take priority. During my working years I continued to see this same mistake in many others, particularly in technically educated people who in other ways were very capable. . . . I still get frustrated when attempting to convey ideas and concepts to others. However, clear, persuasive phrasing has been absolutely critical in my career."

*—**Dennis Willoughby,** P.E., retired Director of Operations for IPSCO's Tubular Division, and a Consultant who advises re: equipment design and product flow for new pipe mills*

Choosing the right words is essential to meeting workplace readers' needs. Here are several factors that should govern your vocabulary choices:

Choose the Right Technical Level for your reader or range of readers. Pages 28–30 of *Technical Communication* illustrate three levels of technicality, highly technical, semi-technical, and non-technical. The following example lists three descriptions of an automotive tire, Nokian's Hakkapeliitta WR "All-Weather Plus" product.

Non-technical level: this introduction to a consumer review is aimed at consumers

The Nokian WR is a contradiction in terms: it is an all-season tire that carries the severe snow rating from Transport Canada. It is the only all-season tire to achieve that rating—even many winter tires don't have it.

Semi-technical level: this expert review is aimed at knowledgeable consumers

The WR features a silica rubber compound and an 'arrowhead' directional tread pattern that is designed to expel water and snow while allowing the tread blocks to remain in contact with the ground. Its "driving safety indicator" displays numbers in the tire's tread, to gauge the tire's remaining life.

Highly-technical level: this description is aimed at technically-trained tire reps and wholesalers

The WR All-Weather PLUS is made of an HD silica compound that offers excellent grip. Lateral grip numbers vary from 0.82g to 0.875g, which rank the WR in the 91st percentile and higher. Its hysteresis rolling resistance (HRR) has been calculated by 3D finite element modeling to be less than 68% of the norm. The tire features an 'arrowhead' directional tread pattern that expels water and snow while the tread blocks continue to contact the ground. A unique feature called the "driving safety indicator" incorporates numbers displayed along the centre of the tire's tread in addition to the usual wear bars. A new tire's numbers read "8 6 4" indicating the number of millimetres of tread depth remaining. As the tire wears and the higher numbers disappear, drivers can gauge how much life is left in their tires. A proprietary information pin provides temperature readings at road height. The tire carries the Severe Service Emblem. Sizes range from 235/75R15 (6.5 rim) to 275/40R20XL (9.5 in. in rim). Median tire weight is 32.5 lbs. and tread depth is 14/32.

Use Precise, Accurate Phrasing

Don't write "the reset button *on the dash*" when your reader needs to know the exact location of that button (as in "the reset button *3.4 cm. to the right of the ignition slot*").

Here are some other examples of vague or abstract phrasing that needs to be more precise:

Abstract Term	Precise Version
a luxurious condominium	the condominium has imported tile, glass walls, large rooms with views of the lake, and a built-in audio system
the area has an abundance of old growth trees	the south-facing slopes of the area are covered primarily by Douglas Fir (Cascade dry cool variant); 90 percent of the observed specimens stand 100' or more.

(Continued)

Abstract Term	Precise Version
the walkway is a disaster	several of the support pillars have been washed away and over half the planking has rotted to the point that it will not support loads over 100 pounds
the computers are outdated, and they need replacement	The computers have only 256 Kb of RAM and hard drives of 15 GB or less. Our current editing tasks require a minimum of 3 GB Dual Channel RAM, 200 GB hard drives, duo core processors, and 768MB graphics cards.

Maintain an Objective Tone

You can write objective prose partly through identifying your physical point of view:

> The downflow meter is positioned in the pipe, underneath the bridge deck. We recorded its position and current condition through a camcorder that we manoeuvred into position at the northeast end of the pipe. Sufficient light was provided by using the camcorder's built-in LED light.

Also, maintain objectivity in your phrasing:

> *Don't write:* Clearly the crew is woefully understaffed.
> *Write:* The five-person crew is four days behind schedule, even though they have worked 10-hour days; three additional workers are required.

Using third person helps achieve an objective tone. The first person seems natural and sensible for reporting direct observations or actions (as in "we installed battery-powered smoke alarms in each hallway of the four-storey residence"). However, first person is not always necessary and may even intrude, as in the following example, where it would be better to focus on the recommendations, not on who is recommending the actions:

> In this report, *we have outlined* all the necessary measures that Glendale Developments will need to follow to develop this site, including the design of a storm water system.
>
> In brief, *our recommendations according to land development guidelines are as follows:*

Here's a more objective version, which sounds more logical and less prone to personal opinion:

> *This report outlines* all the necessary measures the Glendale Developments will need to follow to develop this site, including the design of a storm water system.
>
> In brief, *land development guidelines have led to the following recommendations:*

Avoid Pompous Language

In school, you may have been rewarded for using the biggest words you could find, but business and technical readers won't necessarily be impressed.

> **Grammar at Work: use the right word, not the biggest word**
>
> "...intelligent people use their large vocabulary only to give clear, exact meaning—never to show off. Big minds use little words; little minds use big words."
>
> *—From "Clear Writing: Ten Principles of Clear Statement"*
> *© the Gunning-Mueller Clear Writing Institute, accessed at*
> *https://muextension.missouri.edu/explore/comm/cm0201.htm*

If two words express essentially the same meaning, always choose the word with fewer syllables. (Write *use* instead of *utilize*, or *mislead* instead of *prevaricate*.)

Remember that *so* means the same as *accordingly*, that *start* or *begin* could replace *activate*, and that *get* means the same as *acquire*.

We're talking about **plain language**, the rallying cry a worldwide movement that tries to make government documents, legal statements, scientific descriptions, business disclosures, and technical reports easy to read and understand.

> **Grammar at Work: why use plain language?**
>
> "Plain language results in end products that meet readers' needs. Plain language is a courtesy to your readers, telling them what they want to know quickly and clearly. Plain language doesn't just happen. It is planned. Planning includes understanding the subject, determining what you want to achieve with the document, and knowing who all the readers are, inside and outside your organization."
>
> *—Judith Whitehead, Vankellers Editorial and Writing Services*

The Practice Exercises on page 607 provide you with a chance to choose plain language alternatives for pompous phrasing. If you're interested in learning more about plain language, visit these online resources:

The U.S. Securities and Exchange Commission has placed its Plain English Handbook at *http://www.sec.gov/pdf/handbook.pdf* (highly recommended!)

British writers have led the way in the fight against pompous, garbled writing: *http://www.plainenglish.co.uk/*

In the U.S., Bill Clinton and Al Gore promoted plain English. Their efforts have led to this initiative: *http://www.plainlanguage.gov/*

Avoid Over-Reliance on Jargon

Every line of study and work has its specialized vocabulary, its jargon. Such terms save time and promote understanding, as long as the terms are understood by the reader, not just by the writer. Even then, jargon can be overused and can get downright silly. For example, a Canadian engineer invented the term, *modular vertical retaining device*, which he promptly reduced to the acronym *MVRD*, for obvious reasons. Can you guess what he meant in phrases such as "the MVRD in the southwest quadrant"? He meant "the southwest wall"! That's right; he thought "wall" was too simple a word for an educated person to use.

On the other hand, jargon terms like SAIL (the Stanford Artificial Intelligence Lab) has a very specific meaning for people in artificial intelligence research. These days, you can keep up specialized vocabularies through such sites as *Cool Jargon of the Day* (where I found the SAIL term) or Jon Storm's list of computer jargon at *http://www.jonstorm.com/glossary/*

Please **avoid useless jargon** of the type immortalized in Philip Broughton's buzzword system. Examples include *systematized third-generation hardware* and *balanced incremental programming.* We can't reproduce his system here, but you can find it at these sites:
http://nathancreative.com/buzzphrase.html
http://www.acronymfinder.com/buzzgen.asp
http://www.copywriting-on-demand.com/buzzword-generator.htm

Honeywell has taken the systematic buzzword projector a step further. The Simplified Modular Prose Writing System (SIMP) is described at *http://www.copywriting-on-demand.com/THINK-SIMP-LY.pdf*

WRITING CONCISELY

Busy workplace readers appreciate concise, readable documents that don't waste their time. This workbook demonstrates on pages 556 and 557 that **short sentences** make reading easier. Now we're going to see how to trim unnecessary words <u>within</u> sentences.

Avoid Unnecessary Words in Phrases

Many phrases can be simplified with no loss in meaning:

Wordy:	*Concise:*
an innumerable number of tiny veins	countless tiny veins
at this point in time	now
bright green in color	green (or, bright green)
absolutely complete	complete
during the time that	when, during
completely free	free

See the Practice Exercises on page for more phrases that you can trim.

Avoid Unnecessary Qualifiers

Wordy:	*Concise:*
personally, I believe	I believe
very unique	unique
owing to the fact that	because

Use Active Verbs Instead of Linking Verbs

Wordy:	*Concise:*
I am of the opinion that	I believe

There are not many people who can present a report on this subject in so precise a manner.

Few people can report this subject so precisely.

Avoid *there is, there are,* and *it is* Constructions

Wordy: There is a short in the cable that can interfere with signal splitting.
Concise: A short in the cable can interfere with signal splitting.

Wordy: There are several reasons why we can not hire this candidate.
Concise: Several reasons prevent our hiring this candidate

Wordy: It is necessary for them to change the study method.
Concise: They must change the study method.

Place Action in Verbs; Axe Extra Verbs

In the following examples the real action lies buried in a noun or adjective.
Wordy: Give me a call.
Concise: Call me.

Wordy: Provide a recommendation for...
Concise: Recommend...

Wordy: Ralph is a man who enjoys a task that is challenging.
Concise: Ralph enjoys a challenging task.

Wordy: The technologist has the job of translating the engineer's designs into working plans. [Here, the action is placed in the object.]
Concise: Technologists translate engineering designs into working plans.

Avoid Unnecessary Prepositions

Wordy: under the impression that...
Concise: believing that...

Wordy: at the present time
Concise: now

Wordy: in the event that
Concise: if

Wordy: The editor *of* the company newsletter recently received an award *for* writing.
Concise: The company newsletter editor recently received a writing award.

WRITING CLEARLY

This workbook's "Basic Grammar" section illustrates techniques that make connections clear:

- Make each pronoun refer to one easily-identified antecedent (page 524).
- Ensure that each pronoun agrees with its antecedent (pages 525–526).
- Always write a noun or noun phrase immediately after a reference pronoun such as *this, that, these,* or *those* (pages 524–525).

Grammar at Work: don't waste words

When writing a business plan,

- Avoid unnecessary jargon
- Economize on words
- Use short crisp sentences and bullet points
- Concentrate on relevant and significant issues
- Break the text into numbered paragraphs, sections etc.

—From PlanWare's Plan Write Business Planner website, at http://www.business-planware.com/business-plan-when.htm

- Use the right pronoun case (pages 525, 526, and 527).
- Make subjects and verbs agree (pages 533–534)

Then, the "Sentence Grammar" chapter shows how to create clear, readable sentences, using techniques such as the following:

- Write straightforward SVO and SVC sentences (pages 556–557).
- Keep subjects and verbs together (page 560).
- Avoid overlong sentence openers (pages 559–560).
- Avoid faulty coordination (page 564).
- Avoid faulty parallelism (page 564).

Finally, the "Punctuation" chapter shows how commas and other punctuation are so important in conveying your exact meaning.

You should also **avoid ambiguous phrasing** such as

Most students will party on Friday night.

Does the above sentence mean that the students will go to a party this Friday night, or do they "party" every Friday night? And who are "most students"? Most of the students at a particular college or university, or students in general? And would those students be at Canadian schools, or is the writer referring to all North American students?

Here are some possible meanings that the writer had in mind:

Most students whom I know party every Friday night.
Most of the students in my dorm are going to Friday night's party at Nevin Hall.
Most Canadian university students relax at Friday night parties.

Yes, I know that the context in which the sentence appears could probably help a reader get some sense of the writer's intended meaning, but why should the reader be forced to engage in detective work? Ambiguity works well in poetry—it helps enrich the bounty of possible meanings that bounce off each other—but ambiguity is a definite "no-no" in technical writing. Consider these statements:

All steel is prone to rust. [Under what conditions? For example, does steel rebar rust when it's encased in concrete? And does "all steel" include stainless steel?]

Set up the monitoring station at the corner of 8th Street and Monroe. [That intersection has four possible setup locations—SE, SW, NE, and NW.]

Write Readable Paragraphs

Most of the paragraphs we write are standard body paragraphs that provide information, description, and analysis. Technical subjects can become rather dense with detail, so clear paragraph development is essential. Here are four critical aspects of readable paragraphs:

1. Each paragraph must deal with only one subject or a specific aspect of a subject.
2. Each paragraph requires a topic statement that identifies the paragraph's topic and signals the purpose of the paragraph. That topic statement might require one sentence, two sentences, or perhaps just part of a sentence. (Pages 117–119 in the 4th Canadian edition *of Technical Communication* discuss topic statements.)
3. Each paragraph should use the pattern that best suits its content and purpose. Examples of patterns that suit technical topics appear on pages 121–126 in *Technical Communication.*
4. Transitional words and phrases link ideas within a paragraph.

In the following paragraph, the topic statement is underlined and the transitions are bolded.

> For the Text Enrichment Site (TES) that will accompany the 4th Canadian edition of Technical Communication, <u>I propose a new **Job Search** section that includes *some old and some new features*</u>. *Previously posted material* includes an application package, *but* that package *now* forms the basis for an exercise that asks students to evaluate the applicant's letter and résumé. *Other new material* would include a list of online resources for job seekers, a sample "compliance matrix" for a specific job search, and a hyperlinked electronic job search portfolio that includes streaming video. *I'm particularly excited about the electronic portfolio* because no other TES that I've seen has this kind of business writing sample.

Now here's a paragraph that doesn't really have an effective topic statement, partly because it tries to cover two topics. It also lacks transitions and it seems to wander off topic.

> Smoke can contain several types of particles. Fires exposed to abundant oxygen burn at high temperature and with small amount of smoke produced. Smoke particles might be mostly composed of ash, or even condensed aerosol of water. High temperatures produce nitrogen oxides. Sulfur content yields sulfur dioxide. Carbon and hydrogen are almost completely oxidized to carbon dioxide and water. Fires burning with lack of oxygen can produce many compounds. These are often toxic. When carbon doesn't completely burn, it produces carbon monoxide. Nitrogen-containing materials can yield hydrogen cyanide, ammonia, and nitrogen oxides. Fires are often dangerous to fight.

The following edited version now includes two paragraphs, each with its own topic. Each paragraph has a topic statement (underlined) that says what the paragraph is about. Each now includes useful transitions (in italics) that link everything together.

> *The makeup of smoke depends on the fuel and on the available oxygen.* Fires exposed to abundant oxygen burn at high temperatures and with small amounts of smoke produced: smoke particles are mostly composed of ash, or even condensed aerosol of water. High temperatures also produce nitrogen oxides and sulfur content yields sulfur dioxide. In those hot fires, carbon and hydrogen are almost completely oxidized to carbon dioxide and water.
>
> Fires burning with lack of oxygen can produce many compounds. Many of them toxic. *For example,* when carbon doesn't completely burn, it produces carbon monoxide. *Also,* nitrogen-containing materials can yield hydrogen cyanide, ammonia, and nitrogen oxides. *Therefore,* these types of fires are often dangerous to fight.

Here are some **transitional words and phrases:**

- **go-ahead words** – and, therefore, furthermore, also, for instance
- **new-idea words** – thus, so, and so, therefore, consequently
- **summary words** – as a result, at last, finally, in conclusion, as we've seen
- **change-idea words** – but, yet, nevertheless, otherwise, although, despite, however, conversely, on the other hand
- **link-cause-and-effect words** – that caused, as a result, that produced, consequently
- **referring words** – they, these, though, not one, all but two, without exception
- **restricting and qualifying words** – provided, in case, if, lest, when, occasionally, even if, never

WRITING STRONG PROSE

Clear, concise writing helps convey your credibility to the reader, as do the technical content and the overall structure, and the visual presentation of your document. Now, here are some other factors that help convey that sense of authority needed for your reader to take your document seriously.

1. **Use the active voice.**
   Don't write, "The report was written by me."
   Write, "I wrote the report," which is shorter and more powerful.

   The difference between active and passive voice can be more dramatically shown in a longer passage, such as these geotechnical recommendations concerning the foundation design of a proposed hockey arena. (Italics identify the passive verbs.)

   > ***Passive voice, wordy and annoying because it's not easy to read:***
   > As indicated in Section 4.1, *it is recommended* that the entire building *be founded* on a minimum 1.0 meter thick layer of granular fill placed and compacted as specified in Section 4.2. If the *above is carried out*, then the proposed arena *can be supported* by spread and/or strip footings and *designed* using an allowable bearing pressure of 145 kpa.
   >
   > For the heavier column loads, *it is recommended* that these piles *are supported* with piles end bearing on bedrock. *It is anticipated* that the piles could range from about 2.0 meters to in excess of 15 meters within the center and west side of the

proposed building location, respectively. However, *it is recommended* that additional boreholes *be drilled* to confirm the actual pile length.
[124 words]

Active voice, more concise and more readable:
As Section 4.1 <u>indicates</u>, we <u>recommend</u> founding the entire building on at least 1.0 meter of granular fill, placed and compacted as specified in Section 4.2. Then, spread and/or strip <u>footings can support</u> the proposed arena, if designed for an allowable bearing pressure of 145 kpa.

We <u>recommend</u> supporting the heavier column with piles that <u>bear</u> on bedrock. These piles <u>could range</u> from about 2.0 meters in the center of proposed building location to more than 15 meters at west side. However, additional boreholes *should be drilled* to confirm the actual pile length.
[94 words]

In the above edited version, underlined words indicate the active voice. Notice that the edited version retains one case of passive voice, to emphasize what is done rather than who should drill the holes. (Who drills the holes is irrelevant at this point).

2. **Reserve the passive voice for special meanings.**
Although you should write in the active voice whenever possible, you'll find the passive voice useful when you want to emphasize what happened, rather than who made it happen, or if you do not want to offend the reader:

The project has been completed on time, and on budget.

The remediation work has not been completed according to the terms of the contract.

3. **Provide specific facts and figures** when they're required to support an argument or to impress the reader.

Don't write: This proposal will benefit the City of Johnsonville's water system.

Write: Implementing the water treatment methods described in this proposal will remove the threat of a Cryptosporidium outbreak in the City of Johnsonville's water system.

Don't write: A high water table caused the clay to swell and create a large broken mound in the basement floor.

Write: When the water table rose to within 4.5 meters of the surface, the clay became swollen, resulting in a roughly rectangular mound 7.4 meters long, 1.73 meters wide, and .82 meters high in the center of the basement floor. The center of this mound is cracked along its long axis. (See Figure 2.)

4. **Use direct phrasing.**
Readers appreciate sentences that get to the point as quickly as possible. Yes, many sentences need to begin with a transitional word or phrase, but the following sentences open with superfluous or awkward phrases:

Indirect prepositional phrase and subsequent passive voice:
From the previous assessments completed (Section 3.3.1), potential bottle necks were identified, and in some cases, assigned improvement priorities. [19 words]

More direct:
The previous assessments (Section 3.3.1) identified potential bottle necks and, in some cases, assigned improvement priorities. [16 words]

Indirect prepositional phrase and subsequent passive voice:
With the methods described above, and having an inspector on site during critical production periods, damage will be minimized. [19 words]

More direct:
These methods, monitored by an on-site inspector during critical production periods, will minimize damage. [14 words]

Practice Session 1—Identify Wordy Phrasing

Underline wordy phrases and circle unnecessary words in each of the following sentences. You will find answers for these exercises on page 637.

1. Return that spectrometer to the person named Gordon Burns when you have finished using it.
2. Will the ratepayers make payment of the development costs for the proposed riverside trail system?
3. Some, though not all, air toxins come from absolutely natural sources such as burning forest fires and the wearing away of soil erosion.
4. The Nissan Maxima SE sports sedan automobile that I have for sale is silver in colour.
5. There are several aviation-related businesses that lease land and facilities from YVR.

Practice Session 2—Reduce Wordiness

In the space provided beside each phrase, write a simpler version of the phrase. You will find answers for these exercises on page 637.

fewer in number
for the reason that
goes under the name of
surround on all sides
if conditions are such that
small in size
in view of the fact that
I personally feel
it is often the case that
repeat again
proceed ahead

it would appear that
final conclusion
lenticular in character
equally as good
oval in shape
exhibited good growth
prior to
the fish in question
serves the function of being
it is possible that the cause is

Practice Session 3—Identify Empty Jargon and Pompous Phrasing

Underline all empty jargon and pompous phrases. In the space provided above each line, write simpler or more familiar words or phrases. You will find answers for these exercises on page 638.

> I am in agreement with your proposed solution to the overtime problem, which seems increasingly vexatious to both management and the union, because the current way of allocating overtime work is unfair to employees and is not in keeping with overall management policy. However, I am not enamoured with the projected costs of your proposed approach, which appears burdensome for our company. Therefore, it is my considered opinion that a re-working of the overtime pay scale will be necessary, particularly because we are in a heavy debt load situation at the moment.

Practice Session 4—Identify Paragraphing Techniques

1. Underline the topic statement in the following paragraph.
   - Does that statement cover the paragraph's content? Yes No Partly
   - Does it signal the paragraph's purpose? Yes No Partly
2. If necessary, improve the phrasing of the topic statement, in the space above it.
3. Circle the transitional words in this paragraph. If necessary, add transitional words in the spaces above the lines.
4. Strike a line through (~~like this~~) any errors in spelling, grammar, or punctuation, and write the corrected version on the line above the error.

You will find answers for this exercise on page 638.

> You'll like our floors. A quality hardwood floor adds warmth, elegance, and increases the value of your home. It strengthens and stabilizes the inherent structure of your home. Because of ease of maintenance, and hardness, wood flooring allows you to have the healthiest of living environments. Also, hypoallergenic. Our company offers a full range of wood species, colours, sizes, as well as finishes to meet the needs of the most discerning wood flooring buyer. Each floor we deliver reflects the many years of development in state of the art production, our Premium finish is the most wear resistant finish on the market.

Improvement Exercises—Sentences

The following sentences may contain phrasing that is wordy, overrun with jargon, pompous, weak, imprecise, or indirect. If so, improve the phrasing in the spaces provided.

Also, correct errors in sentence structure, pronoun usage, adjectives and adverbs, conjunctions, prepositions, spelling, or punctuation. You will find answers for these exercises on pages 639 and 640 .

1. The use of the report would be to enable the Maintenance Department at CanaWood's Kelowna plywood plant to demonstrate feasibility of the roller screw in this application to upper management in order to proceed with in-plant testing.
2. We did research on the ISA server by Microsoft. This is a software firewall that is installed on a computer or server.
3. As you requested, the following progress report is provided with regard to the status of our study on Wastewater Management in Oyama that is being prepared for the Oyama Concerned Citizens Committee.
4. The report will review wastewater management issues for the community and make recommendations for further progress in mitigating nutrient loading to area lakes from wastewater discharges.
5. The following is a summary of the progress to date of our project.
6. The assessment was completed as a requirement in order to secure financing for the project through Natural Resources Canada.
7. Understanding the job requirements and roles in shipping, shift work can be advantageous.
8. In the following memo I will describe the activities of the proposed workshop series.
9. Our research regarding your marketing tools identified a security hole in your external network. This helped us create a software tool that is easy to use, but powerful enough to prevent security breaches.
10. I have often been an attendee at your concerts.
11. The writing instructors are assessing participants' writing competencies and are using their education, experience, available computer resources, and optimum pedagogical practices to provide assistance through on-site counselling to the majority of participants that have dysfunctional barriers to effective communication.
12. In conclusion, with the recent improvements in drainage control along West Sitkum Road, the majority of the recommendations of the 1996 assessment are completed, and the risk of sedimentation to local water domestic water supplies is minimized.
13. With having our computer website, an interactive inventory is required.
14. A few of the plant species were unavailable at the time of planting and were substituted with more of the available species.
15. Within the College there are computer laboratory facilities that offer specialized training opportunities.
16. Water quality monitoring in Richmond Creek upstream and downstream the proposed outfall site should take place, beginning two years in advance of plant start-up.
17. Both species have a preference for colder water as is likely to occur in this lake.
18. Our mortgage software automatically calculates the effects of rising inter-

est rates, your income, various amortization periods, coordinating with fluctuating property values, property taxes, compares to your pre-approved credit rating, payment schedules, then requests quotes from 18 Canadian lenders.

19. The study area is not within close proximity to the Fraser River.
20. An important component of this initiative will be establishing targets and reporting on achievements against these targets. This will assist in ensuring accountability and transparency in all areas.

Improvement Exercise—Paragraph

The following paragraph may contain phrasing that is wordy, weak, imprecise, or indirect. If so, improve the phrasing. Also, correct errors in sentence structure, pronoun usage, verb tenses, spelling, or punctuation. Finally, improve the paragraph's structure by creating an effective topic statement and by adding transitions. You will find answers for this exercises on page 640.

> Cork has been used as a flooring material for more than one hundred years (100), it provides outstanding acoustical and thermal insulation, it really cushions the foot, it is resistant to moisture damage and decay. With its surface treatment of 5 coats of UV-cured acrylic finish which contains no volatile organic compounds, Cork is definitely easy to clean. A light cleaning with a damp mop will be maintaining it's new appearance. Cork flooring is proving to be very durable. Most manufactures offer a good warannty on everything except water damage.

Document Critique 1—Structure, Phrasing, and Mechanics

A golf club manufacturer has designed a set of hybrid irons that help "average" players address two failings of "normal" iron sets:

1. Most mid-to-high handicappers (players who shoot in the mid-80s or higher) find that they don't hit their long irons (3 and 4 irons) consistently well and they don't hit the ball far enough with these irons even when they make a good swing.
2. If a golfer buys hybrids—clubs that are easy to hit because they combine the best features of irons and fairway woods—to replace the 3 and 4 irons, then there is a large "gap" between the 4 hybrid and the 5 iron. (A good player with a consistent swing would hit each successive club about 15 yards farther than the previous one; for example, a 6 iron might propel the ball about 160 yards and a 5 iron about 175 yards. However, the gap between a 4 hybrid and a 5 iron might be 25 or even 30 yards.)

Woodsman Golf has designed an integrated set of irons that includes

- two hybrids (equivalents of 3 and 4 irons) and
- nine irons that incorporate technology found in the hybrids. These irons include the numbers 5, 6, 7, 8, 9, and 10, and the pitching wedge, gap wedge, and sand wedge.

Woodsman's marketing director has written the following draft of a product description that will be "placed" in a golf magazine.

Your Task

Proofread and edit the draft. Look for errors in grammar, spelling, punctuation, and mechanics and improve the phrasing to make it clear, concise, and suitable for an enthusiastic but non-technical audience. Also, improve the paragraphing where necessary. You will find an edited version of this document on page 640.

The Woodsman 993 hybrid set of irons bridges the gap between irons and hybrids. Club designer Ed Ring made those choices. He increased the lofts on all the irons, he replaced the 3 iron and 4 iron with hybrids, the remaining eight irons have hollow heads and extreme perimeter weighting.

The 993 hybrid 3 and hybrid 4. The 3 has 20 degrees of loft, the 4 hybrid has 22. The lofts on the 5, 6, and 7 irons are four degrees stronger than standard, at 24, 27, and 30°. The 34° 8 iron is 3 degrees stronger, the 9 iron is two degrees stronger, at 39°. Then the pitching wedge is 44° as compared to the standard 48°, the gap wedge is 50°, the sand wedge 55 degrees.

Hollow heads, a thin face, a huge cavity back is filled with a light (only 5 grams) carbon composite cap. The 35 grams thus saved have been moved to the bottom and back of the head. The Iron has a low deep center of gravity that launches the ball high. Combining this high launch angel with less loft than normal makes the ball go further with each club. A person who would hit a ball 135 yards with a standard 8 iron will hit it 145 or 150 yards with the woodsman 993 7 iron. That's important because the ball will still come in nice and high with good spin, so it will stick on the green.

At the top end of the set, an average player will hit the ball 175 yards with the 5 iron and 190 yards with the 4 hybrid a useful gap between clubs. The set is available with Rifle steel shafts or with Aldila graphite shafts. Designed to match the 993 heads.

NOTE *GolfSpyder.com explains "loft" at http://www.golfspyder.com/golf-club-loft.html*

Notes and Answer: Document Critique

Document Critique 2—Structure and Phrasing

A student has drafted the following summary of a report that has resulted from a geotechnical investigation of the subsurface and bedrock conditions that underlie the proposed site of a hockey arena. Although some details of the summary have been fictionalized, the report is based on an actual situation.

Here's your task:

1. Read the entire summary to understand what it's about. If necessary, consult a dictionary or online search engine to learn the meanings of terms such as *surficial* and *berm.*
2. Review and, if necessary, edit each paragraph in the document to ensure that each has an effective topic statement, that the paragraph flows logically and smoothly, and that the reader can easily move from one paragraph to the next.
3. Improve the sentence structure and phrasing where necessary.
4. Correct errors in grammar, spelling, punctuation, and mechanics.

You will find an edited version of this document on page 641.

SUMMARY

With the proposed project, the purpose of the investigation was to determine the subsurface soil/bedrock conditions at the proposed building location and based on our interpretation of this information, to provide comments and recommendations thereby pertaining to the geotechnical aspects of the proposed arena site, locating on the actual northwest corner of the intersection of seventeenth avenue and Corcoran road.

Therefore the results of the investigation indicates that the east half of the proposed building site consists of a bedrock knoll while the west is underlain by 0.5 to 4.0 meters of fill materials followed by up to 0.9 meters of loose organic soils. The fills and/or organic soils are underlain by native deposits of stiff clayey silt and clay. The bedrock surface which will require drilling and blasting to the proposed design grade elevations and native stiff clayey silt and clay will provide a suitable base on which the proposed arena facility. As indicated in Section 4.1, it is receommended that the entire building be founded on a minimum 1.0 meter thick layer of granular fill placed and compacted as specified in Section 4.2. A soil weight of 2000 kilograms per cubic meter may be used in the design calculations. Observations and borehole results indicate that approximately 3⁄4 of the proposed arena site is underlain by end dumped fills ranging from 0.3 to 1.8 meters thick followed by a thin layer of surficial organic soils. The above surficial soils and fills are underlain by an interlayer sequence of clay, silty clay, and clayey silt. It is also understood that the proposed design will include an approximate 3.7 meter high berm around 3⁄4 of the proposed building. The influence of this around the proposed arena, could result in an additional 50 to 70 millimetres of recompression settlements. In order to minimize potential total and differential settlements of the proposed structure it is recommended that consideration be given to a preloading of the proposed area site in question.

A alternat option for locating the actual location of the arena considers the proposed arena to be located within the north portion of the site where the fill thickness is relatively thin and/or nonexistent. The granular fill that presently overlie the proposed arena site have essentially performed as a preload that has been in place for an estimated period of about twenty-one years, more or less. It is therefore logically concluded that prefoundation treatment of this site would only involve over excavating to remove any further fills and/or surface organic soils beneath the proposed building. That would be cheaper than the option proposed and investigated in this report's report.

Smith Consulting Ltd. has carried out a geotechnical investigatin at the above noted site. To confirm the inferred surface conditions testing, included moisture content determination and Atterberg Limit tests.

[465 words]

Notes and Answer: Document Critique

CHAPTER 29

Answer Key

DIAGNOSTIC TEST

1. E
2. D
3. E
4. C
5. E
6. A
7. E
8. B
9. D
10. C
11. C
12. B
13. A
14. D
15. B
16. E
17. D
18. C
19. A
20. E
21. A
22. B
23. B
24. A
25. B
26. A
27. A
28. B
29. B
30. A
31. B
32. A
33. B
34. B
35. B
36. B
37. B
38. A
39. B
40. A
41. D
42. B
43. D
44. D
45. E
46. A
47. A
48. E
49. B
50. E
51. A
52. A
53. B
54. A
55. A
56. B
57. A
58. B
59. B
60. A

NOUNS

Practice Session—Nouns

1. *specialties*
2. *Celsius*
3. *shelves*
4. *editor-in-chief's*
5. *RVs and boats*
6. *Ryan Collins's*
7. *pit boss*
8. *Bill's and Wanda's reports*
9. *data*
10. *1980s*

Improvement Exercises—Nouns

In items 1 through 5, underline the common nouns and circle the proper nouns.

1. Each of the consultants wrote a report about Riverbend Dam's projected cost overruns.
2. In this book, "grammatical" refers to effective, well-formed phrases and sentences.
3. Grammar studies the rules governing the use of language, as Dr. Benson has stated many times.
4. Written technical communication is not the only subject covered in *Technical Communication*, a book designed for present and future technical communicators.
5. Brick walls can withstand considerably higher temperatures than concrete board walls.

In items 6 through 10, underline the subjects and circle the objects.

6. Each of the consultants wrote a report about Riverbend Dam's projected cost overruns.
7. In this book, the term "grammatical" refers to effective, well-formed phrases and sentences.
8. Grammar studies the rules governing the use of language, as Dr. Benson has stated many times.
9. Written technical communication is not the only subject covered in *Technical Communication*, a book designed for present and future technical communicators.
10. Brick walls can withstand considerably higher temperatures than concrete board walls.
11. trucks
12. criteria
13. Sundin's
14. partners'; company's
15. software
16. procedures than our
17. Rene Corbeil's
18. stimuli
19. phones; signals
20. shorelines

Document Critique—Nouns

(The underlined words indicate where errors have been corrected.)

MEMO

To:	Harlan Devonshire, Field Supervisor
From:	Arjun Atwal, Accounting Office
Date:	June 24, 2009
Subject:	Expense Claims

We have had difficulty establishing the accuracy of recent expense claims submitted by your exploration group, especially those claims submitted this past month.

Would you please review all your team members' expense claims before they are sent to our office? I'm sure that you know when claims are excessive and you'll be able to correct them before we have to deal with them.

As an example of what I mean, I've attached Rose Francis' claim for this May. I find it hard to believe that she could spend $900 on camp supplies in addition to the food allowance!

PRONOUNS

Practice Session—Pronouns

1. me
2. its
3. who
4. his or her
5. its
6. its
7. whom
8. Toni Colette and I
9. who
10. its

Improvement Exercises—Pronouns

1. them
2. whom
3. its
4. whose
5. its
6. his or her
7. your
8. We
9. me
10. company's
11. All the team at EBS, including me, look forward to hearing from you.
12. These dense patches of forest are not a vulnerable ecosystem. The forest patches are in generally good condition, but they are found on steep slopes and would be best left undisturbed by development.
13. A new water intake at Lambeau Lake will require a new structure to be built below the current water level of 112 feet. In order to allow construction at an elevation of about 92 feet, the lake level has to be dropped at least 20 feet.
14. The housing used to protect the stream meters is a 2-inch galvanized pipe, which rests flush with the riprap boulders on the left bank.

15. The system includes two cigar-sized dataloggers that contain both pressure transducers and temperature recorders. These dataloggers are housed in protective casings.
16. Canadian National Railways (CN) has used a GIS-based railway Information System to map the location of all known streams that are crossed by its railways.
17. Box type concrete culverts were constructed with a concrete skirt (Figure 15) downstream of the outlet, in order to reduce scour that would block fish passage below the skirt.
18. Certain specifications govern the transfer of vinyl records to MP3 files.
19. Just between you and me, our network specifications will not meet Microsoft's standards.
20. Martin Technologies has just announced who it has chosen as its main supplier of cable and peripherals.
21. It's time for the company to review all its recruiting practises.
22. Frances and Donna have each told their clients about the new line of excavators.
23. Austin St. Pierre of St. John's Ambulance Services will explain its new billing policy.
24. In Calgary, officials ended their (intersection) red light camera program after statistics showed a 40 percent drop in ticketable offenses.
25. Researching this report taught me about management techniques.

Document Critique—Pronouns

(The underlined words indicate where errors have been corrected.)

Concept Architectural Designs

MEMO

To:	Devin Marchand, Architectural Technologist
From:	Shirley Tostenson, Managing Partner
Date:	April 16, 2009
Subject:	Preliminary Research for Potential Project

We are in the preliminary stages of preparing a proposal to design Halifax's potential Seaport Redevelopment project. I am assigning you to conduct research that will place our proposal in context.

Please review all the available literature on the following group of waterfront developments: Granville Island, Vancouver; the Distillery District, Toronto; The Custard Factory, Birmingham, England; The Forks, Winnipeg. Make note of each development's capitalization, scope, end uses, community involvement, sources of capital, and architectural themes, and its blend of commercial, retail, arts and crafts, and residential uses.

Complete the survey by April 25 and bring the results directly to me. This is a high priority, so drop everything else that you are doing. Don't discuss this outside of the office; we don't want this leaking out to those who might be also submitting a proposal.

VERBS

Practice Session—Verbs

1. is
2. have
3. sings
4. was
5. was
6. needs
7. his or her
8. was, were
9. were
10. laid

Improvement Exercises—Verbs

1. Our group conducted the experiment.
2. We'll prepare a final report when we receive your comments.
3. A list of upcoming squash games has been posted on the bulletin board. *Passive voice suits this sentence because it's irrelevant who posted the list.*
4. Following a storm in March 2008, woody debris, boulders, and gravel were removed from the site.
5. The engineering firm submitted its proposal three days early.
6. The following report summarizes the project's progress to date.
7. The report also includes comments that estimate ecosystem richness and the presence of invasive alien species.
8. Successive approximations converts analogue to digital signals by comparing the unknown input against a known input produced by the D/A converter.
9. Our firm uses their software for tracking traffic on our website.
10. Freeware.com provides the best option for reliable data on who uses open source software.
11. In March 2009, Northern Nurseries and Landscaping began its reconstruction of MacDonald Creek's banks.
12. A new crib wall was built in July 2008.
13. I believe that online gambling threatens small local casinos.
14. The test method and the answer key are faulty.
15. The system includes two cigar-sized dataloggers, each of which contains a pressure transducer and a temperature recorder. The dataloggers are housed in protective casings.
16. My instructor's facilitative role provides learning opportunities.
17. I will graduate from George Brown College's Health Informatics program on May 26.
18. No work program was planned for at the time of this environmental assessment.
19. Allowing the engine to breathe easier typically produces 15 more horsepower.
20. The following analysis combines an assessment, a comparison, and a recommendation for doubling next year's research budget.

21. Every time I suggested an alternative plan, my boss raised budget objections.
22. The guidance document's rough draft recommends labelling pharmaceuticals that would pose an environmental risk when released into the water supply.
23. He must have grown four inches over the summer holidays!
24. The Accident Prevention Board likes to hold informal sessions that include all stakeholders.
25. The Accident Prevention Board comprises seven members from a wide range of industrial occupations.
26. There are some oranges in the fruit bowl.
27. Each of the winners receives $500 and his or her choice of Corel software.
28. The media have their own agenda regarding the Kyoto Accord.

Document Critique—Verbs

(The underlined words indicate where errors have been corrected.)

Concept Architectural Designs

MEMO

To:	Shirley Tostenson, Managing Partner
From:	Devin Marchand, Architectural Technologist
Date:	April 22, 2009
Subject:	Preliminary Research for Potential Project

As you have requested, I have researched several waterfront developments. As you will see in the attached research overview, some very exciting developments have happened in Canada and in England.

I have found most of the information about the respective waterfront developments from the internet. However, most of the internet material is supplied by the development corporations themselves. So, that information is suspect. That's why I then went to newspaper archives for the Vancouver, Toronto, Birmingham, and Winnipeg daily papers. The business sections were especially useful.

Also, I was able to get documents from the planning offices in the city of Vancouver and the city of Winnipeg. I have a friend in City Hall in Toronto; she was able to give me background details of the proposals submitted to the City for the Distillery District development. I received those details last week. I have phoned the City Clerk in Birmingham. He promised to send a package of materials that describe the whole Custard Factory development, complete with construction costs. I hope the package comes because there was not much else available.

Thanks for assigning me this research project, which has been very interesting.

ADJECTIVES AND ADVERBS

Practice Session

1. Two dedicated teams desperately want to win the Vanier Cup, which is awarded annually to the champion of CIS football.
2. Biodiesel has a higher cetane level than petroleum diesel.
3. The Canadian cement industry claims that it has steadily improved energy efficiency in its manufacturing processes.
4. Improved indoor air quality probably reduces the number of sick days claimed by workers.
5. Despite urgent requests from the local health authorities, the mine repeatedly refused to install modern water treatment methods.
6. He has done well with the aging equipment at his disposal.
7. The Earth Home system provides fully integrated, self-sufficient buildings.
8. Compressed earth bricks are environmentally sustainable because they require comparatively little energy to produce and very little energy to transport.
9. The sales manager will work closely with the plant manager to plan just-in-time deliveries.
10. Someone has inadvertently left the specimen case on the loading dock.

Improvement Exercises—Adjectives and Adverbs

1. Don't think badly of me because I tried to improve our working conditions.
2. According to Bobbie Cruz in the IT department, every computer hard drive eventually fails.
3. They advised us to move slowly and carefully when working with those volatile chemicals.
4. We must conserve depleted, scarce, non-renewable resources or face the consequences.
5. Reported rollover rates for vans and SUVs are considerably higher than for sedans.
6. He was clearly the stronger of the two of them.
7. The maple syrup harvest is way earlier than usual this year, perhaps because of global warming.
8. The researchers made an honest mistake when they miscalculated the size of the honey bee population in Ontario.
9. Global cooling surely is more likely than global warming in the next 50 years.
10. *C*
11. In March 2009, Northern Landscaping discovered a near collapse of the Arduin Reservoir dike.
    Adjective *He ran near the prison walls.*
12. He is usually late for meetings that require him to present a project update.
    Adjective *The train arrived two hours late at Victoria Station.*
13. Please report daily about the progress of labour contract negotiations.
    Adverb The Globe and Mail *delivers its daily paper to my door.*
14. Three times this season he has been reprimanded for playing fast and loose with the fishery regulations.
    Adverb *The new BMW is a very fast car.*

15. She responded to the dissident workers' grievances very <u>well</u>, don't you agree?
    Adverb *I am not well.*
16. Please submit the <u>monthly</u> production figures by the second day of the following month.
    Adjective *We get paid monthly.*
17. Do you think that our boss is a <u>well</u> woman?
    Adjective *Trial lawyers need to speak well in public.*
18. The <u>early</u> indications are that the real estate bubble is about to burst.
    Adjective *If you don't arrive early, the best seats will be taken.*
19. Just how <u>hard</u> did you try to make the exam questions difficult?
    Adverb *Yes, that was a hard exam.*
20. *The Globe and Mail*'s <u>weekly</u> "Career" section has recently focused on the changing demographics of the Canadian work force.
    Adjective *I check the water heater weekly because we've had so many problems with leaking heaters.*

Document Critique—Adjectives and Adverbs

(The underlined words indicate where errors have been corrected.)

Christopher Metals

MEMO

To: Shift Foremen

From: Augusta Brown, General Manager

Date: May 22, 2009

Subject: Reducing Toxic <u>Emissions</u> at our Plant

As you might have heard, we received a D⁻ from Environment Canada following <u>their</u> December site visit. Apparently we have <u>six</u> months to clean up <u>our</u> act—the <u>inspectors</u> will be here again in November. If <u>our</u> sulphur and hydrochloric acid readings have not been reduced by 50 percent, they'll move to close us down.

To be honest, I don't think we've <u>been</u> doing that badly. For example, <u>our</u> culvert mill and <u>our</u> lead coating facility <u>don't have</u> <u>any</u> more free-flowing smoke stacks—the emission capture equipment diverts the gases to the holding chamber <u>where</u> the gases <u>are</u> chilled and the toxic elements are filtered out. But that's not good enough for the government, I guess.

I'm attaching some literature on equipment <u>that's</u> supposed to reduce sulphuric and hydrochloric acid <u>emissions</u>. Would you please read the descriptions and look at the diagrams of the equipment to see whether we could fit such devices into <u>our</u> existing setups? I mean, you know <u>your</u> areas inside out, so <u>you'll</u> know if the equipment will work in <u>our</u> plant.

Pay particular attention to the rugged low-cost low-maintenance air pollution control equipment sold by Herring Engineering. How much of it would we need? Can we cut into our ductwork to install it? The price looks right, so look at the Herring stuff really carefully

Let's discuss this next Tuesday in our regular production meeting.

CONJUNCTIONS, PREPOSITIONS, AND INTERJECTIONS

Practice Session 1

1. The Vanier Cup is awarded annually to the champion of CIS football.
2. Improved indoor air quality probably reduces the number of sick days claimed by workers.
3. Despite urgent requests from the local health authorities, the mine repeatedly refused to install modern water treatment methods.
4. The news media are very interested in the global warming issue.
5. Someone has inadvertently left the specimen case on the loading dock.

Practice Session 2

Conjunction	Type of conjunction	Relationship expressed
and	coordinating	connects the compound subject, "research and understanding"
that	subordinating	introduces subordinate clause, "longer autumns may be..."
but	subordinating	introduces subordinate clause, "they release CO_2 when ..."
so	subordinating	introduces subordinate clause, "more CO_2 is being absorbed ..."
however	conjunctive adverb	acts as transition into contrasting statement
so	subordinating	introduces subordinate clause, "more CO_2 is being released ..."
because	subordinating	introduces subordinate clause, "soil microbes are ..."
and	coordinating	connects two subordinate clauses

Practice Session 3

Prepositional phrase	Type of modifying phrase	Word or phrase modified
in Ottawa	adverb	says where the owl "captured media attention"
in the House of Commons	adverb	says where the petition was tabled
for a national park	adjective	modifies "plans"
in the South Okanagan	adjective	modifies "park"
by B.C. Southern MP Alex Atamanenko	adverb	says who submitted the petition
to a meeting	adverb	says when
of the National Park Network	adjective	says what kind of meeting
with representatives	adjective	says more about the meeting—with whom?
with Parks Canada officials	adverb	modifies "worked"
of view	adjective	modifies "points"

Improvement Exercises—Conjunctions, Prepositions, and Interjections

1. Where is the new computer projection system?
2. Clearly, we have to improve the communication among the production team, the sales people and the shipping people.
3. Either the transmission bolt threads are stripping when the engine torque increases because they're made of too soft steel or the engine might be too powerful for this type of transmission.
4. Michelle damaged the portable oscilloscope when she tried to jam it into a metal container that wasn't large enough.
5. Please remember to not place the GPS receiver beside equipment that emits a strong magnetic field.
6. The maple syrup harvest involves way more work than most people realize.
7. Way to go! That set of schematics represents the best work you've done for our firm.

8. Big hybrid SUVs, such as the Toyota Highlander, the Chevrolet Tahoe, and the GMC Yukon, are now getting up to 30 miles per Imperial gallon.
9. Neither the diehard Ottawa football fans nor the corporate community believe that a CFL football team can flourish in Ottawa.
10. ***C***

Document Critique—Prepositions and Conjunctions

(The underlined words indicate where errors have been corrected.)

Christopher Metals

MEMO

To: Shift Foremen

From: Augusta Brown, General Manager

Date: June 2, 2009

Subject: Reducing Toxic Emissions at Our Plant

Thank you for your useful comments in yesterday's meeting. I know we differ with each other on some points, but overall our experience points toward three alternatives.

Alternative 1—upgrade our emission capture equipment. I thought that our existing equipment is state of the art; however, as Jim reported, it's already showing signs of aging and needs new filtering and storage add-ons. This alternative is probably the least expensive.

Alternative 2—shut down the galvanizing facility. This section of the plant requires the most expensive work, but it generates 65 percent of our income. So I don't want to shut it down.

Alternative 3—shut down the culvert mill, sell its equipment, and use the sale funds to expand and modernize our galvanizing facility. Not only would this strategy get rid of the culvert mill, which is barely covering operating costs, but it would allow us to expand production of galvanized pipe, which is in high demand. Beside these benefits, as Jeanine pointed out, new ways of capturing and storing galvanizing by-products have been developed.

There seems to be more research to do, as we look into this issue. Let's meet again on Monday.

SENTENCE EXERCISES

Practice Session 1

1. You will need to return that spectrometer to Gordon Burns.
2. Will the ratepayers pay the development costs for the proposed riverside trail system?
3. Some air toxins come from natural sources such as forest fires and soil erosion.
4. Air toxins pose a serious threat to human health in all parts of the world.
5. The ozone layer in southern Canada thinned by an annual average of about 6 percent in the late 1990s.

Practice Session 2

6. complex
7. simple
8. compound-complex
9. compound-complex
10. simple

Practice Session 3—Identify Sentence Errors

Underline each example of a comma splice (CS), fused sentence (FS), dangling modifier (DM), misplaced modifier (MM), sentence fragment (frag), disruptive modifier (DisM), faulty coordination (coord), or faulty parallelism (//) in the following sentences. In the space above the underlined error, write the appropriate symbol (CS, DM, etc.)

11. The Ekati mine has cost Dia Met about $536 million <u>and</u> (**coord**) is 70% complete.
12. <u>When grading the site</u> (**DM**), two-way radios, which allow surveyors to communicate from a distance, are used.
13. Most people like to relax after a hard day's work <u>in front of the TV</u> (**MM**).
14. <u>After completing the project under budget</u> (**DM**), the head engineer rewarded me with a promotion.
15. The employee persuaded his boss to grant a pay raise <u>with logical arguments</u> (**MM**).
16. Many municipalities created, <u>for the benefit of local farmers</u> (**DisM**), policy that provided for minimal monitoring of animal waste runoff.
17. The Integration comparator is also quite <u>popular</u> (**CS**), it is used most commonly in digital multimeters.
18. <u>When manufacturing a car chassis</u> (**DM**), materials need to be strong and lightweight.
19. The objectives of this assessment were to ascertain whether the completed work is in compliance with the prescriptions <u>and that (//) the drainage</u> along the road might have been improved.
20. The lake will be temporarily drained during the drawdown (**FS**) it will then increase in size during the re-wetting phase of the project.

Improvement Exercises—Sentences

1. Storm water pond construction<u>, which was completed following best management practices,</u> did not cause negative environmental impacts.
2. The plan area<u>, which includes about 390 ha,</u> is bound by Powers Creek to the east, Highway 97 to the north, the District of Peachland to the west, and Okanagan Lake to the south.
3. If the native trees are lost or damaged during the construction process, we'll plant three trees for every one that needs replacing. <u>This over-planting</u> will

ensure an 80 percent survival of shrubs and a 100 percent survival of trees after three years.

4. Watering these plants will ensure quick root growth if they're watered twice weekly for the first two weeks and, depending on the weather, if they're watered once a week for four weeks thereafter.
5. The entire ESB team looks forward to hearing from you.
6. One of his finer projects was the Penticton Channel recreation area; he helped design this project and he oversaw its construction.
7. This proposal outlines the proposed research that will need to be conducted and the solution to the problem that we will implement.
8. Erecting a breakwater wall will divert the currents, thereby eliminating beach erosion.
9. Facial expressions include raising or lowering the eyebrows, squinting, and clenching the jaw.
10. pH measures the acidity or alkalinity of water. Many organisms that live in the water are sensitive to changes in pH.
11. These steps will help protect you from the sun's harmful rays: keep sun exposure to a minimum, especially between 10 a.m. and 3 p.m., wear wide-brimmed hats, wear sunscreen with Sun Protection Factor of 15 or greater, and reapply the sunscreen frequently.
12. Google Inc. tried to persuade members of the public to refrain from using "google" as a verb because it feared the dilution of its trademark. Google Inc. remembered what happened to brand names like Kleenex and Aspirin and Trampoline, and Google noted the increasing popularity of the word, to the point where the word became entrenched in dictionaries such as the Oxford English Dictionary.
13. On the RAR database, we will submit a post-development/construction report that summarizes the development, outlining the degree of compliance with the above measures and demonstrating that the SPEA is protected.
14. The proposed "F" shaped dock, which consists of a 1.8 m wide mainstem, will be made of perforated material.
15. ***C***
16. The average person spends 3,220 hours stuck in traffic, but only minutes planning his or her retirement.
17. Client A has not attended regularly, but he continues to make contact with our counsellors.
18. Smoking is allowed only in the gazebos at this campus.
19. Each of us has a responsibility to the organization.
20. We observed the clients at the Centre trying their very best in the aptitude tests.
21. If you know the answer, it is easy. However, not everyone knows the answer.
22. After you send the message, the following screen will appear.
23. Specialty NiCd batteries have a niche market in the area of cordless and wireless telephones, emergency lighting, model airplanes, and power tools.
24. With a relatively low internal resistance, a NiCd battery can supply high surge currents. This feature makes them a favourable choice for remote controlled

electric model aeroplanes, boats, and cars, as well as cordless power tools and camera flash units.

25. This workshop series has three objectives:
    - developing strategies for structuring documents,
    - learning how to proofread and edit other's documents, and
    - improving ones' efficiency in writing.
26. Please feel free to contact me if you require further clarification.
27. This first tier of the assessment process is completed by the supplier.
28. Roughly 100 pharmaceuticals have now been identified in rivers, lakes, and coastal waters throughout Europe and in North America, in concentrations that have alarmed environmental protection agencies.
29. The European Medicines Agency recommends additional testing of drugs to learn how they break down when they enter surface or underground water supplies.
30. One worry for pharmaceutical companies is that increased testing could translate into costly delays for the release of new drugs.

Document Critique—Sentences

(The underlined words indicate where errors have been corrected.)

Corrine Maltais

From: Billie Cochrane <bcochrane@on.gc.ca>

To: Corrine Maltais <cmaltais@on.gc.ca>

Sent: Friday, June 27, 2008 11:19 AM

Subject: Conflicting Responsibilities for the Georgian Bay Project

As my project leader, will you answer my question about what I'm supposed to be doing on the boat? When I took on this summer student placement, I thought that I and the other student would just be observing procedures and collecting data, not doing all the grunt work on the boat. Isn't that what sailors are for?

Here's what's been happening—

- On Monday, I and Jeannie (she's the other student) had to coil all the ropes and check for flaws in the ropes. That's very hard work, let me tell you: those ropes are heavy and some of them are dirty, too.
- Then on Tuesday the captain made us clean the decks. He said that we're the ones getting the deck dirty with all our fish samples and we came on board with muddy boots after checking the mud flats at 3 Moon bay. That's a big boat actually, and we had to use mops and then hand scrub with those hard sponge things. Why don't they have proper motorized cleaning equipment on board?
- Wednesday we sailed to Parker Point to get water samples and to check for fish mortality. Do you remember that we had heard reports that fish were washing up on shore? We didn't see any, though, so maybe the reports were for another point. That was a good day: we collected samples from 17 lakeshore locations and 5 deep water locations, we observed three outflow pipes and we took samples from those outflows. One of them—I think it was the pulp mill around the

corner from Parker Point—was really disgusting. The colour was muddy red and it smells like sulphur and diesel fuel, which is a really foul combination for sure.

- As you know, we spent yesterday in the lab with your techs as they checked the samples for toxic substances. They found very high levels of dieldrin and lindan, which was surprising because I thought that those pollutants were in decline. At least, that's what Professor Gorsline said.
- This morning Jeannie and I went down to the boat to retrieve some equipment and the captain said that we had to clean the cabin and the storage lockers down below. "Whoa," I said, "that's not what I came here for. I'm a fourth-year biology student, and I'm going to tell Dr Maltais what's going on." And he said, "Go right ahead; I don't care, but it's my boat and you'll do what I tell you when you're on board. That's what he said. Well, I came right up to see you but you were in a meeting so Jeannie said I had better write to you right away.

Thanks for listening. Will you talk to the captain?

PUNCTUATION EXERCISES

Practice Session—Punctuation

1. **a.**
2. **b.**
3. **b.**
4. **c.**
5. **b.**
6. **a.**
7. **a.**
8. **c.**
9. **c.**
10. **c.**

Improvement Exercises—Punctuation

1. The Trackstick has over 1 MB of memory, which can store months of travel information.
2. *C*
3. The Trackstick has several applications: employee monitoring, vehicle tracking, speed control, photo tours, public safety, and law enforcement
4. CEO Hernan Hesse says that the Trackstick II offers upgraded features and accuracy compared to the original device.
5. The device receives signals from 24 orbiting satellites that precisely calculate its position on this planet.
6. The property is owned by Northern Tent Vacations. The company's president, Carlo DeValero, has authorized Green Consultants to apply for environmental approvals required for development.
7. Don't worry about the condition of its transmission; the rest of the car is in really good shape.
8. The proposed wharf will be the same length and appearance and it will use the same materials as the adjacent wharf.
9. She orchestrated and wrote a major update of a maintenance manual.
10. Shortly after he graduated with an engineering diploma, he developed a process for evaluating the quality of concrete as it is poured.
11. Prominent scientists such as Henri Casselle have questioned the popular beliefs about global warming.

12. Art Burns's designs won the Granby Award for high-density housing projects this year.
13. Well, they own the fishing rights, so we should back off.
14. The Canadian dollar—as strong as it is—has hurt U.S. exports that are paid in U.S. dollars.
15. The Leafs post-2005 regular season records leave a lot to be desired.
16. The rocket burst into flames upon re-entry into the earth's atmosphere.
17. Generation Y workers are not all that different from any other "generation" of workers, according to workplace analyst Barbara Moses.
18. This grammar workbook, which supplements your *Technical Communication* textbook, provides hundreds of exercises.
19. The Spanish say, *hasta mañana* and that's exactly how I feel about wanting tomorrow to be here now!
20. On 10 June 2004, a British Airways Boeing 777 suffered a serious fuel leak as it took off from Heathrow Airport.
21. Lack of documentation, or poor documentation, costs your company money.
22. The total cost of a single call answered by a help desk technician is $20 or more, depending on the length of the call.
23. On its website, Innovatia reports on the costs of distributing poorly written documentation.
24. The Regional Aquatics Monitoring Program (RAMP) is an industry-funded multi-stakeholder initiative.
25. The Athabasca River has high year-to-year fluctuations in its flow patterns.
26. "I'd be shocked if we learned that the cause of the flooding was one of the valves installed last week," said Roger Desroches, Managing Director.
27. Unconscious bias may cause some doctors to be more likely to recommend knee replacement surgery to men than to women, according to a recent study.
28. Compared with men, women have the surgery when their arthritis is at a more advanced stage. This fact perhaps explains why women tend to do more poorly than men after knee replacement.
29. The water quality in the Athabasca River in the fall of 2005 was better than in the previous year.
30. On March 25, 2008 *The Globe and Mail* carried a story about Biovail's involvement in a series of frauds that distorted reports of earnings and revenue.
31. The US Securities and Exchange Commission said Biovail executives were "obsessed with meeting quarterly and annual earnings guidance," and engaged in a "corrupt strategy" to do so.
32. In the United States, Sirius Satellite Radio Inc. has taken over its rival XM Satellite Radio Holdings Inc., which means that the Canadian subsidiaries will also merge.
33. Montreal's waterfront district, once a bustling scene of shipping and manufacturing, has almost become a ghost town. However, current private and public investment plans promise to rejuvenate the area.
34. The Canadian fashion industry is not centred in one location. Rather, it's found in Winnipeg, Montreal, Toronto, and Vancouver, and, of all places, in Vernon, British Columbia, the home of Far West and Valhalla Pure.

35. Several media networks, including traditional media companies like Forbes Inc., are trying to lure advertisers away from Google Inc. and Yahoo Inc. by offering one-stop shopping for ad placement.
36. Each of the consultants wrote a report about Riverbend Dam's projected cost overruns.
37. In this book, the term "grammatical" refers to effective, well-formed phrases and sentences.
38. Rollover rates for SUVs are nearly twice that of sedans, and 30 percent higher than that of pickup trucks.
39. *C*
40. Sundin's career as a Toronto Maple Leaf appears to be ending, which is really too bad.
41. Don't expect your cellular phones to receive strong signals in the far northern Arctic.
42. According to Rene Corbeil's report, the bridge is no longer safe, but we knew that.
43. Blogging has real advantages for companies that possess clear goals and a workforce whose ambitions align with the company's.
44. Guerrilla email (www.guerilla-mail.com) supplies disposable email addresses that expire after 15 minutes, so you can register a software program or service but not receive spam later on.
45. A study by York University professor Dr Robert Kozinets shows that consumers of technology are governed partly by their view of the role that technology plays in their lives and in society.

Document Critique—Punctuation

(The underlined words indicate where errors have been corrected.)

Billie Cochrane

From:	Corrine Maltais <cmaltais@on.gc.ca>
To:	Billie Cochrane <bcochrane@on.gc.ca>
Sent:	Monday, June 30, 2008 7:48 AM
Subject:	Conflicting Responsibilities for the Georgian Bay Project

Thank you for drawing my attention to your experiences on the Great Lake Queen, our research vessel. I have spoken with Captain Blair who's denying the accusation made by you and Jeannie Brock.

Let me respond to each of your comments;

- On Monday, you say that Captain Blair forced you and Jeannie to coil all the ropes and check for flaws. He says that he asked you to help him and the two sailors, but only for 15 minutes because they had a particularly difficult time with the anchor rope that had somehow become kinked. He said that after you helped with the anchor rope—which he appreciated by the way—he saw you coiling some dock lines. However, he says he didn't order you to do that.

- He said that on Tuesday all six of you, including him, cleaned the deck.
- On Friday, you went to retrieve the collection equipment. According to Captain Blair, he asked you to clean the cabin because you had left a number of items lying around during Wednesday's trip to Parker Point. Also, he claims that you and Jeannie didn't clean up the galley after you prepared lunch. By the way, the captain said that he and the crew appreciated your offer to cook lunch on Wednesday and it was good, too, he said.

So here's where we're at. I think we (you, Jeannie, the captain, and I) need to get together to discuss your formal roles in the research team while you're on board the Great Lake Queen. We also need to talk about the things that team members do to help each other out and to work as a team. Often, these things go beyond the formal defined roles, you know. I'll set up a meeting for this Wednesday before you sail to The Ramsey shoals. Watch for an email later today, which will set the time we should meet on the boat.

By the way, you mentioned that your professor had said that dieldrin and lindane are in decline in the Great Lakes. Probably his comments were based on a flawed study conducted by the Michigan Fish and Game League. Their results have since been shown to have been based on a too small sample and solely on levels of those chemicals found in one fish species.

MECHANICS EXERCISES

Practice Session—Mechanics

1. Great chefs can prepare low calorie meals that taste every bit as good as meals loaded with calories.
2. Fourteen students came late to the exam. They were denied entrance to the exam hall.
3. Boy, I'm glad I didn't have to study Latin in school.
4. The consensus among my friends is that we should take off the 2009–2010 year so that we can live and work at the Whistler resort during the 2010 Olympic games.
5. I went to see a counsellor about my grades that were too low. They said that I should just work harder.
6. Whole areas of Thailand's beachfront tourist resorts and locals' homes were wiped out by the tsunami in December 2004.
7. The Thai government reported 8,457 confirmed deaths in the wake of the tsunami caused by the 2004 Indian Ocean earthquake on 26 December 2004.
8. More than three years after the massive earthquake and subsequent tsunamis on 26 December 2004 devastated countries around the Indian Ocean, recovery programs undertaken by Red Cross and its partner national societies continue to provide assistance to those communities most affected by the disaster.
9. Canadians were particularly generous in providing aid to the countries affected by that disaster.
10. The RCMP face criticism for several recent incidents which have eroded trust in our national police force.

Improvement Exercises—Mechanics

1. This MP3 player has over three MB of memory that can store thousands of songs.
2. Forty-six percent of all hockey games that go to overtime are settled in the first five minutes of the first overtime period.
3. The Acura MDX offers a 300 horsepower motor.
4. The office has ordered three Dell Inspiron 1525 laptops for field work.
5. Dell offers 24-hour technical support for all its products.
6. Although Dell is the most prominent of the online computer sales companies, there are several other similar outfits operating in Canada.
7. The client responded with a very negative assessment of our proposed approach: "This proposal fails to meet even our most basic requirements."
8. Since the Royal Bank Cup was inaugurated in 1996, only two teams have won the cup twice, the Aurora Tigers (2007 and 2004), and the Vernon Vipers (1996 and 1999).
9. The North American Free Trade Agreement (NAFTA) has supporters and detractors in all three countries, Canada, the United States and Mexico.
10. Dr Judy diSantos, MD, is a leading expert on the effects of workplace second-hand smoke.
11. He is a prime candidate for our quality control position, because he has had similar experience in the steel industry.
12. The structure was completely destroyed when the roof beams gave way under the snow load.
13. They should have reported the cracks that were developing in the support beams.
14. The three main principles of successful road construction are illustrated by the Howth project.
15. Always ensure that the lock down lever has been properly set at the 3 o'clock position.
16. In Canada, provincial governments have accredited 434 post-secondary colleges and universities.
17. Besides the publicly funded and accredited institutions, 49 for-profit institutions have been authorized to grant specific credentials.
18. If you know where to look, you'll find all kinds of scholarships and bursaries available to Canadian and foreign students.
19. The AUCC (Association of Universities and Colleges of Canada) administers more than 150 scholarship, fellowship and internship programs.
20. Canadians' standard of living has long depended on their competitiveness in an international trading economy where their natural resources afford an advantage
21. [We] ensure that postsecondary educational opportunities are affordable and that no qualified individual is denied access because of financial circumstances.
22. Editing rates are considerably lower in the United States than in Canada, perhaps because of greater competition.
23. *C*
24. In 2006 the University of Toronto enrolled over 64,000 full time students.

25. The highest 2007–2008 college and university tuition fees were at BC's Trinity Western University, at $16 500.
26. York University's course handout kits are classified carbon neutral, which means they are produced using environmentally responsible printing practices that include incorporating locally produced papers manufactured using sound forestry practices and increased recycled fibre content.
27. *C*
28. Virtually anybody can make biodiesel, because it is so easy you can even make it in your own kitchen.

Document Critique—Mechanics

(The underlined words indicate where errors have been corrected.)

Let's examine some of the claims made by environmental opportunists such as Carbon Footprint, a company that makes money from selling carbon offsets.

Claim number one:

> "At Carbon Footprint, our belief is that climate change will only be addressed if each and every one of us takes responsible steps to **REDUCE** their [sic] CO_2 emissions."

I've been looking for evidence that CO_2 emissions 1.), actually cause global warming and that 2.), global warming is necessarily a bad thing. Here's what I've found at Carbon Footprint's website: I see scientific evidence that temperatures have been rising (0.7 degrees C in the past 100 years, world wide) and that glaciers have been melting (24,000 kms^2 of Arctic ice in 30 years). But I don't see any evidence that released CO_2 has had anything to do with it. Yes, the increase in CO_2 emissions has been linked with warming, with evidence of those patterns going back four hundred thousand years, but where's the connection? One has to prove correlation, not just timing. You could just as easily say that periodic global warming causes greater CO_2 emissions and that interspersed global cooling caused lower CO_2 emissions.

Claim number two:

> "Even though the hole in the ozone layer doesn't contribute to global warming. [sic] We should still be concerned about the affects [sic] of increased UV light."

Regardless of their claims Carbon Footprint hasn't proved this either. Why should we just take their word for it? The company provides no evidence at their website that the "hole in the ozone layer doesn't contribute to global warming". None. Zilch.

The important thing to remember about Carbon Footprint:

> "From this web site only - you can offset your CO_2 emissions while you shop on-line. Every purchase you make on-line via the links on this page will count towards our carbon offset programme - including reforestation and clean energy projects globally."

So, we see what Carbon Footprints all about—money! When its propaganda makes you feel guilty enough, then you buy its services and you shop with its partners, such as eBay, Amazon books, and Napster. Or you buy its Ultra bright windup Eco Torch.

Don't be fooled by what the media give you; don't be fooled by outfits like Carbon Footprint, who are in the business of selling guilt about global warming. Let's put our energy into dealing with the impacts of warming instead of succumbing to the arrogant human assumption that we can cause a whole planet to change its climate.

VOCABULARY AND STYLE EXERCISES

Practice Session 1—Identify Wordy Phrasing

1. Return that spectrometer to the person named Gordon Burns when you have finished using it.
2. Will the ratepayers make payment of the development costs for the proposed riverside trail system?
3. Some, though not all, air toxins come from absolutely natural sources such as burning forest fires and the wearing away of soil erosion.
4. The Nissan Maxima SE sports sedan automobile that I have for sale is silver in colour.
5. There are several aviation-related businesses that lease land and facilities from YVR.

Practice Session 2—Reduce Wordiness

In the space provided beside each phrase, write a simpler version of the phrase.

fewer in number	*fewer*	it would appear that	*apparently*
for the reason that	*because*	final conclusion	*finally*
goes under the name of	*called*	lenticular in character	*lens shaped*
surround on all sides	*surround*	equally as good	*equal*
if conditions are such that	*if*	oval in shape	*oval*
small in size	*small*	disappear from view	*disappear*
in view of the fact that	*therefore, so*	exhibited good growth	*grew well*
I personally feel	*I feel*	prior to	*before*
it is often the case that	*often*	the fish in question	*the fish*
repeat again	*repeat*	serves the function of being	*is*
proceed ahead	*go, proceed*	it is possible that the cause is	*possibly*

Practice Session 3—Identify Empty Jargon and Pompous Phrasing

agree irritates
I am in agreement with your proposed solution to the overtime problem, which seems increasingly
our overtime scheduling system
vexatious to both management and the union, because the current way of
doesn't match
allocating overtime work is unfair to employees and is not in keeping with overall
I don't like
management policy. However, I am not enamoured with the projected costs of your
is too expensive
proposed approach, which appears burdensome for our company. Therefore, it is
I believe we'll need to renegotiate overtime pay
my considered opinion that a re-working of the overtime pay scale will be
the company is deep in debt
necessary, particularly because we are in a heavy debt load situation at the moment.

Practice Session 4—Identify Paragraphing Techniques

1. Circle the topic statement in the following paragraph.

- Does that statement cover the paragraph's content? **Partly**
- Does it signal the paragraph's purpose? **No**

You'll like our floors for a variety of reasons. *warmth and elegance,*
You'll like our floors. A quality hardwood floor adds ~~warmth, elegance~~, and
For example, hardwood
increases the value of your home. It strengthens and stabilizes the inherent
Also, because its hard surface is easy to maintain,
structure of your home. ~~Because of ease of maintenance, and hardness,~~ wood flooring allows you to have the healthiest of living environments,
and it is *You'll be glad to hear that our*
~~Also,~~ hypoallergenic. ~~Our~~ company offers a full range of wood species, colours,
and
sizes, ~~as well as~~ finishes to meet the needs of the most discerning wood flooring
has been flawlessly milled and then finished with our
buyer. Each floor we deliver ~~reflects the many years of development in state~~
Premium finish, which provides the best wear characteristics on the market.
~~of the art production~~, ~~our Premium finish is the most wear resistant finish on the market.~~

NOTE *The proper spelling of "state of the art" is "state-of-the-art" when it is attributive, that is, when it functions as an adjective in front of a noun.*

Improvement Exercises—Sentences

1. The report would enable the Maintenance Department at CanaWood's Kelowna plywood plant to show upper management that the roller screw is feasible in this application, so that management will approve in-plant testing.
2. We researched the Microsoft's ISA server, a software firewall that is installed on a computer or server.
3. The following progress report answers your request about the status of our study of wastewater management in Oyama, which is being prepared for the Oyama Concerned Citizens Committee.
4. The report will review the community's wastewater management issues and recommend further progress in reducing nutrient loading from wastewater discharges to area lakes.
5. The following summarizes the project's progress to date.
6. The assessment met Natural Resources Canada's requirement for its project financing.
7. When one understands the job requirements and roles in shipping, one can see the advantages of shift work.
8. The following memo describes the activities of the proposed workshop series.
9. Our research about your marketing tools identified a security hole in your external network. This discovery helped us create a software tool that is easy to use, but powerful enough to prevent security breaches.
10. I have often attended your concerts.
11. The writing instructors assess participants' writing skills and use their knowledge, teaching experience, and available computer resources to help those participants who don't communicate well.
12. So, the recent drainage control improvements along West Sitkum Road, which have completed most of the 1996 assessment's recommendations, have minimized the risk of sedimentation in local domestic water supplies.
13. Our website requires an interactive inventory.
14. A few of the plant species were unavailable at the time of planting, so we planted more of the available species.
15. The College computer laboratory facilities offer specialized training.
16. Water quality should be monitored in Richmond Creek, upstream and downstream of the proposed outfall site, beginning two years before the plant starts up.
17. Both species prefer colder water, which usually occurs in this lake.
18. Our mortgage software automatically calculates the effects of rising interest rates, your income, and various amortization periods. The software then coordinates with fluctuating property values and property taxes and compares the results to your pre-approved credit rating and possible payment schedules. Finally it requests quotes from 18 Canadian lenders.
19. The study area is not close to the Fraser River.
20. An important part of this project will be to establish goals and report whether these goals have been met. This process will help ensure total accountability and transparency.

Improvement Exercise—Paragraph

Cork has been a flooring material for over one hundred years because of its features:

- it provides outstanding acoustical and thermal insulation,
- it cushions the foot,
- it resists moisture damage and decay, and
- it has proved very durable, as evidenced by manufacturers' warranties that cover all damage except water damage.

Also, cork is easy to clean because of its five coats of UV-cured acrylic finish that contains no volatile organic compounds. A light cleaning with a damp mop will maintain the floor's new appearance.

Document Critique 1—Structure, Phrasing, and Mechanics

The Woodsman 993 hybrid set of irons bridges the gap between irons and hybrids, as designed by Ed Ring. In order to create an evenly spaced set that has hybrid characteristics throughout the set, he increased the lofts on all the irons, he replaced the 3 iron and 4 iron with hybrids, and he gave the remaining eight irons hollow heads and extreme perimeter weighting.

The 993's lofts vary from traditional settings. The hybrid 3 and hybrid 4 have 20 degrees of loft and 22 degrees, respectively, which is four degrees stronger than standard. The lofts on the 5, 6, and 7 irons are also four degrees stronger than standard, at 24, 27, and 30 degrees. However, starting with the 8 iron, the set starts to come closer to standard specifications: the 34-degree 8 iron is 3 degrees stronger, the 9 iron is two degrees stronger, at 39 degrees. Then the pitching wedge is 44 degrees (as compared to the standard 48 degrees), the gap wedge is 50 degrees, and the sand wedge is 55 degrees.

The strong lofts would ordinarily make the ball fly lower than normal, but Ring's design compensates for those lofts. The heads have hollow heads, a thin face, and a huge cavity back that is filled with a light (only 5 grams) carbon composite cap. The 35 grams thus saved have been moved to the bottom and back of the head. Thus, the iron has a low, deep centre of gravity that launches the ball high. Combining this high launch angle with less loft than normal makes the ball go farther with each club. A person who would hit a ball 135 yards with a standard 8 iron will hit it 145 or 150 yards with the Woodsman 993 7 iron. That distance gain is not penalized because the ball will still come in nice and high with good spin, so it will stick on the green.

An average player will hit the ball 175 yards with the 5 iron and 190 yards with the 4 hybrid, a useful gap between clubs, depending on which shaft the player chooses. The set is available with Rifle steel shafts or with Aldila graphite shafts, which have been designed to match the 993 heads.

Document Critique 2—Structure and Phrasing

SUMMARY

Smith Consulting Ltd. has conducted a geotechnical investigation of subsurface soil and bedrock conditions at the proposed arena location at the northwest corner of 17th Avenue and Corcoran Road. This report interprets the geotechnical data and recommends an approach based on that interpretation.

In addition to observing the surface conditions, the investigative methods determined moisture content and ran Atterberg Limit tests. These tests confirmed inferences that had been based on the observations and tests of surface conditions.

The investigation revealed that the east half of the proposed building site consists of a bedrock knoll while the west is underlain by 0.5 to 4.0 metres of fill materials followed by up to 0.9 metres of loose organic soils. The fills and/or organic soils are underlain by native deposits of stiff clayey silt and clay.

The bedrock surface will require drilling and blasting to the proposed design grade elevations and the native stiff clayey silt and clay will provide a suitable base for the proposed arena facility. As indicated in Section 4.1, the entire building should be founded on a minimum of 1.0 metre thick of granular fill placed and compacted as specified in Section 4.2. A soil weight of 2000 kilograms per cubic metre may be used in the design calculations.

Observations and borehole results indicate that approximately three-quarters of the proposed arena site is underlain by end dumped fills ranging from 0.3 to 1.8 metres thick followed by a thin layer of surficial organic soils. The above surficial soils and fills are further underlain by an interlayer sequence of clay, silty clay, and clayey silt. Also, the proposed design will include an approximate 3.7 metre high berm around three-quarters of the proposed building. This berm could add 50 to 70 millimetres of recompression settlements. In order to minimize potential differential settlements under the proposed structure, the proposed arena site should be preloaded.

An alternate option for locating the arena favours the north portion of the site where the fill thickness is relatively thin and/or nonexistent. The granular fill that presently overlies the proposed arena site has essentially preloaded the site for an estimated 21 years. Therefore, a pre-foundation treatment of this site would require excavating only to remove any further fills and/or surface organic soils beneath the proposed building. That approach would be cheaper than the option investigated in this report.

[391 words]

CHAPTER 30

Correction Symbols

Symbol	Meaning
ab	abbreviation
active	use active voice instead of passive voice
address	change address (1st person, 2nd person, or 3rd person point of view)
amb	ambiguous phrasing
bias	biased tone
ca	faulty pronoun case
cap	capitalization
coh	paragraph lacks coherence (doesn't flow; lacks transitions)
cs	comma splice
coord	faulty coordination
DM	dangling modifier
emph	change emphasis
frag	sentence fragment (incomplete thought)
jarg	needless jargon
ind ph	indirect phrasing (make it direct!)
len	paragraph length
lev	level of technicality
logic	faulty logic
MM	misplaced modifier
mng	meaning unclear
om	omitted word
over	overstatement

Symbol	Meaning
***par** (or //)*	faulty (or lack of) parallelism
p	punctuation error
***P** (or ¶)*	start new paragraph
pomp	pompous phrasing
prep	wrong preposition or excess prepositions
pro agr	pronoun doesn't agree with antecedent
***pro ref** (or ref)*	faulty or vague pronoun reference
ro	run-on sentence
seq	sequence of development in a paragraph
sexist	sexist usage
sp	spelling error
sub	faulty subordination
s/v agr	subject/verb agreement
th op	"there is" or "there are" sentence openers
trans	transition—faulty or needed
ts	topic sentence
un	paragraph lacks unity
var	more sentence variety required
w	wordy phrasing
wo	word order problem
ww	wrong word
#	problem with numbers usage

CHAPTER 31

Appendix A: Punctuating Lists

The way we should punctuate a list depends on the nature of that list. For example, **a simple list** of single items or short phrases may not require internal or end punctuation.

The College has six Business instructors at its downtown campus:

- *Joyce Gruber*
- *Rocky St. Pierre*
- *Magnus Halvorson*
- *Rita O'Toole*
- *Davinder Bains*
- *Yee Ling Chan*

However, the writer who wishes to present **the list as a complete sentence** that's easier to read than a normally formatted sentence would need to include the following punctuation and coordinating conjunction.

The College has six Business instructors at its downtown campus:

- *Joyce Gruber,*
- *Rocky St. Pierre,*
- *Magnus Halvorson,*
- *Rita O'Toole,*
- *Davinder Bains, and*
- *Yee Ling Chan.*

Let's say that the **list contains phrases of more than two words.** One choice would use a series of commas, a conjunction, and end punctuation.

The College now includes several diploma programs:

- *a comprehensive Business Administration program,*
- *three trades programs,*
- *an aviation maintenance course, and*
- *a new nursing program.*

But—there seems to be an exception to every rule! The following list, which appears in the 4th Canadian edition of *Technical Communication*, doesn't punctuate each phrase. The authors envisioned **a simple list, not an integrated sentence.**

Although you might not anticipate a career as a "writer," your writing skills will be tested routinely in situations like these:

- *proposing various projects to management or to clients*
- *contributing articles to employee newsletters*
- *describing a product to employees or customers*
- *writing procedures and instructions for employees or customers*
- *justifying to management a request for funding or personnel*
- *editing and reviewing documents written by colleagues*
- *designing material that will be read on a computer screen*

Another example (that **requires additional internal punctuation**) could use a series of semi-colons that would correspond to the way semi-colons would be used in a complex sentence. First, here's that "normal" sentence:

The College now includes several diploma programs: a comprehensive Business Administration program, offered annually; three trades programs, offered as demand requires; an aviation maintenance course, at the airport; and a new nursing program, slated for 2009.

That sentence would be easier to read in a bulleted list:

The College now includes several diploma programs:

- *a comprehensive Business Administration program, offered annually;*
- *three trades programs, offered as demand requires;*
- *an aviation maintenance course, at the airport; and*
- *a new nursing program, slated for 2009.*

Lists of clauses can use semi-colons, as in the following **integrated sentence list**.

The College now includes several diploma programs:

- *a comprehensive Business Administration program is offered annually;*
- *three trades programs will be offered as demand requires;*
- *an aviation maintenance course has been started at the airport; and*
- *a new nursing program is slated for 2009.*

Or, normal end punctuation might be used, as in this example from *Technical Communication*, 4th Canadian edition[6] (p. 5).

To a large extent, that information is stored and transmitted electronically. Several electronic technologies, collectively known as information technology (IT), enhance the speed, volume, and variety of means of creating and transmitting messages:

- *Integrated software facilitates the inclusion of verbal, graphic, and video elements from word processors, internet sources, digital recording and storage media, electronic spreadsheets and databases, and oral presentation software.*

---

6. Lannon, John M., and Don Klepp. *Technical Communication*, 4th Canadian Edition. Toronto: Pearson Longman, 2006.

- *Basic email helps people exchange ideas and information, while email attachments allow for sophisticated formatting of documents.*
- *Wireless laptop computers allow users to receive and send email from locations (hotel conference rooms, airport lounges, classrooms, etc.) that support wireless transmission.*

Bulleted or numbered lists of sub-paragraphs present few punctuation challenges—each sub-paragraph uses its "normal" punctuation. The following list appears in the 4th Canadian edition of *Technical Communication* (p. 6).

These technologies have had a profound effect on office communication:

- *Small and medium-sized companies, which comprise 95 percent of all Canadian businesses, are slower than large companies to adopt emerging technologies such as VoIP, wireless networking, and videoconferencing. However, almost all have desktop computers and email access, and many have laptops, PDAs, cell phones, and websites. (Lima "Small firms . . . E2)*
- *Instead of being housed in one location, the virtual company may have branches in widespread locations, or just one central office, to which employees "commute" electronically. Such arrangements require workers to be skillfu communicators who must master the latest technologies, use prop e-communication etiquette, and know how to compensate for the lack of f to-face contact (Marron C1). A special class of worker has emerged "virtual assistant," who works on contract, at home, for one or more firms. A tual assistant might answer phones, direct emails, produce and edit documents, update websites, or maintain databases and inventories. He/she can even go into a client firm's computer (via an internet connection) to work on material stored on that computer's hard drive. (Buckler E5)*
- *Instead of relying on secretaries, most managers compose and send their own messages via email. Many also compose, design, and deliver their own reports and proposals.*
- *On desktop publishing networks, the composition, layout, graphic design, and printing of external documents and Web pages are done in-house.*
- *Paper documents (such as résumés) can be optically scanned and stored electronically. Many other documents are stored as PDF files.*
- *Computer-supported cooperative work systems, instant messaging, and videoconferencing enable employees worldwide to converse in real time. Email listservs announce daily developments in prices, policies, and procedures.*

CHAPTER 32

Appendix B: Accidental Humour

The following sentences weren't written by gag writers employed by Rick Mercer or David Letterman. These examples of accidental humour have appeared in student assignments and in actual workplace documents. In the end, though, each bit of levity isn't all that funny because it reflects badly on the person responsible for the mangled English.

- *The trends set by music itself and the natural transitions it goes through is also strong evidence that popular music is popular today.* (This hilarious bit of circular "reasoning" reminds me of the CBC half-time interview with a Winnipeg Blue Bomber defensive back who proudly said during the interview: "Football! I love football. If it wasn't for football, I wouldn't be in football today!")
- *In light of my accomplishments and skills I demonstrated; Wal-Mart promoted me to the curtsy desk. Working the curtsy desk is a real pleasure because it is so demeaning.* (This amazing "confession" appeared in an actual application letter for a marketing position. I think the writer meant "courtesy desk" and "demanding," not "curtsy desk" and "demeaning." At least, I hope so. By the way, the writer's application was unsuccessful.)
- *Never place a power chord within a mouse.* (This sensible admonition appeared in an electronics student's project manual. When I first read the above sentence, I imagined some 120 dB Metallica power chords bouncing a computer mouse around.)
- *I am 17 years old and I have been on a motorcycle since I was 5 years old.* (Life hasn't been easy for this writer! For example, just imagine his saddle sores.)
- *There are about 60 passengers aboard on each cruise. The single tourists make up 66 percent, of which a little more than half are usually male.* (But apparently, they're not <u>always</u> male!)
- *This industry reached a new plato in 2007.* (While writing about adventure tourism, this writer became rather philosophical.)
- *The job market is really tough these days, especially for those in child care, so we have to bare with it.* (This sentence in a five-page job search plan made me wonder whether the writer was paying tuition for child-care studies by working as a stripper.)

- *I also enjoy a strong bake ground in english and have a firm grasp for writing.* (This job applicant may have a strong grip, but he can't spell.)
- *Our trip to southern California and Mexico showed us the full spectre of the hospitality industry.* (What are the odds that this person changed careers after his hotel management class's extended field trip?)
- *Will detonation skiers visit Intrawest's new resort?* (We certainly hope not!)